THE MODERN LIBRARY
of the World's Best Books

THE COMPLETE WORKS OF HOMER

THE ILIAD

AND

THE ODYSSEY

THE COMPLETE WORKS OF HOMER

THE ILIAD AND THE ODYSSEY

THE ILIAD DONE INTO ENGLISH PROSE

BY

ANDREW LANG, WALTER LEAF, ERNEST MYERS

THE ODYSSEY DONE INTO ENGLISH PROSE

BY

S. H. BUTCHER AND ANDREW LANG

BENNETT A. CERF • DONALD S. KLOPFER

THE MODERN LIBRARY

NEW YORK

THE COMPLETE WORKS OF HOMER

The Iliad and the Odyssey

>>

These are the Modern Library "Giants" now ready in identical format:

G1. Count Leo Tolstoy. *War and Peace.*
G2. James Boswell. *The Life of Samuel Johnson.*
G3. Victor Hugo. *Les Miserables.*
G4. The Complete Poems of Keats and Shelley.
G5. Plutarch's Lives (*The Dryden Translation*).
G6 *and* G7. Edward Gibbon. *The Decline and Fall of the Roman Empire. Complete and unabridged in two volumes.*
G8. Jane Austen. *The Complete Novels of Jane Austen.*
G9. G. F. Young. *The Medici. With* 32 *illustrations in aquatone.*
G10. Twelve Famous Plays of the Restoration and Eighteenth Century.
G11. The Essays of Montaigne (*The John Florio Translation*).
G12. Sir Walter Scott. *Quentin Durward, Ivanhoe, Kenilworth.*
G13. Thomas Carlyle. *The French Revolution. With* 16 *illustrations in aquatone.*
G14. Thomas Bulfinch. *Bulfinch's Mythology. With* 16 *illustrations in aquatone.*
G15. Miguel de Cervantes. *Don Quixote. With* 16 *illustrations in aquatone by Gustave Doré.*
G16. Thomas Wolfe. *Look Homeward, Angel.*
G17. Robert Browning. *The Poems and Plays of Robert Browning.*
G18. Henrik Ibsen. *Eleven Plays of Henrik Ibsen.*

>>

Manufactured in the United States of America
Bound for THE MODERN LIBRARY *by H. Wolff*

CONTENTS

THE ILIAD

Book VI

Book VII

Book VIII

Book IX

Book X

Book XI

Book XII

THE ODYSSEY

THE ILIAD

PREFATORY NOTE

THE execution of this version of the *Iliad* has been entrusted to the three Translators in the following three parts:—

Books	I—IX	W. LEAF.
"	X—XVI	A. LANG.
"	XVII—XXIV	E. MYERS.

Each Translator is therefore responsible for his own portion; but the whole has been revised by all three Translators, and the rendering of passages or phrases recurring in more than one portion has been determined after deliberation in common. Even in these, however, a certain elasticity has been deemed desirable.

On a few doubtful points, though very rarely, the opinion of two of the Translators has had to be adopted to the suppression of that held by the third. Thus, for instance, the Translator of Books X—XVI would have preferred "c" and "us" to "k" and "os" in the spelling of all proper names.

The text followed has been that of La Roche (Leipzig, 1873). Where the balance of evidence, external and internal, has seemed to the Translator to be against the genuineness of any passage, such passage has been enclosed in square brackets [ ].

The Translator of Books X—XVI has to thank Mr. R. W. RAPER, Fellow of Trinity College, Oxford, for his valuable aid in revising the proof-sheets of these Books.

The sacred soil of Ilios is rent
  With shaft and pit; foiled waters wander slow
Through plains where Simois and Scamander went
  To war with gods and heroes long ago.
Not yet to dark Cassandra lying low
  In rich Mycenae do the Fates relent;
The bones of Agamemnon are a show,
  And ruined is his royal monument.
The dust and awful treasures of the dead
  Hath Learning scattered wide; but vainly thee,
Homer, she meteth with her Lesbian lead,
  And strives to rend thy songs, too blind is she
To know the crown on thine immortal head
  Of indivisible supremacy.

A. L.

Athwart the sunrise of our western day
  The form of great Achilles, high and clear,
  Stands forth in arms, wielding the Pelian spear.
The sanguine tides of that immortal fray,
Swept on by gods, around him surge and sway,
  Wherethrough the helms of many a warrior peer,
  Strong men and swift, their tossing plumes uprear.
But stronger, swifter, goodlier he than they,
More awful, more divine. Yet mark anigh;
  Some fiery pang hath rent his soul within,
    Some hovering shade his brows encompasseth.
What gifts hath Fate for all his chivalry?
  Even such as hearts heroic oftenest win;
    Honour, a friend, anguish, untimely death.

E. M.

BOOK I

How Agamemnon and Achilles fell out at the siege of Troy; and Achilles withdrew himself from battle, and won from Zeus a pledge that his wrong should be avenged on Agamemnon and the Achaians.

SING, goddess, the wrath of Achilles Peleus' son, the ruinous wrath that brought on the Achaians woes innumerable, and hurled down into Hades many strong souls of heroes, and gave their bodies to be a prey to dogs and all winged fowls; and so the counsel of Zeus wrought out its accomplishment from the day when first strife parted Atreides king of men and noble Achilles.

Who then among the gods set the twain at strife and variance? Even the son of Leto and of Zeus; for he in anger at the king sent a sore plague upon the host, that the folk began to perish, because Atreides had done dishonour to Chryses the priest. For he had come to the Achaians' fleet ships to win his daughter's freedom, and brought a ransom beyond telling; and bare in his hands the fillet of Apollo the Far-darter upon a golden staff; and made his prayer unto all the Achaians, and most of all to the two sons of Atreus, orderers of the host: "Ye sons of Atreus and all ye well-greaved Achaians, now may the gods that dwell in the mansions of Olympus grant you to lay waste the city of Priam, and to fare happily homeward; only set ye my dear child free, and accept the ransom in reverence to the son of Zeus, far-darting Apollo."

Then all the other Achaians cried assent, to reverence the priest and accept his goodly ransom; yet the thing pleased not the heart of Agamemnon son of Atreus, but he roughly sent him away, and laid stern charge upon him, saying: "Let me not find thee, old man, amid the hollow ships, whether tarrying now or returning again hereafter, lest the staff and fillet of the god avail thee naught. And her will I not set free; nay, ere that shall old age come on her in our house, in Argos, far from her native land, where she shall ply the loom and serve my couch. But depart, provoke me not, that thou mayest the rather go in peace."

So said he, and the old man was afraid and obeyed his word, and fared silently along the shore of the loud-sounding sea. Then went that aged man apart and prayed aloud to king Apollo, whom Leto of the fair locks bare: "Hear me, god of the silver bow, that standest over Chryse and holy Killa, and rulest Tenedos with might, O Smintheus! If ever I built a temple gracious in thine eyes, or if ever I burnt to thee fat flesh of thighs of bulls or goats, fulfil thou this my desire; let the Danaans pay by thine arrows for my tears."

So spake he in prayer, and Phoebus Apollo heard him, and came down from the peaks of Olympus wroth at heart, bearing on his shoulders his bow and covered quiver. And the arrows clanged upon his shoulders in his wrath, as the god moved; and he descended like to night. Then he sate him aloof from the ships, and let an arrow fly; and there was heard a dread clanging of the silver bow. First did he assail the mules and fleet dogs, but afterward, aiming at the men his piercing dart, he smote; and the pyres of the dead burnt continually in multitude.

Now for nine days ranged the god's shafts through the host; but on the tenth Achilles summoned the folk to assembly, for in his mind did goddess Hera of the white arms put the thought, because she had pity on the Danaans when she beheld them perishing. Now when they had gathered and were met in assembly, then Achilles fleet of foot stood up and spake among them: "Son of Atreus, now deem I that we shall return wandering home again—if verily we might escape death—if war at once and pestilence must indeed ravage the Achaians. But come, let us now inquire of some soothsayer or priest, yea, or an interpreter of dreams—seeing that a dream too is of Zeus—who shall say wherefore Phoebus Apollo is so wroth, whether he blame us by reason of vow or hetacomb; if perchance he would accept the savour of lambs or unblemished goats, and so would take away the pestilence from us."

So spake he and sate him down; and there stood up before them Kalchas son of Thestor, most excellent far of augurs, who knew both things that were and that should be and that had been before, and guided the ships of the Achaians to Ilios by his soothsaying that Phoebus Apollo bestowed on him. He of good intent made harangue and spake amid them: "Achilles, dear to Zeus, thou biddest me tell the wrath of Apollo, the king that smiteth afar. Therefore will I speak; but do thou make covenant with me, and swear that verily with all thy heart thou wilt aid me both by word and deed. For of a truth I deem that I shall provoke one that ruleth all the Argives with might, and whom the Achaians obey. For a king is more of might when he is wroth with a meaner man; even though for the one day he swallow his anger, yet doth he still keep his displeasure thereafter in his breast till he accomplish it. Consider thou, then, if thou wilt hold me safe."

And Achilles fleet of foot made answer and spake to him: "Yea, be of good courage, speak whatever soothsaying thou knowest; for by Apollo dear to Zeus, him by whose worship thou, O Kalchas, declarest thy soothsaying to the Danaans, no man while I live and behold light on earth shall lay violent hands upon thee amid the hollow ships; no man of all the Danaans, not even if thou mean Agamemnon, that now avoweth him to be greatest far of the Achaians."

Then was the noble seer of good courage, and spake:

"Neither by reason of a vow is he displeased, nor for any hecatomb, but for his priest's sake to whom Agamemnon did despite, and set not his daughter free and accepted not the ransom; therefore hath the Far-darter brought woes upon us, yea, and will bring. Nor will he ever remove the loathly pestilence from the Danaans till we have given the bright-eyed damsel to her father, unbought, unransomed, and carried a holy hecatomb to Chryse; then might we propitiate him to our prayer."

So said he and sate him down, and there stood up before them the hero son of Atreus, wide-ruling Agamemnon, sore displeased; and his dark heart within him was greatly filled with anger, and his eyes were like flashing fire. To Kalchas first spake he with look of ill: "Thou seer of evil, never yet hast thou told me the thing that is pleasant. Evil is ever the joy of thy heart to prophesy, but never yet didst thou tell any good matter nor bring it to pass. And now with soothsaying thou makest harangue among the Danaans, how that the Far-darter bringeth woes upon them because, forsooth, I would not take the goodly ransom of the damsel Chryseis, seeing I am the rather fain to keep her own self within mine house. Yea, I prefer her before Klytaimnestra my wedded wife; in no wise is she lacking beside her, neither in favour nor stature, nor wit nor skill. Yet for all this will I give her back, if that is better; rather would I see my folk whole than perishing. Only make ye me ready a prize of honour forthwith, lest I alone of all the Argives be disprized, which thing beseemeth not; for ye all behold how my prize is departing from me."

To him then made answer fleet-footed goodly Achilles: "Most noble son of Atreus, of all men most covetous, how shall the great-hearted Achaians give thee a meed of honour? We know naught of any wealth of common store, but what spoil soe'er we took from captured cities hath been apportioned, and it beseemeth not to beg all this back from the folk. Nay, yield thou the damsel to the god, and we

Achaians will pay thee back threefold and fourfold, if ever Zeus grant us to sack some well-walled town of Troy-land."

To him lord Agamemnon made answer and said: "Not in this wise, strong as thou art, O godlike Achilles, beguile thou me by craft; thou shalt not outwit me nor persuade me. Dost thou wish, that thou mayest keep thy meed of honour, for me to sit idle in bereavement, and biddest me give her back? Nay, if the great-hearted Achaians will give me a meed suited to my mind, that the recompense be equal—but if they give it not, then I myself will go and take a meed of honour, thine be it or Aias', or Odysseus' that I will take unto me; wroth shall he be to whomsoever I come. But for this we will take counsel hereafter; now let us launch a black ship on the great sea, and gather picked oarsmen, and set therein a hecatomb, and embark Chryseis of the fair cheeks herself, and let one of our counsellors be captain, Aias or Idomeneus or goodly Odysseus, or thou, Peleides, most redoubtable of men, to do sacrifice for us and propitiate the Far-darter."

Then Achilles fleet of foot looked at him scowling and said: "Ah me, thou clothed in shamelessness, thou of crafty mind, how shall any Achaian hearken to thy bidding with all his heart, be it to go a journey or to fight the foe amain? Not by reason of the Trojan spearmen came I hither to fight, for they have not wronged me; never did they harry mine oxen nor my horses, nor ever waste my harvest in deep-soiled Phthia, the nurse of men; seeing there lieth between us long space of shadowy mountains and sounding sea; but thee, thou shameless one, followed we hither to make thee glad, by earning recompense at the Trojans' hands for Menelaos and for thee, thou dog-face! All this thou reckonest not nor takest thought thereof; and now thou threatenest thyself to take my meed of honour, wherefor I travailed much, and the sons of the Achaians gave it me. Never win I meed like unto thine, when the Achaians sack any populous citadel of Trojan men; my hands bear the brunt of furious war, but when the apportioning cometh then is thy meed far ampler, and I betake me to the ships with some small thing, yet mine own, when I have fought to weariness. Now will I depart to Phthia, seeing it is far better to return home on my beaked ships; nor am I minded here in dishonour to draw thee thy fill of riches and wealth."

Then Agamemnon king of men made answer to him: "Yea, flee, if thy soul be set thereon. It is not I that beseech thee to tarry for my sake; I have others by my side that shall do me honour, and above all Zeus, lord of counsel. Most hateful art thou to me of all kings, fosterlings of Zeus; thou ever lovest strife and wars and fightings. Though thou be very strong, yet that I ween is a gift to thee of God. Go home with thy ships and company and lord it among thy Myrmidons; I reck not aught of thee nor care I for thine indignation; and this shall be my threat to thee: seeing Phoebus Apollo bereaveth me of Chryseis, her with my ship and my company will I send back; and mine own self will I go to thy hut and take Briseis of the fair cheeks, even that thy meed of honour, that thou mayest well know how far greater I am than thou, and so shall another hereafter abhor to match his words with mine and rival me to my face."

So said he, and grief came upon Peleus' son, and his heart within his shaggy breast was divided in counsel, whether to draw his keen blade from his thigh and set the company aside and so slay Atreides, or to assuage his anger and curb his soul. While yet he doubted thereof in heart and soul, and was drawing his great sword from his sheath, Athene came to him from heaven, sent forth of the white-armed goddess Hera, whose heart loved both alike and had care for them. She stood behind Peleus' son and caught him by his golden hair, to him only visible, and of the rest no man beheld her. Then Achilles marvelled, and turned him about, and straightway knew Pallas Athene; and terribly shone her eyes. He spake to her winged words, and said: "Why now art thou come hither, thou daughter of aegis-bearing Zeus? Is it to behold the insolence of Agamemnon son of Atreus? Yea, I will tell thee that I deem shall even be brought to pass: by his own haughtinessess shall he soon lose his life."

Then the bright-eyed goddess Athene spake to him again: "I came from heaven to stay thine anger, if perchance thou wilt hearken to me, being sent forth of the white-armed goddess Hera, that loveth you twain alike and careth for you. Go to now, cease from strife, and let not thine hand draw the sword; yet with words indeed revile him, even as it shall come to pass. For thus will I say to thee, and so it shall be fulfilled; hereafter shall goodly gifts come to thee, yea in threefold measure, by reason of this despite; hold thou thine hand, and hearken to us."

And Achilles fleet of foot made answer and said to her: "Goddess, needs must a man observe the saying of you twain, even though he be very wroth at heart; for so is the better way. Whosoever obeyeth the gods, to him they gladly hearken."

He said, and stayed his heavy hand on the silver hilt, and thrust the great sword back into the sheath, and was not disobedient to the saying of Athene; and she forthwith was departed to Olympus, to the other gods in the palace of aegis-bearing Zeus.

Then Peleus' son spake again with bitter words to Atreus' son, and in no wise ceased from anger: "Thou heavy with wine, thou with face of dog and heart of deer, never didst thou take courage to arm for battle among thy folk or to lay ambush with the princes of the Achaians; that to thee were even as death. Far better booteth it, forsooth, to seize for thyself the meed of honour of every man through the wide host of the Achaians that speaketh contrary to thee. Folk-devouring king! seeing thou rulest men of naught; else were this despite, thou son of Atreus, thy last. But I will speak my word to thee, and swear a mighty oath therewith: verily by this staff that shall no more put forth leaf or twig, seeing it hath for ever left its trunk among the hills, neither shall it grow green again, because the axe hath stripped it of leaves and bark; and now the sons of the Achaians that exercise judgment bear it in their hands, even they that by Zeus' command watch over the traditions—so shall this be a mighty oath in thine eyes—verily shall longing for Achilles come hereafter upon the sons of the Achaians one and all; and then wilt thou in no wise avail to save them, for all thy grief, when multitudes fall dying before manslaying Hector. Then shalt thou tear thy heart within thee for anger that thou didst in no wise honour the best of the Achaians."

So said Peleides and dashed to earth the staff studded with golden nails, and himself sat down; and over against him Atreides waxed furious. Then in their midst rose up Nestor, pleasant of speech, the clear-voiced orator of the Pylians, he from whose tongue flowed discourse sweeter than honey. Two generations of mortal men already had he seen perish, that had been of old time born and nurtured with him in goodly Pylos, and he was king among the third. He of good intent made harangue to them and said: "Alas, of a truth sore lamentation cometh upon the land of Achaia. Verily Priam would be glad and Priam's sons, and all the Trojans would have great joy of heart, were they to hear all this tale of strife between you twain that are chiefest of the Danaans in counsel and chiefest in battle. Nay, hearken to me; ye are younger both than I. Of old days held I converse with better men even than you, and never did they make light of me. Yea, I never beheld such warriors, nor shall behold, as were Peirithoos and Dryas shepherd of the host and Kaineous and Exadios and godlike Polyphemos [and Theseus son of Aigeus, like to the immortals]. Mightiest of growth were they of all men upon the earth; mightiest they were and with the mightiest fought they, even the wild tribes of the mountain caves, and destroyed them utterly. And with these held I converse, being come from Pylos, from a distant land afar; for of themselves they summoned me. So I played my part in fight; and with them could none of men that are now on earth do battle. And they laid to heart my counsels and hearkened to my voice. Even so hearken ye also, for better is it to hearken. Neither do thou, though thou art very great, seize from him his damsel, but leave her as she was given at the first by the sons of the Achaians to be a meed of honour; nor do thou, son of Peleus, think to strive with a king, might against might; seeing that no common honour pertaineth to a sceptred king to whom Zeus apportioneth glory. Though thou be strong, and a goddess mother bare thee, yet his is the greater place, for he is king over more. And thou, Atreides, abate thy fury; nay, it is even I that beseech thee to let go thine anger with Achilles, who is made unto all the Achaians a mighty bulwark of evil war."

Then lord Agamemnon answered and said: "Yea verily, old man, all this thou sayest is according unto right. But this fellow would be above all others, he would be lord of all and king among all and captain to all; wherein I deem none will hearken to him. Though the immortal gods made him a spearman, do they therefore put revilings in his mouth for him to utter?"

Then goodly Achilles brake in on him and answered: "Yea, for I should be called coward and man of naught, if I yield to thee in every matter, howsoe'er thou bid. To others give now thine orders, not to me [play master; for thee I deem that I shall no more obey]. This, moreover, will I say to thee, and do thou lay it to thy heart. Know that not by violence will I strive for the damsel's sake, neither with thee nor any other; ye gave and ye have taken away. But of all else that is mine beside my fleet black ship, thereof shalt thou not take anything or bear it away against my will. Yea, go to now, make trial, that all these may see; forthwith thy dark blood shall gush about my spear."

Now when the twain had thus finished the battle of violent words, they stood up and dissolved the assembly beside the Achaian ships. Peleides went his way to his huts and trim ships with Menoitios' son and his company; and Atreides launched a fleet ship on the sea, and picked twenty oarsmen therefor, and embarked the hecatomb for the god, and brought Chryseis of the fair cheeks and set her therein; and Odysseus of many devices went to be their captain.

So these embarked and sailed over the wet ways; and Atreides bade the folk purify themselves. So they purified themselves, and cast the defilements into the sea and did sacrifice to Apollo, even unblemished hecatombs of bulls and goats, along the shore of the unvintaged sea; and the sweet savour arose to heaven eddying amid the smoke.

Thus were they busied throughout the host; but Agamemnon ceased not from the strife wherewith he threatened Achilles at the first; he spake to Talthybios and Eurybates that were his heralds and nimble squires: "Go ye to the tent of Achilles Peleus' son, and take Briseis of the fair cheeks by the hand and lead her hither; and if he give her not, then will I myself go, and more with me, and seize her; and that will be yet more grievous for him."

So saying he sent them forth, and laid stern charge upon them. Unwillingly went they along the beach of the unvintaged sea, and came to the huts and ships of the Myrmidons. Him found they sitting beside his hut and black ship; nor when he saw them was Achilles glad. So they in dread and reverence of the king stood, and spake to him no word, nor questioned him. But he knew in his heart, and spake to them: "All hail, ye heralds, messengers of Zeus and men, come near; ye are not guilty in my sight, but Agamemnon that sent you for the sake of the damsel Briseis. Go now, heaven-sprung Patroklos, bring forth the damsel, and give them her to lead away. Moreover, let the twain themselves be my witness before the face of the blessed gods and mortal men, yea and of him, that king untoward, against the day when there cometh need of me hereafter to save them all from shameful wreck. Of a truth he raveth with baleful mind, and hath not knowledge to look before and after, that so his Achaians might battle in safety beside their ships."

So said he, and Patroklos hearkened to his dear comrade, and led forth from the hut Briseis of the fair cheeks, and gave them her to lead away. So these twain took their way back along the Achaians' ships, and with them went the woman all unwilling. Then Achilles wept anon, and sat him down apart, aloof from his comrades on the beach of the grey sea, gazing across the boundless main; he stretched forth his hands and prayed instantly to his dear mother: "Mother, seeing thou didst of a truth bear me to so brief span of life, honour at the least ought the Olympian to have granted me, even Zeus that thundereth on high; but now doth he not honour me, no, not one whit. Verily Atreus' son, wide-ruling Agamemnon, hath done me dishonour; for he hath taken away my meed of honour and keepeth her of his own violent deed."

So spake he weeping, and his lady mother heard him as she sate in the sea-depths beside her aged sire. With speed arose she from the grey sea, like a mist, and sate her before the face of her weeping son, and stroked him with her hand, and spake and called on his name: "My child, why weepest thou? What sorrow hath entered into thy heart? Speak it forth, hide it not in thy mind, that both may know it."

Then with heavy moan Achilles fleet of foot spake to her: "Thou knowest it; why should I tell this to thee that knowest all! We had fared to Thebe, the holy city of Eëtion, and laid it waste and carried hither all the spoils. So the sons of the Achaians divided among them all aright;

and for Atreides they set apart Chryseis of the fair cheeks. But Chryses, priest of Apollo the Far-darter, came unto the fleet ships of the mail-clad Achaians to win his daughter's freedom, and brought a ransom beyond telling, and bare in his hands the fillet of Apollo the Far-darter upon a golden staff, and made his prayer unto all the Achaians, and most of all to the two sons of Atreus, orderers of the host. Then all the other Achaians cried assent, to reverence the priest and accept his goodly ransom; yet the thing pleased not the heart of Agamemnon son of Atreus, but he roughly sent him away and laid stern charge upon him. So the old man went back in anger; and Apollo heard his prayers, seeing he loved him greatly, and he aimed against the Argives his deadly darts. So the people began to perish in multitudes, and the god's shafts ranged everywhither throughout the wide host of the Achaians. Then of full knowledge the seer declared to us the oracle of the Far-darter. Forthwith I first bade propitiate the god; but wrath gat hold upon Atreus' son thereat, and anon he stood up and spake a threatening word, that hath now been accomplished. Her the glancing-eyed Achaians are bringing on their fleet ship to Chryse, and bear with them offerings to the king; and the other but now the heralds went and took from my hut, even the daughter of Briseus, whom the sons of the Achaians gave me. Thou therefore, if indeed thou canst, guard thine own son; betake thee to Olympus and beseech Zeus by any deed or word whereby thou ever didst make glad his heart. For oft have I heard thee proclaiming in my father's halls and telling that thou alone amid the immortals didst save the son of Kronos, lord of the storm-cloud, from shameful wreck, when all the other Olympians would have bound him, even Hera and Poseidon and Pallas Athene. Then didst thou, O goddess, enter in and loose him from his bonds, having with speed summoned to high Olympus him of the hundred arms whom gods call Briareus, but all men call Aigaion; for he is mightier even than his father—so he sate him by Kronion's side rejoicing in his triumph, and the blessed gods feared him withal and bound not Zeus. This bring thou to his remembrance and sit by him and clasp his knees, if perchance he will give succour to the Trojans; and for the Achaians, hem them among their ships' sterns about the bay, given over to slaughter; that they may make trial of their king, and that even Atreides, wide-ruling Agamemnon, may perceive his blindness, in that he honoured not at all the best of the Achaians."

Then Thetis weeping made answer to him: "Ah me, my child, why reared I thee, cursed in my motherhood? Would thou hadst been left tearless and griefless amid the ships, seeing thy lot is very brief and endureth no long while; but now art thou made short-lived alike and lamentable beyond all men; in an evil hour I bare thee in our halls. But I will go myself to snow-clad Olympus to tell this thy saying to Zeus, whose joy is in the thunder, if perchance he may hearken to me. But tarry thou now amid thy fleet-faring ships, and continue wroth with the Achaians, and refrain utterly from battle: for Zeus went yesterday to Okeanos, unto the noble Ethiopians for a feast, and all the gods followed with him; but on the twelfth day will he return to Olympus, and then will I fare to Zeus' palace of the bronze threshold, and will kneel to him and think to win him."

So saying she went her way and left him there, vexed in spirit for the fair-girdled woman's sake, whom they had taken perforce despite his will: and meanwhile Odysseus came to Chryse with the holy hecatomb. When they were now entered within the deep haven, they furled their sails and laid them in the black ship, and lowered the mast by the forestays and brought it to the crutch with speed, and rowed her with oars to the anchorage. Then they cast out the mooring stones and made fast the hawsers, and so themselves went forth on to the sea-beach, and forth they brought the hecatomb for the Far-darter Apollo, and forth came Chryseis withal from the seafaring ship. Then Odysseus of many counsels brought her to the altar and gave her into her father's arms, and spake unto him: "Chryses, Agamemnon king of men sent me hither to bring thee thy daughter, and to offer to Phoebus a holy hecatomb on the Danaans' behalf, wherewith to propitiate the king that hath now brought sorrow and lamentation on the Argives."

So saying he gave her to his arms, and he gladly took his dear child; and anon they set in order for the god the holy hecatomb about his well-builded altar; next washed they their hands and took up the barley meal. Then Chryses lifted up his hands and prayed aloud for them: "Hearken to me, god of the silver bow that standest over Chryse and holy Killa, and rulest Tenedos with might; even as erst thou heardest my prayer, and didst me honour, and mightily afflictedst the people of the Achaians, even so now fulfil me this my desire; remove thou from the Danaans forthwith the loathly pestilence."

So spake he in prayer, and Phoebus Apollo heard him. Now when they had prayed and sprinkled the barley meal, first they drew back the victims' heads and slaughtered them and flayed them, and cut slices from the thighs and wrapped them in fat, making a double fold, and laid raw collops thereon, and the old man burnt them on cleft wood and made libation over them of gleaming wine; and at his side the young men in their hands held five-pronged forks. Now when the thighs were burnt and they had tasted the vitals, then sliced they all the rest and pierced it through with spits, and roasted it carefully, and drew all off again. So when they had rest from the task and had made ready the banquet, they feasted, nor was their heart aught stinted of the fair banquet. But when they had put away from them the desire of meat and drink, the young men crowned the bowls with wine, and gave each man his portion after the drink-offering had been poured into the cups. So all day long worshipped they the god with music, singing the beautiful paean, the sons of the Achaians making music to the Far-darter; and his heart was glad to hear. And when the sun went down and darkness came on them, they laid them to sleep beside the ship's hawsers; and when rosy-fingered Dawn appeared, the child of morning, then set they sail for the wide camp of the Achaians; and Apollo the Far-darter sent them a favouring gale. They set up their mast and spread the white sails forth, and the wind filled the sail's belly and the dark wave sang loud about the stem as the ship made way, and she sped across the wave, accomplishing her journey. So when they were now come to the wide camp of the Achaians, they drew up their black ship to land high upon the sands, and set in line the long props beneath her; and themselves were scattered amid their huts and ships.

But he sat by his swift-faring ships, still wroth, even the heaven-sprung son of Peleus, Achilles fleet of foot; he betook him neither to the assembly that is the hero's glory, neither to war, but consumed his heart in tarrying in his place, and yearned for the war-cry and for battle.

Now when the twelfth morn thereafter was come, then the gods that are for ever fared to Olympus all in company, led of Zeus. And Thetis forgat not her son's charge, but rose up from the sea-wave, and at early morn mounted up to great heaven and Olympus. There found she Kronos' son of the far-sounding voice sitting apart from all on the topmost peak of many-ridged Olympus. So she sat before his face and with her left hand clasped his knees, and with her right touched him beneath his chin, and spake in prayer to king Zeus son of Kronos: "Father Zeus, if ever I gave thee aid amid the immortal gods, whether by word or deed, fulfil thou this my desire: do honour to my son, that is doomed to earliest death of all men: now hath Agamemnon king of men done him dishonour, for he hath taken away his meed of honour and keepeth her of his own violent deed.

But honour thou him, Zeus of Olympus, lord of counsel; grant thou victory to the Trojans the while, until the Achaians do my son honour and exalt him with recompense."

So spake she; but Zeus the cloud-gatherer said no word to her, and sat long time in silence. But even as Thetis had clasped his knees, so held she by him clinging, and questioned him yet a second time: "Promise me now this thing verily, and bow thy head thereto; or else deny me, seeing there is naught for thee to fear; that I may know full well how I among all gods am least in honour."

Then Zeus the cloud-gatherer, sore troubled, spake to her: "Verily it is a sorry matter, if thou wilt set me at variance with Hera, whene'er she provoketh me with taunting words. Even now she upbraideth me ever amid the immortal gods, and saith that I aid the Trojans in battle. But do thou now depart again, lest Hera mark aught; and I will take thought for these things to fulfil them. Come now, I will bow my head to thee, that thou mayest be of good courage; for that, of my part, is the surest token amid the immortals; no word of mine is revocable nor false nor unfulfilled when the bowing of my head hath pledged it."

Kronion spake, and bowed his dark brow, and the ambrosial locks waved from the king's immortal head; and he made great Olympus quake.

Thus the twain took counsel and parted; she leapt therewith into the deep sea from glittering Olympus, and Zeus fared to his own palace. All the gods in company arose from their seats before their father's face; neither ventured any to await his coming, but they stood up all before him. So he sate him there upon his throne; but Hera saw, and was not ignorant how that the daughter of the Ancient of the sea, Thetis the silver-footed, had devised counsel with him. Anon with taunting words spake she to Zeus the son of Kronos: "Now who among the gods, thou crafty of mind, hath devised counsel with thee? It is ever thy good pleasure to hold aloof from me and in secret meditation to give thy judgments, nor of thine own good will hast thou ever brought thyself to declare unto me the thing thou purposest."

Then the father of gods and men made answer to her: "Hera, think not thou to know all my sayings; hard they are for thee, even though thou art my wife. But whichsoever it is seemly for thee to hear, none sooner than thou shall know, be he god or man. Only when I will to take thought aloof from the gods, then do not thou ask of every matter nor make question."

Then Hera the ox-eyed queen made answer to him. "Most dread son of Kronos, what word is this thou hast spoken? Yea, surely of old I have not asked thee nor made question, but in every quietness thou devisest all thou wilt. But now is my heart sore afraid lest thou have been won over by silver-footed Thetis, daughter of the Ancient of the sea, for she at early morn sat by thee and clasped thy knees. To her I deem thou gavest a sure pledge that thou wilt do honour to Achilles, and lay many low beside the Achaians' ships."

To her made answer Zeus the cloud-gatherer: "Lady, Good lack! ever art thou imagining, nor can I escape thee; yet shalt thou in no wise have power to fulfil, but wilt be the further from my heart; that shall be even the worse for thee. And if it be so, then such must my good pleasure be. Abide thou in silence and hearken to my bidding, lest all the gods that are in Olympus keep not off from thee my visitation, when I put forth my hands unapproachable against thee."

He said, and Hera the ox-eyed queen was afraid, and sat in silence, curbing her heart; but throughout Zeus' palace the gods of heaven were troubled. Then Hephaistos the famed craftsman began to make harangue among them, to do kindness to his dear mother, white-armed Hera: "Verily this will be a sorry matter, neither any more endurable, if ye twain thus fight for mortals' sakes, and bring wrangling among the gods; neither will there any more be joy of the goodly feast, seeing that evil triumpheth. So I give counsel to my mother, though herself is wise, to do kindness to our dear father Zeus, that our father upbraid us not again and cast the banquet in confusion. What if the Olympian, the lord of the lightning, will to dash us from our seats! for he is strongest far. Nay, approach thou him with gentle words, then will the Olympian forthwith be gracious unto us."

So speaking he rose up and set in his dear mother's hand the twy-handled cup, and spake to her: "Be of good courage, mother mine, and endure, though thou art vexed, lest I behold thee, that art so dear, chastised before mine eyes, and then shall I not be able for all my sorrow to save thee; for the Olympian is a hard foe to face. Yea, once ere this, when I was fain to save thee, he caught me by my foot and hurled me from the heavenly threshold; all day I flew, and at the set of sun I fell in Lemnos, and little life was in me. There did the Sintian folk forthwith tend me for my fall."

He spake, and the white-armed goddess Hera smiled, and smiling took the cup at her son's hand. Then he poured wine to all the other gods from right to left, ladling the sweet nectar from the bowl. And laughter unquenchable arose amid the blessed gods to see Hephaistos bustling through the palace.

So feasted they all day till the setting of the sun; nor was their soul aught stinted of the fair banquet, nor of the beauteous lyre that Apollo held, and the Muses singing alternately with sweet voice.

Now when the bright light of the sun was set, these went each to his own house to sleep, where each one had his palace made with cunning device by famed Hephaistos the lame god; and Zeus the Olympian, the lord of lightning, departed to his couch where he was wont of old to take his rest, whenever sweet sleep visited him. There went he up and slept, and beside him was Hera of the golden throne.

BOOK II

How Zeus beguiled Agamemnon by a dream; and of the assembly of the Achaians and their marching forth to battle. And of the names and numbers of the hosts of the Achaians and the Trojans.

Now all other gods and chariot-driving men slept all night long, only Zeus was not holden of sweet sleep; rather was he pondering in his heart how he should do honour to Achilles and destroy many beside the Achaians' ships. And this design seemed to his mind the best, to wit, to send a baneful dream upon Agamemnon son of Atreus. So he spake, and uttered to him winged words: "Come now, thou baneful Dream, go to the Achaians' fleet ships, enter into the hut of Agamemnon son of Atreus, and tell him every word plainly as I charge thee. Bid him call to arms the flowing-haired Achaians with all speed, for that now he may take the wide-wayed city of the Trojans. For the immortals that dwell in the halls of Olympus are no longer divided in counsel, since Hera hath turned the minds of all by her beseeching, and over the Trojans sorrows hang."

So spake he, and the Dream went his way when he had heard the charge. With speed he came to the Achaians' fleet ships, and went to Agamemnon son of Atreus, and found him sleeping in his hut, and ambrosial slumber poured over him. So he stood over his head in seeming like unto the son of Neleus, even Nestor, whom most of all the elders Agamemnon honoured; in his likeness spake to him the heavenly Dream:

"Sleepest thou, son of wise Atreus tamer of horses? To sleep all night through beseemeth not one that is a counsellor, to whom peoples are entrusted and so many cares belong. But now hearken straightway to me, for I am a messenger to thee from Zeus, who though he be afar yet hath great care for thee and pity. He biddeth thee call to arms the flowing-haired Achaians with all speed, for that now thou mayest take the wide-wayed city of the Trojans. For the immortals that dwell in the halls of Olympus are no longer divided in counsel, since Hera hath turned the minds of all by her beseeching, and over the Trojans sorrows hang by the will of Zeus. But do thou keep this in thy heart, nor let forgetfulness come upon thee when honeyed sleep shall leave thee."

So spake the Dream, and departed and left him there, deeming in his mind things that were not to be fulfilled. For indeed he thought to take Priam's city that very day; fond man, in that he knew not the plans that Zeus had in mind, who was willed to bring yet more grief and wailing on Trojans alike and Danaans throughout the course of stubborn fights. Then woke he from sleep, and the heavenly voice was in his ears. So he rose up sitting, and donned his soft tunic, fair and bright, and cast around him his great cloak, and beneath his glistering feet he bound his fair sandals, and over his shoulder cast his silver-studded sword, and grasped his sires' sceptre, imperishable for ever, wherewith he took his way amid the mail-clad Achaians' ships.

Now went the goddess Dawn to high Olympus, foretelling daylight to Zeus and all the immortals; and the king bade the clear-voiced heralds summon to the assembly the flowing-haired Achaians. So did those summon, and these gathered with speed.

But first the council of the great-hearted elders met beside the ship of king Nestor the Pylos-born. And he that had assembled them framed his cunning counsel: "Hearken, my friends. A dream from heaven came to me in my sleep through the ambrosial night, and chiefly to goodly Nestor was very like in shape and bulk and stature. And it stood over my head and charged me saying: 'Sleepest thou, son of wise Atreus tamer of horses? To sleep all night through beseemeth not one that is a counsellor, to whom peoples are entrusted and so many cares belong. But now hearken straightway to me, for I am a messenger to thee from Zeus, who though he be afar yet hath great care for thee and pity. He biddeth thee call to arms the flowing-haired Achaians with all speed, for that now thou mayest take the wide-wayed city of the Trojans. For the immortals that dwell in the palaces of Olympus are no longer divided in counsel, since Hera hath turned the minds of all by her beseeching, and over the Trojans sorrows hang by the will of Zeus. But keep thou this in thy heart.' So spake the dream and was flown away, and sweet sleep left me. So come, let us now call to arms as we may the sons of the Achaians. But first I will speak to make trial of them as is fitting, and will bid them flee with their benched ships; only do ye from this side and from that speak to hold them back."

So spake he and sate him down; and there stood up among them Nestor, who was king of sandy Pylos. He of good intent made harangue to them and said: "My friends, captains and rulers of the Argives, had any other of the Achaians told us this dream we might deem it a false thing, and rather turn away therefrom; but now he hath seen it who of all Achaians avoweth himself far greatest. So come, let us call to arms as we may the sons of the Achaians."

So spake he, and led the way forth from the council, and all the other sceptred chiefs rose with him and obeyed the shepherd of the host; and the people hastened to them. Even as when the tribes of thronging bees issue from some hollow rock, ever in fresh procession, and fly clustering among the flowers of spring, and some on this hand and some on that fly thick; even so from ships and huts before the low beach marched forth their many tribes by companies to the place of assembly. And in their midst blazed forth

Rumour, messenger of Zeus, urging them to go; and so they gathered. And the palace of assemblage was in an uproar, and the earth echoed again as the hosts sate them down, and there was turmoil. Nine heralds restrained them with shouting, if perchance they might refrain from clamour, and hearken to their kings, the fosterlings of Zeus. And hardly at the last would the people sit, and keep them to their benches and cease from noise. Then stood up lord Agamemnon bearing his sceptre, that Hephaistos had wrought curiously. Hephaistos gave it to king Zeus son of Kronos, and then Zeus gave it to the messenger-god the slayer of Argus; and king Hermes gave it to Pelops the charioteer, and Pelops again gave it to Atreus shepherd of the host. And Atreus dying left it to Thyestes rich in flocks, and Thyestes in his turn left it to Agamemnon to bear, that over many islands and all Argos he should be lord. Thereon he leaned and spake his saying to the Argives:

"My friends, Danaan warriors, men of Ares' company, Zeus Kronos' son hath bound me with might in grievous blindness of soul; hard of heart is he, for that erewhile he promised me and pledged his nod that not till I had wasted well-walled Ilios should I return; but now see I that he planned a cruel wile and biddeth me return to Argos dishonoured, with the loss of many of my folk. So meseems it pleaseth most mighty Zeus, who hath laid low the head of many a city, yea, and shall lay low; for his is highest power. Shame is this even for them that come after to hear; how so goodly and great a folk of the Achaians thus vainly warred a bootless war, and fought scantier enemies, and no end thereof is yet seen. For if perchance we were minded, both Achaians and Trojans, to swear a solemn truce, and to number ourselves, and if the Trojans should gather together all that have their dwellings in the city, and we Achaians should marshal ourselves by tens, and every company choose a Trojan to pour their wine, then would many tens lack a cup-bearer: so much, I say, do the sons of the Achaians outnumber the Trojans that dwell within the city. But allies from many cities, even warriors that wield the spear, are therein, and they hinder me perforce, and for all my will suffer me not to waste the populous citadel of Ilios. Already have nine years of great Zeus passed away, and our ships' timbers have rotted and the tackling is loosed; while there our wives and little children sit in our halls awaiting us; yet is our task utterly unaccomplished wherefor we came hither. So come, even as I shall bid let us all obey. Let us flee with our ships to our dear native land; for now shall we never take wide-wayed Troy."

So spake he, and stirred the spirit in the breasts of all throughout the multitude, as many as had not heard the council. And the assembly swayed like high sea-waves of the Icarian Main that east wind and south wind raise, rushing upon them from the clouds of father Zeus; and even as when the west wind cometh to stir a deep cornfield with violent blast, and the ears bow down, so was all the assembly stirred, and they with shouting hasted toward the ships; and the dust from beneath their feet rose and stood on high. And they bade each man his neighbour to seize the ships and drag them into the bright salt sea, and cleared out the launching ways, and the noise went up to heaven of their hurrying homewards; and they began to take the props from beneath the ships.

Then would the Argives have accomplished their return against the will of fate, but that Hera spake a word to Athene: "Out on it, daughter of aegis-bearing Zeus, unwearied maiden! Shall the Argives thus indeed flee homeward to their dear native land over the sea's broad back? But they would leave to Priam and the Trojans their boast, even Helen of Argos, for whose sake many an Achaian hath perished in Troy, far away from his dear native land. But go thou now amid the host of the mail-clad Achaians; with thy gentle words refrain thou every man, neither suffer them to draw their curved ships down to the salt sea."

So spake she, and the bright-eyed goddess Athene disregarded not; but went darting down from the peaks of Olympus, and came with speed to the fleet ships of the Achaians. There found she Odysseus standing, peer of Zeus in counsel, neither laid he any hand upon his decked black ship, because grief had entered into his heart and soul. And bright-eyed Athene stood by him and said: "Heaven-sprung son of Laertes, Odysseus of many devices, will ye indeed fling yourselves upon your benched ships to flee homeward to your dear native land? But ye would leave to Priam and the Trojans their boast, even Helen of Argos, for whose sake many an Achaian hath perished in Troy, far from his dear native land. But go thou now amid the host of the Achaians, and tarry not; and with thy gentle words refrain every man, neither suffer them to draw their curved ships down to the salt sea."

So said she, and he knew the voice of the goddess speaking to him, and set him to run, and cast away his mantle, the which his herald gathered up, even Eurybates of Ithaca, that waited on him. And himself he went to meet Agamemnon son of Atreus, and at his hand received the sceptre of his sires, imperishable for ever, wherewith he took his way amid the ships of the mail-clad Achaians.

Whenever he found one that was a captain and a man of mark, he stood by his side, and refrained him with gentle words: "Good sir, it is not seemly to affright thee like a coward, but do thou sit thyself and make all thy folk sit down. For thou knowest not yet clearly what is the purpose of Atreus' son; now is he but making trial, and soon he will afflict the sons of the Achaians. And heard we not all of us what he spake in the council? Beware lest in his anger he evilly entreat the sons of the Achaians. For proud is the soul of heaven-fostered kings; because their honour is of Zeus, and the god of counsel loveth them."

But whatever man of the people he saw and found him

shouting, him he drave with his sceptre and chode him with loud words: "Good sir, sit still and hearken to the words of others that are thy betters; but thou art no warrior, and a weakling, never reckoned whether in battle or in council. In no wise can we Achaians all be kings here. A multitude of masters is no good thing; let there be one master, one king, to whom the son of crooked-counselling Kronos hath granted it, [even the sceptre and judgments, that he may rule among you]."

So masterfully ranged he the host; and they hasted back to the assembly from ships and huts, with noise as when a wave of the loud-sounding sea roareth on the long beach and the main resoundeth.

Now all the rest sat down and kept their place upon the benches, only Thersites still chattered on, the uncontrolled of speech, whose mind was full of words many and disorderly, wherewith to strive against the chiefs idly and in no good order, but even as he deemed that he should make the Argives laugh. And he was ill-favoured beyond all men that came to Ilios. Bandy-legged was he, and lame of one foot, and his two shoulders rounded, arched down upon his chest; and over them his head was warped, and a scanty stubble sprouted on it. Hateful was he to Achilles above all and to Odysseus, for them he was wont to revile. But now with shrill shout he poured forth his upbraidings upon goodly Agamemnon. With him the Achaians were sore vexed and had indignation in their souls. But he with loud shout spake and reviled Agamemnon: "Atreides, for what art thou now ill content and lacking? Surely thy huts are full of bronze and many women are in thy huts, the chosen spoils that we Achaians give thee first of all, whene'er we take a town. Can it be that thou yet wantest gold as well, such as some one of the horse-taming Trojans may bring from Ilios to ransom his son, whom I perchance or some other Achaian have led captive; or else some young girl, to know in love, whom thou mayest keep apart to thyself? But it is not seemly for one that is their captain to bring the sons of the Achaians to ill. Soft fools, base things of shame, ye women of Achaia and men no more, let us depart home with our ships, and leave this fellow here in Troy-land to gorge him with meeds of honour, that he may see whether our aid avail him aught or no; even he that hath now done dishonour to Achilles, a far better man than he; for he hath taken away his meed of honour and keepeth it by his own violent deed. Of a very surety is there no wrath at all in Achilles' mind, but he is slack; else this despite, thou son of Atreus, were thy last."

So spake Thersites, reviling Agamemnon shepherd of the host. But goodly Odysseus came straight to his side, and looking sternly at him with hard words rebuked him: "Thersites, reckless in words, shrill orator though thou art, refrain thyself, nor aim to strive simply against kings. For I deem that no mortal is baser than thou of all that with the sons of Atreus came before Ilios. Therefore were it well that thou shouldest not have kings in thy mouth as thou talkest, and utter revilings against them and be on the watch for departure. We know not yet clearly how these things shall be, whether we sons of the Achaians shall return for good or for ill. Therefore now dost thou revile continually Agamemnon son of Atreus, shepherd of the host, because the Danaan warriors give him many gifts, and so thou talkest tauntingly. But I will tell thee plain, and that I say shall even be brought to pass: if I find thee again raving as now thou art, then may Odysseus' head no longer abide upon his shoulders, nor may I any more be called father of Telemachos, if I take thee not and strip from thee thy garments, thy mantle and tunic that cover thy nakedness, and for thyself send thee weeping to the fleet ships, and beat thee out of the assembly with shameful blows."

So spake he, and with his staff smote his back and shoulders: and he bowed down and a big tear fell from him, and a bloody weal stood up from his back beneath the golden sceptre. Then he sat down and was amazed, and in pain with helpless look wiped away the tear. But the rest, though they were sorry, laughed lightly at him, and thus would one speak looking at another standing by: "Go to, of a truth Odysseus hath wrought good deeds without number ere now, standing foremost in wise counsels and setting battle in array, but now is this thing the best by far that he hath wrought among the Argives, to wit, that he hath stayed this prating railer from his harangues. Never again, forsooth, will his proud soul henceforth bid him revile the kings with slanderous words."

So said the common sort; but up rose Odysseus waster of cities, with the sceptre in his hand. And by his side bright-eyed Athene in the likeness of a herald bade the multitude keep silence, that the sons of the Achaians, both the nearest and the farthest, might hear his words together and give heed to his counsel. He of good intent made harangue to them and said: "Atreides, now surely are the Achaians for making thee, O king, most despised among all mortal men, nor will they fulfil the promise that they pledged thee when they still were marching hither from horse-pasturing Argos; that thou shouldest not return till thou hadst laid well-walled Ilios waste. For like young children or widow women do they wail each to the other of returning home. Yea, here is toil to make a man depart disheartened. For he that stayeth away but one single month far from his wife in his benched ship fretteth himself when winter storms and the furious sea imprison him; but for us, the ninth year of our stay here is upon us in its course. Therefore do I not marvel that the Achaians should fret beside their beaked ships; yet nevertheless is it shameful to wait long and to depart empty. Be of good heart, my friends, and wait a while, until we learn whether Kalchas be a true prophet or no. For this thing verily we know well in our hearts, and ye all are witnesses thereof, even as many as the fates of death have not borne away.

It was as it were but yesterday or the day before that the Achaians' ships were gathering in Aulis, freighted with trouble for Priam and the Trojans; and we round about a spring were offering on the holy altars unblemished hecatombs to the immortals, beneath a fair plane-tree whence flowed bright water, when there was seen a great portent; a snake blood-red on the back, terrible, whom the god of Olympus himself had sent forth to the light of day, sprang from beneath the altar and darted to the plane-tree. Now there were there the brood of a sparrow, tender little ones, upon the topmost branch, nestling beneath the leaves; eight were they and the mother of the little ones was the ninth, and the snake swallowed these cheeping pitifully. And the mother fluttered around wailing for her dear little ones; but he coiled himself and caught her by the wing as she screamed about him. Now when he had swallowed the sparrow's little ones and the mother with them, the god who revealed him made of him a sign; for the son of crooked-counselling Kronos turned him to stone, and we stood by and marvelled to see what was done. So when the dread portent brake in upon the hecatombs of the gods, then did Kalchas forthwith prophesy, and said: 'Why hold ye your peace, ye flowing-haired Achaians? To us hath Zeus the counsellor shown this great sign, late come, of late fulfilment, the fame whereof shall never perish. Even as he swallowed the sparrow's little ones and herself, the eight wherewith the mother that bare the little ones was the ninth, so shall we war there so many years, but in the tenth year shall we take the wide-wayed city.' So spake the seer; and now are all these things being fulfilled. So come, abide ye all, ye well-greaved Achaians, even where ye are, until we have taken the great city of Priam."

So spake he, and the Argives shouted aloud, and all round the ships echoed terribly to the voice of the Achaians as they praised the saying of godlike Odysseus. And then spake among them knightly Nestor of Gerenia: "Out on it; in very truth ye hold assembly like silly boys that have no care for deeds of war. What shall come of our covenants and our oaths? Let all counsels be cast into the fire and all devices of warriors and the pure drink-offerings and the right hands of fellowship wherein we trusted. For we are vainly striving with words nor can we find any device at all, for all our long tarrying here. Son of Atreus, do thou still, as erst, keep steadfast purpose and lead the Argives amid the violent fray; and for these, let them perish, the one or two Achaians that take secret counsel—though fulfilment shall not come thereof—to depart to Argos first, before they know whether the promise of aegis-bearing Zeus be a lie or no. Yea, for I say that most mighty Kronion pledged us his word that day when the Argives embarked upon their fleet ships, bearing unto the Trojans death and fate; for by his lightning upon our right he manifested signs of good. Therefore let no man hasten to depart home till each have lain by some Trojan's wife and paid back his strivings and groans for Helen's sake. But if any man is overmuch desirous to depart homewards, let him lay his hand upon his decked black ship, that before all men he may encounter death and fate. But do thou, my king, take good counsel thyself, and hearken to another that shall give it; the word that I speak, whate'er it be, shall not be cast away. Separate thy warriors by tribes and by clans, Agamemnon, that clan may give aid to clan and tribe to tribe. If thou do thus and the Achaians hearken to thee, then wilt thou know who among thy captains and who of the common sort is a coward, and who too is brave; for they will fight each after their sort. So wilt thou know whether it is even by divine command that thou shalt not take the city, or by the baseness of thy warriors and their ill skill in battle."

And lord Agamemnon answered and said to him: "Verily hast thou again outdone the sons of the Achaians in speech, old man. Ah, father Zeus and Athene and Apollo, would that among the Achaians I had ten such councillors; then would the city of king Priam soon bow beneath our hands, captive and wasted. But aegis-bearing Zeus, the son of Kronos, hath brought sorrows upon me, in that he casteth my lot amid fruitless wranglings and strifes. For in truth I and Achilles fought about a damsel with violent words, and I was first to be angry; but if we can only be at one in council, then will there no more be any putting off the day of evil for the Trojans, no not for an instant. But now go ye to your meal that we may join battle. Let each man sharpen well his spear and bestow well his shield, and let him well give his fleet-footed steeds their meal, and look well to his chariot on every side and take thought for battle, that all day long we may contend in hateful war. For of respite shall there intervene no, not a whit, only that the coming of night shall part the fury of warriors. On each man's breast shall the baldrick of his covering shield be wet with sweat, and his hand shall grow faint about the spear, and each man's horse shall sweat as he draweth the polished chariot. And whomsoever I perceive minded to tarry far from the fight beside the beaked ships, for him shall there be no hope hereafter to escape the dogs and birds of prey."

So spake he, and the Argives shouted aloud, like to a wave on a steep shore, when the south wind cometh and stirreth it; even on a jutting rock, that is never left at peace by the waves of all winds that rise from this side and from that. And they stood up and scattered in haste throughout the ships, and made fires in the huts and took their meal. And they did sacrifice each man to one of the everlasting gods, praying for escape from death and the tumult of battle. But Agamemnon king of men slew a fat bull of five years to most mighty Kronion, and called the elders, the princes of the Achaian host, Nestor first and king Idomeneus, and then the two Aiantes and Tydeus' son, and sixthly Odysseus peer of Zeus in counsel. And Menelaos of the loud war-cry came to him unbidden, for he knew in his heart how his brother toiled. Then stood they around the bull and took the barley meal. And Agamemnon made his prayer in their midst and said: "Zeus, most glorious, most great, god of the storm-cloud, that dwellest in the heaven, vouchsafe that the sun set not upon us nor the darkness come near, till I have laid low upon the earth Priam's palace smirched with smoke, and burnt the doorways thereof with consuming fire, and rent on Hector's breast his doublet cleft with the blade; and about him may full many of his comrades prone in the dust bite the earth."

So spake he, but not as yet would Kronion grant him fulfilment; he accepted the sacrifice, but made toil to wax unceasingly.

Now when they had prayed and sprinkled the barley meal they first drew back the bull's head and cut his throat and flayed him, and cut slices from the thighs and wrapped them in fat, making a double fold, and laid raw collops thereon. And these they burnt on cleft wood stript of leaves, and spitted the vitals and held them over Hephaistos' flame. Now when the thighs were burnt and they had tasted the vitals, then sliced they all the rest and pierced it through with spits, and roasted it carefully and drew all off again. So when they had rest from the task and had made ready the banquet, they feasted, nor was their heart aught stinted of the fair banquet. But when they had put away from them the desire of meat and drink, then did knightly Nestor of Gerenia open his saying to them: "Most noble son of Atreus, Agamemnon king of men, let us not any more hold long converse here, nor for long delay the work that god putteth in our hands; but come, let the heralds of the mail-clad Achaians make proclamation to the folk and gather them throughout the ships; and let us go thus in concert through the wide host of the Achaians, that the speedier we may arouse keen war."

So spake he and Agamemnon king of men disregarded not. Straightway he bade the clear-voiced heralds summon to battle the flowing-haired Achaians. So those summoned and these gathered with all speed. And the kings, the fosterlings of Zeus that were about Atreus' son, eagerly marshalled them, and bright-eyed Athene in the midst, bearing the holy aegis that knoweth neither age nor death, whereon wave an hundred tassels of pure gold, all deftly woven and each one an hundred oxen worth. Therewith she passed dazzling through the Achaian folk, urging them forth; and in every man's heart she roused strength to battle without ceasing and to fight. So was war made sweeter to them than to depart in their hollow ships to their dear native land. Even as ravaging fire kindleth a boundless forest on a mountain's peaks, and the blaze is seen from afar, even so as they marched went the dazzling gleam from the innumerable bronze through the sky even unto the heavens.

And as the many tribes of feathered birds, wild geese or cranes or long-necked swans, on the Asian mead by Kaystrios' stream, fly hither and thither joying in their plumage, and with loud cries settle ever onwards, and the mead resounds; even so poured forth the many tribes of warriors from ships and huts into the Skamandrian plain. And the earth echoed terribly beneath the tread of men and horses. So stood they in the flowery Skamandrian plain, unnumbered as are leaves and flowers in their season. Even as the many tribes of thick flies that hover about a herdsman's steading in the spring season, when milk drencheth the pails, even in like number stood the flowing-haired Achaians upon the plain in face of the Trojans, eager to rend them asunder. And even as the goatherds easily divide the ranging flocks of goats when they mingle in the pasture, so did their captains marshal them on this side and on that, to enter into the fray, and in their midst lord Agamemnon, his head and eyes like unto Zeus whose joy is in the thunder, and his waist like unto Ares and his breast unto Poseidon. Even as a bull standeth out far foremost amid the herd, for he is pre-eminent amid the pasturing kine, even such did Zeus make Atreides on that day, pre-eminent among many and chief amid heroes.

Tell me now, ye Muses that dwell in the mansions of Olympus—seeing that ye are goddesses and are at hand and know all things, but we hear only a rumour and know not anything—who were the captains of the Danaans and their lords. But the common sort could I not number nor name, nay, not if ten tongues were mine and ten mouths, and a voice unwearied, and my heart of bronze within me, did not the Muses of Olympus, daughters of aegis-bearing Zeus, put into my mind all that came to Ilios. So will I tell the captains of the ships and all the ships in order.

Of the Boiotians Peneleos and Leitos were captains, and Arkesilaos and Prothoënor and Klonios; these were they that dwelt in Hyria and rocky Aulis and Schoinos and Skolos and Eteonos full of ridges, Thespeia and Graia and Mykalessos with wide lawns; and that dwelt about Harma and Eilesion and Erythrai, and they that possessed Eleon and Peteon and Hyle, Okalea and the stablished fortress of Medeon, Kopai and Eutresis and Thisbe haunt of doves; and they of Koroneia and grassy Haliartos, and that possessed Plataia and that dwelt in Glisas, and that possessed the stablished fortress of lesser Thebes and holy Onchestos, Poseidon's bright grove; and that possessed Arne rich in vineyards, and Mideia and sacred Nisa and Anthedon on the furthest borders. Of these there came fifty ships, and in each one embarked young men of the Boiotians an hundred and twenty. And they that dwelt in Aspledon and Orchomenos of the Minyai were led of Askalaphos and Ialmenos, sons of Ares, whom Astyoche conceived of the mighty god in the palace of Aktor son of Azeus, having entered her upper chamber, a stately maiden; for mighty Ares lay with her privily. And with them sailed thirty hollow ships.

And the Phokians were led of Schedios and Epistrophos,

sons of great-hearted Iphitos son of Naubolos; these were they that possessed Kyparissos and rocky Pytho and sacred Krisa and Daulis and Panopeus, and they that dwelt about Anemoreia and Hyampolis, yea, and they that lived by the goodly river Kephisos and possessed Lilaia by Kephisos' springs. And with them followed forty black ships. So they marshalled the ranks of the Phokians diligently, and had their station hard by the Boiotians on the left.

And of the Lokrians the fleet son of Oileus was captain, Aias the less, that was not so great as was the Telamonian Aias but far less. Small was he, with linen corslet, but with the spear he far outdid all the Hellenes and Achaians. These were they that dwelt in Kynos and Opus and Kalliaros and Bessa and Skarphe and lovely Augeiai and Tarphe and Thronion, about the streams of Boagrios. And with Aias followed forty black ships of the Lokrians that dwell over against holy Euboia.

And the Abantes breathing fury, they that possessed Euboia and Chalkis and Eiretria and Histiaia rich in vines, and Kerinthos by the sea and the steep fortress of Dios, and they that possessed Karystos, and they that dwelt in Styra, all these again were led of Elephenor of the stock of Ares, even the son of Chalkodon, and captain of the proud Abantes. And with him followed the fleet Abantes with hair flowing behind, spearmen eager with ashen shafts outstretched to tear the corslets on the breasts of the foes. And with him forty black ships followed.

And they that possessed the goodly citadel of Athens, the domain of Erechtheus the high-hearted, whom erst Athene daughter of Zeus fostered when Earth, the grain-giver, brought him to birth;—and she gave him a resting-place in Athens in her own rich sanctuary; and there the sons of the Athenians worship him with bulls and rams as the years turn in their courses—these again were led of Menestheus son of Peteos. And there was no man upon the face of earth that was like him for the marshalling of horsemen and warriors that bear the shield. Only Nestor rivalled him, for he was the elder by birth. And with him fifty black ships followed.

And Aias led twelve ships from Salamis, [and brought them and set them where the battalions of the Athenians stood].

And they that possessed Argos and Tiryns of the great walls, Hermione and Asine that enfold the deep gulf, Troizen and Eïonai and Epidauros full of vines, and the youths of the Achaians that possessed Aigina and Mases, these were led of Diomedes of the loud war-cry and Sthenelos, dear son of famous Kapaneus. And the third with them came Euryalos, a godlike warrior, the son of king Mekisteus son of Talaos. But Diomedes of the loud war-cry was lord over all. And with them eighty black ships followed.

And of them that possessed the stablished fortress of Mykene and wealthy Corinth and stablished Kleonai, and dwelt in Orneiai and lovely Araithyrea and Sikyon, wherein Adrestos was king at the first; and of them that possessed Hyperesie and steep Gonoessa and Pellene, and dwelt about Aigion and through all the coast-land and about broad Helike, of them did lord Agamemnon son of Atreus lead an hundred ships. With him followed most and goodliest folk by far; and in their midst himself was clad in flashing bronze, all glorious, and was pre-eminent amid all warriors, because he was goodliest and led folk far greatest in number.

And of them that possessed Lakedaimon lying low amid the rifted hills, and Pharis and Sparta and Messe, the haunt of doves, and dwelt in Bryseiai and lovely Augeiai, and of them too that possessed Amyklai and the sea-coast fortress of Helos, and that possessed Laas and dwelt about Oitylos, of these was the king's brother leader, even Menelaos of the loud war-cry, leader of sixty ships, and these were arrayed apart. And himself marched among them confident in his zeal, urging his men to battle: and his heart most of all was set to take vengeance for his strivings and groans for Helen's sake.

And of them that dwelt in Pylos and lovely Arene and Thryon the fording-place of Alpheios, and in stablished Aipy, and were inhabitants of Kyparisseis and Amphigeneia and Pteleos and Helos and Dorion—where the Muses met Thamyris the Thracian, and made an end of his singing, as he was faring from Oichalia, from Eurytos the Oichalian; for he averred with boasting that he would conquer, even did the Muses themselves sing against him, the daughters of aegis-bearing Zeus; but they in their anger maimed him, moreover they took from him the high gift of song and made him to forget his harping—of all these was knightly Nestor of Gerenia leader, and with him sailed ninety hollow ships.

And of them that possessed Arkadia beneath the steep mountain of Kyllene, beside the tomb of Aipytos, where are warriors that fight hand to hand; and of them that dwelt in Pheneos and Orchomenos abounding in flocks, and Rhipe and Stratie and windy Enispe, and that possessed Tegea and lovely Mantineia, and possessed Stymphelos and dwelt in Parrhasie, of these was Ankaios' son lord Agapenor leader, even of sixty ships; and in each ship embarked many Arkadian warriors skilled in fight. For Agamemnon king of men himself gave them benched ships wherewith to cross the wine-dark sea, even he the son of Atreus; for matters of seafaring concerned them not.

And they too that inhabited Bouprasion and goodly Elis, so much thereof as Hyrmine and Myrsinos upon the borders and the Olenian rock and Aleision bound between them, of these men there were four captains, and ten swift ships followed each one, and many Epeians embarked thereon. So some were led of Amphimachos and Thalpios, of the lineage of Aktor, sons one of Kteatos and one of Eurytos; and of some was stalwart Diores captain, son of Amarynkes;

and of the fourth company godlike Polyxeinos was captain, son of king Agasthenes Augeias' son.

And them of Doulichion and the holy Echinean Isles that stand beyond the sea over against Elis, even these did Meges lead, the peer of Ares, Phyleides to wit, for he was begotten of knightly Phyleus dear to Zeus, him that erst changed his habitation to Doulichion for anger against his father. And with him followed forty black ships.

And Odysseus led the great-hearted Kephallenians, them that possessed Ithaka and Neriton with quivering leafage, and dwelt in Krokyleia and rugged Aigilips, and them that possessed Zakynthos and that dwelt in Samos, and possessed the mainland and dwelt in the parts over against the isles. Them did Odysseus lead, the peer of Zeus in counsel, and with him followed twelve ships with vermilion prow.

And of the Aitolians Thoas was captain, the son of Andraimon, even of them that dwelt in Pleuron and Olenos and Pylene, and Chalkis on the sea-shore and rocky Kalydon. For the sons of great-hearted Oineus were no more, neither did he still live, and golden-haired Meleagros was dead, to whose hands all had been committed, for him to be king of the Aitolians. And with Thoas there followed forty black ships.

And of the Cretans Idomeneus the famous spearman was leader, even of them that possessed Knosos and Gortys of the great walls, Lyktos and Miletos and chalky Lykastos and Phaistos and Rhytion, stablished cities all; and of all others that dwelt in Crete of the hundred cities. Of these men was Idomeneus the famous spearman leader, and Meriones peer of the man-slaying war-god. With these followed eighty black ships.

And Tlepolemos, Herakles' son goodly and tall, led from Rhodes nine ships of the lordly Rhodians, that dwelt in Rhodes in threefold ordering, in Lindos and Ialysos and chalky Kameiros. These were led of Tlepolemos the famous spearman, that was born to great Herakles by Astyocheia, whom he had brought away from Ephyre by the river Selleëis, when he laid waste many cities of strong men, fosterlings of Zeus. Now when Tlepolemos had grown to manhood within the strong palace walls, anon he slew his own father's dear uncle, an old man now, Likymnios of the stock of Ares. Then with speed built he ships and gathered much folk together, and went fleeing across the deep, because the other sons and grandsons of great Herakles threatened him. So he came to Rhodes a wanderer, enduring hardships, and his folk settled by kinship in three tribes, and were loved of Zeus that is king among gods and men; and Kronion poured upon them exceeding great wealth.

Nireus, moreover, led three trim ships from Syme, Nireus son of Aglaia and king Charopos, Nireus the most beauteous man that came up under Ilios of all the Danaans, after the noble son of Peleus. Howbeit he was a weakling, and a scanty host followed him.

And of them that possessed Nisyros and Krapathos and Kasos and Kos the city of Eurypylos, and the Kalydnian Isles, of them Pheidippos and Antiphos were leaders, the two sons of king Thessalos son of Herakles. With them were arrayed thirty hollow ships.

Now all moreover that dwelt in the Pelasgian Argos and inhabited Alos and Alope and Trachis and possessed Phthia and Hellas the home of fair women, and were called Myrmidons and Hellenes and Achaians; of all these, even fifty ships, Achilles was captain. But these took no thought of noisy war; for there was no man to array them in line of battle. For fleet-footed goodly Achilles lay idle amid the ships, wroth for the sake of a damsel, Briseis of the lovely hair, whom he had won from Lyrnessos with much travail, what time he laid waste Lyrnessos and the walls of Thebe, and overthrew Mynes and Epistrophos, warriors that bare the spear, sons of king Euenos Selepos' son. For her sake lay Achilles sorrowing; but soon was he to arise again.

And of them that possessed Phylake and flowery Pyrasos, Demeter's sanctuary, and Iton mother of flocks, and Antron by the sea-shore and Pteleos couched in grass, of all these was warlike Protesilaos leader while yet he lived; but now ere this the black earth held him fast. His wife with marred visage was left alone in Phylake, yea, and his bridal chamber half builded; for a Dardanian warrior slew him as he leapt from his ship far first of the Achaians. Yet neither were his men leaderless, though they sorrowed for their leader; for Podarkes of the stock of Ares marshalled them, son of Phylakos' son Iphiklos was he, the lord of many flocks, own brother of great-hearted Protesilaos, and younger-born than he: but the other was alike the elder and the braver, even Protesilaos, that mighty man of war. Yet did not the host lack at all a leader, only they yearned for the noble dead. With him followed forty black ships.

And of them that dwelt in Pherai by the Boibeian mere, in Boibe and Glaphyre and stablished Iolkos, of them, even eleven ships, Admetos' dear son was leader, Eumelos whom Alkestis, fair among women, bare to Admetos, she that was most beauteous to look upon of the daughters of Pelias.

And of them that dwelt in Methone and Thaumakie, and possessed Meliboia and rugged Olizon, of these, even seven ships, was Philoktetes leader, the cunning archer; and in each ship sailed fifty oarsmen skilled to fight amain with the bow. But their captain lay enduring sore pain in the isle of goodly Lemnos, where the sons of the Achaians left him sick of a grievous wound from a deadly water-snake. There lay he pining; yet were the Argives soon to bethink them beside their ships of king Philoktetes. Yet neither were his men leaderless, only they sorrowed for their leader; but Medon marshalled them, Oileus' bastard son, whom Rhene bare to Oileus waster of cities.

And of them that possessed Trikke and terraced Ithome and that possessed Oichalia city of Eurytos the Oichalian, of these again Asklepios' two sons were leaders, the cunning leeches Podaleirios and Machaon. And with them were arrayed thirty hollow ships.

And of them that possessed Ormenios and the fountain of Hypereia, and possessed Asterion and the white crests of Titanos, of these was Eurypylos leader, Euaimon's glorious son; and with him forty black ships followed.

And of them that possessed Argissa and dwelt in Gyrtona, Orthe and Elone and the white city of Oloosson, of these was captain unflinching Polypoites, son of Peirithoos that immortal Zeus begat: and Polypoites did famed Hippodameia conceive of Peirithoos on that day when he took vengeance of the shaggy wild folk, and thrust them forth from Pelion and drave them to the Aithikes. And Polypoites ruled not alone, but with him was Leonteus of the stock of Ares, son of high-hearted Koronos Kaineus' son. And with them forty black ships followed.

And Gouneus from Kyphos led two-and-twenty ships, and with him followed the Enienes and unflinching Peraibians that had pitched their homes about wintry Dodona, and dwelt on the tilth about lovely Titaresios that poureth his fair-flowing stream into Peneios. Yet doth he not mingle with the silver eddies of Peneios, but floweth on over him like unto oil, seeing that he is an offspring from the water of Styx, the dread river of the oath.

And the Magnetes were led of Prothoos son of Tenthredon, even they that dwelt about Peneios and Pelion with trembling leafage. These did fleet Prothoos lead, and with him forty black ships followed.

So these were the leaders of the Danaans and their captains. Now tell me, O Muse, who among them was first and foremost, of warriors alike and horses that followed the sons of Atreus. Of horses they of Pheres' son were far goodliest, those that Eumelos drave, swift as birds, like of coat, like of age, matched to the measure of a levelling line across their backs. These were reared in Peraia by Apollo of the silver bow, two mares carrying onward the terror of battle. But of warriors far best was the Telamonian Aias, while the wrath of Achilles yet endured; for he was greatest of all, he and his horses that bore him, even Peleus' noble son. But he lay idle among his seafaring ships, in sore wrath against Agamemnon Atreus' son, shepherd of the host; and his folk along the sea-shore sported with quoits and with casting of javelins and archery; and the horses each beside his own chariot stood idle, champing clover and parsley of the marsh, and their lords' chariots lay well covered up within the huts, while the men yearned for their warrior chief, and wandered hither and thither through the camp and fought not.

So marched they then as though all the land were consuming with fire; and the earth groaned beneath them as at the wrath of Zeus whose joy is in the thunder, when he lasheth the earth about Typhoeus in the country of the Arimoi, where men say is Typhoeus' couch. Even so groaned the earth aloud at their tread as they went: and with speed advanced they across the plain.

Now fleet Iris the wind-footed went to the Trojans, a messenger from aegis-bearing Zeus, with a grievous message. These were holding assembly at Priam's gate, being gathered all together both young men and old. And fleet-footed Iris stood hard by and spake to them; and she made her voice like to the voice of Polites son of Priam, who was the sentinel of the Trojans and was wont to sit trusting in his fleetness upon the barrow of Aisyetes of old, and on the top thereof wait the sallying of the Achaians forth from their ships. Even in his likeness did fleet-footed Iris speak to Priam: "Old man, words beyond number are still pleasant to thee as erst in the days of peace; but war without respite is upon us. Of a truth have I very oft ere now entered into battles of the warriors, yet have I never seen so goodly a host and so great; for in the very likeness of the leaves of the forest or the sands of the sea are they marching along the plain to fight against the city. But Hector, thee do I charge beyond all to do even as I shall say. Seeing that the allies are very many throughout Priam's great city, and diverse men, being scattered abroad, have diverse tongues; therefore let each one give the word to those whose chieftain he is, and them let him lead forth and have the ordering of his countrymen."

So spake she, and Hector failed not to know the voice of the goddess, and straightway dismissed the assembly, and they rushed to arms. And the gates were thrown open wide, and the host issued forth, footmen and horsemen, and mighty din arose.

Now there is before the city a certain steep mound apart in the plain, with a clear way about it on this side and on that; and men indeed call this "Batieia," but the immortals call it "The tomb of lithe Myrine." There did the Trojans and their allies divide their companies.

Amid the Trojans great Hector of the glancing helm was leader, the son of Priam; with him the greatest hosts by far and the goodliest were arrayed, eager warriors of the spear.

But the Dardanians were led of the princely son of Anchises, Aineias, whom bright Aphrodite conceived to Anchises amid the spurs of Ida, a goddess wedded to a mortal. Neither was he alone; with him were Antenor's two sons, Archelochos and Akamas, well skilled in all the ways of war.

And of them that dwelt in Zeleia beneath the nethermost foot of Ida, the men of substance that drink the dark waters of Aisepos, even the Troes; of these Lykaon's glorious son was leader, Pandaros, to whom Apollo himself gave the bow.

And of them that possessed Adresteia and the land of Apaisos and possessed Pityeia and the steep hill of Tereia, of these Adrestos was captain, and Amphios of the linen corslet, the two sons of Merops of Perkote, that beyond all men knew soothsaying, and would have hindered his children marching to murderous war. But they gave him no heed, for the fates of black death led them on.

And they that dwelt about Perkote and Praktios and possessed Sestos and Abydos and bright Arisbe, these were led of Hyrtakos' son Asios, a prince of men, Asios son of Hyrtakos, whom his tall sorrel steeds brought from Arisbe, from the river Selleëis.

And Hippothoos led the tribes of the Pelasgians that fight with spears, them that inhabited deep-soiled Larisa. These were led of Hippothoos and Pylaios of the stock of Ares, twain sons of Pelasgian Lethos son of Teutamos.

And the Thracians were led of Akamas and hero Peiroos, even all they that the strong stream of Hellespont shutteth in. And Euphemos was captain of the Kikonian spearmen, the son of Troizenos Keos' son, fosterling of Zeus.

But Pyraichmes led the Paionians with curving bows, from far away in Amydon, from the broad stream of Axios, Axios whose water is the fairest that flowest over the face of the earth.

And Pylaimenes of rugged heart led the Paphlagonians from the land of the Eneti, whence is the breed of wild mules. This folk were they that possessed Kytoros and dwelt about Sesamon, and inhabited their famed dwellings round the river Parthenios and Kromna and Aigialos and lofty Erythini.

And the Alizones were led of Odios and Epistrophos, from far away in Alybe, where is the birthplace of silver.

And the Mysians were led of Chromis and Ennomos the augur, yet with all his auguries warded he not black fate from him, but was vanquished by the hand of fleet-footed Aiakides in the river, when he made havoc of the Trojans there and of the rest.

And Phorkys and godlike Askanios led the Phrygians from far Askania, and these were eager to fight in the battle-throng.

And the Maionians were commanded of Mesthles and

Antiphos, Talaimenes' two sons, whose mother was the Gygaian mere. So these led the Maionians, whose birthplace was under Tmolos.

But Nastes led the Karians, uncouth of speech, that possessed Miletos and the mountain of Phthires, of leafage numberless, and the streams of Maiandros and the steep crest of Mykale. These were led of Amphimachos and Nastes: Nastes and Amphimachos the glorious children of Nomion. And he came, forsooth, to battle with golden attire like a girl—fond man: that held not back in any wise grievous destruction, but he was vanquished by the hands of fleet-footed Aiakides in the river, and wise-hearted Achilles carried away his gold.

And Sarpedon and blameless Glaukos led the Lykians from far away in Lykia by eddying Xanthos.

BOOK III

How Menelaos and Paris fought in single combat; and Aphrodite rescued Paris. And how Helen and Priam beheld the Achaian host from the walls of Troy.

Now when they were arrayed, each company with their captains, the Trojans marched with clamour and with shouting like unto birds, even as when there goeth up before heaven a clamour of cranes which flee from the coming of winter and sudden rain, and fly with clamour towards the streams of ocean, bearing slaughter and fate to the Pigmy men, and in early morn offer cruel battle. But on the other side marched the Achaians in silence breathing courage, eager at heart to give succour man to man.

Even as when the south wind sheddeth mist over the crests of a mountain, mist unwelcome to the shepherd, but to the robber better than night, and a man can see no further than he casteth a stone; even so thick arose the gathering dust-clouds at their tread as they went; and with all speed they advanced across the plain.

So when they were now come nigh in onset on each other, godlike Alexandros played champion to the Trojans, wearing upon his shoulders panther-skin and curved bow and sword; and he brandished two bronze-headed spears and challenged all the chieftains of the Argives to fight him man to man in deadly combat. But when Menelaos dear to Ares marked him coming in the forefront of the multitude with long strides, then even as a lion is glad when he lighteth upon a great carcase, a horned stag, or a wild goat that he hath found, being an hungered; and so he devoureth it amain, even though the fleet hounds and lusty youths set upon him;

even thus was Menelaos glad when his eyes beheld godlike Alexandros; for he thought to take vengeance upon the sinner. So straightway he leapt in his armour from his chariot to the ground.

But when godlike Alexandros marked him appear amid the champions, his heart was smitten, and he shrank back into the host of his comrades, avoiding death. And even as a man that hath seen a serpent in a mountain glade starteth backward and trembling seizeth his feet beneath him, and he retreateth back again, and paleness hath hold of his cheeks, even so did godlike Alexandros for fear of Atreus' son shrink back into the throng of lordly Trojans. But Hector beheld and upbraided him with scornful words: "Ill Paris, most fair in semblance, thou deceiver woman-mad, would thou hadst been unborn and died unwed. Yea, that were my desire, and it were far better than thus to be our shame and looked at askance of all men. I ween that the flowing-haired Achaians laugh, deeming that a prince is our champion only because a goodly favour is his; but in his heart is there no strength nor any courage. Art thou indeed such an one that in thy seafaring ships thou didst sail over the deep with the company of thy trusty comrades, and in converse with strangers didst bring back a fair woman from a far country, one that was by marriage daughter to warriors that bear the spear, that she might be a sore mischief to thy father and city and all the realm, but to our foes a rejoicing, and to thyself a hanging of the head? And canst thou not indeed abide Menelaos dear to Ares? Thou mightest see what sort of warrior is he whose lovely wife thou hast. Thy lyre will not avail thee nor the gifts of Aphrodite, those thy locks and fair favour, when thou grovellest in the dust. But the Trojans are very cowards: else ere this hadst thou donned a robe of stone for all the ill thou hast wrought."

And godlike Alexandros made answer to him again: "Hector, since in measure thou chidest me and not beyond measure—thy heart is ever keen, even as an axe that pierceth a beam at the hand of a man that shapeth a ship's timber with skill, and thereby is the man's blow strengthened; even such is thy heart undaunted in thy breast. Cast not in my teeth the lovely gifts of golden Aphrodite; not to be flung aside are the gods' glorious gifts that of their own good will they give; for by his desire can no man win them. But now if thou wilt have me do battle and fight, make the other Trojans sit down and all the Achaians, and set ye me in the midst, and Menelaos dear to Ares, to fight for Helen and all her wealth. And whichsoever shall vanquish and gain the upper hand, let him take all the wealth aright, and the woman, and bear them home. And let the rest pledge friendship and sure oaths; so may ye dwell in deep-soiled Troy, and let them depart to Argos pasture-land of horses, and Achaia home of fair women."

So spake he, and Hector rejoiced greatly to hear his saying, and went into the midst and restrained the battalions of the Trojans, with his spear grasped by the middle; and they all sate them down. But the flowing-haired Achaians kept shooting at him, aiming with arrows and casting stones. But Agamemnon king of men cried aloud: "Refrain, ye Argives; shoot not, ye sons of the Achaians; for Hector of the glancing helm hath set himself to say somewhat."

So spake he, and they refrained from battle and made silence speedily. And Hector spake between the two hosts. "Hear of me, Trojans and well-greaved Achaians, the saying of Alexandros, for whose sake strife hath come about. He biddeth the other Trojans and all the Achaians to lay down their goodly armour on the bounteous earth, and himself in the midst and Menelaos dear to Ares to fight alone for Helen and all her wealth. And whichsoever shall vanquish and gain the upper hand, let him take all the wealth aright, and the woman, and bear them home; but let all of us pledge friendship and sure oaths."

So spake he, and they all kept silence and were still.

Then in their midst spake Menelaos of the loud war-cry: "Hearken ye now to me, too; for into my heart most of all is grief entered; and I deem that the parting of Argives and Trojans hath come at last; seeing ye have endured many ills because of my quarrel and the first sin of Alexandros. And for whichsoever of us death and fate are prepared, let him lie dead: and be ye all parted with speed. Bring ye two lambs, one white ram and one black ewe, for earth and sun; and let us bring one for Zeus. And call hither great Priam, that he may pledge the oath himself, seeing he hath sons that are overweening and faithless, lest any by transgression do violence to the oath of Zeus; for young men's hearts are ever lifted up. But wheresoever an old man entereth in, he looketh both before and after, whereby the best issue shall come for either side."

So spake he, and Achaians and Trojans were glad, deeming that they should have rest from grievous war. So they refrained their chariots to the ranks, and themselves alighted and doffed their arms. And these they laid upon the earth each close to each, and there was but small space between. And Hector sent two heralds to the city with all speed, to bring the lambs, and to call Priam. And lord Agamemnon sent forth Talthybios to go to the hollow ships, and bade him bring a ram; and he was not disobedient to noble Agamemnon.

Now Iris went with a message to white-armed Helen in the likeness of her husband's sister, the spouse of Antenor's son, even her that lord Helikaon Antenor's son had to wife, Laodike fairest favoured of Priam's daughters. And in the hall she found Helen weaving a great purple web of double fold, and embroidering thereon many battles of horse-taming Trojans and mail-clad Achaians, that they had endured for her sake at the hands of Ares. So fleet-footed Iris stood by her side and said: "Come hither, dear sister, that thou mayest see the wondrous doings of horse-taming Trojans and mail-clad Achaians. They that erst waged tearful war upon each other in the plain, eager for deadly battle, even they sit now in silence, and the battle is stayed, and they lean upon their shields, and the tall spears are planted by their sides. But Alexandros and Menelaos dear to Ares will fight with their tall spears for thee; and thou wilt be declared the dear wife of him that conquereth."

So spake the goddess, and put into her heart sweet longing for her former husband and her city and parents.

Forthwith she veiled her face in shining linen, and hastened from her chamber, letting fall a round tear; not unattended, for there followed with her two handmaidens, Aithre daughter of Pittheus and ox-eyed Klymene. Then came she straightway to the place of the Skaian gates. And they that were with Priam and Panthoos and Thymoites and Lampos and Klytios and Hiketaon of the stock of Ares, Oukalegon withal and Antenor, twain sages, being elders of the people, sat at the Skaian gates. These had now ceased from battle for old age, yet were they right good orators, like grasshoppers that in a forest sit upon a tree and utter their lily-like voice; even so sat the elders of the Trojans upon the tower. Now when they saw Helen coming to the tower they softly spake winged words one to the other: "Small blame is it that Trojans and well-greaved Achaians should for such a woman long time suffer hardships; marvellously like is she to the immortal goddesses to look upon. Yet even so, though she be so goodly, let her go upon their ships and not stay to vex us and our children after us."

So said they, and Priam lifted up his voice and called to Helen: "Come hither, dear child, and sit before me, that thou mayest see thy former husband and thy kinsfolk and thy friends. I hold thee not to blame; nay, I hold the gods to blame who brought on me the dolorous war of the Achaians—so mayest thou now tell me who is this huge hero, this Achaian warrior so goodly and great. Of a truth there are others even taller by a head; yet did mine eyes never behold a man so beautiful nor so royal; for he is like unto one that is a king."

And Helen, fair among women, spake and answered him: "Reverend art thou to me and dread, dear father of my lord; would that sore death had been my pleasure when I followed thy son hither, and left my home and my kinsfolk and my daughter in her girlhood and the lovely company of mine age-fellows. But that was not so, wherefore I pine with weeping. Now will I tell thee that whereof thou askest me and enquirest. This is Atreides, wide-ruling Agamemnon, one that is both a goodly king and mighty spearman. And he was husband's brother to me, ah shameless me; if ever such an one there was."

So said she, and the old man marvelled at him, and said: "Ah, happy Atreides, child of fortune, blest of heaven; now know I that many sons of the Achaians are subject to thee. Erewhile fared I to Phrygia, the land of vines, and there saw I that the men of Phrygia, they of the nimble steeds, were very many, even the hosts of Otreus and godlike Mygdon, that were then encamped along the banks of Sangarios. For I too being their ally was numbered among them on the day that the Amazons came, the peers of men. Yet were not even they so many as are the glancing-eyed Achaians."

And next the old man saw Odysseus, and asked: "Come now, tell me of this man too, dear child, who is he, shorter by a head than Agamemnon son of Atreus, but broader of shoulder and of chest to behold? His armour lieth upon the bounteous earth, and himself like a bell-wether rangeth the ranks of warriors. Yea, I liken him to a thick-fleeced ram ordering a great flock of white ewes."

Then Helen sprung of Zeus made answer to him: "Now this is Laertes' son, crafty Odysseus, that was reared in the realm of Ithaka, rugged though it be, and is skilled in all the ways of wile and cunning device."

Then sage Antenor made answer to her: "Lady, verily

the thing thou sayest is true indeed, for erst came goodly Odysseus hither also on an embassage for thee, in the company of Menelaos dear to Ares; and I gave them entertainment and welcomed them in my halls, and learnt the aspect of both and their wise devices. Now when they mingled with the Trojans in the assembly, while all stood up Menelaos overpassed them all by the measure of his broad shoulders; but when both sat down, Odysseus was the more stately. And when they began to weave the web of words and counsel in the face of all, then Menelaos harangued fluently, in few words, but very clearly, seeing he was not long of speech, neither random, though in years he was the younger. But whenever Odysseus full of wiles rose up, he stood and looked down, with eyes fixed upon the ground, and waved not his staff whether backwards or forwards, but held it stiff, like to a man of no understanding; one would deem him to be churlish, and naught but a fool. But when he uttered his great voice from his chest, and words like unto the snowflakes of winter, then could no mortal man contend with Odysseus; then marvelled we not thus to behold Odysseus' aspect."

And thirdly the old man saw Aias, and asked: "Who then is this other Achaian warrior, goodly and great, preeminent among the Argives by the measure of his head and broad shoulders?"

And long-robed Helen, fair among women, answered: "This is huge Aias, bulwark of the Achaians. And on the other side amid the Cretans standeth Idomeneus like a god, and about him are gathered the captains of the Cretans. Oft did Menelaos dear to Ares entertain him in our house whene'er he came from Crete. And now behold I all the other glancing-eyed Achaians, whom well I could discern and tell their names; but two captains of the host can I not see, even Kastor tamer of horses and Polydeukes the skilful boxer, mine own brethren, whom the same mother bare. Either they came not in the company from lovely

Lakedaimon; or they came hither indeed in their seafaring ships, but now will not enter into the battle of the warriors, for fear of the many scornings and revilings that are mine."

So said she; but them the life-giving earth held fast there in Lakedaimon, in their dear native land.

Meanwhile were the heralds bearing through the city the holy oath-offerings, two lambs and strong-hearted wine, the fruit of the earth, in a goat-skin bottle. And the herald Idaios bare the shining bowl and golden cups; and came to the old man and summoned him and said: "Rise, thou son of Laomedon. The chieftains of the horse-taming Trojans and mail-clad Achaians call on thee to go down into the plain, that ye may pledge a trusty oath. But Alexandros and Menelaos dear to Ares will fight with their long spears for the lady's sake; and let lady and treasure go with him that shall conquer. And may we that are left pledge friendship and trusty oaths and dwell in deep-soiled Troy, and they shall depart to Argos pasture-land of horses and Achaia home of fair women."

So said he, and the old man shuddered and bade his companions yoke the horses; and they with speed obeyed. Then Priam mounted and drew back the reins, and by his side Antenor mounted the splendid chariot. So the two drave the fleet horses through the Skaian gates to the plain. And when they had come even to the Trojans and Achaians, they went down from the chariots upon the bounteous earth, and marched into the midst of Trojans and Achaians. Then forthwith rose up Agamemnon king of men, and up rose Odysseus the man of wiles; and the lordly heralds gathered together the holy oath-offerings of the gods, and mingled the wine in a bowl, and poured water over the princes' hands. And Atreides put forth his hand and drew his knife that hung ever beside his sword's great sheath, and cut the hair from off the lambs' heads; and then the heralds portioned it among the chief of the Trojans and Achaians. Then in their midst Atreus' son lifted up his hands and prayed aloud: "Father Zeus, that rulest from Ida, most glorious, most great, and thou Sun that seest all things and hearest all things, and ye Rivers and thou Earth, and ye that in the underworld punish men outworn, whosoever sweareth falsely; be ye witnesses, and watch over the faithful oath. If Alexandros slay Menelaos, then let him have Helen to himself and all her possessions; and we will depart on our seafaring ships. But if golden-haired Menelaos slay Alexandros, then let the Trojans give back Helen and all her possessions and pay the Argives the recompense that is seemly, such as shall live among men that shall be hereafter. But if so be that Priam and Priam's sons will not pay the recompense unto me when Alexandros falleth, then will I fight on thereafter for the price of sin, and abide here till I compass the end of war."

So said he, and cut the lambs' throats with the pitiless knife. Them he laid gasping upon the ground, failing of breath, for the knife had taken their strength from them; and next they drew the wine from the bowl into the cups, and poured it forth and prayed to the gods that live for ever. And thus would say many an one of Achaians and Trojans: "Zeus most glorious, most great, and all ye immortal gods, which folk soe'er be first to sin against the oaths, may their brains be so poured forth upon the earth even as wine, theirs and their children's and let their wives be made subject unto strangers."

So spake they, but the son of Kronos vouchsafed not yet fulfilment. And in their midst Priam of the seed of Dardanos uttered his saying: "Hearken to me, Trojans and well-greaved Achaians. I verily will return back to windy Ilios, seeing that I can in no wise bear to behold with mine eyes my dear son fighting with Menelaos dear to Ares. But Zeus knoweth, and all the immortal gods, for whether of the twain the doom of death is appointed."

So spake the godlike man, and laid the lambs in his chariot, and entered in himself, and drew back the reins;

and by his side Antenor mounted the splendid chariot. So they departed back again to Ilios; and Hector son of Priam and goodly Odysseus first meted out a space, and then they took the lots, and shook them in a bronze-bound helmet, to know whether of the twain should first cast his spear of bronze. And the people prayed and lifted up their hands to the gods; and thus would say many an one of Achaians and Trojans: "Father Zeus, that rulest from Ida, most glorious, most great; whichsoe'er it be that brought this trouble upon both peoples, vouchsafe that he may die and enter the house of Hades; that so for us peace may be assured and trusty oaths."

So said they; and great Hector of the glancing plume shook the helmet, looking behind him; and quickly leapt forth the lot of Paris. Then the people sat them down by ranks where each man's high-stepping horses and inwrought armour lay. And upon his shoulders goodly Alexandros donned his beauteous armour, even he that was lord to Helen of the lovely hair. First upon his legs set he his greaves, beautiful, fastened with silver ankle-clasps; next upon his breast he donned the corslet of his brother Lykaon, and fitted it upon himself. And over his shoulders cast he his silver-studded sword of bronze, and then a shield great and sturdy. And on his mighty head he set a wrought helmet of horse-hair crest, whereover the plume nodded terribly, and he took him a strong spear fitted to his grasp. And in like wise warlike Menelaos donned his armour.

So when they had armed themselves on either side in the throng, they strode between Trojans and Achaians, fierce of aspect, and wonder came on them that beheld, both on the Trojans tamers of horses and on the well-greaved Achaians. Then took they their stand near together in the measured space, brandishing their spears in wrath each against other. First Alexandros hurled his far-shadowing spear, and smote on Atreides' round shield; but the bronze brake not through, for its point was turned in the stout shield. Next Menelaos son of Atreus lifted up his hand to cast, and made prayer to father Zeus: "King Zeus, grant me revenge on him that was first to do me wrong, even on goodly Alexandros, and subdue thou him at my hands; so that many an one of men that shall be hereafter may shudder to wrong his host that hath shown him kindness."

So said he, and poised his far-shadowing spear, and hurled, and smote on the round shield of the son of Priam. Through the bright shield went the ponderous spear and through the inwrought breastplate it pressed on; and straight beside his flank the spear rent the tunic, but he swerved and escaped black death. Then Atreides drew his silver-studded sword, and lifted up his hand and smote the helmet-ridge; but the sword shattered upon it into three, yea four, and fell from his hand. Thereat Atreides looked up to the wide heaven and cried: "Father Zeus, surely none of the gods is crueller than you. Verily I thought to have gotten vengeance on Alexandros for his wickedness, but now my sword breaketh in my hand, and my spear sped from my grasp in vain, and I have not smitten him."

So saying, he leapt upon him and caught him by his horse-hair crest, and swinging him round dragged him towards the well-greaved Achaians; and he was strangled by the embroidered strap beneath his soft throat, drawn tight below his chin to hold his helm. Now would Menelaos have dragged him away and won glory unspeakable, but that Zeus' daughter Aphrodite was swift to mark, and tore asunder for him the strap of slaughtered ox's hide; so the helmet came away empty in his stalwart hand. Thereat Menelaos cast it with a swing toward the well-greaved Achaians, and his trusty comrades took it up; and himself sprang back again eager to slay him with spear of bronze. But Aphrodite snatched up Paris, very easily as a goddess may, and hid him in thick darkness, and set him down in his fragrant perfumed chamber; and herself went to summon Helen. Her she found on the high tower, and about her the Trojan women thronged. So with her hand she plucked her perfumed raiment and shook it and spake to her in the likeness of an aged dame, a woolcomber that was wont to work for her fair wool when she dwelt in Lakedaimon, whom too she greatly loved. Even in her likeness fair Aphrodite spake: "Come hither; Alexandros summoneth thee to go homeward. There is he in his chamber and inlaid bed, radiant in beauty and vesture; nor wouldst thou deem him to be come from fighting his foe, but rather to be faring to the dance, or from the dance to be just resting and set down."

So said she, and stirred Helen's soul within her breast; and when now she marked the fair neck and lovely breast and sparkling eyes of the goddess, she marvelled straightway and spake a word and called upon her name: "Strange queen, why art thou desirous now to beguile me? Verily thou wilt lead me further on to some one of the peopled cities of Phrygia or lovely Maionia, if there too thou hast perchance some other darling among mortal men, because even now Menelaos hath conquered goodly Alexandros, and will lead me, accursed me, to his home. Therefore thou comest hither with guileful intent. Go and sit thou by his side, and depart from the way of the gods; neither let thy feet ever bear thee back to Olympus, but still be vexed for his sake and guard him till he make thee his wife or perchance his slave. But thither will I not go—that were a sinful thing—to array the bed of him; all the women of Troy will blame me hereafter; and I have griefs untold within my soul."

Then in wrath bright Aphrodite spake to her: "Provoke me not, rash woman, lest in mine anger I desert thee, and hate thee even as now I love thee beyond measure, and lest I devise grievous enmities between both, even betwixt Trojans and Achaians, and so thou perish in evil wise."

So said she, and Helen sprung of Zeus was afraid, and went wrapped in her bright radiant vesture, silently, and the

Trojan women marked her not; and the goddess led the way.

Now when they were come to the beautiful house of Alexandros the handmaidens turned straightway to their tasks, and the fair lady went to the high-roofed chamber; and laughter-loving Aphrodite took for her a chair and brought it, even she the goddess, and set it before the face of Paris. There Helen took her seat, the child of aegis-bearing Zeus, and with eyes turned askance spake and chode her lord: "Thou comest back from battle; would thou hadst perished there, vanquished of that great warrior that was my former husband. Verily it was once thy boast that thou wast a better man than Menelaos dear to Ares, in the might of thine arm and thy spear. But go, now, challenge Menelaos dear to Ares to fight thee again face to face. Nay, but I, even I, bid thee refrain, nor fight a fight with golden-haired Menelaos man to man, neither attack him recklessly, lest perchance thou fall to his spear anon."

And Paris made answer to her and said: "Chide not my soul, lady, with cruel taunts. For now indeed hath Menelaos vanquished me with Athene's aid, but another day may I do so unto him; for we too have gods with us. But come now, let us have joy of love upon our couch; for never yet hath love so enwrapped my heart—not even then when first I snatched thee from lovely Lakedaimon and sailed with thee on my seafaring ships, and in the isle of Kranaë had converse with thee upon thy couch in love—as I love thee now and sweet desire taketh hold upon me." So saying he led the way to the couch, and the lady followed with him.

Thus laid they them upon their fretted couch; but Atreides the while strode through the host like to a wild beast, if anywhere he might set eyes on godlike Alexandros. But none of the Trojans or their famed allies could discover Alexandros to Menelaos dear to Ares. Yet surely did they in no wise hide him for kindliness, could any have seen him; for he was hated of all even as black death. So

Agamemnon king of men spake among them there: "Hearken to me, Trojans and Dardanians and allies. Now is victory declared for Menelaos dear to Ares; give ye back Helen of Argos and the possessions with her, and pay ye the recompense such as is seemly, that it may live even among men that shall be hereafter." So said Atreides, and all the Achaians gave assent.

BOOK IV

How Pandaros wounded Menelaos by treachery; and Agamemnon exhorted his chief captains to battle.

Now the gods sat by Zeus and held assembly on the golden floor, and in the midst the lady Hebe poured them their nectar: they with golden goblets pledged one another, and gazed upon the city of the Trojans. Then did Kronos' son essay to provoke Hera with vexing words, and spake maliciously: "Twain goddesses hath Menelaos for his helpers, even Hera of Argos and Alalkomenean Athene. Yet these sit apart and take their pleasure in beholding; but beside that other ever standeth laughter-loving Aphrodite and wardeth off fate from him, and now hath she saved him as he thought to perish. But of a truth the victory is to Menelaos dear to Ares; so let us take thought how these things shall be; whether once more we shall arouse ill war and the dread battle-din, or put friendship between the foes. Moreover if this were welcome to all and well pleasing, may the city of king Priam yet be an habitation, and Menelaos take back Helen of Argos."

So said he, but Athene and Hera murmured thereat, who were sitting by him and devising ills for the Trojans. Now Athene held her peace and said not anything, for wrath at father Zeus, and fierce anger gat hold upon her: but Hera's breast contained not her anger, and she spake: "Most dread son of Kronos, what word is this thou hast spoken? How hast thou the will to make my labour void and of none effect, and the sweat of my toil that I sweated, when my horses were wearied with my summoning of the host, to be the plague of Priam and his sons? Do as thou wilt; but we other gods do not all approve thee."

Then in sore anger Zeus the cloud-gatherer spake to her: "Good lack, how have Priam and Priam's son done thee such great wrong that thou art furiously minded to sack the stablished citadel of Ilios? Perchance wert thou to enter within the gates and long walls and devour Priam raw, and Priam's sons and all the Trojans, then mightest thou assuage thine anger. Do as thou art minded, only let not this quarrel hereafter be to me and thee a sore strife between us both. And this moreover will I say to thee, and do thou lay it to thy heart; whene'er I too be of eager mind to lay waste a city where is the race of men that are dear to thee, hinder thou not my wrath, but let me be, even as I yield to thee of free will, yet with soul unwilling. For of all cities beneath sun and starry heaven that are the dwelling of mortal men, holy Ilios was most honoured of my heart, and Priam and the folk of Priam of the good ashen spear. For never did mine altar lack the seemly feast, even drink-offering and burnt-offering, the worship that is our due."

Then Hera the ox-eyed queen made answer to him: "Of a surety three cities are there that be dearest far to me, Argos and Sparta and wide-wayed Mykene; these lay thou waste whene'er they are found hateful to thy heart; not for them will I stand forth, nor do I grudge thee them. For even if I be jealous and would forbid thee to overthrow them, yet will my jealousy not avail, seeing that thou art stronger far than I. Still must my labour too not be made of none effect; for I also am a god, and my lineage is even as thine and Kronos the crooked counsellor begat me to the place of honour in double wise, by birthright, and because I am named thy spouse, and thou art king among all the immortals. Let us indeed yield each to other herein, I to thee and thou to me, and the rest of the immortal gods will follow with us; and do thou with speed charge Athene to betake her to the fierce battle din of Trojans and Achaians, and to essay that the Trojans may first take upon them to do violence to the Achaians in their triumph, despite the oaths."

So said she, and the father of men and gods disregarded not; forthwith he spake to Athene winged words: "Betake thee with all speed to the host, to the midst of Trojans and Achaians, and essay that the Trojans may first take upon them to do violence to the Achaians in their triumph, despite the oaths."

So spake he, and roused Athene that already was set thereon; and from Olympus' heights she darted down. Even as the son of Kronos the crooked counsellor sendeth a star, a portent for mariners or a wide host of men, bright shining, and therefrom are scattered sparks in multitude; even in such guise sped Pallas Athene to earth, and leapt into their midst; and astonishment came on them that beheld, on horse-taming Trojans and well-greaved Achaians. And thus would many an one say, looking at his neighbour: "Of a surety either shall sore war and the fierce battle din return again; or else Zeus doth stablish peace between the foes, even he that is men's dispenser of battle."

Thus would many an one of Achaians and Trojans say. Then the goddess entered the throng of Trojans in the likeness of a man, even Antenor's son Laodokos, a stalwart warrior, and sought for godlike Pandaros, if haply she might find him. Lykaon's son found she, the noble and stalwart standing, and about him the stalwart ranks of the shield-bearing host that followed him from the streams of Aisepos. So she came near and spake winged words: "Wilt thou now hearken to me, thou wise son of Lykaon? Then wouldst thou take heart to shoot a swift arrow at Menelaos, and wouldst win favour and glory before all the Trojans and before king Alexandros most of all. Surely from him first of any wouldst thou receive glorious gifts, if perchance he see Menelaos, Atreus' warrior son, vanquished by thy dart and brought to the grievous pyre. Go to now, shoot at glorious Menelaos, and vow to Apollo, the son of light, the lord of archery, to sacrifice a goodly hecatomb of firstling lambs when thou art returned to thy home, in the city of holy Zeleia."

So spake Athene, and persuaded his fool's heart. Forthwith he unsheathed his polished bow of horn of a wild ibex that he himself had erst smitten beneath the breast as it came forth from a rock, the while he awaited in a lurking-place; and had pierced it in the chest, so that it fell backward on the rock. Now from its head sprang there horns of sixteen palms; these the artificer, even the worker in horn, joined cunningly together, and polished them all well and set the tip of gold thereon. So he laid it down when he had well strung it, by resting it upon the ground; and his staunch comrades held their shields before him, lest the warrior sons of the Achaians should first set on them, ere Menelaos, Atreus' warrior son, were smitten. Then opened he the lid of his quiver and took forth a feathered arrow, never yet shot, a source of grievous pangs; and anon he laid the bitter dart upon the string and vowed to Apollo, the son of light, the lord of archery, to sacrifice a goodly hecatomb of firstling lambs when he should have returned to his home in the city of holy Zeleia. Then he took the notch and string of oxes' sinew together, and drew, bringing to his breast the string, and to the bow the iron head. So when he had now bent the great bow into a round, the horn twanged, and the string sang aloud, and the keen arrow leapt eager to wing his way amid the throng.

But the blessed gods immortal forgat not thee, Menelaos; and before all the daughter of Zeus, the driver of the spoil, who stood before thee and warded off the piercing dart. She turned it just aside from the flesh, even as a mother driveth a fly from her child that lieth in sweet slumber; and with her own hand guided it where the golden buckles of the belt were clasped and the doubled breastplate met them. So the bitter arrow lighted upon the firm belt;

through the inwrought belt it sped and through the curiously wrought breastplate it pressed on and through the taslet he wore to shield his flesh, a barrier against darts; and this best shielded him, yet it passed on even through this. Then did the arrow graze the warrior's outermost flesh, and forthwith the dusky blood flowed from the wound.

As when some woman of Maionia or Karia staineth ivory with purple, to make a cheek-piece for horses, and it is laid up in the treasure chamber, and many a horseman prayeth for it to wear; but it is laid up to be a king's boast, alike an adornment for his horse and a glory for his charioteer; even in such wise, Menelaos, were thy shapely thighs stained with blood and thy legs and thy fair ankles beneath.

Thereat shuddered Agamemnon king of men when he saw the black blood flowing from the wound. And Menelaos dear to Ares likewise shuddered; but when he saw how thread and barbs were without, his spirit was gathered in his breast again. Then lord Agamemnon moaned deep, and spake among them, holding Menelaos by the hand; and his comrades made moan the while: "Dear brother, to thy death, me seemeth, pledged I these oaths, setting thee forth to fight the Trojans alone before the face of the Achaians; seeing that the Trojans have so smitten thee, and trodden under foot the trusty oaths. Yet in no wise is an oath of none effect, and the blood of lambs and pure drink-offerings and the right hands of fellowship wherein we trusted. For even if the Olympian bring not about the fulfilment forthwith, yet doth he fulfil at last, and men make dear amends, even with their own heads and their wives and little ones. Yea of a surety I know this in heart and soul; the day shall come for holy Ilios to be laid low, and Priam and the folk of Priam of the good ashen spear; and Zeus the son of Kronos enthroned on high, that dwelleth in the heaven, himself shall brandish over them all his lowring aegis, in indignation at this deceit. Then shall all this not be void; yet shall I have sore sorrow for thee, Menelaos, if thou die and fulfil the lot of life. Yea in utter shame should I return to thirsty Argos, seeing that the Achaians will forthwith bethink them of their native land, and so should we leave to Priam and the Trojans their boast, even Helen of Argos. And the earth shall rot thy bones as thou liest in Troy with thy task unfinished: and thus shall many an overweening Trojan say as he leapeth upon the tomb of glorious Menelaos: 'Would to God Agamemnon might so fulfil his wrath in every matter, even as now he led hither the host of the Achaians for naught, and hath gone home again to his dear native land with empty ships, and hath left noble Menelaos behind.' Thus shall men say hereafter: in that day let the wide earth gape for me."

But golden-haired Menelaos encouraged him and said: "Be of good courage, neither dismay at all the host of the Achaians. The keen dart lighted not upon a deadly spot; my glistering belt in front stayed it, and the kirtle of mail beneath, and the taslet that the coppersmiths fashioned."

Then lord Agamemnon answered him and said: "Would it may be so, dear Menelaos. But the leech shall feel the wound, and lay thereon drugs that shall assuage thy dire pangs."

So saying he spake to godlike Talthybios, his herald: "Talthybios, with all speed call Machaon hither, the hero son of Asklepios the noble leech, to see Menelaos, Atreus' warrior son, whom one well skilled in archery, some Trojan or Lykian, hath wounded with a bow-shot, to his glory and our grief."

So said he, and the herald heard him and disregarded not, and went his way through the host of mail-clad Achaians to spy out the hero Machaon. Him he found standing, and about him the stalwart ranks of the shield-bearing host that followed him from Trike, pasture land of horses. So he came near and spake his winged words: "Arise, thou son of Asklepios. Lord Agamemnon calleth thee to see Menelaos, captain of the Achaians, whom one well skilled in archery, some Trojan or Lykian, hath wounded with a bow-shot, to his glory and our grief."

So saying he aroused his spirit in his breast, and they went their way amid the throng, through the wide host of the Achaians. And when they were now come where was golden-haired Menelaos wounded, and all as many as were chieftains gathered around him in a circle, the godlike hero came and stood in their midst, and anon drew forth the arrow from the clasped belt; and as it was drawn forth the keen barbs were broken backwards. Then he loosed the glistering belt and the kirtle of mail beneath and taslet that the coppersmiths fashioned; and when he saw the wound where the bitter arrow had lighted, he sucked out the blood and cunningly spread thereon soothing drugs, such as Cheiron of his good will had imparted to his sire.

While these were tending Menelaos of the loud war-cry, the ranks of shield-bearing Trojans came on; so the Achaians donned their arms again, and bethought them of the fray. Now wouldest thou not see noble Agamemnon slumbering, nor cowering, nor unready to fight, but very eager for glorious battle. He left his horses and his chariot adorned with bronze; and his squire, even Eurymedon son of Ptolemaios Peiraieus' son, kept apart the snorting steeds; and he straitly charged him to have them at hand whenever weariness should come upon his limbs with marshallings so many; and thus on foot ranged he through the ranks of warriors. And whomsoever of all the fleet-horsed Danaans he found eager, he stood by them and by his words encouraged them: "Ye Argives, relax not in any wise your impetuous valour; for father Zeus will be no helper of liars, but as these were first to transgress against the oaths, so shall their own tender flesh be eaten of the vultures, and we shall bear away their dear wives and little children in our ships, when once we take the stronghold."

But whomsoever he found shrinking from hateful battle, these he chode sore with angry words: "Ye Argives, warriors of the bow, ye men of dishonour, have ye no shame? Why stand ye thus dazed like fawns that are weary with running over the long plain and so stand still, and no valour is found in their hearts at all? Even thus stand ye dazed, and fight not. Is it that ye wait for the Trojans to come near where your good ships' sterns are drawn up on the shore of the grey sea, to see if Kronion will stretch his arm over you indeed?"

So masterfully ranged he through the ranks of warriors. Then came he to the Cretans as he went through the throng of warriors; and these were taking arms around wise Idomeneus; Idomeneus amid the foremost, valiant as a wild boar, and Meriones the while was hastening his hindermost battalions. Then Agamemnon king of men rejoiced to see them, and anon spake to Idomeneus with kindly words: "Idomeneus, more than all the fleet-horsed Danaans do I honour thee, whether in war or in task of other sort or in the feast, when the chieftains of the Argives mingle in the bowl the gleaming wine of the counsellors. For even though all the other flowing-haired Achaians drink one allotted portion, yet thy cup standeth ever full even as mine, to drink as oft as thy soul biddeth thee. Now arouse thee to war like such an one as thou avowest thyself to be of old."

And Idomeneus the captain of the Cretans made answer to him: "Atreides, of very truth will I be to thee a trusty comrade even as at the first I promised and gave my pledge; but do thou urge on all the flowing-haired Achaians, that we may fight with all speed, seeing the Trojans have disannulled the oaths. But for all that death and sorrow hereafter shall be their lot, because they were the first to transgress against the oaths."

So said he, and Agamemnon passed on glad at heart. Then came he to the Aiantes as he went through the throng of warriors; and these twain were arming, and a cloud of footmen followed with them. Even as when a goatherd from a place of outlook seeth a cloud coming across the deep before the blast of the west wind; and to him being afar it seemeth ever blacker, even as pitch, as it goeth along the deep, and bringeth a great whirlwind, and he shuddereth to see it and driveth his flock beneath a cave; even in such wise moved the serried battalions of young men, the fosterlings of Zeus, by the side of the Aiantes into furious war, battalions dark of line, bristling with shields and spears. And lord Agamemnon rejoiced to see them and spake to them winged words, and said: "Aiantes, leaders of the mail-clad Argives, to you twain, seeing it is not seemly to urge you, give I no charge; for of your own selves ye do indeed bid your folk to fight amain. Ah, father Zeus and Athene and Apollo, would that all had like spirit in their breasts; then would king Priam's city soon bow captive and wasted beneath our hands."

So saying he left them there, and went to others. Then found he Nestor, the clear-voiced orator of the Pylians, arraying his comrades, and urging them to fight, around great Pelagon and Alastor and Chromios and lord Haimon and Bias shepherd of the host. And first he arrayed the horsemen with horses and chariots, and behind them the footmen many and brave, to be a bulwark of battle; but the cowards he drave into the midst, that every man, even though he would not, yet of necessity must fight. First he laid charge upon the horsemen; these he bade hold in their horses nor be entangled in the throng. "Neither let any man, trusting in his horsemanship and manhood, be eager to fight the Trojans alone before the rest, nor yet let him draw back, for so will ye be enfeebled. But whensoever a warrior from the place of his own car can come at a chariot of the foe, let him thrust forth with his spear; even so is the far better way. Thus moreover did men of old time lay low cities and walls, because they had this mind and spirit in their breasts."

So did the old man charge them, being well skilled of

yore in battles. And lord Agamemnon rejoiced to see him, and spake to him winged words, and said: "Old man, would to god that, even as thy spirit is in thine own breast, thy limbs might obey and thy strength be unabated. But the common lot of age is heavy upon thee; would that it had come upon some other man, and thou wert amid the young."

Then knightly Nestor of Gerenia answered him: "Atreides, I verily, even I too, would wish to be as on the day when I slew noble Ereuthalion. But the gods in no wise grant men all things at once. As I was then a youth, so doth old age now beset me. Yet even so will I abide among the horsemen and urge them by counsel and words; for that is the right of elders. But the young men shall wield the spear, they that are more youthful than I and have confidence in their strength."

So spake he, and Atreides passed on glad at heart. He found Menestheus the charioteer, the son of Peteos, standing still, and round him were the Athenians, masters of the battle-cry. And hard by stood crafty Odysseus and round about him the ranks of Kephallenians, no feeble folk, stood still; for their host had not yet heard the battle-cry, seeing the battalions of horse-taming Trojans and Achaians had but just bestirred them to move; so these stood still tarrying till some other column of the Achaians should advance to set upon the Trojans and begin the battle. But when Agamemnon king of men saw it, he upbraided them, and spake to them winged words, saying: "O son of king Peteos fosterling of Zeus, and thou skilled in evil wiles, thou cunning of mind, why stand ye shrinking apart, and tarry for others? You beseemeth it to stand in your place amid the foremost and to front the fiery battle; for ye are the first to hear my bidding to the feast, as oft as we Achaians prepare a feast for the counsellors. Then are ye glad to eat roast meat and drink your cups of honey-sweet wine as long as ye will. But now would ye gladly behold it, yea, if ten columns of Achaians in front of you were fighting with the pitiless sword."

But Odysseus of many counsels looked fiercely at him and said: "Atreides, what word is this that hath escaped the barrier of thy lips? How sayest thou that we are slack in battle? When once our Achaians launch furious war on the Trojans, tamers of horses, then shalt thou, if thou wilt, and if thou hast any care therefor, behold Telemachos' dear father mingling with the champions of the Trojans, the tamers of horses. But that thou sayest is empty as air."

Then lord Agamemnon spake to him smiling, seeing how he was wroth, and took back his saying: "Heaven-sprung son of Laertes, Odysseus full of devices, neither do I chide thee beyond measure nor urge thee; for I know that thy heart within thy breast is kindly disposed; for thy thoughts are as my thoughts. Go to, we will make amends hereafter, if any ill word hath been spoken now; may the gods bring it all to none effect."

So saying he left them there and went on to others. The son of Tydeus found he, high-hearted Diomedes, standing still with horses and chariot well compact; and by him stood Sthenelos son of Kapaneus. Him lord Agamemnon saw and upbraided, and spake to him winged words, and said: "Ah, me, thou son of wise Tydeus tamer of horses, why shrinkest thou, why gazest thou at the highways of the battle? Not thus was Tydeus wont to shrink, but rather to fight his enemies far in front of his dear comrades, as they say that beheld him at the task; for never did I meet him nor behold him, but men say that he was pre-eminent amid all. Of a truth he came to Mykene, not in enmity, but as a guest with godlike Polyneikes, to raise him an army for the war that they were levying against the holy walls of Thebes; and they besought earnestly that valiant allies might be given them, and our folk were fain to grant them and made assent to their entreaty, only Zeus showed omens of ill and turned their minds. So when these were departed and were come on their way, and had attained to Asopos deep in rushes, that maketh his bed in grass, there did the Achaians appoint Tydeus to be their ambassador. So he went and found the multitude of the sons of Kadmos feasting in the palace of mighty Eteokles. Yet was knightly Tydeus, even though a stranger, not afraid, being alone amid the multitude of the Kadmeians, but challenged them all to feats of strength, and in every one vanquished he them easily; so present a helper was Athene unto him. But the Kadmeians, the urgers of horses, were wroth, and as he fared back again they brought and set a strong ambush, even fifty young men, whose leaders were twain, Maion son of Haimon, like to the immortals, and Autophonos' son Polyphontes staunch in battle. Still even on these Tydeus brought shameful death; he slew them all, save one that he sent home alone; Maion to wit he sent away in obedience to the omens of heaven. Such was Tydeus of Aitolia; but he begat a son that in battle is worse than he; only in harangue is he the better."

So said he, and stalwart Diomedes made no answer, but had respect to the chiding of the king revered. But the son of glorious Kapaneus answered him: "Atreides, utter not falsehood, seeing thou knowest how to speak truly. We avow ourselves to be better men by far than our fathers were: we did take the seat of Thebes the seven gated, though we led a scantier host against a stronger wall, because we followed the omens of the gods and the salvation of Zeus; but they perished by their own iniquities. Do not thou therefore in any wise have our fathers in like honour with us."

But stalwart Diomedes looked sternly at him, and said: "Brother, sit silent and obey my saying. I grudge not that Agamemnon shepherd of the host should urge on the well-greaved Achaians to fight; for him the glory will attend if the Achaians lay the Trojans low and take holy Ilios; and his will be the great sorrow if the Achaians be laid low.

Go to now, let us too bethink us of impetuous valour."

He spake and leapt in his armour from the chariot to earth, and terribly rang the bronze upon the chieftain's breast as he moved; thereat might fear have come even upon one stout-hearted.

As when on the echoing beach the sea-wave lifteth up itself in close array before the driving of the west wind; out on the deep doth it first raise its head, and then breaketh upon the land and belloweth aloud and goeth with arching crest about the promontories, and speweth the foaming brine afar; even so in close array moved the battalions of the Danaans without pause to battle. Each captain gave his men the word, and the rest went silently; thou wouldest not deem that all the great host following them had any voice within their breasts; in silence feared they their captains. On every man glittered the inwrought armour wherewith they went clad. But for the Trojans, like sheep beyond number that stand in the courtyard of a man of great substance, to be milked of their white milk, and bleat without ceasing to hear their lambs' cry, even so arose the clamour of the Trojans through the wide host. For they had not all like speech nor one language, but their tongues were mingled, and they were brought from many lands. These were urged on of Ares, and those of bright-eyed Athene, and Terror and Rout, and Strife whose fury wearieth not, sister and friend of murderous Ares; her crest is but lowly at the first, but afterward she holdeth up her head in heaven and her feet walk upon the earth. She now cast common discord in their midst, as she fared through the throng and made the lamentation of men to wax.

Now when they were met together and come unto one spot, then clashed they targe and spear and fury of bronze-clad warrior; the bossed shields pressed each on each and mighty din arose. Then were heard the voice of groaning and the voice of triumph together of the slayers and the slain, and the earth streamed with blood. As when two winter torrents flow down the mountains to a watersmeet and join their furious flood within the deep ravine from their great springs, and the shepherd heareth the roaring far off among the hills; even so from the joining of battle came there forth shouting and travail. Antilochos first slew a Trojan warrior in full array, valiant amid the champions, Echepolos son of Thalysios; him was he first to smite upon the ridge of his crested helmet, and he drave the spear into his brow and the point of bronze passed within the bone; darkness clouded his eyes, and he crashed like a tower amid the press of fight. As he fell lord Elephenor caught him by the foot, Chalkodon's son, captain of the great-hearted Abantes, and dragged him from beneath the darts, eager with all speed to despoil him of his armour. Yet but for a little endured his essay; great-hearted Agenor saw him haling away the corpse, and where his side was left uncovered of his buckler as he bowed him down, there smote he him with bronze-tipped spear-shaft and unstrung his limbs. So his life departed from him, and over his corpse the task of Trojans and Achaians grew hot; like wolves leapt they one at another, and man lashed at man.

Next Telamonian Aias smote Anthemion's son, the lusty stripling Simoeisios, whom erst his mother bare beside the banks of Simoeis on the way down from Ida whither she had followed with her parents to see their flocks. Therefore they called him Simoeisios, but he repaid not his dear parents the recompense of his nurture; scanty was his span of life by reason of the spear of great-hearted Aias that laid him low. For as he went he first was smitten on his right breast beside the pap; straight through his shoulder passed the spear of bronze, and he fell to the ground in the dust like a poplar-tree, that hath grown up smooth in the lowland of a great marsh, and its branches grow upon the top thereof; this hath a wainwright felled with gleaming steel, to bend him a felloe for a goodly chariot, and so it lies drying by a river's banks. In such fashion did heaven-sprung Aias slay Simoeisios son of Anthemion; then at him Antiphos of the glancing corslet, Priam's son, made a cast with his keen javelin across the throng. Him he missed, but smote Odysseus' valiant comrade Leukos in the groin as he drew the corpse his way, so that he fell upon it and the body dropped from his hands. Then Odysseus was very wroth at heart for the slaying of him, and strode through the forefront of the battle harnessed in flashing bronze, and went and stood hard by and glanced around him, and cast his bright javelin; and the Trojans shrank before the casting of the hero. He sped not the dart in vain, but smote Demokoon, Priam's bastard son that had come to him from tending his fleet mares in Abydos. Him Odysseus, being wroth for his comrade's sake, smote with his javelin on one temple; and through both temples passed the point of bronze, and darkness clouded his eyes, and he fell with a crash and his armour clanged upon him. Then the forefighters and glorious Hector yielded, and the Argives shouted aloud, and drew the bodies unto them, and pressed yet further onward. But Apollo looked down from Pergamos, and had indignation, and with a shout called to the Trojans. "Arise, ye Trojans, tamers of horses; yield not to the Argives in fight; not of stone nor iron is their flesh, that it should resist the piercing bronze when they are smitten. Moreover Achilles, son of Thetis of the fair tresses, fighteth not, but amid the ships broodeth on his bitter anger."

So spake the dread god from the city; and the Achaians likewise were urged on of Zeus' daughter the Triton-born, most glorious, as she passed through the throng wheresoever she beheld them slackening.

Next was Diores son of Amarynkeus caught in the snare of fate; for he was smitten by a jagged stone on the right leg hard by the ankle, and the caster thereof was captain of the men of Thrace, Peiroos son of Imbrasos that had come from Ainos. The pitiless stone crushed utterly the two sinews and the bones; back fell he in the dust, and stretched out both his hands to his dear comrades, gasping out his soul. Then he that smote him, even Peiroos, sprang at him and pierced him with a spear beside the navel; so all his bowels gushed forth upon the ground, and darkness clouded his eyes. But even as Peiroos departed from him Thoas of Aitolia smote with a spear his chest above the pap, and the point fixed in his lung. Then Thoas came close, and plucked out from his breast the ponderous spear, and drew his sharp sword, wherewith he smote his belly in the midst, and took his life. Yet he stripped not off his armour; for his comrades, the men of Thrace that wear the top-knot, stood around, their long spears in their hands, and albeit he was great and valiant and proud they drave him off from them and he gave ground reeling. So were the two captains stretched in the dust side by side, he of the Thracians and he of the mail-clad Epeians; and around them were many others likewise slain.

Now would none any more enter in and make light of the battle, could it be that a man yet unwounded by dart or thrust of keen bronze might roam in the midst, being led of Pallas Athene by the hand, and by her guarded from the flying shafts. For many Trojans that day and many Achaians were laid side by side upon their faces in the dust.

BOOK V

How Diomedes by his great valour made havoc of the Trojans, and wounded even Aphrodite and Ares by the help of Athene.

But now to Tydeus' son Diomedes Pallas Athene gave might and courage, for him to be pre-eminent amid all the Argives and win glorious renown. She kindled flame unwearied from his helmet and shield, like to the star of summer that above all others glittereth bright after he hath bathed in the ocean stream. In such wise kindled she flame from his head and shoulders and sent him into the midst, where men thronged the thickest.

Now there was amid the Trojans one Dares, rich and noble, priest of Hephaistos; and he had two sons, Phegeus and Idaios, well skilled in all the art of battle. These separated themselves and assailed him face to face, they setting on him from their car and he on foot upon the ground. And when they were now come near in onset on each other, first Phegeus hurled his far-shadowing spear; and over Tydeides' left shoulder the spear point passed, and smote not his body. Then next Tydeides made a spear-cast, and the javelin sped not from his hand in vain, but smote his breast between the nipples, and thrust him from the chariot. So Idaios sprang away, leaving his beautiful car, and dared not to bestride his slain brother; else had neither he himself escaped black fate; but Hephaistos guarded him and saved him in a veil of darkness, that he might not have his aged priest all broken with sorrow. And the son of great-hearted Tydeus drave away the horses and gave them to his men to take to the hollow ships. But when the great-hearted Trojans beheld the sons of Dares, how one was fled, and one was slain beside his chariot, the spirit of all was stirred. But bright-eyed Athene took impetuous Ares by the hand and spake to him and said: "Ares, Ares, blood-stained bane of mortals, thou stormer of walls, can we not now leave the Trojans and Achaians to fight, on whichsoever it be that father Zeus bestoweth glory? But let us twain give place, and escape the wrath of Zeus."

So saying she led impetuous Ares from the battle. Then she made him sit down beside loud Skamandros, and the Danaans pushed the Trojans back. Each one of the captains slew his man; first Agamemnon king of men thrust from his chariot the lord of the Halizonians, great Odios; for as he first turned to flight Agamemnon thrust his dart into his back between his shoulders, and drave it through his breast. And he fell with a crash, and his armour clanged upon him.

And Idomeneus slew Phaistos son of Boros the Maionian, that came from deep-soiled Tarne. Him in the act to mount upon his car spear-famed Idomeneus pierced with his long dart through his right shoulder; and he fell from the car and hateful darkness gat hold of him.

Him then Idomeneus' squires despoiled; and Skamandrios, son of Strophios, cunning in the chase, fell to the keen-pointed spear of Menelaos son of Atreus; even he the mighty hunter, whom Artemis herself had taught to shoot all manner of wild things that the mountain forest breedeth. But now did Archer Artemis avail him naught nor all his marksmanship wherein of old time he excelled; but spear famed Menelaos son of Atreus smote him with his dart as he fled before him, in his back [between his shoulders, and pierced through his breast]. So he fell prone and his armour clanged upon him.

And Meriones slew Phereklos, son of Tekton Harmon's son, whose hands were cunning to make all manner of curious work; for Pallas Athene loved him more than all men. He likewise built Alexandros the trim ships, source of ills, that were made the bane of all the Trojans and of himself, because he knew not the oracles of heaven. Him Meriones pursued, and overtaking him smote him in the right buttock, and right through passed the point straight to the bladder beneath the bone; and he fell to his knees with a cry, and death overshadowed him.

Then Meges slew Pedaios Antenor's son, that was a bastard; yet goodly Theano nurtured him carefully like to her own children, to do her husband pleasure. To him Phyleus' spear-famed son came near, and with keen dart smote him upon the sinew of the head; and right through amid the teeth the point of bronze cleft the tongue's root. So he fell in the dust, and bit the cold bronze with his teeth.

And by Eurypylos, Euaimon's son, noble Hypsenor son of high-hearted Dolopion that was appointed Skamandros' priest and like to a god was held in honour of the folk—by Eurypylos Euaimon's glorious son, he as he fled before him was pursued and smitten on the shoulder with a sword-thrust, and his heavy arm was shorn away. All bleeding the arm fell upon the earth; and over his eyes came gloomy death and forceful fate.

So laboured these in the violent mellay; but of Tydeides man could not tell with whom he were joined, whether he consorted with Trojans or with Achaians. For he stormed across the plain like a winter torrent at the full, that in swift course scattereth the causeys; neither can the long lines of causeys hold it in, nor the fences of fruitful orchards stay its sudden coming when the rain of heaven driveth it; and so before it perish in multitudes the fair works of the sons of men. Thus before Tydeides the serried battalions of the Trojans were overthrown, and they abode him not for all they were so many.

But when Lykaon's glorious son marked him storming across the plain, overthrowing battalions before him, anon he bent his crooked bow against Tydeides, and smote him as he sped onwards, hitting hard by his right shoulder the plate of his corslet; the bitter arrow flew through and held straight upon its way, and the corslet was dabbled with blood. Over him then loudly shouted Lykaon's glorious son: "Bestir you, great-hearted Trojans, urgers of horses; the best man of the Achaians is wounded, and I deem that he shall not for long endure the violent dart, if verily the king, the son of Zeus, sped me on my way from Lykia."

So spake he boasting; yet was the other not vanquished of the swift dart, only he gave place and stood before his horses and his chariot and spake to Sthenelos son of Kapaneus: "Haste thee, dear son of Kapaneus; descend from thy chariot, to draw me from my shoulder the bitter arrow."

So said he, and Sthenelos leapt from his chariot to earth and stood beside him and drew the swift shaft right through, out of his shoulder; and the blood darted up through the pliant tunic. Then Diomedes of the loud war-cry prayed thereat: "Hear me, daughter of aegis-bearing Zeus, unwearied maiden! If ever in kindly mood thou stoodest by my father in the heat of battle, even so now be thou likewise kind to me, Athene. Grant me to slay this man, and bring within my spear-cast him that took advantage to shoot me, and boasteth over me, deeming that not for long shall I see the bright light of the sun."

So spake he in prayer, and Pallas Athene heard him, and made his limbs nimble, his feet and his hands withal, and came near and spake winged words: "Be of good courage now, Diomedes, to fight the Trojans; for in thy breast I have set thy father's courage undaunted, even as it was in knightly Tydeus, wielder of the buckler. Moreover I have taken from thine eyes the mist that erst was on them, that thou mayest well discern both god and man. Therefore if any god come hither to make trial of thee, fight not thou face to face with any of the immortal gods; save only if Aphrodite daughter of Zeus enter into the battle, her smite thou with the keen bronze."

So saying bright-eyed Athene went her way and Tydeides

returned and entered the forefront of the battle; even though erst his soul was eager to do battle with the Trojans, yet now did threefold courage come upon him, as upon a lion whom some shepherd in the field guarding his fleecy sheep hath wounded, being sprung into the fold, yet hath not vanquished him; he hath roused his might, and then cannot beat him back, but lurketh amid the steading, and his forsaken flock is affrighted; so the sheep are cast in heaps, one upon the other, and the lion in his fury leapeth out of the high fold; even so in fury mingled mighty Diomedes with the Trojans.

There slew he Astynoos and Hypeiron shepherd of the host; the one he pierced above the nipple with his bronze-shod dart, the other with his great sword upon the collar-bone beside the shoulder he smote, and severed the shoulder from neck and back. Them left he there, and pursued after Abas and Polvidos, sons of old Eurydamas dreamer of dreams; yet discerned he no dreams for them when they went, but stalwart Diomedes despoiled them. Then went he after Xanthos and Thoon, sons of Phainops, striplings both; but their father was outworn of grievous age, and begat no other son for his possessions after him. Then Diomedes slew them and bereft the twain of their dear life, and for their father left only lamentation and sore distress, seeing he welcomed them not alive returned from battle; and kinsmen divided his substance.

Then caught he two sons of Priam of the seed of Dardanos, riding in one chariot, Echemmon and Chromios. As a lion leapeth among the kine and breaketh the neck of cow or heifer grazing in a woodland pasture, so Tydeus' son thrust in ill wise from their chariot both of them unwilling, and thereafter despoiled them of their arms; and the horses gave he to his comrades to drive them to the ships.

Him Aineias beheld making havoc of the ranks of warriors, and went his way along the battle and amid the hurtling of spears, seeking godlike Pandaros, if haply he might find him. Lykaon's son he found, the noble and stalwart, and stood before his face, and spake a word unto him. "Pandaros, where now are thy bow and thy winged arrows, and the fame wherein no man of this land rivalleth thee, nor any in Lykia boasteth to be thy better? Go to now, lift thy hands in prayer to Zeus and shoot thy dart at this fellow, whoe'er he be that lordeth it here and hath already wrought the Trojans much mischief, seeing he hath unstrung the knees of many a brave man; if indeed it be not some god wroth with the Trojans, in anger by reason of sacrifices; the wrath of god is a sore thing to fall on men."

And Lykaon's glorious son made answer to him: "Aineias, counsellor of the mail-clad Trojans, in everything liken I him to the wise son of Tydeus; I discern him by his shield and crested helmet, and by the aspect of his horses, yet know I not surely if it be not a god. But if it be the man I deem, even the wise son of Tydeus, then not without help of a god is he thus furious, but some immortal standeth beside him with a cloud wrapped about his shoulders and turned aside from him my swift dart even as it lighted. For already have I shot my dart at him and smote his right shoulder right through the breastplate of his corslet, yea and I thought to hurl him headlong to Aidoneus, yet I vanquished him not; surely it is some wrathful god. And I have no steeds at hand nor any chariot whereon to mount—yet in Lykaon's halls are eleven fair chariots, new wrought, with gear all fresh, and cloths spread over them; and beside each standeth a yoke of horses, champing white barley and spelt. Moreover Lykaon the aged spearman at my departing laid instant charge upon me in our well-builded house; he bade me mount horse and chariot to lead the Trojans in the violent mellay; but I obeyed him not—far better had that been!—but spared the horses lest in the great crowd of men they should lack fodder that had been wont to feed their fill. Therefore I left them and am come on foot to

Ilios, trusting to my bow; and now must my bow not help me. Already have I aimed at two princes, Tydeus' and Atreus' sons, and both I smote and surely drew forth blood, yet only roused them the more. Therefore in an evil hour I took from the peg my curved bow on that day when I led my Trojans to lovely Ilios, to do noble Hector pleasure. But if I return and mine eyes behold my native land and wife and great palace lofty-roofed, then may an alien forthwith cut my head from me if I break not this bow with mine hands and cast it upon the blazing fire; worthless is its service to me as air."

Then Aineias captain of the Trojans answered him: "Nay, talk not thus; naught shall be mended before that we with horses and chariot have gone to face this man, and made trial of him in arms. Come then, mount upon my car that thou mayest see of what sort are the steeds of Tros, well skilled for following or for fleeing hither or thither very fleetly across the plain; they will e'en bring us to the city safe and sound, even though Zeus hereafter give victory to Diomedes son of Tydeus. Come therefore, take thou the lash and shining reins, and I will stand upon the car to fight; or else withstand thou him, and to the horses will I look."

To him made answer Lykaon's glorious son: "Aineias, take thou thyself the reins and thine own horses; better will they draw the curved car for their wonted charioteer, if perchance it hap that we must flee from Tydeus' son; lest they go wild for fear and will not take us from the fight, for lack of thy voice, and so the son of great-hearted Tydeus attack us and slay us both and drive away the whole-hooved horses. So drive thou thyself thy chariot and thy horses, and I will await his onset with my keen spear." So saying mounted they upon the well-dight chariot, and eagerly drave the fleet horses against Tydeides. And Sthenelos, the glorious son of Kapaneus, saw them, and anon spake to Tydeides winged words: "Diomedes son of Tydeus, dear to mine heart, I behold two stalwart warriors eager to fight against thee, endued with might beyond measure. The one is well skilled in the bow, even Pandaros, and he moreover boasteth him to be Lykaon's son; and Aineias boasteth himself to be born son of great-hearted Anchises, and his mother is Aphrodite. Come now, let us give place upon the chariot, neither rage thou thus, I pray thee, in the forefront of battle, lest perchance thou lose thy life."

Then stalwart Diomedes looked sternly at him and said: "Speak to me no word of flight, for I ween that thou shalt not at all persuade me; not in my blood is it to fight a skulking fight or cower down; my force is steadfast still. I have no mind to mount the chariot, nay, even as I am will I go to face them; Pallas Athene biddeth me not be afraid. And as for these, their fleet horses shall not take both back from us again, even if one or other escape. And this moreover tell I thee, and lay thou it to heart: if Athene rich in counsel grant me this glory, to slay them both, then refrain thou here these my fleet horses, and bind the reins tight to the chariot rim; and be mindful to leap upon Aineias' horses, and drive them forth from the Trojans amid the well-greaved Achaians. For they are of that breed whereof farseeing Zeus gave to Tros recompense for Ganymede his child, because they were the best of all horses beneath the daylight and the sun. That blood Anchises king of men stole of Laomedon, privily putting mares to them. Thereof a stock was born him in his palace, even six; four kept he himself and reared them at the stall, and the other twain gave he to Aineias deviser of rout. Them could we seize, we should win us great renown."

In such wise talked they one to the other, and anon those other twain came near, driving their fleet horses. First to him spake Lykaon's glorious son: "O thou strong-souled and cunning, son of proud Tydeus, verily my swift dart vanquished thee not, the bitter arrow; so now will I make trial with my spear if I can hit thee."

He spake and poised and hurled his far-shadowing spear, and smote upon Tydeides' shield; right through it sped the point of bronze and reached the breastplate. So over him shouted loudly Lykaon's glorious son: "Thou are smitten on the belly right through, and I ween thou shalt not long hold up thine head; so thou givest me great renown."

But mighty Diomedes unaffrighted answered him: "Thou hast missed, and not hit; but ye twain I deem shall not cease till one or other shall have fallen and glutted with blood Ares the stubborn god of war."

So spake he and hurled; and Athene guided the dart upon his nose beside the eye, and it pierced through his white teeth. So the hard bronze cut through his tongue at the root and the point issued forth by the base of the chin. He fell from his chariot, and his splendid armour gleaming clanged upon him, and the fleet-footed horses swerved aside; so there his soul and strength were unstrung.

Then Aineias leapt down with shield and long spear, fearing lest perchance the Achaians might take from him the corpse; and strode over him like a lion confident in his strength, and held before him his spear and the circle of his shield, eager to slay whoe'er should come to face him, crying his terrible cry. Then Tydeides grasped in his hand a stone—a mighty deed—such as two men, as men now are, would not avail to lift; yet he with ease wielded it all alone. Therewith he smote Aineias on the hip where the thigh turneth in the hip-joint, and this men call the "cup-bone." So he crushed his cup-bone, and brake both sinews withal, and the jagged stone tore apart the skin. Then the hero stayed fallen upon his knees and with stout hand leant upon the earth; and the darkness of night veiled his eyes. And now might Aineias king of men have perished, but that Aphrodite daughter of Zeus was swift to mark, even his mother that conceived him by Anchises as he tended the kine. About her dear son wound she her white arms, and spread before his face a fold of her radiant vesture, to be a covering from the darts, lest any of the fleet-horsed Danaans might hurl the spear into his breast and take away his life.

So was she bearing her dear son away from battle; but the son of Kapaneus forgat not the behest that Diomedes of the loud war-cry had laid upon him; he refrained his own whole-hooved horses away from the tumult, binding the reins tight to the chariot-rim, and leapt on the sleek-coated horses of Aineias, and drave them from the Trojans to the well-greaved Achaians, and gave them to Deïpylos his dear comrade whom he esteemed above all that were his age-fellows, because he was like-minded with himself; and bade him drive them to the hollow ships. Then did the hero mount his own chariot and take the shining reins and forthwith drive his strong-hooved horses in quest of Tydeides, eagerly. Now Tydeides had made onslaught with pitiless weapon on Kypris, knowing how she was a coward goddess and none of those that have mastery in battle of the warriors—no Athene she nor Enyo waster of cities. Now when he had pursued her through the dense throng and come on her, then great-hearted Tydeus' son thrust with his keen spear, and leapt on her and wounded the skin of her weak hand; straight through the ambrosial raiment that the Graces themselves had woven her pierced the dart into the flesh, above the springing of the palm. Then flowed the goddess's immortal blood, such ichor as floweth in the blessed gods; for they eat no bread neither drink they gleaming wine, wherefore they are bloodless and are named immortals. And she with a great cry let fall her son: him Phoebus Apollo took into his arms and saved him in a dusky cloud, lest any of the fleet-horsed Danaans might hurl the spear into his breast and take away his life. But over her Diomedes of the loud war-cry shouted afar: "Refrain thee, thou daughter of Zeus, from war and fighting. Is it not enough that thou beguilest feeble women? But if in battle thou wilt mingle, verily I deem that thou shalt shudder at the name of battle, if thou hear it even afar off."

So spake he, and she departed in amaze and was sore troubled: and wind-footed Iris took her and led her from the throng tormented with her pain, and her fair skin was stained. There found she impetuous Ares sitting, on the battle's left; and his spear rested upon a cloud, and his fleet steeds. Then she fell on her knees and with instant prayer besought of her dear brother his golden-frontleted steeds: "Dear brother, save me and give me thy steeds, that I may win to Olympus, where is the habitation of the immortals. Sorely am I afflicted with a wound wherewith a mortal smote me, even Tydeides, who now would fight even with father Zeus."

So spake she, and Ares gave her his golden-frontleted steeds; and she mounted on the chariot sore at heart. By her side mounted Iris, and in her hands grasped the reins and lashed the horses to start them; and they flew onward nothing loth. Thus soon they came to the habitation of the gods, even steep Olympus. There wind-footed fleet Iris loosed the horses from the chariot and stabled them, and set ambrosial forage before them; but fair Aphrodite fell upon Dione's knees that was her mother. She took her daughter in her arms and stroked her with her hand, and spake and called upon her name: "Who now of the sons of heaven, dear child, hath entreated thee thus wantonly, as though thou wert a wrong-doer in the face of all?"

Then laughter-loving Aphrodite made answer to her: "Tydeus' son wounded me, high-hearted Diomedes, because I was saving from the battle my dear son Aineias, who to me is dearest far of all men. For no more is the fierce battle-cry for Trojans and Achaians, but the Danaans now are fighting even the immortals."

Then the fair goddess Dione answered her: "Be of good heart, my child, and endure for all thy pain; for many of us that inhabit the mansions of Olympus have suffered through men, in bringing grievous woes one upon another. So suffered Ares, when Otos and stalwart Ephialtes, sons of Aloeus, bound him in a strong prison-house; yea in a vessel of bronze lay he bound thirteen months. Then might Ares insatiate of battle have perished, but that the step-mother of Aloeus' sons, fair Eëriboia, gave tidings to Hermes, and he stole away Ares, already pining; for the grievous prison-house was wearing him out. So suffered Hera when Amphitryon's stalwart son smote her on the right breast with a three-barbed arrow, so that pain unassuageable gat hold of her likewise. So suffered awful Hades a swift arrow like the rest, when this same man, the son of aegis-bearing Zeus, smote him in Pylos amid the dead and gave him over to anguish. And he went to the mansion of Zeus and to high Olympus, grieved at heart, pierced through with anguish; for the arrow was driven into his stout shoulder, and vexed his soul. But Paieon spread soothing drugs upon the wound and healed him; seeing that verily he was of no mortal substance. Headstrong man and violent of deed, that recked not of his evil doings, and with his archery vexed the gods that dwell in Olympus! So upon thee was this man sent by the bright-eyed goddess Athene; fond man—for the heart of Tydeus' son knoweth not this, that he of a surety is not long-lived that fighteth with immortals, nor ever do his children prattle upon his knees at his returning from war and terrible fray. Therefore now let Tydeides, though he be very mighty, beware lest one better than thou encounter him; and so Aigialeia, wise daughter of Adrestos, wake from sleep with lamentations all her household, bewailing her wedded lord, the best man of the Achaians, even she that is the brave wife of horse-taming Diomedes."

So saying with both hands she wiped the ichor from the arm; her arm was comforted, and the grievous pangs assuaged. But Athene and Hera beheld, and with bitter words provoked Zeus the son of Kronos. Of them was the bright-eyed goddess Athene first to speak: "Father Zeus, wilt thou indeed be wroth with me whate'er I say? Verily I ween that Kypris was urging some woman of Achaia to join her unto the Trojans whom she so marvellously loveth; and stroking such an one of the fair-robed women of Achaia, she tore upon the golden brooch her delicate hand."

So spake she, and the father of gods and men smiled, and called unto him golden Aphrodite and said: "Not unto thee, my child, are given the works of war; but follow thou after the loving tasks of wedlock, and to all these things shall fleet Ares and Athene look."

Now while they thus spake in converse one with the other, Diomedes of the loud war-cry leapt upon Aineias, knowing full well that Apollo himself had spread his arms over him; yet reverenced he not even the great god, but still was eager to slay Aineias and strip from him his glorious armour. So thrice he leapt on him, fain to slay him, and thrice Apollo beat back his glittering shield. And when the fourth time he sprang at him like a god, then Apollo the Far-darter spake to him with terrible shout: "Think, Tydeides, and shrink, nor desire to match thy spirit with gods; seeing there is no comparison of the race of immortal gods and of men that walk upon the earth."

So said he, and Tydeides shrank a short space backwards, to avoid the wrath of Apollo the Far-darter. Then Apollo set Aineias away from the throng in holy Pergamos where his temple stood. There Leto and Archer Artemis healed him in the mighty sanctuary, and gave him glory; but Apollo of the silver bow made a wraith like unto Aineias' self, and in such armour as his; and over the wraith Trojans and goodly Achaians each hewed the others' bucklers on their breasts, their round shields and fluttering targes.

Then to impetuous Ares said Phoebus Apollo: "Ares, Ares, blood-stained bane of mortals, thou stormer of walls, wilt thou not follow after this man and withdraw him from the battle, this Tydeides, who now would fight even with father Zeus? First in close fight he wounded Kypris in her hand hard by the wrist, and then sprang he upon myself like unto a god."

So saying he sate himself upon the height of Pergamos, and baleful Ares entered among the Trojan ranks and aroused them in the likeness of fleet Akamas, captain of the Thracians. On the heaven-nurtured sons of Priam he called saying: "O ye sons of Priam, the heaven-nurtured king, how long will ye yet suffer your host to be slain of the Achaians? Shall it be even until they fight about our well-builded gates? Low lieth the warrior whom we esteemed like unto goodly Hector, even Aineias son of Anchises great of heart. Go to now, let us save from the tumult our valiant comrade."

So saying he aroused the spirit and soul of every man. Thereat Sarpedon sorely chode noble Hector: "Hector, where now is the spirit gone that erst thou hadst? Thou saidst forsooth that without armies or allies thou wouldest hold the city, alone with thy sisters' husbands and thy brothers; but now can I not see any of these neither perceive them, but they are cowering like hounds about a lion; and we are fighting that are but allies among you. Yea I being an ally am come from very far; far off is Lykia upon eddying Xanthos, where I left my dear wife and infant son, and left my great wealth that each one coveteth that is in need. Yet for all that I urge on my Lykians, and myself am eager to fight my man, though here is naught of mine such as the Achaians might plunder or harry. But thou standest, nay thou dost not even urge all thine hosts to abide and guard their wives. Only beware lest, as though tangled in meshes of all-ensnaring flax, ye be made unto your foeman a prey and a spoil; and they will soon lay waste your well-peopled city. Thee it behoveth to give thought to all these things both by night and day, and to beseech the captains of thy far-famed allies to hold on unflinchingly;

and so shalt thou put away their sore rebuking from thee."

So spake Sarpedon, and his word stung Hector to the heart. Forthwith he leapt from his chariot in his armour to the earth, and brandishing two keen spears went everywhere through the host, urging them to fight, and roused the dread battle-cry. So they were rallied and stood to face the Achaians: and the Argives withstood them in close array and fled not. Even as a wind carrieth the chaff about the sacred threshing-floors when men are winnowing, what time golden-haired Demeter in rush of wind maketh division of grain and chaff, and so the chaff-heaps grow white—so now grew the Achaians white with falling dust which in their midst the horses' hooves beat up into the brazen heaven, as fight was joined again, and the charioteers wheeled round. Thus bare they forward the fury of their hands; and impetuous Ares drew round them a veil of night to aid the Trojans in the battle, ranging everywhere; so fulfilled he the behest of Phoebus Apollo of the golden sword, who bade him rouse the Trojans' spirit when he beheld Pallas Athene departed; for she was helper to the Danaans. And Apollo himself sent forth Aineias from his rich sanctuary and put courage in the heart of him, shepherd of the hosts. So Aineias took his place amid his comrades, and they were glad to see him come among them alive and sound and full of valiant spirit. Yet they questioned him not at all, for all the toil forbade them that the god of the silver bow was stirring and Ares bane of men and Strife raging insatiably.

And on the other side the two Aiantes and Odysseus and Diomedes stirred the Danaans to fight; yet these of themselves feared neither the Trojans' violence nor assaults, but stood like mists that Kronos' son setteth in windless air on the mountain tops, at peace, while the might of the north wind sleepeth and of all the violent winds that blow with keen breath and scatter apart the shadowing clouds. Even so the Danaans withstood the Trojans steadfastly and fled not. And Atreides ranged through the throng exhorting instantly: "My friends, quit you like men and take heart of courage, and shun dishonour in one another's eyes amid the stress of battle. Of men that shun dishonour more are saved than slain, but for them that flee is neither glory found nor any safety."

So saying he darted swiftly with his javelin and smote a foremost warrior, even great-hearted Aineias' comrade Deïkoon son of Pergasos, whom the Trojans held in like honour with Priam's sons, because he was swift to do battle amid the foremost. Him lord Agamemnon smote with his dart upon the shield, and it stayed not the spear, but the point passed through, so that he drave it through the belt into his nethermost belly: and he fell with a crash and his armour clanged upon him.

Then did Aineias slay two champions of the Danaans, even the sons of Diokles, Krethon and Orsilochos, whose father dwelt in stablished Phere, a man full of substance, whose lineage was of the river Alpheios, that floweth in broad stream through the land of the Pylians; Alpheios begat Orsilochos to be king of many men, and Orsilochos begat great-hearted Diokles, and of Diokles were born twin sons, even Krethon and Orsilochos, well skilled in all the ways of war. Now when these were of full age, they bare the Argives company on their black ships to Ilios home of horses, to win recompense for Atreus' sons, Agamemnon and Menelaos; but now the issue of death shrouded them about. Like them, two lions on the mountain tops are nurtured by their dam in the deep forest thickets; and these harry the kine and goodly sheep and make havoc of the farmsteads of men, till in their turn they too are slain at men's hands with the keen bronze; in such wise were these twain vanquished at Aineias' hands and fell like tall pine-trees.

But Menelaos dear to Ares had pity of them in their fall, and strode through the forefront, harnessed in flashing bronze, brandishing his spear; and Ares stirred his courage, with intent that he might fall beneath Aineias' hand. But Antilochos, great-hearted Nestor's son, beheld him, and strode through the forefront; because he feared exceedingly for the shepherd of the host, lest aught befall him and disappoint them utterly of their labour. So those two were now holding forth their hands and sharp spears each against the other, eager to do battle; when Antilochos came and stood hard by the shepherd of the host. But Aineias faced them not, keen warrior though he was, when he beheld two men abiding side by side; so these haled away the corpses to the Achaians' host, and laid the hapless twain in their comrades' arms, and themselves turned back and fought on amid the foremost.

Then slew they Pylaimenes, peer of Ares, captain of the great-hearted Paphlagonians bearers of the shield. Him as he stood still Atreus' son, spear-famed Menelaos, pierced with his javelin, smiting upon the collar-bone; and Antilochos hurled at Mydon, his squire and charioteer, Atymnios' brave son, even as he was wheeling the whole-hooved horses, and with a stone smote his elbow in the midst; so the reins white with ivory fell from his hands to earth, even into the dust. Then Antilochos sprang on him and drave the sword into his temple, and he fell gasping from the well-wrought chariot headlong in the dust on crown and shoulders. A while he stood there, being lighted on deep sand, until his horses spurned him and cast him to earth, even in the dust; and them Antilochos lashed, and drave them to the Achaians' host.

But Hector marked them across the ranks, and sprang on them with a shout, and the battalions of the Trojans followed him in their might: and Ares led them on and dread Enyo, she bringing ruthless turmoil of war, the while Ares wielded in his hands his monstrous spear, and ranged now before Hector's face, and now behind.

Then Diomedes of the loud war-cry shuddered to behold

him; and even as a shiftless man crossing a great plain cometh on a swift-streaming river flowing on to the sea, and seeing it boil with foam springeth backwards, even so now Tydeides shrank back and spake to the host: "Friends, how marvel we that noble Hector is a spearman and bold man of war! Yet ever is there beside him some god that wardeth off destruction; even as now Ares is there by him in likeness of a mortal man. But with faces towards the Trojans still give ground backwards, neither be desirous to fight amain with gods."

So said he, and the Trojans came very close upon them. Then Hector slew two that knew well the battle joy, riding in one chariot, even Menesthes and Anchialos. And the great Telamonian Aias had pity of them in their fall, and came hard by and darted with his bright javelin, and smote Amphios son of Selagos, that dwelt in Paisos, a man rich in substance, rich in meadow land; but fate led him to bring succour to Priam and his sons. Him Telamonian Aias smote upon the belt, and in his nether belly the far-shadowing spear stuck and he fell with a crash. Then glorious Aias ran at him to strip him of his armour, and the Trojans rained on him keen javelins glittering, and his shield caught many thereof. But he set his heel upon the corpse and plucked forth the spear of bronze; only he could not strip from his shoulders all the fair armour therewith, being overwhelmed of spears. Moreover he feared the haughty Trojans' stout defence, they being many and brave that with their spears pressed on him, so that for all he was so great and valiant and proud they thrust him from them; and he was shaken and shrank back.

Thus toiled these in violent battle; and Tlepolemos son of Herakles, valiant and tall, was driven of forceful fate against godlike Sarpedon. Then when the twain were come nigh in onset on each other, even the son and grandson of Zeus the cloud-gatherer, then first to the other spake Tlepolemos: "Sarpedon, counsellor of the Lykians, why must thou be skulking here, being a man unskilled in battle? Falsely do men say that thou art offspring of aegis-bearing Zeus, seeing thou art found lacking greatly beside those men that in days of old were born of Zeus. Ah, what an one do men say was mighty Herakles, even my father the steadfast lion-heart, who erst came hither for Laomedon's mares with but six ships and a scantier host, yet sacked the city of Ilios and made her highways desolate. But thine is a base spirit, and thy folk are minishing. I ween that thou art in no wise come from Lykia to be a bulwark unto the Trojans, for all thy great strength, but that thou shalt be vanquished at my hand and pass the gates of Hades."

Then Sarpedon captain of the Lykians answered him: "Tlepolemos, he verily overthrew holy Ilios by the folly of the proud man Laomedon, that rewarded his good deed with harsh upbraiding, and paid him not the steeds wherefor he came from afar. And for thee I say that slaughter and black death shall come about here at my hands; vanquished by my spear thou shalt yield to me my glory, and thy life to Hades of the goodly steeds."

So spake Sarpedon, and Tlepolemos lifted his ashen spear, and both their long javelins sped from their hands together. Sarpedon smote the midst of his neck, and the grievous point passed right through, and the darkness of night fell on his eyes and shrouded him: and Tlepolemos with long spear smote the other's left thigh, and the point sped through furiously, grazing the bone; but his father yet warded off destruction.

So his goodly comrades bare away godlike Sarpedon from the battle, but the long spear dragging was heavy upon him, and no man marked it or took thought in their haste to draw the ashen spear out from his thigh that he might stand upright; such labour had they in tending him. And over against them the well-greaved Achaians bare Tlepolemos from the battle. And noble Odysseus of the patient soul marked it, and his heart was stirred within him. Then doubted he in mind and soul whether first to pursue the son of Zeus the loud thunderer, or take the lives of the common sort of the Lykians. But it was not destined to great-hearted Odysseus to slay with his keen blade the mighty son of Zeus; so Athene turned his fury upon the multitude of the Lykians. Then slew he Koiranos and Alastor and Chromios and Alkandros and Halios and Noëmon and Prytanis; and yet more Lykians had noble Odysseus slain but that great Hector of the glancing helm was swift to mark him, and strode through the forefront of battle, harnessed in flashing bronze, and brought terror to the Danaans; but Sarpedon the son of Zeus was glad at his coming, and spake to him a word of pain: "O son of Priam, let me not now be left a prey unto the Danaans, but bring me succour; howbeit thereafter let my life depart from me in your city, seeing it might not be that I should return home to my dear native land, to make glad my dear wife and infant son."

So said he, but Hector of the glancing helm spake no word to him, but hastened on, desirous with all speed to thrust back the Argives and take the lives of many. So his goodly comrades made godlike Sarpedon to sit beneath a fair oak-tree of aegis-bearing Zeus, and valiant Pelagon that was his dear comrade thrust forth from his thigh the ashen spear; and his spirit failed him and mist overspread his eyes. Then breathed he again, and the breath of the north wind blew round about him and brought him to life from the grievous swoon of his soul.

Now the Argives before the face of Ares and mail-clad Hector neither turned them round about toward their black ships, nor charged forward in battle, but still fell backward, when they heard of Ares amid the Trojans. And now who first was slaughtered, and who last, by Hector son of Priam and brazen Ares? Even godlike Teuthras, and thereafter Orestes the charioteer, and Trechos spearman of Aitolia, and Oinomaos and Helenos son of Oinops and Oresbios with gleaming taslets, who dwelt in Hyle and had great care of his substance, lying beside the Kephisian mere; and near him dwelt all the Boiotians, inhabiters of a full rich domain.

Now when the white-armed goddess Hera marked them making havoc of the Argives in the press of battle, anon she spake winged words to Athene: "Out on it, thou daughter of aegis-bearing Zeus, unwearied maiden! Was it for naught we pledged our word to Menelaos, that he should not depart till he had laid waste well-walled Ilios,—if thus we let baleful Ares rage? Go to now, let us twain also take thought of impetuous valour."

So said she, and the bright-eyed goddess Athene disregarded not. So Hera the goddess queen, daughter of great Kronos, went her way to harness the gold-frontleted steeds; and Hebe quickly put to the car the curved wheels of bronze, eight-spoked, upon their axle-tree of iron. Golden is their felloe, imperishable, and tires of bronze are fitted thereover, a marvel to look upon; and the naves are of silver, to turn about on either side. And the car is plaited tight with gold and silver thongs, and two rails run round about it. And the silver pole stood out therefrom; upon the end bound she the fair golden yoke, and set thereon the fair breaststraps of gold, and Hera led beneath the yoke the horses fleet of foot, and hungered for strife and the battle-cry. And Athene, daughter of aegis-bearing Zeus, cast down at her father's threshold her woven vesture many-coloured, that herself had wrought and her hands had fashioned, and put on her the tunic of Zeus the cloud-gatherer, and arrayed her in her armour for dolorous battle. About her shoulders cast she the tasselled aegis terrible, whereon is Panic as a crown all round about, and Strife is therein and Valour and horrible Onslaught withal, and therein is the dreadful monster's Gorgon head, dreadful and grim, portent of aegis-bearing Zeus. Upon her head set she the two-crested golden helm with fourfold plate, bedecked with men-at-arms of a hundred cities. Upon the flaming chariot set she her foot, and grasped her heavy spear, great and stout, wherewith she vanquished the ranks of men, even of heroes with whom she of the awful sire is wroth. Then Hera swiftly smote the horses with the lash; self-moving groaned upon their hinges the gates of heaven whereof the Hours are warders, to whom is committed great heaven and Olympus, whether to throw open the thick cloud or set it to. There through the gates guided they their horses patient of the lash. And they found the son of Kronos sitting apart from all the gods on the topmost peak of many-ridged Olympus. Then the white-armed goddess Hera stayed her horses and questioned the most high Zeus, the son of Kronos, and said: "Father Zeus, hast thou no indignation with Ares for these violent deeds? How great and goodly a company of Achaians hath he destroyed recklessly and in unruly wise, unto my sorrow. But here in peace Kypris and Apollo of the silver bow take their pleasure, having set on this mad one that knoweth not any law. Father Zeus, wilt thou at all be wroth with me if I smite Ares and chase him from the battle in sorry plight?"

And Zeus the cloud-gatherer answered and said to her: "Go to now, set upon him Athene driver of the spoil, who most is wont to bring sore pain upon him."

So spake he, and the white-armed goddess Hera disregarded not, and lashed her horses; they nothing loth flew on between earth and starry heaven. As far as a man seeth with his eyes into the haze of distance as he sitteth on a place of outlook and gazeth over the wine-dark sea, so far leap the loudly neighing horses of the gods. Now when they came to Troy and the two flowing rivers, even to where Simoeis and Skamandros join their streams, there the white-armed goddess Hera stayed her horses and loosed them from the car and poured thick mist round about them, and Simoeis made ambrosia spring up for them to graze. So the goddesses went their way with step like unto turtledoves, being fain to bring succour to the men of Argos. And when they were now come where the most and most valiant stood, thronging about mighty Diomedes tamer of horses, in the semblance of ravening lions or wild boars whose strength is nowise feeble, then stood the white-armed goddess Hera and shouted in the likeness of great-hearted Stentor with voice of bronze, whose cry was loud as the cry of fifty other men: "Fie upon you, Argives, base things of shame, so brave in semblance! While yet noble Achilles entered continually into battle, then issued not the Trojans even from the Dardanian gate; for they had dread of his terrible spear. But now fight they far from the city at the hollow ships."

So saying she aroused the spirit and soul of every man. And to Tydeides' side sprang the bright-eyed goddess Athene. That lord she found beside his horses and chariot, cooling the wound that Pandaros with his dart had pierced, for his sweat vexed it by reason of the broad baldrick of his round shield; therewith was he vexed and his arm grew weary, so he was lifting up the baldrick and wiping away the dusky blood. Then the goddess laid her hand on his horses' yoke, and said: "Of a truth Tydeus begat a son little after his own likeness. Tydeus was short of stature, but a man of war; yea even when I would not have him fight nor make display—what time he came apart from the Achaians on an embassage to Thebes, to the midst of the multitude of the Kadmeians, I bade him feast in their halls at peace; but he, possessing his valiant soul as of old time, challenged the young men of the Kadmeians and in everything vanquished [easily; so sure a helper was I unto him]. But for thee, beside thee stand I and guard thee and with all my heart bid thee fight the Trojans; yet either hath weariness of much striving entered into thy limbs, or disheartening terror hath taken hold of thee. If that be so, no offspring art thou of Tydeus, the wise son of Oineus."

And stalwart Diomedes made answer to her and said: "I

know thee, goddess daughter of aegis-bearing Zeus: therefore with my whole heart will I tell thee my thought and hide it not. Neither hath disheartening terror taken hold upon me, nor any faintness, but I am still mindful of thy behest that thou didst lay upon me. Thou forbadest me to fight face to face with all the blessed gods, save only if Zeus' daughter Aphrodite should enter into battle, then to wound her with the keen bronze. Therefore do I now give ground myself and have bidden all the Argives likewise to gather here together; for I discern Ares lording it in the fray."

Then the bright-eyed goddess Athene answered him: "Diomedes son of Tydeus, thou joy of mine heart, fear thou, for that, neither Ares nor any other of the immortals; so great a helper am I to thee. Go to now, at Ares first guide thou thy whole-hooved horses, and smite him hand to hand, nor have any awe of impetuous Ares, raving here, a curse incarnate, the renegade that of late in converse with me and Hera pledged him to fight against the Trojans and give succour to the Argives, but now consorteth with the Trojans and hath forgotten these."

So speaking, with her hand she drew back Sthenelos and thrust him from the chariot to earth, and instantly leapt he down, so the goddess mounted the car by noble Diomedes' side right eagerly. The oaken axle creaked loud with its burden, bearing the dread goddess and the man of might. Then Pallas Athene grasped the whip and reins; forthwith against Ares first guided she the whole-hooved horses. Now he was stripping huge Periphas, most valiant far of the Aitolians, Ochesios' glorious son. Him was blood-stained Ares stripping; and Athene donned the helm of Hades, that terrible Ares might not behold her. Now when Ares scourge of mortals beheld noble Diomedes, he left huge Periphas lying there, where at the first he had slain him and taken away his life, and made straight at Diomedes tamer of horses. Now when they were come nigh in onset on one another, first Ares thrust over the yoke and horses' reins with spear of bronze, eager to take away his life. But the bright-eyed goddess Athene with her hand seized the spear and thrust it up over the car, to spend itself in vain. Next Diomedes of the loud war-cry attacked with spear of bronze; and Pallas Athene drave it home against Ares' nethermost belly, where his taslets were girt about him. There smote he him and wounded him, rending through his fair skin, and plucked forth the spear again. Then brazen Ares bellowed loud as nine thousand warriors or ten thousand cry in battle as they join in strife and fray. Thereat trembling gat hold of Achaians and Trojans for fear, so mightily bellowed Ares insatiate of battle.

Even as gloomy mist appeareth from the clouds when after heat a stormy wind ariseth, even so to Tydeus' son Diomedes brazen Ares appeared amid clouds, faring to wide heaven. Swiftly came he to the gods' dwelling, steep Olympus, and sat beside Zeus son of Kronos with grief at heart, and shewed the immortal blood flowing from the wound, and piteously spake to him winged words: "Father Zeus, hast thou no indignation to behold these violent deeds? For ever cruelly suffer we gods by one another's devices, in shewing men grace. With thee are we all at variance, because thou didst beget that reckless maiden and baleful, whose thought is ever of iniquitous deeds. For all the other gods that are in Olympus hearken to thee, and we are subject every one; only her thou chastenest not, neither in deed nor word, but settest her on, because this pestilent one is thine own offspring. Now hath she urged on Tydeus' son, even overweening Diomedes, to rage furiously against the immortal gods. Kypris first he wounded in close fight, in the wrist of her hand, and then assailed he me, even me, with the might of a god. Howbeit my swift feet bare me away; else had I long endured anguish there amid the grisly heaps of dead, or else had lived strengthless from the smitings of the spear."

Then Zeus the cloud-gatherer looked sternly at him and said: "Nay, thou renegade, sit not by me and whine. Most hateful to me art thou of all gods that dwell in Olympus; thou ever lovest strife and wars and battles. Truly thy mother's spirit is intolerable, unyielding, even Hera's; her can I scarce rule with words. Therefore I deem that by her prompting thou art in this plight. Yet will I no longer endure to see thee in anguish; mine offspring art thou, and to me thy mother bare thee. But wert thou born of any other god unto this violence, long ere this hadst thou been lower than the sons of Heaven."

So spake he and bade Paieon heal him. And Paieon laid assuaging drugs upon the wound [and healed him; seeing he was verily of no mortal substance]. Even as fig juice maketh haste to thicken white milk, that is liquid but curdleth speedily as a man stirreth, even so swiftly healed he impetuous Ares. And Hebe bathed him, and clothed him in gracious raiment, and he sate him down by Zeus son of Kronos, glorying in his might.

Then fared the twain back to the mansion of great Zeus, even Hera of Argos and Alalkomenean Athene, having stayed Ares scourge of mortals from his man-slaying.

BOOK VI

How Diomedes and Glaukos being about to fight, were known to each other, and parted in friendliness. And how Hector returning to the city bade farewell to Andromache his wife.

So was the dread fray of Trojans and Achaians left to itself, and the battle swayed oft this way and that across the plain, as they aimed against each other their bronze-shod javelins, between Simoeis and the streams of Xanthos.

First Aias son of Telamon, bulwark of the Achaians, brake a battalion of the Trojans and brought his comrades salvation, smiting a warrior that was chiefest among the Thracians, Eussoros' son Akamas the goodly and great. Him first he smote upon his thick-crested helmet-ridge and drave into his forehead, so that the point of bronze pierced into the bone; and darkness shrouded his eyes.

Then Diomedes of the loud war-cry slew Axylos Teuthranos' son that dwelt in stablished Arisbe, a man of substance dear to his fellows; for his dwelling was by the roadside and he entertained all men. Howbeit of all these was there then not one to meet the foe before his face and save him from fell destruction; but Diomedes took the life of both of them, even of him and Kalesios his squire that now was the driver of his chariot; so passed both below the earth.

And Euryalos slew Dresos and Opheltios, and followed after Aisepos and Pedasos whom erst the fountain-nymph Abarbarea bare to noble Boukolion. Now Boukolion was son of proud Laomedon, his eldest born, begotten of a mother unwedded; and as he tended his flocks he had converse with the nymph in love, and she conceived and bare twin sons. And lo, the strength of these and their glorious limbs Mekisteus' son unstrung, and stripped the armour from their shoulders. And stubborn Polypoites slew Astyalos, and Odysseus with spear of bronze laid low Pidytes of Perkote, and so did Teukros to goodly Aretaon. Then was Ableros killed by the glistening spear of Antilochos, Nestor's son, and Elatos by Agamemnon king of men; beside the banks of fair-flowing Satnioeis dwelt he in steep Pedasos. And Leïtos the warrior caught Phylakos, as he fled; and Eurypylos slew Melanthios.

Now did Menelaos of the loud war-cry take Adrestos alive; for his horses took flight across the plain, and stumbling in a tamarisk bough brake the curved car at the pole's foot; so they themselves fared towards the city where the rest were fleeing in rout, and their lord rolled from out the car beside the wheel, prone in the dust upon his face. Then came Atreus' son Menelaos to his side bearing his far-shadowing spear. Thereat Adrestos caught him by his knees and besought him: "Take me captive, thou son of Atreus, and accept a worthy ransom; many a treasure is stored up in my father's rich palace, bronze and gold and smithied iron; thereof would my father yield thee ransom beyond the telling, if he but heard that I am alive at the ships of the Achaians."

So spake he, and moved the spirit in his breast. And now had he forthwith given him to his squire to lead him to the Achaians' fleet ships, but that Agamemnon came running to meet him, and spake a word of chiding to him: "Good Menelaos, why art thou so careful of the foeman? Have then such good deeds been wrought thee in thy house by Trojans? Of them let not one escape sheer destruction at our hands, not even the man-child that the mother beareth in her womb; let not even him escape, but all perish together out of Ilios, uncared for and unknown."

So spake the hero and turned his brother's mind with righteous persuasion; so with his hand he thrust the hero

Adrestos from him, and lord Agamemnon smote him in the flank, and he was overthrown, and Atreus' son set his heel upon his chest and plucked forth his ashen spear.

Then Nestor called to the Argives with far-reaching shout: "My friends, Danaan warriors, men of Ares' company, let no man now take thought of spoils to tarry behind, that he may bring the greatest burden to the ships; but let us slay the foemen. Thereafter shall ye at your ease also strip of their spoil the dead corpses about the plain."

So spake he and stirred the spirit and soul of every man. Now had the Trojans been chased again by the Achaians, dear to Ares, up into Ilios, in their weakness overcome, but that Priam's son Helenos, far best of augurs, stood by Aineias' side and Hector's, and spake to them: "Aineias and Hector, seeing that on you lieth the task of war in chief of Trojans and Lykians, because for every issue ye are foremost both for fight and counsel, stand ye your ground, and range the host everywhither to rally them before the gates, ere yet they fall fleeing in their women's arms, and be made a rejoicing to the foe. Then when ye have aroused all our battalions we will abide here and fight the Danaans, though in sore weariness; for necessity presseth us hard: but thou, Hector, go into the city, and speak there to thy mother and mine; let her gather the aged wives to bright-eyed Athene's temple in the upper city, and with her key open the doors of the holy house; and let her lay the robe, that seemeth to her the most gracious and greatest in her hall and far dearest unto herself, upon the knees of beauteous-haired Athene; and vow to her to sacrifice in her temple twelve sleek kine, that have not felt the goad, if she will have mercy on the city and the Trojans' wives and little children. So may she perchance hold back Tydeus' son from holy Ilios, the furious spearman, the mighty deviser of rout, whom in good sooth I deem to have proved himself mightiest of the Achaians. Never in this wise feared we Achilles, prince of men, who they say is born of a goddess; nay, but he that we see is beyond measure furious; none can match him for might."

So spake he, and Hector disregarded not his brother's word, but leapt forthwith from his chariot in his armour to earth, and brandishing two sharp spears passed everywhere through the host, rousing them to battle, and stirred the dread war-cry. So they were rallied and stood to face the Achaians, and the Argives gave ground and ceased from slaughter, and deemed that some immortal had descended from starry heaven to bring the Trojans succour, in such wise rallied they. Then Hector called to the Trojans with far-reaching shout: "Oh high-souled Trojans and ye far-famed allies, quit you like men, my friends, and take thought of impetuous courage, while I depart to Ilios and bid the elders of the council and our wives pray to the gods and vow them hecatombs."

So saying Hector of the glancing helm departed, and the black hide beat on either side against his ankles and his neck, even the rim that ran uttermost about his bossed shield.

Now Glaukos son of Hippolochos and Tydeus' son met in the mid-space of the foes, eager to do battle. Thus when the twain were come nigh in onset on each other, to him first spake Diomedes of the loud war-cry: "Who art thou, noble sir, of mortal men? For never have I beheld thee in glorious battle ere this, yet now hast thou far outstripped all men in thy hardihood, seeing thou abidest my far-shadowing spear. Luckless are the fathers whose children face my might. But if thou art some immortal come down from heaven, then will not I fight with heavenly gods. Nay moreover even Dryas' son mighty Lykurgos was not for long when he strove with heavenly gods, he that erst chased through the goodly land of Nysa the nursing-mothers of frenzied Dionysos; and they all cast their wands upon the ground, smitten with murderous Lykurgos' ox-goad. Then Dionysos fled and plunged beneath the salt sea-wave, and

Thetis took him to her bosom, affrighted, for a mighty trembling had seized him at his foe's rebuke. But with Lykurgos the gods that live at ease were wroth, and Kronos' son made him blind, and he was not for long, because he was hated of all the immortal gods. So would neither I be fain to fight the blessed gods. But if thou art of men that eat the fruit of the field, come nigh, that anon thou mayest enter the toils of destruction."

Then Hippolochos' glorious son made answer to him: "Great-hearted Tydeides, why enquirest thou of my generation? Even as are the generations of leaves such are those likewise of men; the leaves that be the wind scattereth on the earth, and the forest buddeth and putteth forth more again, when the season of spring is at hand; so of the generations of men one putteth forth and another ceaseth. Yet if thou wilt, have thine answer, that thou mayest well know our lineage, whereof many men have knowledge. There is a city Ephyre in the heart of Argos, pasture land of horses, and there dwelt Sisyphos that was craftiest of men, Sisyphos son of Aiolos; and he begat a son, even Glaukos, and Glaukos begat noble Bellerophon. To him the gods granted beauty and lovely manhood; but Proitos in his heart devised ill for him, and being mightier far drave him from the land of the Argives, whom Zeus had made subject to his sceptre. Now Proitos' wife, goodly Anteia, lusted after him, to have converse in secret love, but no whit prevailed she, for the uprightness of his heart, on wise Bellerophon. Then spake she lyingly to king Proitos: "Die, Proitos, or else slay Bellerophon, that would have converse in love with me against my will." So spake she, and anger gat hold upon the king at that he heard. To slay him he forbare, for his soul had shame of that; but he sent him to Lykia, and gave him tokens of woe, graving in a folded tablet many deadly things, and bade him shew these to Anteia's father, that he might be slain. So fared he to Lykia by the blameless convoy of the gods. Now when he came to Lykia and the stream of Xanthos, then did the king of wide Lykia honour him with all his heart; nine days he entertained him and killed nine oxen. And when on the tenth day rosy-fingered dawn appeared, then he questioned him and asked to see what token he bare from his son-in-law, even Proitos. Now when he had received of him Proitos' evil token, first he bade him slay Chimaira the unconquerable. Of divine birth was she and not of men, in front a lion, and behind a serpent, and in the midst a goat; and she breathed dread fierceness of blazing fire. And her he slew, obedient to the signs of heaven. Next fought he with the famed Solymi; this, said he, was the mightiest battle of warriors wherein he entered. And thirdly he slew the Amazons, women peers of men. And as he turned back therefrom, the king devised another cunning wile; he picked from wide Lykia the bravest men, and set an ambush. But these returned nowise home again; for noble Bellerophon slew them all. So when the king now knew that he was the brave offspring of a god, he kept him there, and plighted him his daughter, and gave him the half of all the honour of his kingdom; moreover the Lykians meted him a domain pre-eminent above all, fair with vineyards and tilth to possess it. And his wife bare wise Bellerophon three children, Isandros and Hippolochos and Laodameia. With Laodameia lay Zeus the lord of counsel, and she bare godlike Sarpedon, the warrior with arms of bronze. But when even Bellerophon came to be hated of all the gods, then wandered he alone in the Aleian plain, devouring his own soul, and avoiding the paths of men; and Isandros his son was slain by Ares insatiate of battle, as he fought against the famed Solymi, and his daughter was slain in wrath of gold-gleaming Artemis. But Hippolochos begat me, and of him do I declare me to be sprung; he sent me to Troy and bade me very instantly to be ever the best and to excel all other men, nor put to shame the lineage of my fathers that were of noblest blood in Ephyre and in wide Lykia. This is the lineage and blood whereof I avow myself to be."

So said he, and Diomedes of the loud war-cry was glad. He planted his spear in the bounteous earth and with soft words spake to the shepherd of the host: "Surely then thou art to me a guest-friend of old times through my father: for goodly Oineus of yore entertained noble Bellerophon in his halls and kept him twenty days. Moreover they gave each the other goodly gifts of friendship; Oineus gave a belt bright with purple, and Bellerophon a gold twy-handled cup, the which when I came I left in my palace. But of Tydeus I remember naught, seeing I was yet little when he left me, what time the Achaian host perished at Thebes. Therefore now am I to thee a dear guest-friend in midmost Argos, and thou in Lykia, whene'er I fare to your land. So let us shun each other's spears, even amid the throng; Trojans are there in multitudes and famous allies for me to slay, whoe'er it be that God vouchsafeth me and my feet overtake; and for thee are there Achaians in multitude, to slay whome'er thou canst. But let us make exchange of arms between us, that these also may know how we avow ourselves to be guest-friends by lineage."

So spake the twain, and leaping from their cars clasped each the other by his hand, and pledged their faith. But now Zeus son of Kronos took from Glaukos his wits, in that he made exchange with Diomedes Tydeus' son of golden armour for bronze, the price of five score oxen for the price of nine.

Now when Hector came to the Skaian gates and to the oak-tree, there came running round about him the Trojans' wives and daughters, enquiring of sons and brethren and friends and husbands. But he bade them thereat all in turn pray to the gods; but sorrow hung over many.

But when he came to Priam's beautiful palace, adorned with polished colonnades—and in it were fifty chambers of polished stone, builded hard by one another, wherein Priam's sons slept beside their wedded wives; and for his daughters over against them on the other side within the courtyard were twelve roofed chambers of polished stone builded hard by one another, wherein slept Priam's sons-in-law beside their chaste wives—then came there to meet him his bountiful mother, leading with her Laodike, fairest of her daughters to look on; and she clasped her hand in his, and spake, and called upon his name: "My son, why hast thou left violent battle to come hither? Surely the sons of the Achaians—name of evil!—press thee hard in fight about thy city, and so thy spirit hath brought thee hither, to come and stretch forth thy hands to Zeus from the citadel. But tarry till I bring thee honey-sweet wine, that thou mayest pour libation to Zeus and all the immortals first, and then shalt thou thyself also be refreshed if thou wilt drink. When a man is awearied wine greatly maketh his strength to wax, even as thou art awearied in fighting for thy fellows."

Then great Hector of the glancing helm answered her: "Bring me no honey-hearted wine, my lady mother, lest thou cripple me of my courage and I be forgetful of my might. Moreover I have awe to make libation of gleaming wine to Zeus with hands unwashen; nor can it be in any wise that one should pray to the son of Kronos, god of the storm-cloud, all defiled with blood and filth. But go thou to the temple of Athene, driver of the spoil, with offerings, and gather the aged wives together; and the robe that seemeth to thee the most gracious and greatest in thy palace, and dearest unto thyself, that lay thou upon the knees of beauteous-haired Athene, and vow to her to sacrifice in her temple twelve sleek kine, that have not felt the goad, if she will have mercy on the city and the Trojans' wives and little children. So may she perchance hold back Tydeus' son from holy Ilios, the furious spearman, the mighty deviser of rout. So go thou to the temple of Athene, driver of the spoil; and I will go after Paris, to summon him, if perchance he will hearken to my voice. Would that the earth forthwith might swallow him up! The Olympian fostered him to be a sore bane to the Trojans and to great-hearted Priam, and to Priam's sons. If I but saw him going down to the gates of death, then might I deem that my heart had forgotten its sorrow."

So said he, and she went unto the hall, and called to her handmaidens, and they gathered the aged wives throughout the city. Then she herself went down to her fragrant chamber where were her embroidered robes, the work of Sidonian women, whom godlike Alexandros himself brought from Sidon, when he sailed over the wide sea, that journey wherein he brought home high-born Helen. Of these Hekabe took one to bear for an offering to Athene, the one that was fairest for adornment and greatest, and shone like a star, and lay nethermost of all. Then went she her way and the multitude of aged wives hasted after her.

Now when they came to the temple of Athene in the citadel, fair-cheeked Theano opened them the doors, even Kisseus' daughter, wife of horse-taming Antenor; for her the Trojans had made priestess of Athene. Then lifted they all their hands to Athene with lamentation: and fair-cheeked Theano took the robe and laid it on the knees of beauteous-haired Athene, and lifted up her voice and prayed to the daughter of great Zeus: "Lady Athene, saviour of the city, fair among goddesses, break now Diomedes' spear, and grant moreover that himself may fall prone before the Skaian gates; that we may sacrifice thee now forthwith in thy temple twelve sleek kine, that have not felt the goad, if thou wilt have mercy on the city and the Trojans' wives and little children." So spake she praying, but Pallas Athene denied the prayer.

So were these praying to the daughter of great Zeus; and Hector was come to Alexandros' fair palace, that himself had builded with them that were most excellent carpenters then in deep-soiled Troy-land; these made him his chamber and hall and courtyard hard by to Priam and Hector, in the upper city. There entered in Hector dear to Zeus, and his hand bare his spear, eleven cubits long: before his face glittered the bronze spear-point, and a ring of gold ran round about it. And he found Paris in his chamber busied with his beauteous arms, his shield and breastplate, and handling his curved bow; and Helen of Argos sate among her serving-women and appointed brave handiwork for her handmaidens. Then when Hector saw him he rebuked him with scornful words: "Good sir, thou dost not well to cherish this rancour in thy heart. The folk are perishing about the city and high wall in battle, and for thy sake the battle-cry is kindled and war around this city; yea thyself wouldest thou fall out with another, didst thou see him shrinking from hateful war. Up then, lest the city soon be scorched with burning fire."

And godlike Alexandros answered him: "Hector, since in measure thou chidest me and not beyond measure, therefore will I tell thee; lay thou it to thine heart and hearken to me. Not by reason so much of the Trojans, for wrath and indignation, sate I me in my chamber, but fain would I yield me to my sorrow. Even now my wife hath persuaded me with soft words, and urged me into battle; and I moreover, even I, deem that it will be better so; for victory shifteth from man to man. Go to then, tarry awhile, let me put on my armour of war; or else fare thou forth, and I will follow; and I think to overtake thee."

So said he, but Hector of the glancing helm answered him not a word. But Helen spake to him with gentle words: "My brother, even mine that am a dog, mischievous and abominable, would that on the day when my mother bare me at the first, an evil storm-wind had caught me away to a mountain or a billow of the loud-sounding sea, where the billow might have swept me away before all these things came to pass. Howbeit, seeing the gods devised all these ills in this wise, would that then I had been mated with a better man that felt dishonour and the multitude of men's reproachings. But as for him, neither hath he now sound heart, nor ever will have; thereof deem I moreover that he will reap the fruit. But now come, enter in and sit thee here upon this bench, my brother, since thy heart chiefly trouble hath encompassed, for the sake of me, that am a dog, and for Alexandros' sin; on whom Zeus bringeth evil doom, that even in days to come we may be a song in the ears of men that shall be hereafter."

Then great Hector of the glancing helm answered her: "Bid me not sit, Helen, of thy love; thou wilt not persuade me. Already my heart is set to succour the men of Troy, that have great desire for me that am not with them. But rouse thou this fellow, yea let himself make speed, to overtake me yet within the city. For I shall go into mine house to behold my housefolk and my dear wife, and infant boy; for I know not if I shall return home to them again, or if the gods will now overthrow me at the hands of the Achaians."

So spake Hector of the glancing helm and departed; and anon he came to his well stablished house. But he found not white-armed Andromache in the halls; she with her boy and fair-robed handmaiden had taken her stand upon the tower, weeping and wailing. And when Hector found not his noble wife within, he came and stood upon the threshold, and spake amid the serving-women: "Come tell me now true, my serving-women. Whither went white-armed Andromache forth from the hall? Hath she gone out to my sisters or unto my brothers' fair-robed wives, or to Athene's temple, where all the fair-tressed Trojan women propitiate the awful goddess?"

Then a busy housedame spake in answer to him: "Hector, seeing thou straitly chargest us tell thee true, neither hath she gone out to any of thy sisters or thy brothers' fair-robed wives, neither to Athene's temple, where all the fair-tressed Trojan women are propitiating the awful goddess; but she went to the great tower of Ilios, because she heard the Trojans were hard pressed, and great victory was for the Achaians. So hath she come in haste to the wall, like unto one frenzied; and the nurse with her beareth the child."

So spake the housedame, and Hector hastened from his house back by the same way down the well-builded streets. When he had passed through the great city and was come to the Skaian gates, whereby he was minded to issue upon the plain, then came his dear-won wife, running to meet him, even Andromache daughter of great-hearted Eëtion, Eëtion that dwelt beneath wooded Plakos, in Thebe under Plakos, and was king of the men of Kilikia; for his daughter was wife to bronze-harnessed Hector. So she met him now, and with her went the handmaid bearing in her bosom the tender boy, the little child, Hector's loved son, like unto a beautiful star. Him Hector called Skamandrios, but all the folk Astyanax; for only Hector guarded Ilios. So now he smiled and gazed at his boy silently, and Andromache stood by his side weeping, and clasped her hand in his, and spake and called upon his name. "Dear my lord, this thy hardihood will undo thee, neither hast thou any pity for thine infant boy, nor for me forlorn that soon shall be thy widow; for soon will the Achaians all set upon thee and slay thee. But it were better for me to go down to the grave if I lose thee; for never more will any comfort be mine, when once thou, even thou, hast met thy fate, but only sorrow. Moreover I have no father nor lady mother: my father was slain of goodly Achilles, for he wasted the populous city of the Kilikians, even high-gated Thebe, and slew Eëtion; yet he despoiled him not, for his soul had shame of that, but he burnt him in his inlaid armour and raised a barrow over him; and all about were elm-trees planted by the mountain nymphs, daughters of aegis-bearing Zeus. And the seven brothers that were mine within our halls, all these on the selfsame day went within the house of Hades; for fleet-footed goodly Achilles slew them all amid their kine of trailing gait and white-fleeced sheep. And my mother, that was queen beneath wooded Plakos, her brought he hither with the other spoils, but afterward took a ransom untold to set her free; but in her father's halls was she smitten by the Archer Artemis. Nay, Hector, thou art to me father and lady mother, yea and brother, even as thou art my goodly husband. Come now, have pity and abide here upon the tower, lest thou make thy child an orphan and thy wife a widow. And stay thy folk beside the fig-tree, where best the city may be scaled and the wall is assailable. Thrice came thither the most valiant that are with the two Aiantes and famed Idomeneus and the sons of Atreus and Tydeus' valiant son, and essayed to enter; whether one skilled in soothsaying revealed it to them, or whether their own spirit urgeth and biddeth them on."

Then great Hector of the glancing helm answered her: "Surely I take thought for all these things, my wife; but I have very sore shame of the Trojans and Trojan dames with trailing robes, if like a coward I shrink away from battle. Moreover mine own soul forbiddeth me, seeing I have learnt ever to be valiant and fight in the forefront of the Trojans, winning my father's great glory and mine own. Yea of a surety I know this in heart and soul; the day shall come for holy Ilios to be laid low, and Priam and the folk of Priam of the good ashen spear. Yet doth the anguish of the Trojans hereafter not so much trouble me neither Hekabe's own, neither king Priam's, neither my brethren's, the many and brave that shall fall in the dust before their foemen, as doth thine anguish in the day when some mail-clad Achaian shall lead thee weeping and rob thee of the light of freedom. So shalt thou abide in Argos and ply the loom at another woman's bidding, and bear water from fount Messeis or Hypereia, being grievously entreated, and sore constraint shall be laid upon thee. And then shall one say that beholdeth thee weep: 'This is the wife of Hector, that was foremost in battle of the horse-taming

Trojans when men fought about Ilios.' Thus shall one say hereafter, and fresh grief will be thine for lack of such an husband as thou hadst to ward off the day of thraldom. But me in death may the heaped-up earth be covering, ere I hear thy crying and thy carrying into captivity."

So spake glorious Hector, and stretched out his arm to his boy. But the child shrunk crying to the bosom of his fair-girdled nurse, dismayed at his dear father's aspect, and in dread at the bronze and horse-hair crest that he beheld nodding fiercely from the helmet's top. Then his dear father laughed aloud, and his lady mother; forthwith glorious Hector took the helmet from his head, and laid it, all gleaming, upon the earth; then kissed he his dear son and dandled him in his arms, and spake in prayer to Zeus and all the gods, "O Zeus and all ye gods, vouchsafe ye that this my son may likewise prove even as I, pre-eminent amid the Trojans, and as valiant in might, and be a great king of Ilios. Then may men say of him, 'Far greater is he than his father' as he returneth home from battle; and may he bring with him blood-stained spoils from the foeman he hath slain, and may his mother's heart be glad."

So spake he, and laid his son in his dear wife's arms; and she took him to her fragrant bosom, smiling tearfully. And her husband had pity to see her, and caressed her with his hand, and spake and called upon her name: "Dear one, I pray thee be not of oversorrowful heart; no man against my fate shall hurl me to Hades; only destiny, I ween, no man hath escaped, be he coward or be he valiant, when once he hath been born. But go thou to thine house and see to thine own tasks, the loom and distaff, and bid thine handmaidens ply their work; but for war shall men provide and I in chief of all men that dwell in Ilios."

So spake glorious Hector, and took up his horse-hair crested helmet; and his dear wife departed to her home oft looking back, and letting fall big tears. Anon she came to the well-stablished house of man-slaying Hector, and found therein her many handmaidens, and stirred lamentation in them all. So bewailed they Hector, while yet he lived, within his house: for they deemed that he would no more come back to them from battle, nor escape the fury of the hands of the Achaians.

Neither lingered Paris long in his lofty house, but clothed on him his brave armour, bedight with bronze, and hasted through the city, trusting to his nimble feet. Even as when a stalled horse, full-fed at the manger, breaketh his tether and speedeth at the gallop across the plain, being wont to bathe him in the fair-flowing stream, exultingly; and holdeth his head on high, and his mane floateth about his shoulders, and he trusteth in his glory, and nimbly his limbs bear him to the haunts and pasturage of mares; even so Priam's son Paris, glittering in his armour like the shining sun, strode down from high Pergamos laughingly, and his swift feet bare him. Forthwith he overtook his brother noble Hector, even as he was on the point to turn him away from the spot where he had dallied with his wife. To him first spake godlike Alexandros: "Sir, in good sooth I have delayed thee in thine haste by my tarrying, and came not rightly as thou badest me."

And Hector of the glancing helm answered him and said: "Good brother, no man that is rightminded could make light of thy doings in fight, seeing thou art strong: but thou art wilfully remiss and hast no care; and for this my heart is grieved within me, that I hear shameful words concerning thee in the Trojans' mouths, who for thy sake endure much toil. But let us be going; all this will we make good hereafter, if Zeus ever vouchsafe us to set before the heavenly gods that are for everlasting the cup of deliverance in our halls, when we have chased out of Troy-land the well-greaved Achaians."

BOOK VII

Of the single combat between Aias and Hector, and of the burying of the dead, and the building of a wall about the Achaian ships.

So spake glorious Hector and issued from the gates, and with him went his brother Alexandros; and both were eager of soul for fight and battle. Even as God giveth to longing seamen fair wind when they have grown weary of beating the main with polished oars, and their limbs are foredone with toil, even so appeared these to the longing Trojans.

Then the one of them slew king Areïthoös' son, Menesthios dwelling in Arne, whom Areïthoös the Mace-man and ox-eyed Phylomedusa begat; and the other, even Hector, with his sharp spear smote Eïoneus' neck, beneath his bronze helmet-rim, and unstrung his limbs. And Glaukos son of Hippolochos, captain of the men of Lykia, cast his spear at Iphinoos through the press of battle, even at the son of Dexios, as he sprang up behind his fleet mares, and smote his shoulders; so fell he from his chariot to earth and his limbs were unstrung.

Now when the goddess bright-eyed Athene marked them making havoc of the Argives in the press of battle, she darted down from the crests of Olympus to holy Ilios. But Apollo rose to meet her, for he beheld her from Pergamos, and would have victory for the Trojans. So the twain met each the other by the oak-tree. To her spake first king Apollo son of Zeus: "Why now art thou come thus eagerly from Olympus, thou daughter of great Zeus, and why hath thy high heart sent thee? Surely it is to give the Danaans unequal victory in battle! seeing thou hast no mercy on the Trojans, that perish. But if thou wouldest hearken to me—and it were far better so—let us now stay battle and warring for the day; hereafter shall they fight again, till they reach the goal of Ilios, since thus it seemeth good to your hearts, goddesses immortal, to lay waste this city."

And the goddess bright-eyed Athene made answer to him: "So be it, Far-darter; in this mind I likewise came from Olympus to the midst of Trojans and Achaians. But come, how thinkest thou to stay the battle of the warriors?"

And king Apollo, son of Zeus, made answer to her: "Let us arouse the stalwart spirit of horse-taming Hector, if so be he will challenge some one of the Danaans in single fight man to man to meet him in deadly combat. So shall the bronze-greaved Achaians be jealous and stir up one to fight singly with goodly Hector."

So spake he and the bright-eyed goddess Athene disregarded not. Now Helenos Priam's dear son understood in spirit their resolve that the gods in counsel had approved; and he went to Hector and stood beside him, and spake a word to him: "Hector son of Priam, peer of Zeus in counsel, wouldest thou now hearken at all to me? for I am thy brother. Make the other Trojans sit, and all the Achaians, and thyself challenge him that is best of the Achaians to meet thee man to man in deadly combat. It is not yet thy destiny to die and meet thy doom; for thus heard I the voice of the gods that are from everlasting."

So said he, and Hector rejoiced greatly to hear his saying, and went into the midst and refrained the battalions of the Trojans with his spear grasped by the middle, and they all sate them down: and Agamemnon made the well-greaved Achaians sit. And Athene withal and Apollo of the silver bow, in the likeness of vulture birds, sate them upon a tall oak holy to aegis-bearing father Zeus, rejoicing in their warriors; and the ranks of all of them sate close together, bristling with shields and plumes and spears. Even as there spreadeth across the main the ripple of the west wind newly risen, and the sea grows black beneath it, so sate the ranks of Achaians and Trojans upon the plain. And Hector spake between both hosts: "Hearken to me, Trojans and well-greaved Achaians, that I may speak what my mind within my breast biddeth me. Our oaths of truce Kronos' son, enthroned on high, accomplished not; but evil is his intent and ordinance for both our hosts, until either ye take fair-towered Troy or yourselves be vanquished beside your seafaring ships. But in the midst of you are the chiefest of all the Achaians; therefore now let the man whose heart biddeth him fight with me come hither from among you all to be your champion against goodly Hector. And this declare I, and be Zeus our witness thereto; if that man slay me with the long-edged sword, let him spoil me of my armour and bear it to the hollow ships, but give back my body to my home, that Trojans and Trojans' wives may give me my due of burning in my death. But if I slay him and Apollo vouchsafe me glory, I will spoil him of his armour and bear it to holy Ilios and hang it upon the temple of far-darting Apollo, but his corpse will I render back to the well-decked ships, that the flowing-haired Achaians may entomb him, and build him a barrow beside wide Hellespont. So shall one say even of men that be late born, as he saileth in his benched ship over the wine-dark sea: 'This is the barrow of a man that died in days of old, a champion whom glorious Hector slew.' So shall a man say hereafter, and this my glory shall never die."

So spake he and they all were silent and held their peace; to deny him they were ashamed, and feared to meet him. But at the last stood up Menelaos and spake amid them and chiding upbraided them, and groaned deep at heart: "Ah me, vain threateners, ye women of Achaia and no more men, surely all this shall be a shame, evil of evil, if no one of the Danaans now goeth to meet Hector. Nay, turn ye all to earth and water, sitting there each man disheartened, helplessly inglorious; against him will I myself array me; and from on high the threads of victory are guided of the immortal gods."

So spake he and donned his fair armour. And now, O Menelaos, had the end of life appeared for thee at Hector's hands, seeing he was stronger far, but that the princes of the Achaians started up and caught thee. And Atreus' son himself wide-ruling Agamemnon, took him by his right hand and spake a word and called upon his name: "Thou doest madly, Menelaos fosterling of Zeus; yet is it no time for this thy madness. Draw back, though it be with pain, nor think for contention's sake to fight with one better than thou, with Hector Priam's son, whom others beside thee abhor. Yea, this man even Achilles dreadeth to meet in battle, wherein is the warrior's glory; and Achilles is better far than thou. Go therefore now and sit amid the company of thy fellows; against him shall the Achaians put forth another champion. Fearless though he be and insatiate of turmoil, I ween that he shall be fain to rest his knees, if he escape from the fury of war and terrible fray."

So spake the hero and persuaded his brother's heart with just counsel; and he obeyed. So his squires thereat with gladness took his armour from his shoulders; and Nestor stood up and spake amid the Argives: "Fie upon it, verily sore lamentation cometh on the land of Achaia. Verily old Peleus driver of chariots would groan sore, that goodly counsellor of the Myrmidons and orator, who erst questioned me in his house, and rejoiced greatly, inquiring of the lineage and birth of all the Argives. If he heard now of those that all were cowering before Hector, then would he lift his hands to the immortals, instantly praying that his soul might depart from his limbs down to the house of Hades. Ah would to father Zeus and Athene and Apollo I were young as when beside swift-flowing Keladon the Pylians gathered together to battle and the Arkadians that bear the spear, beneath the walls of Pheia, about the streams of Iardanos. Then stood up for their champion Ereuthalion, a man the peer of gods, bearing upon his shoulders the armour of king Areïthoös that by men and fair-girdled women was surnamed the Mace-man, because he fought not with bow and long spear, but with an iron mace clave the battalions. Him Lykurgos slew by guile, and not by strength, in a narrow way, where his mace of iron saved him not from destruction: ere that, Lykurgos came on him unawares and pierced him through the midst with his dart, and he was hurled backward upon the earth. Then Lykurgos despoiled him of his arms that brazen Ares had given him; and these himself he bare thereafter into the mellay of war. But when Lykurgos grew old within his halls he gave them to Ereuthalion his dear squire to wear. So with his arms upon him he challenged all our best; but they trembled sore and were afraid, and no man took heart. But me my hardy spirit aroused to meet him in my confidence; yet was I youngest in years of all. So fought I with him and Athene vouchsafed me glory. Tallest was he and strongest of men that I have slain; as one of huge bulk he lay spread this way and that. Would to God I were thus young and my strength were sound; then would Hector of the glancing helm soon find his combat. But of those of you that be chieftains of the host of the Achaians, yet desireth no man of good heart to meet Hector face to face."

So the old man upbraided them, and there stood up nine in all. Far first arose Agamemnon king of men, and after him rose Tydeus' son stalwart Diomedes, and after them the Aiantes clothed with impetuous might, and after them Idomeneus and Idomeneus' brother-in-arms Meriones, peer of Enyalios slayer of men, and after them Eurypylos Euaimon's glorious son; and up rose Thoas Andraimon's son and goodly Odysseus. So all these were fain to fight with goodly Hector. And among them spake again knightly Nestor of Gerenia: "Now cast ye the lot from the first unto the last, for him that shall be chosen; for he shall in truth profit the well-greaved Achaians, yea and he shall have profit of his own soul, if he escape from the fury of war and terrible fray."

So said he, and they marked each man his lot and cast them in the helmet of Agamemnon Atreus' son; and the hosts prayed and lifted up their hands to the gods. And thus would one say, looking up to wide heaven: "O father Zeus, vouchsafe that the lot fall upon Aias or Tydeus' son, or else on the king of Mykene rich in gold."

So spake they, and knightly Nestor of Gerenia shook the helmet, and there leapt forth the lot that themselves desired, even the lot of Aias. The herald bare it everywhither through the throng, shewing it from right to left to all the princes of the Achaians; but they knew it not, and every man denied it. But when he came, bearing it everywhither through the throng, to him that had marked it and cast it in the helm, even glorious Aias, then he held forth his hand, and the herald stood by him and put it therein. And Aias saw and knew the token upon the lot, and rejoiced in heart. He cast it by his foot upon the earth, and spake: "My friends, verily the lot is mine, yea and myself am glad at heart, because I deem that I shall vanquish goodly Hector. But come now, while I clothe me in my armour of battle, pray ye the while to Kronos' son king Zeus, in silence to yourselves, that the Trojans hear you not—nay rather, openly if ye will, for we have no fear of any man soever. For none by force shall chase me, he willing me unwilling, neither by skill; seeing I hope that not so skill-less, either, was I born in Salamis nor nurtured."

So said he, and they prayed to Kronos' son, king Zeus; and thus would one speak, looking up to wide heaven: "O father Zeus that rulest from Ida, most glorious, most great, vouchsafe to Aias victory and the winning of great glory. But if thou so lovest Hector indeed, and carest for him, grant unto either equal prowess and renown."

So said they, while Aias arrayed him in flashing bronze. And when he had now clothed upon his flesh all his armour, then marched he as huge Ares coming forth, when he goeth to battle amid heroes whom Kronos' son setteth to fight in fury of heart-consuming strife. So rose up huge Aias, bulwark of the Achaians, with a smile on his grim face: and went with long strides of his feet beneath him, shaking his far-shadowing spear. Then moreover the Argives rejoiced to look upon him, but sore trembling came upon the Trojans, on the limbs of every man, and Hector's own heart beat within his breast. But in no wise could he now flee nor shrink back into the throng of the host, seeing he had challenged him to battle. And Aias came near bearing his tower-like shield of bronze, with sevenfold ox-hide, that Tychios had wrought him cunningly; Tychios far best of curriers, that had his home in Hyle, who made him his glancing shield, of sevenfold hides of stalwart bulls, and overlaid the seven with bronze. This bare Telamonian Aias before his breast, and stood near to Hector, and spake to him threatening: "Hector, now verily shalt thou well know, man to man, what manner of princes the Danaans likewise have among them, even after Achilles, render of men, the lion-hearted. But he amid his beaked seafaring ships lieth in sore wrath with Agamemnon shepherd of the host; yet are we such as to face thee, yea and many of us. But make thou beginning of war and battle."

And great Hector of the glancing helm answered him: "Aias of the seed of Zeus, son of Telamon, chieftain of the host, tempt not thou me like some puny boy or woman that knoweth not deeds of battle. But I well know wars and slaughterings. To right know I, to left know I the wielding of my tough targe; therein I deem is stalwart soldiership. And I know how to charge into the mellay of fleet chariots, and how in close battle to join in furious Ares' dance. Howbeit, I have no mind to smite thee, being such an one as thou art, by spying thee unawares; but rather openly, if perchance I may hit thee."

He spake, and poised his far-shadowing spear, and hurled and smote Aias' dread shield of sevenfold hide upon the uttermost bronze, the eighth layer that was thereon. Through six folds went the stubborn bronze cleaving, but in the seventh hide it stayed. Then heaven-sprung Aias hurled next his far-shadowing spear, and smote upon the circle of the shield of Priam's son. Through the bright shield passed the violent spear, and through the curiously wrought corslet pressed it on; and straight forth beside the flank the spear rent his doublet; but he swerved aside and escaped black death. Then both together with their hands plucked forth their long spears and fell to like ravening lions or wild boars whose might is nowise feeble. Then Priam's son smote the shield's midst with his dart, but the bronze brake not through, for the point turned back; but Aias leapt on him and pierced his buckler, and straight through went the spear and staggered him in his onset, and cleft its way unto his neck, so that the dark blood gushed up. Yet even then did not Hector of the glancing helm cease from fight, but yielded ground and with stout hand seized a stone lying upon the plain, black and rugged and great; therewith hurled he and smote Aias' dread shield of sevenfold ox-hide in the midst upon the boss, and the bronze resounded. Next Aias lifted a far greater stone, and swung and hurled it, putting might immeasurable therein. So smote he the buckler and burst it inwards with the rock like unto a mill-stone, and beat down his knees; and he was stretched upon his back, pressed into his shield; but Apollo straightway raised him up. And now had they been smiting hand to hand with swords, but that the heralds, messengers of gods and men, came, one from the Trojans, one from the mail-clad Achaians, even Talthybios and Idaios, both men discreet. Between the two held they their staves, and herald Idaios spake a word, being skilled in wise counsel: "Fight ye no more, dear sons, neither do battle; seeing Zeus the cloud-gatherer loveth you both, and both are men of war; that verily know we all. But night already is upon us: it is well withal to obey the hest of night."

Then Telamonian Aias answered and said to him: "Idaios, bid ye Hector to speak those words; of his own self he challenged to combat all our best. Let him be first, and I will surely follow as he saith."

Then great Hector of the glancing helm said to him: "Aias, seeing God gave thee stature and might and wisdom, and with the spear thou art excellent above all the Achaians, let us now cease from combat and battle for the day; but hereafter will we fight until God judge between us, giving to one of us the victory. But night already is upon us; it is well withal to obey the hest of night; that so thou mayest rejoice all the Achaians beside their ships, and chiefly the kinsmen and fellows that are thine; and I throughout the great city of king Priam will rejoice the Trojan men and Trojan dames with trailing robes, that with prayer I ween will enter the holy assemblage. But come, let us give each the other famous gifts, that men may thus say, Achaians alike and Trojans: 'These, having fought for sake of heart-consuming strife, parted again reconciled in friendship.'"

So said he, and gave him his silver-studded sword, with scabbard and well-cut baldrick; and Aias gave his belt bright with purple. So they parted and one went to the Achaian host, and one betook him to the throng of Trojans. And these rejoiced to behold him come to them alive and sound, escaped from the fury of Aias and his hands unapproachable; and they brought him to the city saved beyond their hope. And Aias on their side the well-greaved Achaians brought to noble Agamemnon, exulting in his victory.

So when these were come unto the huts of Atreides, then did Agamemnon king of men slay them an ox, a male of five years old, for the most mighty son of Kronos. This they flayed and made ready, and divided it all, and minced it cunningly, and pierced it through with spits, and roasted it carefully, and drew all off again. Then as soon as they had rest from the task and had made ready the meal, they began the feast, nor was their soul aught stinted of the equal banquet. And the hero son of Atreus, wide-ruling Agamemnon, gave to Aias slices of the chine's full length for his honour. And when they had put from them the desire of meat and drink, then first the old man began to weave the web of counsel, even Nestor whose rede of old time was proved most excellent. He of good intent made harangue among them and said: "Son of Atreus and ye other princes of the Achaians, seeing that many flowing-haired Achaians are dead, and keen Ares hath spilt their dusky blood about fair-flowing Skamandros, and their souls have gone down to the house of Hades; therefore it behoveth thee to make the battle of the Achaians cease with daybreak; and we will assemble to wheel hither the corpses with oxen and mules; so let us burn them [a little way from the ships, that each man may bear their bones home to their children, whene'er we return again to our native land]; and let us heap one barrow about the pyre, rearing it from the plain for all alike; and thereto build with speed high towers, a bulwark for our ships and for ourselves. In the midst thereof let us make gates well compact, that through them may be a way for chariot-driving. And without let us dig a deep foss hard by, to be about it and to hinder horses and footmen, lest the battle of the lordly Trojans be heavy on us hereafter."

So spake he and all the chiefs gave assent. But meanwhile there was in the high town of Ilios an assembly of the Trojans, fierce, confused, beside Priam's gate. To them discreet Antenor began to make harangue: "Hearken to me, Trojans and Dardanians and allies, that I may tell you that my soul within my breast commandeth me. Lo, go to now, let us give Helen of Argos and the wealth with her for the sons of Atreus to take away. Now fight we in guilt against the oaths of faith; therefore is there no profit for us that I hope to see fulfilled, unless we do thus."

So spake he and sate him down; and there stood up among them noble Alexandros, lord of Helen beautiful-haired; he made him answer and spake winged words: "Antenor, these words from thee are no longer to my pleasure; yet thou hast it in thee to devise other sayings more excellent than this. But if indeed thou sayest this in earnest, then verily the gods themselves have destroyed thy wit. But I will speak forth amid the horse-taming Trojans, and declare outright; my wife will I not give back; but the wealth I brought from Argos to our home, all that I have a mind to give, and add more of mine own substance."

So spake he and sate him down, and there stood up among them Priam of the seed of Dardanos, the peer of gods in counsel; he of good intent made harangue to them, and said: "Hearken to me, Trojans and Dardanians and allies, that I may tell you that my soul within my breast commandeth me. Now eat your supper throughout the city as of old, and take thought to keep watch, and be wakeful every man. And at dawn let Idaios fare to the hollow ships to tell to Atreus' sons Agamemnon and Menelaos the saying of Alexandros, for whose sake strife is come about: and likewise to ask them this wise word, whether they are minded to refrain from noisy war till we have burned our dead; afterwards will we fight again, till heaven part us and give one or other victory."

So spake he, and they hearkened diligently to him and obeyed; [then took they their supper throughout the host by ranks,] and at dawn Idaios fared to the hollow ships. He found the Danaans in assembly, the men of Ares' company, beside the stern of Agamemnon's ship; and so the loud-voiced herald stood in their midst and said unto them: "Atreides and ye other princes of the Achaians, Priam and all the noble Trojans bade me tell you—if perchance it might find favour and acceptance with you—the saying of Alexandros, for whose sake strife hath come about. The wealth that Alexandros brought in his hollow ships to Troy—would he had perished first—all that he hath a mind to give, and to add more thereto of his substance. But the wedded wife of glorious Menelaos he saith he will not give; yet verily the Trojans bid him do it. Moreover they bade me ask this thing of you; whether ye are minded to refrain from noisy war until we have burned our dead; afterwards will we fight again, till heaven part us and give one or other victory."

So said he and they all kept silence and were still. But at the last spake Diomedes of the loud war-cry in their midst: "Let no man now accept Alexandros' substance, neither Helen's self; known is it, even to him that hath no wit at all, how that the issues of destruction hang already over the Trojans."

So spake he, and all the sons of the Achaians shouted, applauding the saying of horse-taming Diomedes. And then lord Agamemnon spake to Idaios: "Idaios, thyself thou hearest the saying of the Achaians, how they answer thee; and the like seemeth good to me. But as concerning the dead, I grudge you not to burn them; for dead corpses is there no stinting, when they once are dead, of the swift propitiation of fire. And for the oaths let Zeus be witness, the loud-thundering lord of Hera."

So saying he lifted up his sceptre in the sight of all the gods, and Idaios departed back to holy Ilios. Now Trojans and Dardanians sate in assembly, gathered all together to wait till Idaios should come; and he came and stood in their midst and declared his message. Then they made them ready very swiftly for either task, some to bring the dead, and some to seek for wood. And on their part the Argives hasted from their well-decked ships, some to bring the dead and some to seek for wood.

Now the sun was newly beating on the fields as he

climbed heaven from the deep stream of gently-flowing Ocean, when both sides met together. Then was it a hard matter to know each man again; but they washed them with water clean of clotted gore, and with shedding of hot tears lifted them upon the wains. But great Priam bade them not wail aloud; so in silence heaped they the corpses on the pyre, stricken at heart; and when they had burned them with fire departed to holy Ilios. And in like manner on their side the well-greaved Achaians heaped the corpses on the pyre, stricken at heart, and when they had burned them with fire departed to the hollow ships.

And when day was not yet, but still twilight of night, then was the chosen folk of the Achaians gathered together around the pyre, and made one barrow about it, rearing it from the plain for all alike; and thereto built they a wall and lofty towers, a bulwark for their ships and for themselves. In the midst thereof made they gates well-compacted, that through them might be a way for chariot-driving. And without they dug a deep fosse beside it, broad and great, and planted a palisade therein.

Thus toiled the flowing-haired Achaians: and the gods sate by Zeus, the lord of lightning, and marvelled at the great work of the mail-clad Achaians. And Poseidon shaker of earth spake first to them: "O father Zeus, is there any man throughout the boundless earth that will any more declare to the immortals his mind and counsel? Seest thou not how the flowing-haired Achaians have now again built them a wall before their ships, and drawn a fosse around it, but gave not excellent hecatombs to the gods? Verily the fame thereof shall reach as far as the dawn spreadeth, and men will forget the wall that I and Phoebus Apollo built with travail for the hero Laomedon."

And Zeus the cloud-gatherer said to him, sore troubled: "Out on it, far-swaying Shaker of earth, for this thing thou sayest. Well might some other god fear this device, one that were far feebler than thou in the might of his hands:

but thine shall be the fame as far as the dawn spreadeth. Go to now, hereafter when the flowing-haired Achaians be departed upon their ships to their dear native land, then burst thou this wall asunder and scatter it all into the sea, and cover the great sea-beach over with sand again, that the great wall of the Achaians be brought thee to naught."

Such converse held these one with the other, and the sun went down, and the work of the Achaians was accomplished; and they slaughtered oxen amid the huts, and took supper. And many ships from Lemnos, bearing wine, were at hand, sent of Jason's son Euneos, whom Hypsipyle bare to Jason shepherd of the host. And specially for Atreus' sons, Agamemnon and Menelaos, Jason's son gave a freight of wine, even a thousand measures. So the flowing-haired Achaians bought them wine thence, some for bronze and some for gleaming iron, and some with hides and some with whole kine, and some with captives; and they set a rich feast before them. Then all night long feasted the flowing-haired Achaians, and in the city the Trojans and allies; and all night long Zeus the lord of counsel devised them ill with terrible thunderings. Then pale fear gat hold upon them, and they spilt wine from their cups upon the earth, neither durst any drink till he had made libation to most mighty Kronion. Then laid they them to rest and took the boon of sleep.

BOOK VIII

How Zeus bethought him of his promise to avenge Achilles' wrong on Agamemnon: and therefore bade the gods refrain from war, and gave victory to the Trojans.

Now Dawn the saffron-robed was spreading over all the earth, and Zeus whose joy is in the thunder let call an assembly of the gods upon the topmost peak of many-ridged Olympus, and himself made harangue to them and all the gods gave ear: "Hearken to me, all gods and all ye goddesses, that I may tell you that my heart within my breast commandeth me. One thing let none essay, be it goddess or be it god, to wit, to thwart my saying; approve ye it all together, that with all speed I may accomplish these things. Whomsoever I shall perceive minded to go, apart from the gods, to succour Trojans or Danaans, chastened in no seemly wise shall he return to Olympus, or I will take and cast him into misty Tartaros, right far away, where is the deepest gulf beneath the earth; there are the gate of iron and threshold of bronze, as far beneath Hades as heaven is high above the earth: then shall he know how far I am mightiest of all gods. Go to now, ye gods, make trial that ye all may know. Fasten ye a rope of gold from heaven, and all ye gods lay hold thereof and all goddesses; yet could ye not drag from heaven to earth Zeus, counsellor supreme, not though ye toiled sore. But once I likewise were minded to draw with all my heart, then should I draw you up with very earth and sea withal. Thereafter would I bind the rope about a pinnacle of Olympus, and so should all those things be hung in air. By so much am I beyond gods and beyond men."

[So said he, and they all kept silence and were still, marvelling at his saying; for he spake very masterfully. But at the last there spake to them the bright-eyed goddess Athene: "O our father Kronides, supreme of lords, well we know, even we, that thy might is unyielding; yet still have we pity for the Danaan spearmen, that now shall perish and fulfil a grievous fate. Yet will we refrain from battle as thou biddest us, but counsel will we offer to the Argives for their profit, that they perish not all at thy wrath."

Then Zeus the cloud-gatherer smiled at her and said: "Be of good comfort, dear child, Trito-born; I speak not at all of earnest purpose, but I am minded to be kindly to thee."]

So saying he let harness to his chariot his bronze-shod horses, fleet of foot, with flowing manes of gold; and himself clad him with gold upon his flesh, and grasped the whip of gold, well-wrought, and mounted upon his car, and lashed the horses to start them; they nothing loth sped on between earth and starry heaven. So fared he to many-fountained Ida, mother of wild beasts, even unto Gargaros, where is his demesne and fragrant altar. There did the father of men and gods stay his horses, and unloose them from the car, and cast thick mist about them; and himself sate on the mountain-tops rejoicing in his glory, to behold the city of the Trojans and ships of the Achaians.

Now the flowing-haired Achaians took meat hastily among the huts and thereafter arrayed themselves. Likewise the Trojans on their side armed them throughout the town—a smaller host, yet for all that were they eager to fight in battle, of forceful need, for their children's sake and their wives'. And the gates were opened wide and the host issued forth, footmen and horsemen; and mighty din arose.

So when they were met together and come unto one spot, then clashed they targe and spear and fury of bronze-clad warrior; the bossed shields pressed each on each, and mighty din arose. Then were heard the voice of groaning and the voice of triumph together of the slayers and the slain, and the earth streamed with blood.

Now while it yet was morn and the divine day waxed, so long from either side lighted the darts amain and the people fell. But when the sun bestrode mid-heaven, then did the Father balance his golden scales, and put therein two fates of death that layeth men at their length, one for horse-taming Trojans, one for mail-clad Achaians; and he took the scale-yard by the midst and lifted it, and the Achaians' day of destiny sank down. So lay the Achaians' fates on the bounteous earth, and the Trojans' fates were lifted up towards wide heaven. And the god thundered aloud from Ida, and sent his blazing flash amid the host of the Achaians; and they saw and were astonished, and pale fear gat hold upon all.

Then had Idomeneus no heart to stand, neither Agamemnon, neither stood the twain Aiantes, men of Ares' company. Only Nestor of Gerenia stood his ground, he the Warden of the Achaians; neither he of purpose, but his horse was fordone, which noble Alexandros, beauteous-haired Helen's lord, had smitten with an arrow upon the top of the crest where the foremost hairs of horses grow upon the skull; and there is the most deadly spot. So the horse leapt up in anguish and the arrow sank into his brain, and he brought confusion on the steeds as he writhed upon the dart. While the old man leapt forth and with his sword began to hew the traces, came Hector's fleet horses through the tumult, bearing a bold charioteer, even Hector. And now had the old man lost his life, but that Diomedes of the loud war-cry was swift to mark. Terribly shouted he, summoning Odysseus: "Heaven-born son of Laertes, Odysseus of many wiles, whither fleest thou with thy back turned, like a coward in the throng? Beware lest as thou fleest one plant a spear between thy shoulders. Nay, stand thy ground, till we thrust back from the old man his furious foe."

So spake he, but much-enduring noble Odysseus heard him not, but hastened by to the hollow ships of the Achaians. Yet Tydeides, though but one, mingled amid the fighters in the forefront, and took his stand before the steeds of the old man, Neleus' son, and spake to him winged words, and said: "Old man, of a truth young warriors beset thee hard; and thy force is abated, and old age is sore upon thee, and thy squire is but a weakling, and thy steeds are slow. Come then, mount upon my car, that thou mayest see of what sort are the steeds of Tros, well skilled for following or fleeing hither or thither very fleetly across the plain, even those that erst I took from Aineias inspirer of fear. Thine let our squires tend, and these let us guide straight against the horse-taming Trojans, that even Hector may know whether my spear also rageth in my hands."

So said he, and knightly Nestor of Gerenia disregarded not. Then the two squires tended Nestor's horses, even Sthenelos the valiant and kindly Eurymedon: and the other twain both mounted upon Diomedes' car. And Nestor took into his hands the shining reins, and lashed the horses; and soon they drew nigh Hector. Then Tydeus' son hurled at him as he charged straight upon them: him missed he, but his squire that drave his chariot, Eniopeus, high-hearted Thebaios' son, even him as he held the reins, he smote upon the breast beside the nipple. So he fell from out the car, and his fleet-footed horses swerved aside; and there his soul and spirit were unstrung. Then sore grief encompassed Hector's soul for sake of his charioteer. Yet left he him there lying, though he sorrowed for his comrade, and drave in quest of a bold charioteer; and his horses lacked not long a master, for anon he found Iphitos' son, bold Archeptolemos, and him he made mount behind his fleet horses, and gave the reins into his hands.

Then had destruction come and deeds beyond remedy

been wrought, and so had they been penned in Ilios like lambs, had not the father of gods and men been swift to mark. So he thundered terribly and darted his white lightning and hurled it before Diomedes' steeds to earth; and there arose a terrible flame of sulphur burning, and the two horses were affrighted and cowered beneath the car. And the shining reins dropped from Nestor's hands, and he was afraid at heart and spake to Diomedes: "Come now, Tydeides, turn back thy whole-hooved horses to flight: seest thou not that victory from Zeus attendeth not on thee? Now doth Kronos' son vouchsafe glory to this Hector, for the day; hereafter shall he grant it us likewise, if he will. A man may not at all ward off the will of Zeus, not though one be very valiant; he verily is mightier far."

Then Diomedes of the loud war-cry answered him: "Yea verily, old man, all this thou sayest is according unto right. But this is the sore grief that entereth my heart and soul; Hector some day shall say as he maketh harangue amid the Trojans: 'Tydeides betook him to the ships in flight before my face.' So shall he boast—in that day let the wide earth yawn for me."

Then knightly Nestor of Gerenia answered him: "Ah me, thou son of wise Tydeus, that thou shouldest speak on this wise! Even though Hector call thee a base man and coward, yet will not the Trojans hearken to him nor the Dardanians, neither the wives of the great-hearted men of Troy, bearers of the shield, the wives whose lusty bedfellows thou hast laid low in the dust."

So spake he and turned the whole-hooved horses to flight, back through the tumult; and the Trojans and Hector with wondrous uproar poured upon them their dolorous darts. And over him shouted loudly great Hector of the glancing helm: "Tydeides, the fleet-horsed Danaans were wont to honour thee with the highest place, and meats, and cups brimful, but now will they disdain thee; thou art after all no better than a woman. Begone, poor puppet; not for my flinching shalt thou climb on our towers, neither carry our wives away upon thy ships; ere that will I deal thee thy fate."

So said he, and Tydeides was of divided mind, whether to wheel his horses and fight him face to face. Thrice doubted he in heart and soul, and thrice from Ida's mountains thundered Zeus the lord of counsel, and gave to the Trojans a sign, the turning of the course of battle. And Hector with loud shout called to the Trojans: "Trojans and Lykians and Dardanians that love close fight, be men, my friends, and bethink you of impetuous valour. I perceive that of good will Kronion vouchsafeth me victory and great glory, and to the Danaans destruction. Fools, that devised these walls weak and of none account; they shall not withhold our fury, and lightly shall our steeds overleap the delved fosse. But when I be once come amid the hollow ships, then be thought taken of consuming fire, that with fire I may burn the ships and slay the men, [even the Argives amid their ships, in confusion beneath the smoke]."

So spake he and shouted to his steeds, and said: "Xanthos, and thou Podargos, and Aithon and goodly Lampos, now pay me back your tending, even the abundance that Andromache, great-hearted Eëtion's daughter, set before you of honey-hearted wheat, and mingled wine to drink at the heart's bidding, sooner than for me, that verily avow me to be her lusty spouse. Pursue ye now and haste, that we may seize Nestor's shield the fame whereof now reacheth unto heaven, how that it is of gold throughout, armrods and all; and may seize moreover from horse-taming Diomedes' shoulders his richly dight breastplate that Hephaistos wrought cunningly. Could we but take these, then might I hope this very night to make the Achaians to embark on their fleet ships."

So spake he boastfully, and queen Hera had indignation, and stirred her upon her throne and made high Olympus quake, and answered and said to the great god Poseidon: "Out on it, far-swaying Shaker of Earth; not even thine heart within thy breast hath pity on the Danaans perishing. Yet bring they to thee in Helike and Aigai offerings many and gracious: wish thou them victory. Did we but will, we that are confederate with the Danaans, to drive the Trojans back and withhold far-seeing Zeus, then would he vex himself that he should sit there alone in Ida."

Then was the lord the Shaker of earth sore troubled and made answer: "Hera headstrong in speech, what is this thing thou sayest? I am not he that would fain see us all at strife with Zeus Kronion, for he verily is mightier far."

Thus spake they to each other; and now was all the space that from the ships the moat enclosed, even unto the wall, filled full of horses together and shield-bearing warriors pent: so pent them Hector Priam's son, peer of fleet Ares, now that Zeus vouchsafed him glory. And now had he burned the trim ships with blazing fire, but that queen Hera put it in Agamemnon's heart himself to bestir him and swiftly arouse the Achaians. So he went his way along the huts and ships of the Achaians, holding a great cloak of purple in his stalwart hand, and stood by Odysseus' black ship of mighty burden, that was in the midst, so that a voice could be heard to either end, [whether to the huts of Aias son of Telamon, or of Achilles; for these had drawn their trim ships up at the uttermost ends, trusting to their valour and to the might of their hands.] Then shouted he in a piercing voice, and called to the Danaans aloud: "Fie upon you, Argives, ye sorry things of shame, so brave in semblance! Whither are gone our boastings when we said that we were bravest, the boasts ye uttered vaingloriously when in Lemnos, as ye ate your fill of flesh of tall-horned oxen and drank goblets crowned with wine, and said that every man should stand in war to face fivescore yea tenscore Trojans? yet now can we not match one, even this Hector that anon will burn our ships with flame of fire. O

Father Zeus, didst ever thou blind with such a blindness any mighty king, and rob him of great glory? Yet I ween that never in my benched ship passed I by a fair altar of thine on my mad way hither, but upon all I burnt fat and thighs of oxen, being eager to lay waste well-walled Troy. Nay, Zeus, this hope fulfil thou me; suffer that we ourselves at least flee and escape, neither suffer that the Achaians be thus vanquished of the Trojans."

So spake he, and the Father had pity on him as he wept, and vouchsafed him that his folk should be saved and perish not. Forthwith sent he an eagle—surest sign among winged fowl—holding in his claws a fawn, the young of a fleet hind; beside the beautiful altar of Zeus he let fall the fawn, where the Achaians did sacrifice unto Zeus lord of all oracles. So when they saw that the bird was come from Zeus, they sprang the more upon the Trojans and bethought them of the joy of battle.

Now could no man of the Danaans, for all they were very many, boast that he before Tydeus' son had guided his fleet horses forth, and driven them across the trench and fought man to man; first by far was Tydeides to slay a warrior of the Trojans in full array, even Agelaos son of Phradmon. Now he had turned his steeds to flee; but as he wheeled the other plunged the spear into his back between his shoulders, and drave it through his breast. So fell he from his chariot, and his armour clanged upon him.

And after him came Atreus' sons, even Agamemnon and Menelaos, and after them the Aiantes clothed upon with impetuous valour, and after them Idomeneus and Idomeneus' brother in arms Meriones, peer of Enyalios slayer of men, and after them Eurypylos, Euaimon's glorious son. And ninth came Teukros, stretching his back-bent bow, and took his stand beneath the shield of Aias son of Telamon. And so Aias would stealthily withdraw the shield, and Teukros would spy his chance; and when he had shot and smitten one in the throng, then fell such an one and gave up the ghost, and Teukros would return, and as a child beneath his mother, so gat he him to Aias; who hid him with the shining shield.

Now who first of the Trojans was slain of noble Teukros? Orsilochos first and Ormenos and Ophelestes and Daitor and Chromios and godlike Lykophontes and Amopaon Polyaimon's son and Melanippos; [all these in turn laid he upon the bounteous earth.] And Agamemnon king of men rejoiced to behold him making havoc with his stalwart bow of the battalions of the Trojans, and he came and stood by his side and spake to him, saying: "Teukros, dear heart, thou son of Telamon, prince of the host, shoot on in this wise, if perchance thou mayest be found the salvation of the Danaans and glory of thy father Telamon; who nurtured thee when thou wast little, and reared thee, though a bastard, in his house; exalt thou him to honour, though he be afar. Moreover I will say to thee that which shall indeed be fulfilled. If aegis-bearing Zeus and Athene vouchsafe me to lay waste the stablished city of Ilios, in thine hand first, after myself, will I bestow the meed of honour, be it a tripod or two steeds with their chariot, or a woman that shall go up into thy bed."

And noble Teukros made answer and said to him: "Most noble son of Atreus, why urgest thou me that myself am eager? Verily with such strength as is in me forbear I not, but ever since we drave them towards Ilios I watch with my bow to slay the foemen. Eight long-barbed arrows have I now sped, and all are buried in the flesh of young men swift in battle; only this mad dog can I not smite."

He said, and shot another arrow from the string right against Hector; and his heart was fain to smite him. Yet him he missed, but noble Gorgythion, Priam's good son, he smote with an arrow in the breast, him born of a mother wedded from Aisyme, even fair Kastianeira, of favour like unto the gods. Even as in a garden a poppy droopeth its head aside, being heavy with fruit and the showers of spring; so bowed he aside his head laden with his helm.

And Teukros shot another arrow from the string, right against Hector, and his heart was fain to smite him. Yet missed he once again, for Apollo turned the dart away; but Archeptolemos, Hector's bold charioteer, he smote on the breast beside the nipple as he hasted into battle: so he fell from his car and his fleet-footed horses swerved aside; and there his soul and spirit were unstrung. Then sore grief encompassed Hector's soul for his charioteer's sake; yet left he him, though he sorrowed for his comrade, and bade Kebriones his own brother, being hard by, take the chariot reins; and he heard and disregarded not. And himself he leapt to earth from the resplendent car, with a terrible shout; and in his hand he caught a stone, and made right at Teukros, and his heart bade him smite him. Now Teukros had plucked forth from his quiver a keen arrow, and laid it on the string; but even as he drew it back, Hector of the glancing helm smote him with the jagged stone, as he aimed eagerly against him, even beside his shoulder, where the collar-bone fenceth off neck and breast, and where is the most deadly spot; and he brake the bowstring, and his hand from the wrist grew numb, and he stayed fallen upon his knee, and his bow dropped from his hand. But Aias disregarded not his brother's fall, but ran and strode across him and hid him with his shield. Then two trusty comrades bent down to him, even Mekisteus son of Echios and goodly Alastor, and bare him, groaning sorely, to the hollow ships. And once again the Olympian aroused the spirit of the Trojans. So they drove the Achaians straight toward the deep fosse, and amid the foremost went Hector exulting in his strength. And even as when a hound behind wild boar or lion, with swift feet pursuing snatcheth at him, at flank or buttock, and watcheth for him as he wheeleth, so Hector pressed hard on the flowing-haired Achaians, slaying ever the hindmost, and they fled on. But when they were passed in flight through palisade and fosse, and many were fallen beneath the Trojans' hands, then halted they and tarried beside the ships, calling one upon another, and lifting up their hands to all the gods prayed each one instantly. But Hector wheeled round his beauteous-maned steeds this way and that, and his eyes were as the eyes of Gorgon or Ares bane of mortals.

Now at the sight of them the white-armed goddess Hera had compassion, and anon spake winged words to Athene: "Out on it, thou child of aegis-bearing Zeus, shall not we twain any more take thought for the Danaans that perish, if only for this last time? Now will they fill up the measure of evil destiny and perish by one man's onslaught; seeing that he is furious now beyond endurance, this Hector son of Priam, and verily hath wrought many a deed of ill."

And the bright-eyed goddess Athene made answer to her, "Yea in good sooth, may this fellow yield up strength and life, and perish at the Argives' hands in his native land; only mine own sire is furious, with no good intent, headstrong, ever sinful, the foiler of my purposes. Neither remembereth he at all those many times and oft that I saved his son fordone with Eurystheus' tasks. For he would make lament toward heaven, and me would Zeus speed forth from heaven to succour him. Had I but known all this in my prudent heart, what time Eurystheus sent him forth to the house of Hades the Warder of the Gate, to bring from Erebos the hound of loathed Hades, then had he not escaped the sheer stream of the water of Styx. But now Zeus hateth me, and fulfilleth the purposes of Thetis, that kissed his knees and with her hand touched his beard, beseeching him to do honour to Achilles waster of cities. Verily the day shall come when he shall call me again his bright-eyed darling. But now make thou ready our whole-hooved horses, while I enter in to the palace of aegis-bearing Zeus and gird me in my armour for battle, that I may see if Priam's son, Hector of the glancing helm, shall be glad at the appearing of us twain amid the highways of the battle. Surely shall many a Trojan likewise glut dogs and birds with fat and flesh, fallen dead at the ships of the Achaians."

So said she, and the white-armed goddess Hera disregarded not. So Hera, the goddess queen, daughter of great Kronos, went her way and harnessed the golden-frontleted steeds; and Athene, daughter of aegis-bearing Zeus, cast down at her father's threshold her woven vesture many-coloured, that herself had wrought and her hands had fashioned; and put on her the tunic of Zeus the cloud-gatherer, and arrayed her in her armour for dolorous battle. Upon the flaming chariot set she her foot, and grasped her heavy spear great and stout, wherewith she vanquisheth the ranks of men, even of heroes with whom she of the awful sire is wroth. Then Hera swiftly smote the horses with the lash; self-moving groaned upon their hinges the gates of heaven whereof the Hours are warders, to whom is committed great heaven and Olympus, whether to throw open the thick cloud or set it to. There through the gates guided they their horses patient of the lash.

But when father Zeus beheld from Ida, he was sore wroth, and sped Iris golden-winged to bear a message: "Go thy way, fleet Iris, turn them back neither suffer them to face me; for in no happy wise shall we join in combat. For thus will I declare, and even so shall the fulfilment be; I will maim their fleet horses in the chariot, and them will I hurl out from the car, and will break in pieces the chariot; neither within the courses of ten years shall they heal them of the wounds the thunderbolt shall tear; that the bright-eyed one may know the end when she striveth against her father. But with Hera have I not so great indignation nor wrath: seeing it ever is her wont to thwart me, whate'er I have decreed."

So said he, and whirlwind-footed Iris arose to bear the message, and departed from the mountains of Ida unto high Olympus. And even at the entrance of the gates of Olympus many-folded she met them and stayed them, and told them the saying of Zeus: "Whither hasten ye? Why are your hearts furious within your breasts? Kronides forbiddeth you to give the Argives succour. For thus the son of Kronos threatened, even as he will fulfil; to wit, to maim your fleet horses in the chariot, and you will he hurl out from the car, and break the chariot in pieces; neither within the courses of ten years shall ye heal you of the wounds that the thunderbolt shall tear; that thou, bright-eyed goddess, mayst know the end when thou strivest against thy father. But with Hera hath he not so great indignation nor wrath; seeing it ever is her wont to thwart him, whate'er he have decreed. But most fell art thou, reckless vixen! if thou indeed wilt dare to lift thy huge spear against the face of Zeus."

So said fleet-footed Iris, and departed; but Hera spake to Athene and said: "Out on it, thou child of aegis-bearing Zeus, I verily would no more have us war against Zeus for mortals' sake. Of them let one man perish and another live, even as the lot falleth; and for him, let him take counsel for himself in his heart, and give judgment for Trojans and for Danaans, as is meet."

So saying she turned back her whole-hooved horses. Then the Hours unyoked them their beauteous-maned horses, and tethered them to their ambrosial mangers, and leant the chariots against the shining faces of the gateway; and the goddesses sate them upon their golden thrones amid the throng of all the gods, and were grieved at heart.

And father Zeus drave from Ida his fair-wheeled chariot and horses unto Olympus, and came unto the session of the gods. For him also the noble Shaker of Earth unyoked the steeds, and set the car upon the stand, and spread a cloth thereover; and far-seeing Zeus himself sate upon his golden throne, and beneath his feet great Olympus quaked. Only Athene and Hera sate apart from Zeus, and spake no word to him neither questioned him. But he was ware thereof in his heart, and said, "Why are ye thus vexed, Athene and Hera? Surely ye are not wearied of making havoc in glorious battle of the Trojans, for whom ye cherish bitter hate! Howsoever, seeing that my might is so great and my hands invincible, all the gods that are in Olympus could not turn me, and for you twain, trembling erst gat hold upon your bright limbs ere that ye beheld war and war's fell deeds. For thus will I declare, and even so had the fulfilment been—never had ye, once smitten with the thunderbolt, fared on your chariots back unto Olympus where is the habitation of the immortals."

So spake he, and Athene and Hera murmured, that were sitting by him and devising ills for the Trojans. Now Athene held her peace, and said not anything, for wrath at father Zeus, and fierce anger gat hold upon her; but Hera's heart contained not her anger, and she spake: "Most dread son of Kronos, what word is this thou hast said? Well know we, even we, that thy might is no wise puny; yet still have we pity for the Danaan spearmen, that now shall perish and fill up the measure of grievous fate. [Yet will we refrain from battle, if thou biddest us; but counsel will we offer to the Argives, such as shall profit them, that they perish not all at thy wrath.]"

And Zeus the cloud-gatherer answered and said: "At morn shalt thou behold most mighty Kronion, if thou wilt have it so, O Hera, ox-eyed queen, making yet more havoc of the vast army of Argive spearmen; for headlong Hector shall not refrain from battle till that Peleus' son fleet of foot has arisen beside the ships, that day when these shall fight amid the sterns in most grievous stress, around Patroklos fallen. Such is the doom of heaven. And for thine anger reck I not, not even though thou go to the nethermost bounds of earth and sea, where sit Iapetos and Kronos and have no joy in the beams of Hyperion the Sun-god, neither in any breeze, but deep Tartaros is round about them. Though thou shouldest wander till thou come even thither, yet reck I not of thy vexation, seeing there is no thing more unabashed than thou."

So said he, but white-armed Hera spake him no word. And the sun's bright light dropped into Ocean, drawing black night across Earth the grain-giver. Against the Trojans' will daylight departed, but welcome, thrice prayed for, to the Achaians came down the murky night.

Now glorious Hector made an assembly of the Trojans, taking them apart from the ships, beside the eddying river, in an open space where was found a spot clear of dead. And they came down from their chariots to the ground to hear the word that Hector, dear unto Zeus, proclaimed. He in his hand held his spear eleven cubits long; before his face gleamed the spear-head of bronze, and a ring of gold ran round about it. Thereon he leaned and spake to the Trojans, saying: "Hearken to me, Trojans and Dardanians and allies. I thought but now to make havoc of the ships and all the Achaians and depart back again to windy Ilios; but dusk came too soon, and that in chief hath now saved the Argives and the ships beside the beach of the sea. So let us now yield to black night, and make our supper ready; unyoke ye from the chariots your fair-maned horses, and set fodder beside them. And from the city bring kine and goodly sheep with speed; and provide you with honey-hearted wine, and corn from your houses, and gather much wood withal, that all night long until early-springing dawn we may burn many fires, and the gleam may reach to heaven; lest perchance even by night the flowing-haired Achaians strive to take flight over the broad back of the sea. Verily must they not embark upon their ships unvexed, at ease; but see ye that many a one of them have a wound to nurse even at home, being stricken with arrow or keen-pointed spear as he leapeth upon his ship; that so many another man may dread to wage dolorous war on the horse-taming men of Troy. And let the heralds dear to Zeus proclaim throughout the city that young maidens and old men of hoary heads camp round the city on the battlements builded of the gods; and let the women folk burn a great fire each in her hall; and let there be a sure watch set, lest an ambush enter the city when the host is absent. Thus be it, great-hearted Trojans, as I proclaim; the counsel that now is sound, let that stand spoken; further will I proclaim at dawn amid the horse-taming men of Troy. I pray with good hope to Zeus and all the gods, to drive from hence these dogs borne onward by the fates, [them that the fates bear on in the black ships]. Howbeit for the night will we guard our own selves, and at morn by daybreak, arrayed in our armour, let us awake keen battle at the hollow ships. I will know whether Tydeus' son stalwart Diomedes shall thrust me from the ships back to the wall, or I shall lay him low with my spear and bear away his gory spoils. To-morrow shall he prove his valour, whether he can abide the onslaught of my spear. But he amid the foremost, I ween, shall lie stricken, and many comrades round about their lord at the rising of to-morrow's sun. Would that I were immortal and ageless all my days and honoured like as Athene is honoured and Apollo, so surely as this day bringeth the Argives ill."

So Hector made harangue, and the Trojans clamoured applause. And they loosed their sweating steeds from the yoke, and tethered them with thongs, each man beside his chariot; and from the city they brought kine and goodly sheep with speed, and provided them with honey-hearted wine and corn from their houses, and gathered much wood withal; [and sacrificed to the immortals unblemished hecatombs]. And from the plain the winds bare into heaven the sweet savour. [But the blessed gods regaled not themselves nor would they aught thereof; for sore was holy Ilios hated of them, and Priam and the folk of Priam of the good ashen spear.] But these with high hopes sate them all night along the highways of the battle, and their watchfires burned in multitude. Even as when in heaven the stars about the bright moon shine clear to see, when the air is windless, and all the peaks appear and the tall headlands and glades, and from heaven breaketh open the infinite air, and all stars are seen, and the shepherd's heart is glad; even in like multitude between the ships and the streams of Xanthos appeared the watchfires that the Trojans kindled in front of Ilios. A thousand fires burned in the plain and by the side of each sate fifty in the gleam of blazing fire. And the horses champed white barley and spelt, and standing by their chariots waited for the throned Dawn.

BOOK IX

How Agamemnon sent an embassage to Achilles, beseeching him to be appeased; and how Achilles denied him.

THUS kept the Trojans watch; but the Achaians were holden of heaven-sent panic, handmaid of palsying fear, and all their best were stricken to the heart with grief intolerable. Like as two winds stir up the main, the home of fishes, even the north wind and the west wind that blow from Thrace, coming suddenly; and the dark billow straightway lifteth up its crest and casteth much tangle out along the sea; even so was the Achaians' spirit troubled in their breast.

But Atreides was stricken to the heart with sore grief, and went about bidding the clear-voiced heralds summon every man by name to the assembly, but not to shout aloud; and himself he toiled amid the foremost. So they sat sorrowful in assembly, and Agamemnon stood up weeping like unto a fountain of dark water that from a beetling cliff poureth down its black stream; even so with deep groaning he spake amid the Argives and said: "My friends, leaders and captains of the Argives, Zeus son of Kronos hath bound me with might in grievous blindness of soul; hard of heart is he, for that erewhile he promised and gave his pledge that not till I had laid waste well-walled Ilios should I depart, but now hath planned a cruel wile, and biddeth me return in dishonour to Argos with the loss of many of my folk. Such meseemeth is the good pleasure of most mighty Zeus that hath laid low the heads of many cities, yea and shall lay low; for his is highest power. So come, even as I shall bid let us all obey; let us flee with our ships to our dear native land, for now shall we never take wide-wayed Troy."

So said he, and they all held their peace and kept silence. Long time were the sons of the Achaians voiceless for grief, but at the last Diomedes of the loud war-cry spake amid them and said: "Atreides, with thee first in thy folly will I contend, where it is just, O king, even in the assembly; be not thou wroth therefor. My valour didst thou blame in chief amid the Danaans, and saidst that I was no man of war but a coward; and all this know the Argives both young and old. But the son of crooked-counselling Kronos hath endowed thee but by halves; he granted thee to have the honour of the sceptre above all men, but valour he gave thee not, wherein is highest power. Sir, deemest thou that the sons of the Achaians are thus indeed cowards and weaklings as thou sayest? But and if thine own heart be set on departing, go thy way; the way is before thee, and thy ships stand beside the sea, even the great multiude that followed thee from Mykene. But all the other flowing-haired Achaians will tarry here until we lay waste Troy. Nay, let them too flee on their ships to their dear native land; yet will we twain, even I and Sthenelos, fight till we attain the goal of Ilios; for in God's name are we come."

So said he, and all the sons of the Achaians shouted aloud, applauding the saying of horse-taming Diomedes. Then knightly Nestor arose and said amid them: "Tydeides, in battle art thou passing mighty, and in council art thou best among thine equals in years; none of all the Achaians will make light of thy word nor gainsay it; but thou hast not made a full end of thy words. Moreover thou art a young man indeed, and mightest even be my son, my youngest-born; yet thou counsellest prudently the princes of the Achaians, because thou speakest according unto right. But lo, I that avow me to be older than thou will speak forth and expound everything; neither shall any man despise my saying, not even the lord Agamemnon. A tribeless, lawless, homeless man is he that loveth bitter civil strife. Howbeit now let us yield to black night and make ready our meal; and let the sentinels bestow them severally along the deep-delved fosse without the wall. This charge give I to the young men; and thou, Atreides, lead then the way, for thou art the most royal. Spread thou a feast for the councillors; that is thy place and seemly for thee. Thy huts are full of wine that the ships of the Achaians bring thee by day from Thrace across the wide sea; all entertainment is for thee, being king over many. In the gathering of many shalt thou listen to him that deviseth the most excellent counsel; sore need have all the Achaians of such as is good and prudent, because hard by the ships our foemen are burning their watch-fires in multitude; what man can rejoice thereat? This night shall either destroy or save the host."

So said he, and they gladly hearkened to him and obeyed. Forth sallied the sentinels in their harness, around Thrasymedes Nestor's son, shepherd of the host, and Askalaphos and Ialmenos sons of Ares, and Meriones and Aphareus and Deïpyros and Kreion's son noble Lykomedes. Seven were the captains of the sentinels, and with each went fivescore young men bearing their long spears in their hands; and they took post midway betwixt fosse and wall, and kindled a fire and made ready each man his meal.

Then Atreides gathered the councillors of the Achaians, and led them to his hut, and spread before them an abundant feast. So they put forth their hands to the good cheer that lay before them. And when they had put away from them the desire of meat and drink, then the old man first began to weave his counsel, even Nestor, whose rede of old time was approved the best. He of good intent spake to them and said: "Most noble son of Atreus, Agamemnon king of men, in thy name will I end and with thy name begin, because thou art king over many hosts, and to thy hand Zeus hath entrusted sceptre and law, that thou mayest take counsel for thy folk. Thee therefore more than any it behoveth both to speak and hearken, and to accomplish what another than thou may say, when his heart biddeth him speak for profit: wheresoever thou leadest all shall turn on thee, so I will speak as meseemeth best. No other man shall have a more excellent thought than this that I bear in mind from old time even until now, since the day when thou, O heaven-sprung king, didst go and take the damsel Briseis from angry Achilles' hut by no consent of ours. Nay, I right heartily dissuaded thee; but thou yieldedst to thy proud spirit, and dishonouredest a man of valour whom even the immortals honoured; for thou didst take and keepest from him his meed of valour. Still let us even now take thought how we may appease him and persuade him with gifts of friendship and kindly words."

And Agamemnon king of men answered and said to him: "Old sir, in no false wise hast thou accused my folly. Fool was I, I myself deny it not. Worth many hosts is he whom Zeus loveth in his heart, even as now he honoureth this man and destroyeth the host of the Achaians. But seeing I was a fool in that I yielded to my sorry passion, I will make amends and give a recompense beyond telling. In the midst of you all I will name the excellent gifts; seven tripods untouched of fire, and ten talents of gold and twenty gleaming caldrons, and twelve stalwart horses, winners in the race, that have taken prizes by their speed. No lack-wealth were that man, neither undowered of precious gold, whose substance were as great as the prizes my whole-hooved steeds have borne me off. And seven women will I give, skilled in excellent handiwork, Lesbians whom I chose me from the spoils the day that he himself took stablished Lesbos, surpassing womankind in beauty. These will I give him, and with them shall be she whom erst I took from him, even the daughter of Briseus; moreover I will swear a great oath that never I went up into her bed nor had with her converse as is the wont of mankind, even of men and women. All these things shall be set straightway before him; and if hereafter the gods grant us to lay waste the great city of Priam, then let him enter in when we Achaians be dividing the spoil, and lade his ship full of gold and bronze, and himself choose twenty Trojan women, the fairest that there be after Helen of Argos. And if we win to the richest of lands, even Achaian Argos, he shall be my son and I will hold him in like honour with Orestes, my stripling boy that is nurtured in all abundance. Three daughters are mine in my well-builded hall, Chrysothemis and Laodike and Iphianassa; let him take of them which he will, without gifts of wooing, to Peleus' house; and I will add a great dower such as no man ever yet gave with his daughter. And seven well-peopled cities will I give him, Kardamyle and Enope and grassy Hire and holy Pherai and Antheia deep in meads, and fair Aipeia and Pedasos land of vines. And all are nigh to the salt sea, on the uttermost border of sandy Pylos; therein dwell men abounding in flocks and kine, men that shall worship him like a god with gifts, and beneath his sway fulfil his prosperous ordinances. All this will I accomplish so he but cease from wrath. Let him yield; Hades I ween is not to be softened neither overcome, and therefore is he hatefullest of all gods to mortals. Yea, let him be ruled by me, inasmuch as I am more royal and avow me to be the elder in years."

Then knightly Nestor of Gerenia answered and said: "Most noble son of Atreus, Agamemnon king of men, now are these gifts not lightly to be esteemed that thou offerest king Achilles. Come therefore, let us speed forth picked men to go with all haste to the hut of Peleus' son Achilles. Lo now, whomsoever I appoint let them consent. First let Phoinix dear to Zeus lead the way, and after him great Aias and noble Odysseus; and for heralds let Odios and Eurybates be their companions. And now bring water for our hands, and bid keep holy silence, that we may pray unto Zeus the son of Kronos, if perchance he will have mercy upon us."

So said he, and spake words that were well-pleasing unto

all. Forthwith the heralds poured water on their hands, and the young men crowned the bowls with drink and gave each man his portion after they had poured the libation in the cups. And when they had made libation and drunk as their heart desired, they issued forth from the hut of Agamemnon son of Atreus. And knightly Nestor of Gerenia gave them full charge, with many a glance to each, and chiefest to Odysseus, how they should essay to prevail on Peleus' noble son.

So the twain went along the shore of the loud-sounding sea, making instant prayer to the earth-embracer, the Shaker of the Earth, that they might with ease prevail on Aiakides' great heart. So they came to the huts and ships of the Myrmidons, and found their king taking his pleasure of a loud lyre, fair, of curious work, with a silver cross-bar upon it; one that he had taken from the spoils when he laid Eëtion's city waste. Therein he was delighting his soul, and singing the glories of heroes. And over against him sate Patroklos alone in silence, watching till Aiakides should cease from singing. So the twain came forward, and noble Odysseus led the way, and they stood before his face; and Achilles sprang up amazed with the lyre in his hand, and left the seat where he was sitting, and in like manner Patroklos when he beheld the men arose. Then Achilles fleet of foot greeted them and said: "Welcome; verily ye are friends that are come—sore indeed is the need—even ye that are dearest of the Achaians to me even in my wrath."

So spake noble Achilles and led them forward, and made them sit on settles and carpets of purple; and anon he spake to Patroklos being near: "Bring forth a greater bowl, thou son of Menoitios; mingle stronger drink, and prepare each man a cup, for dearest of men are these that are under my roof."

So said he, and Patroklos hearkened to his dear comrade. He cast down a great fleshing-block in the fire-light, and laid thereon a sheep's back and a fat goat's, and a great hog's chine rich with fat. And Automedon held them for him, while Achilles carved. Then he sliced well the meat and pierced it through with spits, and Menoitios' son, that godlike hero, made the fire burn high. Then when the fire was burned down and the flame waned, he scattered the embers and laid the spits thereover, resting them on the spit-racks, when he had sprinkled them with holy salt. Then when he had roasted the meat and apportioned it in the platters, Patroklos took bread and dealt it forth on the table in fair baskets, and Achilles dealt the meat. And he sate him over against godlike Odysseus by the other wall, and bade his comrade Patroklos do sacrifice to the gods; so he cast the first-fruits into the fire. Then put they forth their hands to the good cheer lying before them. And when they had put from them the desire of meat and drink, Aias nodded to Phoinix. But noble Odysseus marked it, and filled a cup with wine and pledged Achilles: "Hail, O Achilles! The fair feast lack we not either in the hut of Agamemnon son of Atreus neither now in thine; for feasting is there abundance to our heart's desire, but our thought is not for matters of the delicious feast; nay, we behold very sore destruction, thou fosterling of Zeus, and are afraid. Now is it in doubt whether we save the benched ships or behold them perish, if thou put not on thy might. Nigh unto ships and wall have the high-hearted Trojans and famed allies pitched their camp, and kindled many fires throughout their host, and ween that they shall no more be withheld but will fall on our black ships. And Zeus son of Kronos sheweth them signs upon the right by lightning, and Hector greatly exulteth in his might and rageth furiously, trusting in Zeus, and recketh not of god nor man, for mighty madness hath possessed him. He prayeth bright Dawn to shine forth with all speed, for he hath passed his word to smite off from the ships the ensigns' tops, and to fire the hulls with devouring flame, and hard thereby to make havoc of the Achaians confounded by the smoke.

Therefore am I sore afraid in my heart lest the gods fulfil his boastings, and it be fated for us to perish here in Troy-land, far from Argos pasture-land of horses. Up then! if thou art minded even at the last to save the failing sons of the Achaians from the war-din of the Trojans. Thyself shalt have grief hereafter, and when the ill is done is there no way to find a cure therefor; in good time rather take thou thought to ward the evil day from the Danaans. Friend, surely to thee thy father Peleus gave commandment the day he sent thee to Agamemnon forth from Phthia: 'My son, strength shall Athene and Hera give thee if they will; but do thou refrain thy proud soul in thy breast, for gentlemindedness is the better part; and withdraw from mischievous strife, that so the Argives may honour thee the more, both young and old.' Thus the old man charged thee, but thou forgettest. Yet cease now at the last, and eschew thy grievous wrath; Agamemnon offereth thee worthy gifts, so thou wilt cease from anger. Lo now, hearken thou to me, and I will tell thee all the gifts that in his hut Agamemnon promised thee: seven tripods untouched of fire, and ten talents of gold and twenty gleaming caldrons and twelve stalwart horses, winners in the race, that have taken prizes by their speed. No lackwealth were that man, neither undowered of precious gold, whose substance were as great as the prizes Agamemnon's steeds have borne him off. And seven women will he give, skilled in excellent handiwork, Lesbians whom he chose him from the spoils the day that thou thyself tookest Lesbos, surpassing womankind in beauty. These will he give thee, and with them shall be she whom erst he took from thee, even the daughter of Briseus; moreover he will swear a great oath that never he went up into her bed nor had with her converse as is the wont of mankind, O king, even of men and women. All these things shall be set straightway before thee; and if hereafter the gods grant us to lay waste the great city of Priam, then enter thou in when we Achaians be dividing the spoil, and lade thy ship full of gold and bronze, and thyself choose twenty Trojan women, the fairest that there be after Helen of Argos. And if we win to the richest of lands, even Achaian Argos, thou shalt be his son and he will hold thee in like honour with Orestes, his stripling boy that is nurtured in all abundance. Three daughters are his in his well-builded hall, Chrysothemis and Laodike and Iphianassa; take thou of them which thou wilt, without gifts of wooing, to Peleus' house; and he will add a great dower such as no man ever yet gave with his daughter. And seven well-peopled cities will he give thee, Kardamyle and Enope and grassy Hire and holy Pherai and Antheia deep in meads, and fair Aipeia and Pedasos land of vines. And all are nigh to the sea, on the uttermost border of sandy Pylos; therein dwell men abounding in flocks and kine, men that shall worship thee like a god with gifts, and beneath thy sway fulfil thy prosperous ordinances. All this will he accomplish so thou but cease from wrath. But and if Agamemnon be too hateful to thy heart, both he and his gifts, yet have thou pity on all the Achaians that faint throughout the host; these shall honour thee as a god, for verily thou wilt earn exceeding great glory at their hands. Yea now mightest thou slay Hector, for he would come very near thee in his deadly madness, because he deemeth that there is no man like unto him among the Danaans that the ships brought hither."

And Achilles fleet of foot answered and said unto him: "Heaven-sprung son of Laertes, Odysseus of many wiles, in openness must I now declare unto you my saying, even as I am minded and as the fulfilment thereof shall be, that ye may not sit before me and coax this way and that. For hateful to me even as the gates of hell is he that hideth one thing in his heart and uttereth another: but I will speak what meseemeth best. Not me, I ween, shall Agamemnon son of Atreus persuade, nor the other Danaans, seeing we were to have no thank for battling with the foemen ever without respite. He that abideth at home hath equal share with him that fighteth his best, and in like honour are held both the coward and the brave; death cometh alike to the untoiling and to him that hath toiled long. Neither have I any profit for that I endured tribulation of soul, ever staking my life in fight. Even as a hen bringeth her unfledged chickens each morsel as she winneth it, and with herself it goeth hard, even so I was wont to watch out many a sleepless night and pass through many bloody days of battle, warring with folk for their women's sake. Twelve cities of men have I laid waste from ship-board, and from land eleven, I do you to wit, throughout deep-soiled Troy-land; out of all these took I many goodly treasures and would bring and give them all to Agamemnon son of Atreus, and he staying behind amid the fleet ships would take them and portion out some few but keep the most. Now some he gave to be meeds of honour to the princes and the kings, and theirs are left untouched; only from me of all the Achaians took he my darling lady and keepeth her—let him sleep beside her and take his joy! But why must the Argives make war on the Trojans? why hath Atreides gathered his host and led them hither? is it not for lovely-haired Helen's sake? Do then the sons of Atreus alone of mortal men love their wives? surely whatsoever man is good and sound of mind loveth his own and cherisheth her, even, as I too loved mine with all my heart, though but the captive of my spear. But now that he hath taken my meed of honour from mine arms and hath deceived me, let him not tempt me that know him full well; he shall not prevail. Nay, Odysseus, let him take counsel with thee and all the princes to ward from the ships the consuming fire. Verily without mine aid he hath wrought many things, and built a wall and dug a foss about it wide and deep, and set a palisade therein; yet even so can he not stay murderous Hector's might. But so long as I was fighting amid the Achaians, Hector had no mind to array his battle far from the wall, but scarce came unto the Skaian gates and to the oak-tree; there once he awaited me alone and scarce escaped my onset. But now, seeing I have no mind to fight with noble Hector, I will to-morrow do sacrifice to Zeus and all the gods, and store well my ships when I have launched them on the salt sea—then shalt thou see, if thou wilt and hast any care therefor, my ships sailing at break of day over Hellespont, the fishes' home, and my men right eager at the oar; and if the great Shaker of the Earth grant me good journey, on the third day should I reach deep-soiled Phthia. There are my great possessions that I left when I came hither to my hurt; and yet more gold and ruddy bronze shall I bring home hence, and fair-girdled women and grey iron, all at least that were mine by lot; only my meed of honour hath he that gave it me taken back in his despitefulness, even lord Agamemnon son of Atreus. To him declare ye everything even as I charge you, openly, that all the Achaians likewise may have indignation, if haply he hopeth to beguile yet some other Danaan, for that he is ever clothed in shamelessness. Verily not in my face would he dare to look, though he have the front of a dog. Neither will I devise counsel with him nor any enterprise, for utterly he hath deceived me and done wickedly; but never again shall he beguile me with fair speech—let this suffice him. Let him begone in peace; Zeus the lord of counsel hath taken away his wits. Hateful to me are his gifts, and I hold him at a straw's worth. Not even if he gave me ten times, yea twenty, all that now is his, and all that may come to him otherwhence, even all the revenue of Orchomenos or Egyptian Thebes where the treasure-houses are stored fullest—Thebes of the hundred gates, whence sally forth two hundred warriors through each with horses and chariots—nay, nor gifts in number as sand or dust; not even so shall Agamemnon persuade my soul till he have paid me back all the bitter despite. And the daughter of Agamemnon son of Atreus will I not wed, not were she rival of golden Aphrodite for fairness and for handiwork matched bright-eyed Athene—not even then will I wed her; let him choose him of the Achaians another that is his peer and is more royal than I. For if the gods indeed preserve me and I come unto my home, then will Peleus himself seek me a wife. Many Achaian maidens are there throughout Hellas and Phthia, daughters of princes that ward their cities; whomsoever of these I wish will I make my dear lady. Very often was my high soul moved to take me there a wedded wife, a help meet for me, and have joy of the possessions that the old man Peleus possesseth. For not of like worth with life hold I even all the wealth that men say was possessed of the well-peopled city of Ilios in days of peace gone by, before the sons of the Achaians came; neither all the treasure that the stone threshold of the archer Phoebus Apollo encompasseth in rocky Pytho. For kine and goodly flocks are to be had for the harrying, and tripods and chestnut horses for the purchasing; but to bring back man's life neither harrying nor earning availeth when once it hath passed the barrier of his lips. For thus my goddess mother telleth me, Thetis the silver-footed, that twain fates are bearing me to the issue of death. If I abide here and besiege the Trojans' city, then my returning home is taken from me, but my fame shall be imperishable; but if I go home to my dear native land, my high fame is taken from me, but my life shall endure long while, neither shall the issue of death soon reach me. Moreover I would counsel you all to set sail homeward, seeing ye shall never reach your goal of steep Ilios; of a surety far-seeing Zeus holdeth his hand over her and her folk are of good courage. So go your way and tell my answer to the princes of the Achaians, even as is the office of elders, that they may devise in their hearts some other better counsel, such as shall save them their ships and the host of the Achaians amid the hollow ships: since this counsel availeth them naught that they have now devised, by reason of my fierce wrath. But let Phoinix now abide with us and lay him to rest, that he may follow with me on my ships to our dear native land to-morrow, if he will; for I will not take him perforce."

So spake he, and they all held their peace and were still, and marvelled at his saying; for he denied them very vehemently. But at the last spake to them the old knight Phoinix, bursting into tears, because he was sore afraid for the ships of the Achaians: "If indeed thou ponderest departure in thy heart, glorious Achilles, and hast no mind at all to save the fleet ships from consuming fire, because that wrath hath entered into thy heart; how can I be left of thee, dear son, alone thereafter? To thee did the old knight Peleus send me the day he sent thee to Agamemnon forth from Phthia, a stripling yet unskilled in equal war and in debate wherein men wax pre-eminent. Therefore sent he me to teach thee all these things, to be both a speaker of words and a doer of deeds. So would I not be left alone of thee, dear son, not even if god himself should take on him to strip my years from me, and make me fresh and young as in the day when first I left Hellas the home of fair women, fleeing from strife against my father Amyntor son of Ormenos: for he was sore angered with me by reason of his lovely-haired concubine, whom he ever cherished and wronged his wife my mother. So she besought me continually by my knees to go in first unto the concubine, that the old man might be hateful to her. I hearkened to her and did the deed; but my sire was ware thereof forthwith and cursed me mightily, and called the dire Erinyes to look that never should any dear son sprung of my body sit upon my knees; and the gods fulfilled his curse, even Zeus of the underworld and dread Persephone. [Then took I counsel to slay him with the keen sword; but some immortal stayed mine anger, bringing to my mind the people's voice and all the reproaches of men, lest I should be called a father-slayer amid the Achaians.] Then would my soul no more be refrained at all within my breast to tarry in the halls of mine angered father. Now my fellows and my kinsmen came about me with many prayers, and refrained me there within the halls, and slaughtered many goodly sheep and shambling kine with crooked horns; and many swine rich with fat were stretched to singe over the flames of Hephaistos, and wine from that old man's jars was drunken without stint. Nine nights long slept they all night around my body; they kept watch in turn, neither were the fires quenched, one beneath the colonnade of the fenced courtyard and another in the porch before the chamber doors. But when the tenth dark night was come upon me, then burst I my cunningly fitted chamber doors, and issued forth and overleapt the courtyard fence lightly, unmarked of watchmen and handmaidens. Then fled I far through Hellas of wide lawns, and came to deep-soiled Phthia, mother of flocks, even unto king Peleus; and he received me kindly and cherished me as a father cherisheth his only son, his stripling heir of great possessions; and he made me rich and gave much people to me, and I dwelt in the uttermost part of Phthia and was king over the Dolopians. Yea, I reared thee to this greatness, thou godlike Achilles, with my heart's love; for with none other wouldest thou go unto the feast, neither take meat in the hall, till that I had set thee upon my knees and stayed thee with the savoury morsel cut first for thee, and put the wine-cup to thy lips. Oft hast thou stained the doublet on my breast with sputtering of wine in thy sorry helplessness. Thus I suffered much with thee and much I toiled, being mindful that the gods in nowise created any issue of my body; but I made thee my son, thou godlike Achilles, that thou mayest yet save me from grievous destruction. Therefore, Achilles, rule thy high spirit; neither beseemeth it thee to have a ruthless heart. Nay, even the very gods can bend, and theirs withal is loftier majesty and honour and might. Their hearts by incense and reverent vows and drink-offering and burnt-offering men turn with prayer, so oft as any transgresseth and doeth sin. Moreover Prayers of penitence are daughters of great Zeus, halting and wrinkled and of eyes askance, that have their task withal to go in the steps of Sin. For Sin is strong and fleet of foot, wherefore she far outrunneth all prayers, and goeth before them over all the earth making men fall, and Prayers follow behind to heal the harm. Now whosoever reverenceth Zeus' daughters when they draw near, him they greatly bless and hear his petitions; but when one denieth them and stiffly refuseth, then depart they and make prayer unto Zeus the son of Kronos that sin may come upon such an one, that he may fall and pay the price. Nay, Achilles, look thou too that there attend upon the daughters of Zeus the reverence that bendeth the heart of all men that be right-minded. For if Atreides brought thee not gifts and foretold thee not more hereafter, but were ever furiously wroth, then I were not he that should bid thee cast aside thine anger and save the Argives, even in their sore need of thee. But now he both offereth thee forthwith many gifts, and promiseth thee more hereafter, and hath sent heroes to beseech thee, the best men chosen throughout the host of the Achaians and that to thyself are dearest of the Argives; dishonour not thou their petition nor their journey hither; though erst it were no wrong that thou wast wroth. Even in like manner have we heard the fame of those heroes that were of old, as oft as furious anger came on any; they might be won by gifts and prevailed upon by speech. This tale have I in mind of old time and not of yesterday, even as it was; and I will tell it among you that all are friends. The Kuretes fought and the staunch Aitolians about the city of Kalydon, and slew one another, the Aitolians defending lovely Kalydon, the Kuretes eager to lay it waste in war. For Artemis of the golden throne had brought a plague upon them, in wrath that Oineus offered her not the harvest first-fruits on the fat of his garden land; for all the other gods had their feast of hecatombs, and only to the daughter of great Zeus offered he not, whether he forgat or marked it not; and therein sinned he sore in his heart. So the Archer-goddess was wroth and sent against him a creature of heaven, a fierce wild boar, white-tusked, that wrought sore ill continually on Oineus' garden land; many a tall tree laid he low utterly, even root and apple blossom therewith. But him slew Meleagros the son of Oineus, having gathered together from many cities huntsmen and hounds; for not of few men could the boar be slain, so mighty was he; and many an one brought he to the grievous pyre. But the goddess made much turmoil over him and tumult concerning the boar's head and shaggy hide, between the Kuretes and great-hearted Aitolians. Now so long as Meleagros dear to Ares fought, so long it went ill with the Kuretes, neither dared they face him without their city walls, for all they were very many. But when Meleagros grew full of wrath, such as swelleth the hearts of others likewise in their breasts, though they be wise of mind, then in anger of heart at his dear mother Althaia he tarried beside his wedded wife, fair Kleopatra, daughter of Marpessa fair-ankled daughter of Euenos, and of Ides that was strongest of men that were then upon the earth; he it was that took the bow to face the king Phoebus Apollo for sake of the fair-ankled damsel. And she was called Alkyone of her father and lady mother by surname in their hall, because her mother in the plight of the plaintive halcyon-bird wept when the far-darter Phoebus Apollo snatched her away. By her side lay Meleagros, brooding on his grievous anger, being wroth by reason of his mother's curses: for she, grieved for her brethren's death, prayed instantly to the gods, and with her hands likewise beat instantly upon the fertile earth, calling on Hades and dread Persephone, while she knelt upon her knees and made her bosom wet with tears, to bring her son to death; and Erinnys that walketh in darkness, whose heart knoweth not ruth, heard her from Erebos. Now was the din of foemen about their gates quickly risen, and a noise of battering of towers; and the elders of the Aitolians sent the best of the god's priests and besought him to come forth and save them, with promise of a mighty gift; to wit, they bade him, where the plain of lovely Kalydon was fattest, to choose him out a fair demesne of fifty plough-gates, the half thereof vine-land and the half open plough-land, to be cut from out the plain. And old knightly Oineus prayed him instantly, and stood upon the threshold of his high-roofed chamber, and shook the morticed doors to beseech his son; him too his sisters and his lady mother prayed instantly—but he denied them yet more—instantly too his comrades prayed, that were nearest him and dearest of all men. Yet even so persuaded they not his heart within his breast, until his chamber was now hotly battered and the Kuretes were climbing upon the towers and firing the great city. Then did his fair-girdled wife pray Meleagros with lamentation, and told him all the woes that come on men whose city is taken; the warriors are slain, and the city is wasted of fire, and the children and the deep-girdled women are led captive of strangers. And his soul was stirred to hear the grievous tale, and he went his way and donned his glittering armour. So he saved the Aitolians from the evil day, obeying his own will; but they paid him not now the gifts many and gracious; yet nevertheless he drave away destruction. But be not thine heart thus minded, neither let heaven so guide thee, dear son; that were a hard thing, to save the ships already burning. Nay, come for the gifts; the Achaians shall honour thee even as a god. But if without gifts thou enter into battle the bane of men, thou wilt not be held in like honour, even though thou avert the fray."

And Achilles fleet of foot made answer and said to him: "Phoinix my father, thou old man fosterling of Zeus, such honour need I in no wise; for I deem that I have been honoured by the judgment of Zeus, which shall abide upon me amid my beaked ships as long as breath tarrieth in my body and my limbs are strong. Moreover I will say this thing to thee and lay thou it to thine heart; trouble not my soul by weeping and lamentation, to do the pleasure of warrior Atreides; neither beseemeth it thee to cherish him, lest thou be hated of me that cherish thee. It were good that thou with me shouldest vex him that vexeth me. Be thou king even as I, and share my sway by halves, but these shall bear my message. So tarry thou here and lay thee to rest in a soft bed, and with break of day will we consider whether to depart unto our own, or to abide."

He spake, and nodded his brow in silence unto Patroklos to spread for Phoinix a thick couch, that the others might bethink them to depart from the hut with speed. Then spake to them Aias, Telamon's godlike son, and said: "Heaven-sprung son of Laertes, Odysseus of many wiles, let us go hence; for methinks the purpose of our charge will not by this journey be accomplished; and we must tell the news, though it be no wise good, with all speed unto the Danaans, that now sit awaiting. But Achilles hath wrought his proud soul to fury within him—stubborn man, that recketh naught of his comrades' love, wherein we worshipped him beyond all men amid the ships—unmerciful! Yet doth a man accept recompense of his brother's murderer or for his dead son; and so the man-slayer for a great price abideth in his own land, and the kinsman's heart is appeased, and his proud soul, when he hath taken the recompense. But for thee, the gods have put within thy breast a spirit implacable and evil, by reason of one single damsel. And now we offer thee seven damsels, far best of all, and many other gifts besides; entertain thou then a kindly spirit, and have respect unto thine home; because we are guests of thy roof, sent of the multitude of Danaans, and we would fain be nearest to thee and dearest beyond all other Achaians, as many as there be."

And Achilles fleet of foot made answer and said to him: "Aias sprung of Zeus, thou son of Telamon, prince of the folk, thou seemest to speak all this almost after mine own mind; but my heart swelleth with wrath as oft as I bethink me of those things, how Atreides entreated me arrogantly among the Argives, as though I were some worthless sojourner. But go ye and declare my message; I will not take thought of bloody war until that wise Priam's son, noble Hector, come to the Myrmidons' huts and ships, slaying the Argives, and smirch the ships with fire. But about mine hut and black ship I ween that Hector, though he be very eager for battle, shall be refrained."

So said he, and they took each man a two-handled cup, and made libation and went back along the line of ships; and Odysseus led the way. And Patroklos bade his fellows and handmaidens spread with all speed a thick couch for Phoinix; and they obeyed and spread a couch as he ordained, fleeces and rugs and fine flock of linen. Then the old man laid him down and tarried for bright Dawn. And Achilles slept in the corner of the morticed hut, and by his side lay a woman that he brought from Lesbos, even Phorbas' daughter fair-cheeked Diomede. And on the other side Patroklos lay, and by his side likewise fair-girdled Iphis, whom noble Achilles gave him at the taking of steep Skyros, the city of Enyeus.

Now when those were come unto Atreides' huts, the sons of the Achaians stood up on this side and on that, and pledged them in cups of gold, and questioned them; and Agamemnon king of men asked them first: "Come now, tell me, Odysseus full of praise, thou great glory of the Achaians; will he save the ships from consuming fire, or said he nay, and hath wrath yet hold of his proud spirit?"

And steadfast goodly Odysseus answered him: "Most noble son of Atreus, Agamemnon king of men, he yonder hath no mind to quench his wrath, but is yet more filled of fury, and spurneth thee and thy gifts. He biddeth thee take counsel for thyself amid the Argives, how to save the ships and folk of the Achaians. And for himself he threateneth that at break of day he will launch upon the sea his trim well-benched ships. Moreover he said that he would counsel all to sail for home, because ye now shall never reach your goal of steep Ilios; surely far-seeing Zeus holdeth his hand over her and her folk are of good courage. Even so said he, and here are also these to tell the tale that were my companions, Aias and the two heralds, both men discreet. But the old man Phoinix laid him there to rest, even as Achilles bade him, that he may follow with him on his ships to his dear native land to-morrow, if he will; for he will not take him perforce."

So said he, and they all held their peace and were still, marvelling at his saying, for he harangued very vehemently. Long were the sons of the Achaians voiceless for grief, but at the last Diomedes of the loud war-cry spake amid them: "Most noble son of Atreus, Agamemnon king of men, would thou hadst never besought Peleus' glorious son with offer of gifts innumerable; proud is he at any time, but now hast thou yet far more encouraged him in his haughtiness. Howbeit we will let him bide, whether he go or tarry; hereafter he shall fight, whenever his heart within him biddeth and god arouseth him. Come now, even as I shall say let us all obey. Go ye now to rest, full to your hearts' desire of meat and wine, wherein courage is and strength; but when fair rosy-fingered Dawn appeareth, array thou with all speed before the ships thy folk and horsemen, and urge them on; and fight thyself amid the foremost."

So said he, and all the princes gave assent, applauding the saying of Diomedes tamer of horses. And then they made libation and went every man to his hut, and there laid them to rest and took the boon of sleep.

BOOK X

How Diomedes and Odysseus slew Dolon, a spy of the Trojans, and themselves spied on the Trojan camp, and took the horses of Rhesos, the Thracian king.

Now beside the ships the other leaders of the whole Achaian host were sleeping all night long, by soft Sleep overcome, but Agamemnon son of Atreus, shepherd of the host, sweet Sleep held not, so many things he debated in his mind. And even as when the lord of fair-tressed Hera lighteneth, fashioning either a mighty rain unspeakable, or hail, or snow, when the flakes sprinkle all the ploughed lands, or fashioning perchance the wide mouth of bitter war, even so oft in his breast groaned Agamemnon, from the very deep of his heart, and his spirits trembled within him. And whensoever he looked toward that Trojan plain, he marvelled at the many fires that blazed in front of Ilios, and at the sound of flutes and pipes, and the noise of men; but whensoever to the ships he glanced and the host of the Achaians, then rent he many a lock clean forth from his head, to Zeus that is above, and greatly groaned his noble heart.

And this in his soul seemed to him the best counsel, to go first of all to Nestor son of Neleus, if perchance he might contrive with him some right device that should be for the warding off of evil from all the Danaans.

Then he rose, and did on his doublet about his breast and beneath his shining feet he bound on fair sandals, and thereafter clad him in the tawny skin of a lion fiery and great, a skin that reached to the feet, and he grasped his spear.

And even in like wise did trembling fear take hold on Menelaos, (for neither on his eyelids did Sleep settle down,) lest somewhat should befall the Argives, who verily for his sake over wide waters were come to Troy-land, with fierce war in their thoughts.

With a dappled pard's skin first he covered his broad shoulders, and he raised and set on his head a casque of bronze, and took a spear in his strong hand. Then went he on his way to rouse his brother, that mightily ruled over all the Argives, and as a god was honoured by the people. Him found he harnessing his goodly gear about his shoulders, by the stern of the ship, and glad to his brother was his coming. Then Menelaos of the loud war-cry first accosted him: "Wherefore thus, dear brother, art thou arming? Wilt thou speed forth any of thy comrades to spy on the Trojans? Nay, terribly I fear lest none should undertake for thee this deed, even to go and spy out the foemen alone through the ambrosial night; needs must he be a man right hardy of heart."

Then the lord Agamemnon answered him and spake: "Need of good counsel have I and thou, Menelaos fosterling of Zeus, of counsel that will help and save the Argives and the ships, since the heart of Zeus hath turned again. Surely on the sacrifices of Hector hath he set his heart rather than on ours. For never did I see, nor heard any tell, that one man devised so many terrible deeds in one day, as Hector, dear to Zeus, hath wrought on the sons of the Achaians, unaided; though no dear son of a goddess is he, nor of a god. He hath done deeds that methinks will be a sorrow to the Argives, lasting and long, such evils hath he devised against the Achaians. But go now, run swiftly by the ships, and summon Aias and Idomeneus, but I will betake me to noble Nestor, and bid him arise, if perchance he will be fain to go to the sacred company of the sentinels and lay on them his command. For to him above others would they listen, for his own son is chief among the sentinels, he and the brother in arms of Idomeneus, even Meriones, for to them above all we entrusted this charge."

Then Menelaos of the loud war-cry answered him: "How meanest thou this word wherewith thou dost command and exhort me? Am I to abide there with them, waiting till thou comest, or run back again to thee when I have well delivered to them thy commandment?"

Then the king of men, Agamemnon, answered him again: "There do thou abide lest we miss each other as we go, for many are the paths through the camp. But call aloud, wheresoever thou goest, and bid men awake, naming each man by his lineage, and his father's name, and giving all their dues of honour, nor be thou proud of heart. Nay rather let us ourselves be labouring, for even thus did Zeus from our very birth dispense to us the heaviness of toil."

So he spake, and sent his brother away, having clearly laid on him his commandment. Then went he himself after Nestor, the shepherd of the host, whom he found by his hut and black ship, in his soft bed: beside him lay his fair dight arms, a shield, and two spears, and a shining helmet. Beside him lay his glittering girdle wherewith the old man was wont to gird himself when he harnessed him for war, the bane of men, and led on the host, for he yielded not to grievous old age. Then he raised him on his elbow, lifting his head, and spake to the son of Atreus, inquiring of him with this word: "Who art thou that farest alone by the ships, through the camp, in the dark night, when other mortals are sleeping? Seekest thou one of thy mules, or of thy comrades? speak, and come not silently upon me. What need hast thou?"

Then the king of men, Agamemnon, answered him: "O Nestor, son of Neleus, great glory of the Achaians, thou shalt know Agamemnon, son of Atreus, whom above all men Zeus hath planted for ever among labours, while my breath abides within my breast, and my knees move. I wander thus, for that sweet sleep rests not on mine eyes, but war is my care, and the troubles of the Achaians. Yea, greatly I fear for the sake of the Danaans, nor is my heart firm, but I am tossed to and fro, and my heart is leaping from my breast, and my good knees tremble beneath me. But if thou wilt do aught, since neither on thee cometh sleep, let us go thither to the sentinels, that we may see them, lest they be fordone with toil and drowsihead, and so are slumbering, and have quite forgotten to keep watch. And hostile men camp hard by, nor know we at all but that they are keen to do battle in the night."

Then knightly Nestor of Gerenia answered him: "Most renowned son of Atreus, Agamemnon king of men, assuredly not all his designs will wise-counselling Zeus fulfil for Hector, even all that now he thinketh; nay methinks he will contend with even more troubles if but Achilles turn back his heart from grievous anger. And verily will I follow after thee, but let us also rouse others again, both the son of Tydeus, spearman renowned, and Odysseus, and swift Aias, and the strong son of Phyleus. But well it would be if one were to go and call those also, the godlike Aias, and Idomeneus the prince; for their ships are furthest of all, and nowise close at hand. But Menelaos will I blame, dear as he is and worshipful, yea, even if thou be angry with me, nor will I hide my thought, for that he slumbereth, and to thee alone hath left the toil; now should he be toiling among all the chiefs and beseeching them, for need no longer tolerable is coming upon us."

And the king of men, Agamemnon, answered him again: "Old man, another day I even bid thee blame him, for often is he slack, and willeth not to labour, yielding neither to unreadiness nor heedlessness of heart, but looking toward me, and expecting mine instance. But as now he awoke far before me, and came to me, and him I sent forward to call those concerning whom thou inquirest. But let us be gone, and them shall we find before the gates, among the sentinels, for there I bade them gather."

Then knightly Nestor of Gerenia answered him: "So will none of the Argives be wroth with him or disobey him, whensoever he doth urge any one, and give him his commands."

So spake he and did on his doublet about his breast, and beneath his bright feet he bound goodly shoon, and all around him buckled a purple cloak, with double folds and wide, and thick down all over it.

And he took a strong spear, pointed with sharp bronze, and he went among the ships of the mail-clad Achaians. Then Odysseus first, the peer of Zeus in counsel, did knightly Gerenian Nestor arouse out of sleep, with his voice, and quickly the cry came all about his heart, and he came forth from the hut and spake to them saying: "Wherefore thus among the ships and through the camp do ye wander alone, in the ambrosial night; what so great need cometh upon you?"

Then knightly Nestor of Gerenia answered him: "Laertes' son, of the seed of Zeus, Odysseus of many a wile, be not wroth, for great trouble besetteth the Achaians. Nay follow, that we may arouse others too, even all that it behoveth to take counsel, whether we should fly, or fight."

So spake he, and Odysseus of the many counsels came to the hut, and cast a shield bedight about his shoulders, and went after them.

And they went to seek Diomedes, son of Tydeus, and him they found outside his hut, with his arms, and around him his comrades were sleeping with their shields beneath their heads, but their spears were driven into the ground erect on the spikes of the butts, and afar shone the bronze, like the lightning of father Zeus. Now that hero was asleep, and under him was strewn the hide of an ox of the field, but beneath his head was stretched a shining carpet. Beside him went and stood knightly Nestor of Gerenia and stirred him with a touch of his foot, and aroused him, chiding him to his face, saying: "Wake, son of Tydeus, why all night long dost thou sleep? Knowest thou not that the Trojans on the high place of the plain are camped near the ships, and but a little space holdeth them apart?"

So spake he, and Diomedes sprang swiftly up out of sleep, and spake out to him winged words: "Hard art thou, old man, and from toil thou never ceasest. Now are there not other younger sons of the Achaians, who might rouse when there is need each of the kings, going all round the host? but thou, old man, art indomitable."

And him knightly Nestor of Gerenia answered again, "Nay verily, my son, all this that thou sayest is according unto right. Noble sons have I, and there be many of the host, of whom each man might go and call the others. But a right great need hath assailed the Achaians. For now to all of us it standeth on a razor's edge, either pitiful ruin for the Achaians, or life. But come now, if indeed thou dost pity me, rouse swift Aias, and the son of Phyleus, for thou art younger than I."

So spake he, and Diomedes cast round his shoulders the skin of a great fiery lion, that reached to his feet, and he grasped his spear, and started on his way, and roused the others from their place and led them on.

Now when they had come among the assembled sentinels, they found not the leaders of the sentinels asleep, but they all sat wide awake with their arms. And even as hounds keep difficult guard round the sheep in a fold, having heard a hardy wild beast that cometh through the wood among the hills, and much clamour riseth round him of hounds and men, and sleep perisheth from them, even so sweet sleep did perish from their eyes, as they watched through the wicked night, for ever were they turning toward the plains, when they heard the Trojans moving.

And that old man was glad when he saw them, and heartened them with his saying, and calling out to them he spake winged words: "Even so now, dear children, do ye keep watch, nor let sleep take any man, lest we become a cause of rejoicing to them that hate us."

So saying he sped through the moat, and they followed with him, the kings of the Argives, who had been called to the council. And with them went Meriones, and the glorious son of Nestor, for they called them to share their counsel. So they went clean out of the delved fosse, and sat down in the open, where the mid-space was clear of dead men fallen, where fierce Hector had turned again from destroying the Argives, when night covered all. There sat they down, and declared their saying each to the other, and to them knightly Nestor of Gerenia began discourse: "O friends, is there then no man that would trust to his own daring spirit, to go among the great-hearted Trojans, if perchance he might take some straggler of the enemy, yea, or hear perchance some rumour among the Trojans, and what things they devise among themselves, whether they are fain to abide there by the ships, away from the city, or will retreat again to the city, now that they have conquered the Achaians? All this might such an one learn, and back to us come scathless: great would be his fame under heaven among all men, and a goodly gift will be given him. For all the best men that bear sway by the ships, each and all of them will give him a black ewe, with her lamb at her foot, —no chattel may compare with her,—and ever will he be present at feasts and clan-drinkings."

So spake he, and thereon were they all silent, holding their peace, but to them spake Diomedes of the loud war-cry: "Nestor, my heart and manful spirit urge me to enter the camp of the foemen hard by, even of the Trojans: but and if some other man will follow with me, more comfort and more courage will there be. If two go together, one before another perceiveth a matter, how there may be gain therein; but if one alone perceive aught, even so his wit is shorter, and weak his device."

So spake he, and many were they that wished to follow Diomedes. The two Aiantes were willing, men of Ares' company, and Meriones was willing, and right willing the son of Nestor, and the son of Atreus, Menelaos, spearman renowned, yea and the hardy Odysseus was willing to steal into the throng of Trojans, for always daring was his heart within him. But among them spake the king of men, Agamemnon: "Diomedes son of Tydeus, joy of mine heart, thy comrade verily shalt thou choose, whomsoever thou wilt, the best of them that be here, for many are eager. But do not thou, out of reverent heart, leave the better man behind, and give thyself the worse companion, yielding to regard for any, and looking to their lineage, even if one be more kingly born."

So spake he, but was in fear for the sake of fair-haired Menelaos. But to them again answered Diomedes of the loud war-cry: "If indeed ye bid me choose myself a comrade, how then could I be unmindful of godlike Odysseus, whose heart is passing eager, and his spirit so manful in all manner of toils; and Pallas Athene loveth him. But while he cometh with me, even out of burning fire might we both return, for he excelleth in understanding."

Then him again answered the steadfast noble Odysseus: "Son of Tydeus, praise me not overmuch, neither blame me aught, for thou speakest thus among the Argives that themselves know all. But let us be going, for truly the night is waning, and near is the dawn, and the stars have gone onward, and the night has advanced more than two watches, but the third watch is yet left."

So spake they and harnessed them in their dread armour. To the son of Tydeus did Thrasymedes steadfast in war give a two-edged sword, (for his own was left by his ship) and a shield, and about his head set a helm of bull's hide, without cone or crest, that is called a skull-cap, and keeps the heads of stalwart youths. And Meriones gave Odysseus a bow and a quiver, and a sword, and on his head set a helm made of leather, and with many a thong was it stiffly wrought within, while without the white teeth of a boar of flashing tusks were arrayed thick set on either side, well and cunningly, and in the midst was fixed a cap of felt. This casque Autolykos once stole from Amyntor son of Ormenos, out of Eleon, breaking into his well-builded house; and he gave it to Amphidamas of Kythera to take to Skandeia and Amphidamas gave it for a guest-gift to Molos, who gave it to his own son Meriones to wear, and now it was set to cover the head of Odysseus.

So when these twain had harnessed them in their dread armour, they set forth to go, and left there all the best of the host. And to them did Pallas Athene send forth an omen on the right, a heron hard by the way, and they beheld it not with their eyes, through the dark night, but they heard its shrill cry. And Odysseus was glad in the omen of the bird, and prayed to Athene: "Listen to me, thou child of aegis-bearing Zeus that ever in all toils dost stand by me, nor doth any motion of mine escape thee: but now again above all be thou friendly to me, Athene, and grant that we come back with renown to the ships, having wrought a great work, that shall be sorrow to the Trojans."

Next again prayed Diomedes of the loud war-cry: "Listen now likewise to me, thou child of Zeus, unwearied maiden, and follow with me as when with my father thou didst follow, even noble Tydeus, into Thebes, when he went forth as a messenger from the Achaians. And them he left by the Asopos, the mail-clad Achaians, and a honeyed word he bare to the Kadmeians in that place; but on his backward way he devised right terrible deeds, with thee, fair goddess, for eager didst thou stand by him. Even so now stand thou by me willingly, and protect me. And to thee will I sacrifice a yearling heifer, broad of brow, unbroken, that never yet hath man led below the yoke. Her will I sacrifice to thee, and gild her horns with gold."

So spake they in their prayer, and Pallas Athene heard

them. And when they had prayed to the daughter of mighty Zeus, they went forth on their way, like two lions, through the dark night, amid the slaughter, amid the slain men, through the arms and the black blood.

Nay, nor the stout-hearted Trojans did Hector suffer to sleep, but he called together all the best of them, all that were chiefs and leaders of the Trojans, them did he call together, and contrived a crafty counsel: "Who is there that would promise and perform for me this deed, for a great gift? yea his reward shall be sufficient. For I will give him a chariot, and two horses of arching neck, the best that be at the swift ships of the Achaians, to whosoever shall dare the deed, and for himself shall win glory. And the deed is this; to go near the swift-faring ships, and seek out whether the swift ships are guarded, as of old, or whether already, being subdued beneath our hands, the foes are devising of flight among themselves, and have no care to watch through the night, being fordone with dread weariness."

So spake he, but they were all silent and held their peace. Now there was among the Trojans one Dolon, the son of Eumedes the godlike herald, and he was rich in gold, and rich in bronze: and verily he was ill favoured to look upon, but swift of foot; now he was an only son among five sisters. So he spake then a word to the Trojans and to Hector: "Hector, my heart and manful spirit urge me to go near the swift-faring ships, and spy out all. But come, I pray thee, hold up the staff, and swear to me, that verily thou wilt give me the horses and the chariots bedight with bronze that bear the noble son of Peleus. But to thee I will prove no vain spy, nor disappoint thy hope. For I will go straight to the camp, until I may come to the ship of Agamemnon, where surely the chiefs are like to hold council, whether to fight or flee."

So spake he, and Hector took the staff in his hand, and sware to him: "Now let Zeus himself be witness, the loud-thundering lord of Hera, that no other man of the Trojans shall mount those horses, but thou, I declare, shalt rejoice in them for ever."

So spake he, and sware a bootless oath thereto, and aroused Dolon to go. And straightway he cast on his shoulders his crooked bow, and did on thereover the skin of a grey wolf, and on his head a helm of ferret-skin, and took a sharp javelin, and went on his way to the ships from the host. But he was not like to come back from the ships and bring word to Hector.

But when he had left the throng of men and horses, he went forth eagerly on the way, and Odysseus of the seed of Zeus was ware of him as he approached, and said unto Diomedes: "Lo, here is some man, Diomedes, coming from the camp, I know not whether as a spy to our ships, or to strip certain of the dead men fallen. But let us suffer him to pass by us a little way on the plain, and thereafter may we rush on him and take him speedily, and if it chance that he outrun us by speed of foot, ever do thou hem him in towards the ships and away from the camp, rushing on him with thy spear, lest in any wise he escape towards the city."

So they spake, and turning out of the path they lay down among the bodies of the dead; and swiftly Dolon ran past them in his witlessness. But when he was as far off as is the length of the furrow made by mules, (for better far are they than kine, to drag the jointed plough through the deep fallow,) these twain ran after him, and he stood still when he heard the sound, supposing in his heart that they were friends come from among the Trojans to turn him back, at the countermand of Hector. But when they were about a spear-cast off, or even less, he knew them for foemen, and stirred his swift limbs to fly, and speedily they started in pursuit.

And as when two sharp-toothed hounds, well skilled in the chase, press ever hard on a doe or a hare through a wooded land, and it runs screaming before them, even so

Tydeus' son and Odysseus the sacker of cities cut Dolon off from the host, and ever pursued hard after him. But when he was just about to come among the sentinels, in his flight towards the ships, then Athene poured strength into the son of Tydeus, that none of the mail-clad Achaians might boast himself the first to smite, and he come second. And strong Diomedes leaped upon him with the spear, and said: "Stand, or I shall overtake thee with the spear, and methinks that thou shalt not long avoid sheer destruction at my hand."

So spake he, and threw his spear, but of his own will he missed the man, and passing over his right shoulder the point of the polished spear stuck fast in the ground: and Dolon stood still, in great dread and trembling, and the teeth chattered in his mouth, and he was green with fear. Then the twain came up with him, panting, and gripped his hands, and weeping he spake: "Take me alive, and I will ransom myself, for within our house there is bronze, and gold, and smithied iron, wherefrom my father would do you grace with ransom untold, if he should learn that I am alive among the ships of the Achaians."

Then Odysseus of the many counsels answered him and said: "Take courage, let not death be in thy mind, but come speak and tell me truly all the tale, why thus from the host dost thou come all alone among the ships, through the black night, when other mortals are sleeping? Comest thou to strip certain of the dead men fallen, or did Hector send thee forth to spy out everything at the hollow ships, or did thine own spirit urge thee on?"

Then Dolon answered him, his limbs trembling beneath him: "With many a blind hope did Hector lead my wits astray, who vowed to give me the whole-hooved horses of the proud son of Peleus, and his car bedight with bronze: and he bade me fare through the swift black night, and draw nigh the foemen, and seek out whether the swift ships are guarded, as of old, or whether, already, being subdued beneath our hands, they are devising of flight among themselves, and have no care to watch through the night, being fordone with dread weariness."

And smiling thereat did Odysseus of the many counsels make him answer: "Verily now thy soul was set on great rewards, even the horses of the wise son of Aiakos, but hard are they for mortal men to master, and hard to drive, for any but Achilles only, whom a deathless mother bare. But come, tell me all this truly, all the tale: where when thou camest hither didst thou leave Hector, shepherd of the host, and where lie his warlike gear, and where his horses? And how are disposed the watches, and the beds of the other Trojans? And what counsel take they among themselves; are they fain to abide there nigh the ships, afar from the city, or will they return to the city again, seeing that they have subdued unto them the Achaians?"

Then Dolon son of Eumedes made him answer again: "Lo, now all these things will I recount to thee most truly. Hector with them that are counsellors holdeth council by the barrow of godlike Ilos, apart from the din, but as for the guards whereof thou askest, oh hero, no chosen watch nor guard keepeth the host. As for all the watch fires of the Trojans—on them is necessity, so that they watch and encourage each other to keep guard; but, for the allies called from many lands, they are sleeping and to the Trojans they leave it to keep watch, for no wise near dwell the children and wives of the allies."

Then Odysseus of the many counsels answered him and said: "How stands it now, do they sleep amidst the horse-taming Trojans, or apart? tell me clearly, that I may know."

Then answered him Dolon son of Eumedes: "Verily all this likewise will I recount to thee truly. Towards the sea lie the Karians, and Paionians of the bended bow, and the Leleges and Kaukones, and noble Pelasgoi. And towards Thymbre the Lykians have their place, and the haughty Mysians, and the Phrygians that fight from chariots, and Maionians lords of chariots. But wherefore do ye inquire of me thoroughly concerning all these things? for if ye desire to steal into the throng of Trojans, lo, there be those Thracians, new comers, at the furthest point apart from the rest, and among them their king Rhesos, son of Eïoneus. His be the fairest horses that ever I beheld, and the greatest, whiter than snow, and for speed like the winds. And his chariot is fashioned well with gold and silver, and golden is his armour that he brought with him, marvellous, a wonder to behold; such as it is in no wise fit for mortal men to bear, but for the deathless gods. But bring me now to the swift ships, or leave me here, when ye have bound me with a ruthless bond, that ye may go and make trial of me whether I have spoken to you truth, or lies."

Then strong Diomedes, looking grimly on him, said: "Put no thought of escape, Dolon, in thy heart, for all the good tidings thou hast brought, since once thou hast come into our hands. For if now we release thee or let thee go, on some later day wilt thou come to the swift ships of the Achaians, either to play the spy, or to fight in open war, but if subdued beneath my hands thou lose thy life, never again wilt thou prove a bane to the Argives."

He spake, and that other with strong hand was about to touch his chin, and implore his mercy, but Diomedes smote him on the midst of the neck, rushing on him with the sword, and cut through both the sinews, and the head of him still speaking was mingled with the dust. And they stripped him of the casque of ferret's skin from off his head, and of his wolf-skin, and his bended bow, and his long spear, and these to Athene the Giver of Spoil did noble Odysseus hold aloft in his hand, and he prayed and spake a word: "Rejoice, O goddess, in these, for to thee first of all the Immortals in Olympus will we call for aid; nay, but yet again send us on against the horses and the sleeping places of the Thracian men."

So spake he aloud, and lifted from him the spoils on high, and set them on a tamarisk bush, and raised thereon a mark right plain to see, gathering together reeds, and luxuriant shoots of tamarisk, lest they should miss the place as they returned again through the swift dark night.

So the twain went forward through the arms, and the black blood, and quickly they came to the company of Thracian men. Now they were slumbering, fordone with toil, but their goodly weapons lay by them on the ground, all orderly, in three rows, and by each man his pair of steeds. And Rhesos slept in the midst, and beside him his swift horses were bound with thongs to the topmost rim of the chariot. Him Odysseus spied from afar, and showed him unto Diomedes: "Lo, Diomedes, this is the man, and these are the horses whereof Dolon that we slew did give us tidings. But come now, put forth thy great strength; it doth not behove thee to stand idle with thy weapons: nay, loose the horses; or do thou slay the men, and of the horses will I take heed."

So spake he, and into that other bright-eyed Athene breathed might, and he began slaying on this side and on that, and hideously went up their groaning, as they were smitten with the sword, and the earth was reddened with blood. And like as a lion cometh on flocks without a herdsman, on goats or sheep, and leaps upon them with evil will, so set the son of Tydeus on the men of Thrace, till he had slain twelve. But whomsoever the son of Tydeus drew near and smote with the sword, him did Odysseus of the many counsels seize by the foot from behind, and drag him out of the way, with this design in his heart, that the fair-maned horses might lightly issue forth, and not tremble in spirit, when they trod over the dead; for they were not yet used to dead men. But when the son of Tydeus came upon the king, he was the thirteenth from whom he took sweet life away, as he was breathing hard, for an evil dream stood above his head that night, even the seed of Oineus, through the device of Athene. Meanwhile the hardy Odysseus loosed the whole-hooved horses, and bound them together with thongs, and drave them out of the press, smiting them with his bow, since he had not taken thought to lift the shining whip with his hands from the well-dight chariot; then he whistled for a sign to noble Diomedes.

But Diomedes stood and pondered what most daring deed he might do, whether he should take the chariot, where lay the fair-dight armour, and drag it out by the pole, or lift it upon high, and so bear it forth, or whether he should take the life away from yet more of the Thracians. And while he was pondering this in his heart, then Athene drew near, and stood, and spake to noble Diomedes: "Bethink thee of returning, O son of great-hearted Tydeus, to the hollow ships, lest perchance thou come thither in flight, and perchance another god rouse up the Trojans likewise."

So spake she, and he observed the voice of the utterance of the goddess, and swiftly he sprang upon the steeds, and Odysseus smote them with his bow, and they sped to the swift ships of the Achaians.

Nay, nor a vain watch kept Apollo of the silver bow, when he beheld Athene caring for the son of Tydeus; in wrath against her he stole among the crowded press of Trojans, and aroused a counsellor of the Thracians, Hippokoon, the noble kinsman of Rhesos. And he started out of sleep, when he beheld the place desolate where the swift horses had stood, and beheld the men gasping in the death struggle; then he groaned aloud, and called out by name to his comrade dear. And a clamour arose and din unspeakable of the Trojans hasting together, and they marvelled at the terrible deeds, even all that the heroes had wrought, and had gone thereafter to the hollow ships.

But when those others came to the place where they had slain the spy of Hector, there Odysseus, dear to Zeus, checked the swift horses, and Tydeus' son, leaping to the ground, set the bloody spoil in the hands of Odysseus, and again mounted, and lashed the horses, and they sped onward nothing loth [to the hollow ships, for there they fain would be]. But Nestor first heard the sound, and said: "O friends, leaders and counsellors of the Argives, shall I be wrong or speak sooth? for my heart bids me speak. The sound of swift-footed horses strikes upon mine ears. Would to god that Odysseus and that strong Diomedes may even instantly be driving the whole-hooved horses from among the Trojans; but terribly I fear in mine heart lest the bravest of the Argives suffer aught through the Trojans' battle-din."

Not yet was his whole word spoken, when they came themselves, and leaped down to earth, but gladly the others welcomed them with hand-clasping, and with honeyed words. And first did knightly Nestor of Gerenia make question: "Come, tell me now, renowned Odysseus, great glory of the Achaians, how ye twain took those horses? Was it by stealing into the press of Trojans? Or did some god meet you, and give you them? Wondrous like are they to rays of the sun. Ever with the Trojans do I mix in fight, nor methinks do I tarry by the ships, old warrior as I am. But never yet saw I such horses, nor deemed of such. Nay, methinks some god must have encountered you and given you these. For both of you doth Zeus the cloud-gatherer love, and the maiden of aegis-bearing Zeus, bright-eyed Athene."

And him answered Odysseus of the many counsels: "O Nestor, son of Neleus, great glory of the Achaians, lightly could a god, if so he would, give even better steeds than these, for the gods are far stronger than we. But as for these new come horses, whereof, old man, thou askest me, they are Thracian, but their lord did brave Diomedes slay, and beside him all the twelve best men of his company. The thirteenth man was a spy we took near the ships, one that Hector and the other haughty Trojans sent forth to pry upon our camp."

So spake he, and drave the whole-hooved horses through the fosse, laughing; and the other Achaians went with him joyfully. But when they had come to the well-built hut of the son of Tydeus, they bound the horses with well-cut thongs, at the mangers where the swift horses of Diomedes stood eating honey-sweet barley.

And Odysseus placed the bloody spoils of Dolon in the stern of the ship, that they might make ready a sacred offering to Athene. But for themselves, they went into the sea, and washed off the thick sweat from shins, and neck, and thighs. But when the wave of the sea had washed the thick sweat from their skin, and their hearts revived again, they went into polished baths, and were cleansed.

And when they had washed, and anointed them with olive oil, they sat down at supper, and from the full mixing bowl they drew off the honey-sweet wine, and poured it forth to Athene.

BOOK XI

Despite the glorious deeds of Agamemnon, the Trojans press hard on the Achaians, and the beginning of evil comes on Patroklos.

Now Dawn arose from her couch beside proud Tithonos, to bring light to the Immortals and to mortal men. But Zeus sent forth fierce Discord unto the fleet ships of the Achaians, and in her hands she held the signal of war. And she stood upon the huge black ship of Odysseus, that was in the midst, to make her voice heard on either side, both to the huts of Aias, son of Telamon, and to the huts of Achilles, for these twain, trusting in their valour and the might of their hands, had drawn up their trim ships at the two ends of the line. There stood the goddess and cried shrilly in a great voice and terrible, and mighty strength she set in the heart of each of the Achaians, to war and fight unceasingly. And straightway to them war grew sweeter than to depart in the hollow ships to their dear native land.

Then the son of Atreus cried aloud, and bade the Argives arm them, and himself amid them did on the flashing bronze. First he fastened fair greaves about his legs, fitted with ankle-clasps of silver; next again he did his breastplate about his breast, the breastplate that in time past Kinyras gave him for a guest-gift. For afar in Cyprus did Kinyras hear the mighty rumour how that the Achaians were about to sail forth to Troy in their ships, wherefore did Kinyras give him the breastplate, to do pleasure to the king. Now therein were ten courses of black cyanus, and twelve of gold, and twenty of tin, and dark blue snakes writhed up towards the neck, three on either side, like rainbows that the son of Kronos hath set in the clouds, a marvel of the mortal tribes of men. And round his shoulders he cast his sword, wherein shone studs of gold, but the scabbard about it was silver, fitted with golden chains. And he took the richly-dight shield of his valour that covereth all the body of a man, a fair shield, and round about it were ten circles of bronze, and thereon were twenty white bosses of tin, and one in the midst of black cyanus. And thereon was embossed the Gorgon fell of aspect glaring terribly, and about her were Dread and Terror. And from the shield was hung a baldric of silver, and thereon was curled a snake of cyanus; three heads interlaced had he, growing out of one neck. And on his head Agamemnon set a two-crested helm with fourfold plate, and plume of horse-hair, and terribly the crest nodded from above. And he grasped two strong spears, shod with bronze and keen, and far forth from him into the heaven shone the bronze; and thereat Hera and Athene thundered, honouring the king of Mykene rich in gold.

Then each man gave in charge his horses to his charioteer, to hold them in by the fosse, well and orderly, and themselves as heavy men at arms were hasting about, being harnessed in their gear, and unquenchable the cry arose into the Dawn. And long before the charioteers were they arrayed at the fosse, but after them a little way came up the drivers. And among them the son of Kronos aroused an evil din, and from above rained down dew dank with blood out of the upper air, for that he was about to send many strong men down to Hades.

But the Trojans on the other side, on the high ground of the plain, gathered them around great Hector, and noble Polydamas, and Aineias that as a god was honoured by the people of the Trojans, and the three sons of Antenor, Polybos, and noble Agenor, and young Akamas like unto the Immortals. And Hector in the foremost rank bare the circle of his shield. And as from amid the clouds appeareth glittering a baneful star, and then again sinketh within the shadowy clouds, even so Hector would now appear among the foremost ranks, and again would be giving command in the rear, and all in bronze he shone, like the lightning of aegis-bearing father Zeus.

And even as when reapers over against each other drive their swaths through a rich man's field of wheat or barley, and thick fall the handfuls, even so the Trojans and Achaians leaped upon each other, destroying, and neither side took thought of ruinous flight; and equal heads had the battle, and they rushed on like wolves. And woful Discord was glad at the sight, for she alone of the gods was with them in the war; for the other gods were not beside them, but in peace they sat within their halls, where the goodly mansion of each was builded in the folds of Olympus. And they all were blaming the son of Kronos, lord of the storm-cloud, for that he willed to give glory to the Trojans. But of them took the father no heed, but aloof from the others he sat apart, glad in his glory, looking toward the city of the Trojans, and the ships of the Achaians, and the glitter of bronze, and the slayers and the slain.

So long as morning was, and the sacred day still waxed, so long did the shafts of both hosts strike, and the folk fell, but about the hour when a woodman maketh ready his meal, in the dells of a mountain, when he hath tired his hands with felling tall trees, and weariness cometh on his soul, and desire of sweet food taketh his heart, even then the Danaans by their valour brake the battalions, and called on their comrades through the lines. And in rushed Agamemnon first of all, and slew a man, even Bienor, shepherd of the hosts, first himself, and next his comrade Oïleus, the charioteer. He verily leaped from the chariot and stood and faced Agamemnon, but the king smote the brow of him with the sharp spear as he came eagerly on, and his vizor heavy with bronze held not off the spear, but through vizor and bone it sped, and the brain within was all scattered, and so was Oïleus overcome despite his eagerness.

And them did Agamemnon king of men leave in that place, with their breasts gleaming, when he had stripped them of their corslets, and he went on to destroy Isos and Antiphos, two sons of Priam, one born in wedlock, the other a bastard, and both were in one chariot: the bastard held the reins, but renowned Antiphos was fighting by him. These twain did Achilles on the spurs of Ida once bind with fresh withes, taking them as they herded the sheep, and he ransomed them for a price. But now Agamemnon, son of Atreus, of the wide domain, smote Isos on the breast, above the nipple, with his spear, but Antiphos he struck hard by the ear, with the sword, and dashed him from the chariot. Then made he haste, and stripped from them their goodly harness, well knowing who they were, for he had seen them before beside the fleet ships when swift-footed Achilles led them from Ida. And as a lion easily crusheth the young fawns of a swift hind, when that he hath seized them in his strong teeth, and hath come to their lair, and taketh their tender life away,—and the hind, even if she chance to be near at hand, cannot help them, for on herself too cometh dread terror, and swiftly she speedeth through the thick coppice and the woodland, hasting and sweating before the onslaught of the mighty beast,—even so not one of the Trojans did avail to save them from their bane, but themselves were fleeing in fear before the Argives.

Next took he Peisandros and Hippolochos, steadfast in fight. These were sons of wise-hearted Antimachos, who chiefly had taken the gold of Alexandros, goodly gifts, and therefore never would consent to give Helen to fair-haired Menelaos. His two sons then lord Agamemnon took, both being in one car, and together they were driving the swift steeds; for the shining reins had fallen from their hands, and the horses were all distraught with dread, and he set on against them, like a lion,—even the son of Atreus,—but from their chariot the twain did supplicate him: "Take us alive, O son of Atreus, and receive worthy ransom, for in the halls of Antimachos lie many possessions, bronze, and gold, and smithied iron; out of these could our father do thee grace with ransom past telling, if he heard that we twain were alive by the ships of the Achaians."

So did the twain weeping beseech the king with soft words, but they heard a voice wherein was no softness at all: "If indeed ye be the sons of wise Antimachos, who once in the assembly of the Trojans bade slay Menelaos there, when he came on an embassy with godlike Odysseus, nor ever let him return to the Achaians, now verily shall ye pay the price of your father's foul shame."

He spake and dashed Peisandros from his chariot to the earth, smiting him with the spear upon the breast, and he lay supine on the ground. But Hippolochos rushed away, and him too he smote to earth, and cut off his arms and his neck with the sword, then tossed him like a ball of stone to roll through the throng. Then left he them, and where thickest clashed the battalions, there he set on, and with him all the well-greaved Achaians. Footmen kept slaying footmen as they were driven in flight, and horsemen slaying horsemen with the sword, and from beneath them rose up the dust from the plain, stirred by the thundering hooves of horses. And the lord Agamemnon, ever slaying, followed after, calling on the Argives. And as when ruinous fire falleth on dense woodland, and the whirling wind beareth it everywhere, and the thickets fall utterly before it, being smitten by the onset of the fire, even so beneath Agamemnon son of Atreus fell the heads of the Trojans as they fled; and many strong-necked horses rattled empty cars along the highways of the battle, lacking their noble charioteers; but they on the earth were lying, far more dear to the vultures than to their wives.

But Hector did Zeus draw forth from the darts and the dust, from the man-slaying, and the blood, and the din, and the son of Atreus followed on, crying eagerly to the Danaans. And past the tomb of ancient Ilos, son of Dardanos, across the mid plain, past the place of the wild fig-tree they sped, making for the city, and ever the son of Atreus followed shouting, and his invincible hands were defiled with gore. But when they were come to the Skaian gates, and the oak-tree, there then they halted, and awaited each other. But some were still in full flight through the mid plain, like kine that a lion hath scattered, coming on them in the dead of night; all hath he scattered, but to one sheer death appeareth instantly, and he breaketh her neck first, seizing her with strong teeth, and thereafter swalloweth greedily the blood and all the guts; even so lord Agamemnon son of Atreus followed hard on the Trojans, ever slaying the hindmost man, and they were scattered in flight, and on face or back many of them fell from their chariots beneath the hands of Agamemnon, for mightily he raged with the spear. But when he was now about coming below the city, and the steep wall, then did the father of men and gods sit him down on the crests of many-fountained Ida, from heaven descending, with the thunderbolt in his hands.

Then sent he forth Iris of the golden wings, to bear his word: "Up and go, swift Iris, and tell this word unto Hector: So long as he sees Agamemnon, shepherd of the host, raging among the foremost fighters, and ruining the ranks of men, so long let him hold back, but bid the rest of the host war with the foe in strong battle. But when, or smitten with the spear or wounded with arrow shot, Agamemnon leapeth into his chariot, then will I give Hector strength to slay till he come even to the well-timbered ships, and the sun go down, and sacred darkness draw on."

So spake he, and wind-footed swift Iris disobeyed him not,

But Agamemnon ranged among the ranks of men, with spear, and sword, and great stones for throwing, while yet the blood welled warm from his wound. But when the wound waxed dry, and the blood ceased to flow, then keen pangs came on the might of the son of Atreus. And even as when the keen shaft cometh upon a woman in her travail, the piercing shaft that the goddesses of the birth-pangs send, even the Eilithyiai, the daughters of Hera that have bitter pangs in their gift, even so keen pains sank into the might of the son of Atreus. Then leaped he into his chariot, and bade his charioteer drive to the hollow ships, for he was sore vexed at heart. And he called in a piercing voice, and shouted to the Danaans: "O friends, leaders and counsellors of the Argives, do ye now ward from the seafaring ships the harsh din of battle, for Zeus the counsellor suffers me not all day to war with the Trojans."

So spake he, and his charioteer lashed the fair-maned steeds toward the hollow ships, and they flew onward nothing loth, and their breasts were covered with foam, and their bellies were stained with dust, as they bore the wounded king away from the war.

But Hector, when he beheld Agamemnon departed, cried to the Trojans and Lykians with a loud shout: "Ye Trojans and Lykians, and Dardanians that war in close fight, be men, my friends. and be mindful of your impetuous valour. The best man of them hath departed and to me hath Zeus, the son of Kronos, given great renown. But straightway drive ye the whole-hooved horses against the mighty Danaans, that ye may be the masters and bear away the higher glory."

So spake he, and aroused the might and spirit of every man. And even as when some hunter tars on his white-toothed hounds against a boar of the wild, or a lion, even so did Hector, son of Priam, like unto Ares the bane of men, tar on the great-hearted Trojans against the Achaians. Himself with high thoughts he fared among the foremost, and fell upon the fight, like a roaring blast, that leapeth down and stirreth the violet-coloured deep. There whom first, whom last did he slay, even Hector, son of Priam, when Zeus vouchsafed him renown?

Asaios first, and Autonoos, and Opites, and Dolops, son of Klytios, and Opheltios, and Agelaos, and Aisymnos, and Oros, and Hipponoos steadfast in the fight; these leaders of the Danaans he slew, and thereafter smote the multitude, even as when the West Wind driveth the clouds of the white South Wind, smiting with deep storm, and the wave swelleth huge, rolling onward, and the spray is scattered on high beneath the rush of the wandering wind; even so many heads of the host were smitten by Hector.

There had ruin begun, and deeds remedyless been wrought, and now would all the Achaians have fled and fallen among the ships, if Odysseus had not called to Diomedes, son of Tydeus: "Tydeus' son, what ails us that we forget our impetuous valour? Nay, come hither, friend, and take thy stand by me, for verily it will be shame if Hector of the glancing helm take the ships."

And to him strong Diomedes spake in answer: "Verily will I abide and endure, but short will be all our profit, for Zeus, the cloud-gatherer, clearly desireth to give victory to the Trojans rather than to us."

He spake, and drave Thymbraios from his chariot to the ground, smiting him with the spear in the left breast, and Odysseus smote Molion the godlike squire of that prince. These then they let be, when they had made them cease from war, and then the twain fared through the crowd with a din, as when two boars full of valour fall on the hunting hounds; so rushed they on again, and slew the Trojans, while gladly the Achaians took breath again in their flight from noble Hector.

There took they a chariot and two of the best men of the people, two sons of Merops of Perkote, who above all men was skilled in soothsaying, nor would he suffer his children to go to ruinous war; but in no wise did the twain obey him, for the Fates of black death led them on. Them did the son of Tydeus, Diomedes, spearman renowned, deprive of life and spirit, and took away their glorious harness. And Odysseus stripped Hippodamos and Hypeirochos. Then Kronion stretched for them the line of battle level, as he looked down from Ida, and they kept slaying each other. Then Tydeus' son smote the hero Agastrophos, son of Paion, on the hip-joint, with his spear; nor were his horses near, for him to flee, and great blindness was on his spirit; for the squire held them aloof, but on foot he was charging through the foremost fighters, till he lost his life. But Hector quickly spied them among the ranks, and rushed upon them shouting, and with him followed the battalions of the Trojans. And beholding him, Diomedes of the loud war-cry shuddered, and straightway spake to Odysseus that was hard by: "Lo, on us this ruin, even mighty Hector, is rolling: let us stand, and await him, and ward off his onset."

So spake he, and swayed and sent forth his far-shadowing spear, and smote him nor missed, for he aimed at the head, on the summit of the crest, and bronze by bronze was turned, nor reached his fair flesh, for it was stopped by the threefold helm with its socket, that Phoebus Apollo to Hector gave. But Hector sprang back a wondrous way, and mingled with the throng, and he rested, fallen on his knee, and leaned on the ground with his stout hand, and dark night veiled his eyes.

But while Tydeus' son was following after his spear-cast, far through the foremost fighters, where he saw it sink into the earth, Hector gat breath again, and leaping back into his chariot drave out into the throng, and avoided black Fate. Then rushing on with his spear mighty Diomedes spake to him: "Dog, thou art now again escaped from death; yet came ill very nigh thee: but now hath Phoebus Apollo saved thee, to whom thou must surely pray when thou goest amid the clash of spears. Verily I will slay thee yet when I meet thee hereafter, if any god is helper of me too. Now will I make after the rest, whomsoever I may seize."

So spake he, and stripped the son of Paeon, spearman renowned. But Alexandros, the lord of fair-tressed Helen, aimed with his arrows at Tydeides, shepherd of the host; leaning as he aimed against a pillar on the barrow, by men fashioned, of Ilos, son of Dardanos, an elder of the people in time gone by. Now Diomedes was stripping the shining corslet of strong Agastrophos from about his breast, and the shield from his shoulders, and his strong helmet, when Paris drew the centre of his bow; nor vainly did the shaft fly from his hand, for he smote the flat of the right foot of Diomedes, and the arrow went clean through, and stood fixed in the earth; and right sweetly laughing Paris leaped up from his lair, and boasted, and said: "Thou art smitten, nor vainly hath the dart flown forth; would that I had smitten thee in the nether belly, and taken thy life away. So should the Trojans have breathed again from their trouble, they that shudder at thee, as bleating goats at a lion."

But him answered strong Diomedes, no wise dismayed: "Bowman, reviler, proud in thy bow of horn, thou gaper after girls, verily if thou madest trial in full harness, man to man, thy bow and showers of shafts would nothing avail thee, but now thou boastest vainly, for that thou hast grazed the sole of my foot. I care not, more than if a woman had struck me or a senseless boy, for feeble is the dart of a craven man and a worthless. In other wise from my hand, yea, if it do but touch, the sharp shaft flieth, and straightway layeth low its man, and torn are the cheeks of his wife, and fatherless his children, and he, reddening the earth with his blood, doth rot away, more birds than women round him."

So spake he, and Odysseus, spearman renowned, drew near, and stood in front of him, and Diomedes sat down behind him, and drew the sharp arrow from his foot, and a sore pang passed through his flesh. Then sprang he into his car, and bade his charioteer drive back to the hollow ships, for he was hurt at heart. Then Odysseus, spearman renowned, was left alone, nor did one of the Argives abide by him, for fear had fallen on them all. Then in heaviness he spoke to his own great-hearted spirit: "Ah me, what thing shall befall me! A great evil it is if I flee, in dread of the throng; yet worse is this, if I be taken all alone, for the other Danaans hath Kronion scattered in flight. But wherefore doth my heart thus converse with herself? for I know that they are cowards, who flee the fight, but whosoever is a hero in war, him it mainly behoves to stand stubbornly, whether he be smitten, or whether he smite another."

While he pondered thus in heart and spirit, the ranks came on of the Trojans under shield, and hemmed him in the midst, setting among them their own bane. And even as when hounds and young men in their bloom press round a boar, and he cometh forth from his deep lair, whetting his white tusk between crooked jaws, and round him they rush, and the sound of the gnashing of tusks ariseth, and straightway they await his assault, so dread as he is, even so then round Odysseus, dear to Zeus, rushed the Trojans. And first he wounded noble Deïopites, from above, in the shoulder, leaping on him with sharp spear, and next he slew Thoon and Ennomos, and next Chersidamas, being leapt down from his chariot, he smote with the spear on the navel beneath the bossy shield, and he fell in the dust and clutched the ground with the hollow of his hand. These left he, and wounded Charops, son of Hippasos, with the spear, the brother of high-born Sokos. And to help him came Sokos, a godlike man, and stood hard by him, and spake saying: "O renowned Odysseus, insatiable of craft and toil, to-day shalt thou either boast over two sons of Hippasos, as having slain two such men of might, and stripped their harness, or smitten by my spear shalt lose thy life."

So spake he, and smote him on the circle of his shield; through the shining shield passed the strong spear, and through the fair-dight corslet it was thrust, and tore clean off the flesh of the flanks, but Pallas Athene did not suffer it to mingle with the bowels of the hero, and Odysseus knew that the dart had in no wise lighted on a deadly spot, and drawing backward, he spake unto Sokos: "Ah, wretched one, verily sheer destruction is come upon thee. Surely thou hast made me to cease from warring among the Trojans, but here to thee I declare that slaying and black Fate will be upon thee this day, and beneath my spear overthrown shalt thou give glory to me, and thy soul to Hades of the noble steeds."

He spake, and the other turned, and started to flee, and in his back as he turned he fixed the spear, between the shoulders, and drave it through the breast. Then he fell with a crash, and noble Odysseus boasted over him: "Ah, Sokos, son of wise-hearted Hippasos the tamer of horses, the end of death hath come upon and caught thee, nor hast thou avoided. Ah, wretch, thy father and lady mother shall not close thine eyes in death, but birds that eat flesh raw shall tear thee, shrouding thee in the multitude of their wings. But to me, if I die, the noble Achaians will yet give due burial."

So spake he, and drew the mighty spear of wise-hearted Sokos forth from his flesh, and from his bossy shield, and his blood flowed forth when the spear was drawn away, and afflicted his spirit. And the great-hearted Trojans when they beheld the blood of Odysseus, with clamour through the throng came all together against him. But he gave ground, and shouted unto his comrades: thrice he shouted then, as loud as man's mouth might cry, and thrice did Menelaos dear to Zeus hear his call, and quickly he spake to Aias that was hard by him: "Aias, of the seed of Zeus, child of Telamon, lord of the hosts, the shout of Odysseus of the hardy heart rings round me, like as though the Trojans were oppressing him alone among them, and had cut him off in the strong battle. Nay, let us speed into the throng, for better it is to rescue him. I fear lest he suffer some evil, being alone among the Trojans, so brave as he is, and lest great sorrow for his loss come upon the Danaans."

So spake he, and led the way, and the other followed him, a godlike man. Then found they Odysseus dear to Zeus, and the Trojans beset him like tawny jackals from the hills round a wounded horned stag, that a man hath smitten with an arrow from the bow-string, and the stag hath fled from him by speed of foot, as long as the blood is warm and his limbs are strong, but when the swift arrow hath overcome him, then do the ravening jackals rend him in the hills, in a dark wood, and then god leadeth a murderous lion thither, and the jackals flee before him, but he rendeth them, so then, round wise-hearted Odysseus of the crafty counsels, did the Trojans gather, many and mighty, but that hero thrusting on with the spear held off the pitiless day. Then Aias drew near, bearing his shield like a tower, and stood thereby, and the Trojans fled from him, where each man might. Then warlike Menelaos led Odysseus out of the press, holding him by the hand, till the squire drave up the horses.

Then Aias leaped on the Trojans, and slew Doryklos, bastard son of Priam, and thereafter wounded he Pandokos, and he wounded Lysandros, and Pyrasos, and Pylartes. And as when a brimming river cometh down upon the plain, in winter flood from the hills, swollen by the rain of Zeus, and many dry oaks and many pines it sucketh in, and much soil it casteth into the sea, even so renowned Aias charged them, pursuing through the plain, slaying horses and men. Nor was Hector thereof at all, for he was fighting on the left of all the battle, by the banks of the river Skamandros, whereby chiefly fell the heads of men, and an unquenchable cry arose, around great Nestor and warlike Idomeneus. And Hector with them was warring, and terrible things did he, with the spear and in horsemanship, and he ravaged the battalions of the young men. Nor would the noble Achaians have yet given ground from the path, if Alexandros, the lord of fair-tressed Helen, had not stayed Machaon shepherd of the host in his valorous deeds, and smitten him on the right shoulder with a three-barbed arrow. Therefore were the Achaians, breathing valour, in great fear, lest men should seize Machaon in the turning of the fight.

Then Idomeneus spake to noble Nestor: "O Nestor, son of Neleus, great glory of the Achaians, arise, get thee up into thy chariot, and with thee let Machaon go, and swiftly drive to the ships the whole-hooved horses. For a leech is worth many other men, to cut out arrows, and spread soothing medicaments."

So spake he, nor did knightly Nestor of Gerenia disobey him, but straightway gat up into his chariot, and with him went Machaon, son of Asklepios the good leech, and he lashed the horses, and willingly flew they forward to the hollow ships, where they desired to be.

But Kebriones, the charioteer of Hector, beheld the Trojans driven in flight, and spake to him, and said: "Hector, here do we contend with the Danaans, at the limit of the wailful war, but, lo, the other Trojans are driven in flight confusedly, men and horses. And Aias son of Telamon is driving them; well I know him, for wide is the shield round his shoulders. Nay, let us too urge thither the horses and chariot, there where horsemen and footmen thickest in the forefront of evil strife are slaying each other, and the cry goes up unquenchable."

So spake he, and smote the fair-maned horses with the shrill sounding whip, and they felt the lash, and fleetly bore the swift chariot among the Trojans and Achaians, treading on the dead, and the shields, and with blood was sprinkled all the axle-tree beneath, and the rims round the car with the drops from the hooves of the horses, and with drops from the tires about the wheels. And Hector was eager to enter the press of men, and to leap in and break through, and evil din of battle he brought among the Danaans, and brief space rested he from smiting with the spear. Nay, but he ranged among the ranks of other men, with spear, and sword, and with great stones, but he avoided the battle of Aias son of Telamon, [for Zeus would have been wroth with him, if he fought with a better man than himself].

Now father Zeus, throned in the highest, roused dread in Aias, and he stood in amaze, and cast behind him his sevenfold shield of bull's hide, and gazed round in fear upon the throng, like a wild beast, turning this way and that, and slowly retreating step by step. And as when hounds and country folk drive a tawny lion from the mid-fold of the kine, and suffer him not to carry away the fattest of the herd; all night they watch, and he in great desire for the flesh maketh his onset, but takes nothing thereby, for thick the darts fly from strong hands against him, and the burning brands, and these he dreads for all his fury, and in the dawn he departeth with vexed heart; even so at that time departed Aias, vexed at heart, from among the Trojans, right unwillingly, for he feared sore for the ships of the Achaians. And as when a lazy ass going past a field hath the better of the boys with him, an ass that hath had many a cudgel broken about his sides, and he fareth into the deep crop, and wasteth it, while the boys smite him with cudgels, and feeble is the force of them, but yet with might and main they drive him forth, when he hath had his fill of fodder, even so did the high-hearted Trojans and allies, called from many lands, smite great Aias, son of Telamon, with darts on the centre of his shield, and ever followed after him. And Aias would now be mindful of his impetuous valour, and turn again, and hold at bay the battalions of the horse-taming Trojans, and once more he would turn him again to flee. Yet he hindered them all from making their way to the fleet ships, and himself stood and smote between the Trojans and the Achaians, and the spears from strong hands stuck some of them in his great shield, fain to win further, and many or ever they reached his white body stood fast halfway in the earth, right eager to sate themselves with his flesh.

But when Eurypylos, the glorious son of Euaimon, beheld him oppressed by showers of darts, he went and took his stand by him, and cast with his shining spear, and smote Apisaon, son of Phausios, shepherd of the host, in the liver, below the midriff, and straightway loosened his knees; and Eurypylos sprang on him, and stripped the harness from his shoulders.

But when godlike Alexandros beheld him stripping the harness from Apisaon, straightway he drew his bow against Eurypylos, and smote him with a shaft on the right thigh, and the reed of the shaft brake, and weighed down the thigh. Then Eurypylos withdrew back into the host of his comrades, avoiding fate, and with a piercing voice he shouted to the Danaans: "O friends, leaders and counsellors of the Argives, turn and stand and ward off the pitiless day from Aias, that is oppressed with darts, nor methinks will he escape out of the evil din of battle. Nay, stand ye the rather at bay round great Aias, son of Telamon."

So spake Eurypylos being wounded, and they stood close together beside him, sloping the shields on their shoulders, and holding up their spears, and Aias came to meet them, and turned and stood when he reached the host of his comrades.

So they fought like unto burning fire.

But the mares of Neleus all sweating bare Nestor out of the battle, and also carried they Machaon, shepherd of the host. Then the noble Achilles, swift of foot, beheld and was ware of him, for Achilles was standing by the stern of his great ship, watching the dire toil, and the woful rout of battle. And straightway he spake to his own comrade, Patroklos, calling to him from beside the ship, and he heard, and from the hut he came, like unto Ares; and this to him was the beginning of evil. Then the strong son of Menoitios spake first to Achilles: "Why dost thou call me, Achilles, what need hast thou of me?"

Then swift-footed Achilles answered him and spake: "Noble son of Menoitios, dear to my heart, now methinks that the Achaians will stand in prayer about my knees, for need no longer tolerable cometh upon them. But go now, Patroklos dear to Zeus, and ask Nestor who is this that he bringeth wounded from the war. Verily from behind he is most like Machaon, that child of Asklepios, but I beheld not the eyes of the man, for the horses sped past me, straining forward eagerly."

So spake he, and Patroklos obeyed his dear comrade, and started and ran past the ships, and the huts of the Achaians.

Now when they came to the hut of the son of Neleus, they lighted down on the bounteous earth, and the squire, Eurymedon, loosed the horses of that old man from the car, and they dried the sweat from their doublets, standing before the breeze, by the shore of the sea, and thereafter came they to the hut, and sat them down on chairs. And fair-tressed Hekamede mixed for them a mess, Hekamede that the old man won from Tenedos, when Achilles sacked it, and she was the daughter of great-hearted Arsinoos, and her the Achaians chose out for him, because always in counsel he excelled them all. First she drew before them a fair table, polished well, with feet of cyanus, and thereon a vessel of bronze, with onion, for relish to the drink, and pale honey, and the grain of sacred barley, and beside it a right goodly cup, that the old man brought from home, embossed with studs of gold, and four handles there were to it, and round each two golden doves were feeding, and to the cup were two feet below. Another man could scarce have lifted the cup from the table, when it was full, but Nestor the Old raised it easily. In this cup the woman, like unto the goddesses, mixed a mess for them, with Pramnian wine, and therein grated cheese of goats' milk, with a grater of bronze, and scattered white barley thereover, and bade them drink, whenas she had made ready the mess.

So when the twain had drunk, and driven away parching thirst, they took their pleasure in discourse, speaking each to the other. Now Patroklos stood at the doors, a godlike man, and when the old man beheld him, he arose from his shining chair, and took him by the hand, and led him in, and bade him be seated. But Patroklos, from over against him, was for refusing, and spake and said: "No time to sit have I, old man, fosterling of Zeus, nor wilt thou persuade me. Revered and dreaded is he that sent me forth to ask thee who this man is that thou bringest home wounded. Nay, but I know myself, for I see Machaon, shepherd of the host. And now will I go back again, a messenger, to speak a word to Achilles. And well dost thou know, old man, fosterling of Zeus, how terrible a man he is; lightly would he blame even one that is blameless."

Then knightly Nestor of Gerenia answered him again: "Wherefore is Achilles thus sorry for the sons of the Achaians, for as many as are wounded with darts? He knoweth not at all what grief hath arisen in the camp: for the best men lie in the ships, wounded by shaft or smitten by spear. Wounded with the shaft is strong Diomedes, son of Tydeus, and smitten is Odysseus, spearman renowned, and Agamemnon, [and Eurypylos hath been shot with an arrow in the thigh], and this other have I but newly carried out of battle, wounded with an arrow from the bowstring. But Achilles, for all his valiance, careth not for the Danaans, nor pities them at all. Doth he wait till the fleet ships hard by the shore shall burn, maugre the Argives, in the consuming fire, and till we be slain one upon another? For my strength is no longer what it was before in my supple limbs.

Would that I were in such youth, and my might as steadfast, as when a strife was set between the Eleians and ourselves, about a raid on the kine; what time I slew Itymoneus, the brave son of Hypeirochos, a dweller in Elis, when I was driving the spoil. And in fighting for his kine was he smitten in the foremost rank by a spear from my hand, and he fell, and about him were the country folk in great fear. And a prey exceeding abundant did we drive together out of the plain, fifty herds of kine, and as many flocks of sheep, and as many droves of swine, and as many wide flocks of goats, and chestnut horses a hundred and fifty, all mares, and many with their foals at their feet. And these by night we drave within Neleian Pylos to the citadel, and Neleus was glad at heart, for that so much wealth came to me, the first time I went to war. And the heralds cried aloud, with the coming of the dawn, that all men should meet that had a debt owing to them in goodly Elis. And the men that were leaders of the Pylians gathered together and divided all, for to many did the Epeians owe a debt, for few we were, and oppressed, that dwelt in Pylos. For the mighty Herakles had come and oppressed us, in the former years, and all our best men were slain. For twelve sons were we of noble Neleus, whereof I alone was left, and all the others perished. And being lifted up with pride because of these things, the mail-clad Epeians did us despite, and devised deeds of violence. And out of the spoil that old man, even Neleus, took him a herd of kine, and a great flock of sheep, choosing three hundred, and the shepherds with them. For to him was a great debt owing in goodly Elis: four horses, winners of prizes, with their chariot had gone to the games, and were to run for a tripod; but these did Augeias, king of men, hold in bond in that place, but sent away the driver sorrowing for the horses. By which words and deeds was the old man angered, so he chose out much booty, uncountable, and the rest he gave to the people to divide, lest any man should depart deprived by him of his equal share. So we ordered each thing, and offered victims to the gods about the city; and on the third day all the Eleians came together, many men and whole-hooved horses in full array, and with them the two Moliones in their harness, being still but lads, nor yet well skilled in impetuous valour. Now there is a certain city, Thryoessa, a steep burg, far off on Alpheios, the uttermost city of sandy Pylos, round this they pitched their camp, being eager to raze it utterly. But when they had passed through all the plain, to us came Athene by night rushing down from Olympus, with the message that we should arm us. Nor were the folk unwilling that she gathered in Pylos, but right eager for war. Now Neleus would not suffer me to arm myself, but hid my horses away, for he deemed that I knew naught as yet of the deeds of war. Yet even so did I shine among our horsemen, on foot though I was, for so Athene led the fight. There is a river Minyeïos, that falleth into the sea near Arene, where the horsemen of us Pylians waited the fair dawn, and thither those ranks of footmen flowed onward. Thence in full array, and harnessed in our gear, we came at midday to the sacred stream of Alpheios. There to Zeus pre-eminent in might we sacrificed goodly victims, and a bull to Alpheios, and a bull to Poseidon, but to bright-eyed Athene a heifer of the herd, and thereafter took we supper in ranks throughout the camp, and lay down to sleep each man in his arms, about the streams of the river. Now the great-hearted Epeians were gathered round the citadel, being eager to sack it utterly. But ere that might be, there appeared unto them a great deed of war. For when the bright sun came up above the earth, we joined battle, with prayer to Zeus, and Athene. But when the strife of the Pylians and Epeians began, I was the first that slew a man, and got me his whole-hooved steeds,—the warrior Mulios was he, who had to wife fair-haired Agamede, the eldest daughter of Augeias, and she knew all drugs that the wide earth nourisheth. Him as he came on I smote with a bronze-shod spear, and he fell in the dust and I leaped into the car, and stood among the foremost fighters. But the great-hearted Epeians fled this way and that when they saw the man fall, even the leader of the horsemen, who excelled in battle. But I sprang upon them, like a black tempest, and fifty chariots I took, and beside each chariot two men bit the earth with their teeth, subdued beneath my spear. And now should I have overthrown the twin Moliones, sons of Aktor, if their sire, the Earthshaker of wide sway, had not saved them out of the battle, and covered them with a thick mist. There Zeus gave great might to the Pylians, for we followed through the wide plain, slaying the foe and gathering their goodly arms, even till we brought our horses to Bouprasion, rich in wheat, and the rock Olenian, and where is the hill called the hill of Alision, whence Athene turned the people again. There slew I the last man and left him there, but the Achaians drave back their swift horses from Bouprasion to Pylos, and all gave praise, among the gods to Zeus, and among men to Nestor. Such was I, if ever among men I was such an one. But Achilles is for reaping alone the reward of his valour; surely methinks that he will repent, and lament sore when the host perisheth. O friend, surely Menoitios thus gave thee command, on that day when he sent thee out of Phthia to Agamemnon. And we twain were within the house, I and goodly Odysseus, and in the halls heard we all things even as he commanded thee. For we had come to the fair-set halls of Peleus, gathering the host throughout Achaia of the fair dames. There then we found the hero Menoitios within, and thee, and with thee Achilles. And Peleus the Old, the lord of horses, was burning the fat thighs of kine to Zeus, whose joy is in the thunder, in the precinct of his court, and held in his hand a chalice of gold, pouring forth the bright wine upon the burning offerings. And ye were busy about the flesh of the ox, and then stood we in the doorway, and Achilles leaped up in amazement, and took us by the hand, and led us in, and bade us be seated, and set before us well the entertainment of strangers, all that is their due. But when we had taken delight in eating and drinking, I began the discourse, and bade you follow with us, and ye were right eager, and those twain laid on you many commands. Peleus the Old bade his son Achilles be ever the boldest in fight, and preeminent over others, but to thee did Menoitios thus give command, the son of Aktor: 'My child, of lineage is Achilles higher than thou, and thou art elder, but in might he is better far. But do thou speak to him well a word of wisdom, and put it to him gently, and show him what things he should do, and he will obey thee to his profit.' So did the old man give thee command, but thou art forgetful. Nay, but even now speak thou thus and thus to wise-hearted Achilles, if perchance he will obey thee. Who knows but that, God helping, thou mightst stir his spirit with thy persuading? and good is the persuasion of a friend. But if in his heart he be shunning some oracle of God, and his lady mother hath told him somewhat from Zeus, natheless let him send forth thee, and let the rest of the host of the Myrmidons follow with thee, if perchance any light shall arise from thee to the Danaans; and let him give thee his fair harness, to bear into the war, if perchance the Trojans may take thee for him, and withhold them from the strife, and the warlike sons of the Achaians might take breath, being wearied; for brief is the breathing time in battle. And lightly might ye, being unwearied, drive men wearied in the war unto the city, away from the ships and the huts."

So spake he, and roused his heart within his breast, and he started and ran by the ships to Achilles of the seed of Aiakos. But when Patroklos came in his running to the ships of godlike Odysseus, where was their assembly and place of law, and whereby also were their altars of the gods established, there did Eurypylos meet him, Euaimon's son, of the seed of Zeus, wounded in the thigh with an arrow, and limping out of the battle. And sweat ran down streaming from his head and shoulders, and from his cruel wound the black blood was welling, but his mind was unshaken. And the strong son of Menoitios had pity on him when he beheld him, and lamenting he spake winged words: "Ah, wretched men, ye leaders and counsellors of the Danaans. How are ye now doomed, far from your friends and your own country, to feed full with your white fat the swift hounds in Troia! But come, tell me this, Eurypylos, hero and fosterling of Zeus, will the Achaians yet in any wise restrain mighty Hector, or will they perish even now, subdued beneath his spear?"

And to him again did the wounded Eurypylos make answer: "No more, Patroklos of the seed of Zeus, will there be any defence of the Achaians, but they will fall among the black ships. For verily all of them, that afore were bravest, are lying in the ships wounded and smitten by the hands of the Trojans, whose strength is waxing always. But me do thou succour, and lead me to the black ship, and cut the arrow out of my thigh, and wash away the black blood from it with warm water, and smear soft healing drugs thereover, these good herbs whereof they say that thou hast learned from Achilles, whom Cheiron taught, the most righteous of the Centaurs. For of the leeches, Podaleirios and Machaon, one methinks, is wounded in the huts, and himself hath need of a good leech, and the other on the plain abideth the keen battle of the Trojans."

Then the strong son of Menoitios answered him again: "How should these things be? what shall we do, hero Eurypylos? I am on my way to carry a saying to wise-hearted Achilles, even the command of Nestor of Gerenia, warden of the Achaians; nay, but not even so will I be heedless of thee that art wounded."

So spake he, and clasped the shepherd of the host below the breast, and led him to the hut; and the squire when he beheld them cast on the ground the skins of oxen. There he stretched him at length, and cut with a knife the sharp arrow from his thigh, and washed from it the black blood with warm water. And thereon he cast a bitter root rubbing it between his hands, a root that took pain away, and ended all his anguish, and the wound began to dry, and the blood ceased.

BOOK XII

How the Trojans and allies broke within the wall of the Achaians.

So in the huts the strong son of Menoitios was tending the wounded Eurypylos, but still they fought confusedly, the Argives and Trojans. Nor were the fosse of the Danaans and their wide wall above, long to protect them, the wall they had builded for defence of the ships, and the fosse they had drawn round about; for neither had they given goodly hecatombs to the gods, that it might guard with its bounds their swift ships, and rich spoil. Nay, maugre the deathless gods was it builded, wherefore it abode steadfast for no long time. While Hector yet lived, and yet Achilles kept his wrath, and unsacked was the city of Priam the king, so long the great wall of the Achaians likewise abode steadfast. But when all the bravest of the Trojans died, and many of the Argives,—some were taken, and some were left,—and the city of Priam was sacked in the tenth year, and the Argives had gone back in their ships to their own dear country, then verily did Poseidon and Apollo take counsel to wash away the wall, bringing in the might of the rivers, of all that flow from the hills of Ida to the sea. Rhesos there was, and Heptaporos, and Karesos, and Rhodios, Grenikos, and Aisepos, and goodly Skamandros, and Simoeis, whereby many shields and helms fell in the dust, and the generation of men half divine; the mouths of all these waters did Phoebus Apollo turn together, and for nine days he drave their stream against the wall; and still Zeus rained unceasingly, that the quicker he might mingle the wall with the salt sea. And the Shaker of the earth, with his trident in his hands, was himself the leader, and sent forth into the waves all the foundations of beams and stones that the Achaians had laid with toil, and made all smooth by the strong current of Hellespont, and covered again the great beach with sand, when he had swept away the wall, and turned the rivers back to flow in their channel, where of old they poured down their fair flow of water.

So were Poseidon and Apollo to do in the aftertime; but then war and the din of war sounded about the well-builded wall, and the beams of the towers rang beneath the strokes; while the Argives, subdued by the scourge of Zeus, were penned and driven in by the hollow ships, in dread of Hector, the mighty maker of flight, but he, as aforetime, fought like a whirlwind. And as when, among hounds and hunting men, a boar or lion wheeleth him about, raging in his strength, and these array themselves in fashion like a tower, and stand up against him, casting many javelins from their hands; but never is his stout heart confused nor afraid, and his courage is his bane, and often he wheeleth him about, and maketh trial of the ranks of men, and wheresoever he maketh onset there the ranks of men give way, even so Hector went and besought his comrades through the press, and spurred them on to cross the dyke. But his swift-footed horses dared not, but loud they neighed, standing by the sheer edge, for the wide fosse affrighted them, neither easy to leap from hard by, nor to cross, for overhanging banks stood round about it all on either hand, and above it was furnished with sharp stakes that the sons of the Achaians had planted there, thick set and great, a bulwark against hostile men. Thereby not lightly might a horse enter, drawing a well-wheeled chariot; but the footmen were eager, if they might accomplish it. Then Polydamas drew near valiant Hector, and spake to him: "Hector and ye other leaders of the Trojans and allies, foolishly do we drive our fleet horses through the dyke; nay right hard it is to cross, for sharp stakes stand in it, and over against them the wall of the Achaians. Thereby none may go down and fight in chariots, for strait is the place wherein, methinks, we might come by a mischief. For if Zeus that thunders on high is utterly to destroy them in his evil will, and is minded to help the Trojans, verily then I too would desire that even instantly this might be, that the Achaians should perish here nameless far from Argos: but and if they turn again, and we flee back from among the ships, and rush into the delved ditch, then methinks that not even one from among us to bear the tidings will win back to the city before the force of the Achaians when they rally. But come as I declare, let us all obey. Let our squires hold the horses by the dyke, while we being harnessed in our gear as foot soldiers follow all together with Hector, and the Achaians will not withstand us, if indeed the bands of death be made fast upon them."

So spake Polydamas, and his wise word pleased Hector well, and straightway in his harness he leaped from his chariot to the ground. Nor were the other Trojans gathered upon the chariots, but they all leaped forth, when they beheld goodly Hector. There each gave it into the charge of his own charioteer, to keep the horses orderly there by the fosse. And they divided, and arrayed themselves, and ordered in five companies they followed with the leaders.

Now they that went with Hector and noble Polydamas, these were most, and bravest, and most were eager to break the wall, and fight by the hollow ships; and with them followed Kebriones for the third, for Hector had left another man with his chariot, a weaker warrior than Kebriones. The second company Paris led, and Alkathoos, and Agenor: and the third company Helenos led, and godlike Deiphobos, —two sons of Priam,—the third was the warrior Asios, Asios Hyrtakos' son, whom his tall sorrel steeds brought out of Arisbe, from the river Selleëis. And of the fourth company was the brave son of Anchises leader, even Aineias;

and with him were two sons of Antenor, Archelochos and Akamas, both well skilled in all warfare.

And Sarpedon led the glorious allies, and to be with him he chose Glaukos and warlike Asteropaios, for they seemed to him to be manifestly the bravest of all after himself, but he was excellent, yea, above all the host. And these when they had arrayed one another with well-fashioned shields of bulls' hide, went straight and eager against the Danaans, nor deemed that they could longer resist them, but that themselves should fall on the black ships.

Then the rest of the Trojans and the far-famed allies obeyed the counsel of blameless Polydamas, but Asios, son of Hyrtakos, leader of men, willed not to leave his horses there, and his squire the charioteer, but with them he drew near the swift ships, fond man! for never was he, avoiding evil Fates, to return, rejoicing in his horses and chariot, back from the ships to windy Ilios. Nay, ere that the Fate of ill name overshadowed him, by the spear of Idomeneus, the haughty son of Deukalion. For Asios went against the left flank of the ships, whereby the Achaians returned out of the plain with chariots and horses: there he drave through his horses and his car, nor found he the doors shut on the gates, and the long bar, but men were holding them open if perchance they might save any of their comrades fleeing out of the battle towards the ships. Straight thereby held he his horses with unswerving aim, and his men followed him, crying shrilly, for they deemed that the Achaians could no longer hold them off, but that themselves would fall on the black ships: fools, for in the gates they found two men of the bravest, the high-hearted sons of the warrior Lapithae, one the son of Peirithoos, strong Polypoites, and one Leonteus, peer of Ares the bane of men. These twain stood in front of the lofty gates, like high-crested oak-trees in the hills, that for ever abide the wind and rain, firm fixed with roots great and long; even so these twain, trusting to the mightiness of their hands, abode the coming of great

Asios, and fled not. But straight came the Trojans against the well-builded wall, holding their shields of dry bulls' hide on high, with mighty clamour, round the prince Asios, and Iamenos, and Orestes, and Adamas, son of Asios, and Thoon, and Oinomaos. But the other twain for a while, being within the wall, urged the well-greaved Achaians to fight for the ships; but when they saw the Trojans assailing the wall, while the Danaans cried and turned in flight, then forth rushed the twain, and fought in front of the gates like wild boars that in the mountains abide the assailing crew of men and dogs, and charging on either flank they crush the wood around them, cutting it at the root, and the clatter of their tusks waxes loud, till one smite them and take their life away: so clattered the bright bronze on the breasts of the twain, as they were smitten in close fight, for right hardily they fought, trusting to the host above them, and to their own strength.

For the men above were casting with stones from the well-builded towers in defence of themselves and of the huts, and of the swift-faring ships. And like snowflakes the stones fell earthward, flakes that a tempestuous wind, as it driveth the dark clouds, rains thickly down on the bounteous earth: so thick fell the missiles from the hands of Achaians and Trojans alike, and their helms rang harsh and their bossy shields, being smitten with mighty stones. Verily then Asios, son of Hyrtakos, groaned and smote both his thighs, and indignantly he spake: "Father Zeus, verily thou too dost greatly love a lie, for I deemed not that the Achaian heroes could withstand our might and our hands invincible. But they like wasps of nimble body, or bees that have made their dwellings in a rugged path, and leave not their hollow hold, but abide and keep the hunters at bay for the sake of their little ones, even so these men have no will to give ground from the gates, though they are but two, ere they slay or be slain."

So spake he, nor with his speech did he persuade the mind of Zeus, for his will was to give renown to Hector.

[But the others were fighting about the other gates, and hard it were for me like a god to tell all these things, for everywhere around the wall of stone rose the fire divine; the Argives, for all their sorrow, defending the ships of necessity; and all the gods were grieved at heart, as many as were defenders of the Danaans in battle. And together the Lapithae waged war and strife.]

There the son of Peirithoos, mighty Polypoites, smote Damasos with the spear, through the helmet with cheek-pieces of bronze; nor did the bronze helm stay the spear, but the point of bronze brake clean through the bone, and all the brain within was scattered, and the spear overcame him in his eagerness. Thereafter he slew Pylon and Ormenos. And Leonteus of the stock of Ares smote Hippomachos, son of Antimachos, with the spear, striking him on the girdle. Then again he drew his sharp sword from the sheath, and smote Antiphates first in close fight, rushing on him through the throng, that he fell on his back on the ground; and thereafter he brought down Menon, and Iamenos, and Orestes one after the other, to the bounteous earth.

While they were stripping from these the shining arms, the young men who followed with Polydamas and Hector, they that were most in number and bravest, and most were eager to break the wall and set the ships on fire, these still stood doubtful by the fosse, for as they were eager to pass over a bird had appeared to them, an eagle of lofty flight, skirting the host on the left hand. In its talons it bore a blood-red monstrous snake, alive, and struggling still; yea, not yet had it forgotten the joy of battle, but writhed backward and smote the bird that held it on the breast, beside the neck, and the bird cast it from him down to the earth, in sore pain, and dropped it in the midst of the throng; then with a cry sped away down the gusts of the wind. And the Trojans shuddered when they saw the gleaming snake lying in the midst of them; an omen of aegis-bearing Zeus.

Then verily Polydamas stood by brave Hector, and spake: "Hector, ever dost thou rebuke me in the assemblies, though I counsel wisely; since it by no means beseemeth one of the people to speak contrary to thee, in council or in war, but always to increase thy power; but now again will I say all that seemeth to me to be best. Let us not advance and fight with the Danaans for the ships. For even thus, methinks, the end will be, if indeed this bird hath come for the Trojans when they were eager to cross the dyke, this eagle of lofty flight, skirting the host on the left hand, bearing in his talons a blood-red monstrous snake, yet living; then straightway left he hold of him, before he reached his own nest, nor brought him home in the end to give to his nestlings. Even so shall we, though we burst with mighty force the gates and wall of the Achaians, and the Achaians give ground, even so we shall return in disarray from the ships by the way we came; for many of the Trojans shall we leave behind, whom the Achaians will slay with the sword, in defence of the ships. Even so would a soothsayer interpret that in his heart had clear knowledge of omens, and whom the people obeyed."

Then Hector of the glancing helm lowered on him and said: "Polydamas, that thou speakest is no longer pleasing to me; yea, thou knowest how to conceive another counsel better than this. But if thou verily speakest thus in earnest, then the gods themselves have utterly destroyed thy wits; thou that bidst us forget the counsels of loud-thundering Zeus, that himself promised me, and confirmed with a nod of his head! But thou bidst us be obedient to birds long of wing, whereto I give no heed, nor take any care thereof, whether they fare to the right, to the dawn and to the sun, or to the left, to mist and darkness. Nay, for us, let us trust to the counsel of mighty Zeus, who is king over all mortals and immortals. One omen is best, to fight for our own country. And wherefore dost thou fear war and battle?

For if all the rest of us be slain by the ships of the Argives, yet needest thou not fear to perish, for thy heart is not warlike, nor enduring in battle. But if thou dost hold aloof from the fight, or winnest any other with thy words to turn him from war, straightway by my spear shalt thou be smitten, and lose thy life."

So spake he, and led on, and they followed with a wondrous din; and Zeus that joyeth in the thunder roused from the hills of Ida a blast of wind, which bare the dust straight against the ships; and he made weak the heart of the Achaians, but gave renown to the Trojans and to Hector. Trusting then in his omens, and their might, they strove to break the great wall of the Achaians. They dragged down the machicolations of the towers, and overthrew the battlements, and heaved up the projecting buttresses, that the Achaians set first in the earth, to be the props of the towers. These they overthrew, and hoped to break the wall of the Achaians. Nor even now did the Danaans give ground from the path, but closed up the battlements with shields of bulls' hides, and cast from them at the foemen as they went below the walls.

Now the two Aiantes went everywhere on the towers, ever urging, and arousing the courage of the Achaians. One they would accost with honeyed words, another with hard words they would rebuke, whomsoever they saw utterly giving ground from the fight: "O friends, whosoever is eminent, or whosoever is of middle station among the Argives, ay, or lower yet, for in no wise are all men equal in war, now is there work for all, and this yourselves well know. Let none turn back to the ships, for that he hath heard one threatening aloud; nay, get ye forward, and cheer another on, if perchance Olympian Zeus, the lord of lightning, will grant us to drive back the assault, and push the foe to the city."

So these twain shouted in the front, and aroused the battle of the Achaians. But as flakes of snow fall thick on a winter day, when Zeus the Counsellor hath begun to snow, showing forth these arrows of his to men, and he hath lulled the winds, and he snoweth continually, till he hath covered the crests of the high hills, and the uttermost headlands, and the grassy plains, and rich tillage of men; and the snow is scattered over the havens and shores of the grey sea, and only the wave as it rolleth in keeps off the snow, but all other things are swathed over, when the shower of Zeus cometh heavily, so from both sides their stones flew thick, some towards the Trojans, and some from the Trojans against the Achaians, while both sides were smitten, and over all the wall the din arose.

Yet never would the Trojans, then, and renowned Hector have broken the gates of the wall, and the long bar, if Zeus the Counsellor had not roused his son Sarpedon against the Argives, like a lion against the kine of crooked horn. Straightway he held forth his fair round shield, of hammered bronze, that the bronze-smith had hammered out, and within had stitched many bulls' hides with rivets of gold, all round the circle, this held he forth, and shook two spears; and sped on his way, like a mountain-nurtured lion, that long lacketh meat, and his brave spirit urgeth him to make assail on the sheep, and come even against a well-builded homestead. Nay, even if he find herdsmen thereby, guarding the sheep with hounds and spears, yet hath he no mind to be driven without an effort from the steading, but he either leapeth on a sheep, and seizeth it, or himself is smitten in the foremost place with a dart from a strong hand. So did his heart then urge on the godlike Sarpedon to rush against the wall, and break through the battlements. And instantly he spake to Glaukos, son of Hippolochos: "Glaukos, wherefore have we twain the chiefest honour,—seats of honour, and messes, and full cups in Lykia, and all men look on us as gods? And wherefore hold we a great demesne by the banks of Xanthos, a fair demesne of orchard-land, and wheat-bearing tilth? Therefore now it behoveth us to take our stand in the first rank of the Lykians, and encounter fiery battle, that certain of the well-corsleted Lykians may say, 'Verily our kings that rule Lykia be no inglorious men, they that eat fat sheep, and drink the choice wine honey-sweet: nay, but they are also of excellent might, for they war in the foremost ranks of the Lykians.' Ah, friend, if once escaped from this battle we were for ever to be ageless and immortal, neither would I fight myself in the foremost ranks, nor would I send thee into the war that giveth men renown, but now—for assuredly ten thousand fates of death do every way beset us, and these no mortal may escape nor avoid—now let us go forward, whether we shall give glory to other men, or others to us."

So spake he, and Glaukos turned not apart, nor disobeyed him, and they twain went straight forward, leading the great host of the Lykians.

Then Menestheus son of Peteos shuddered when he beheld them, for against his tower they went, bringing with them ruin; and he looked along the tower of the Achaians if perchance he might see any of the leaders, that would ward off destruction from his comrades, and he beheld the two Aiantes, insatiate of war, standing there, and Teukros hard by, newly come from his hut; but he could not cry to be heard of them, so great was the din, and the noise went up unto heaven of smitten shields and helms with horse-hair crests, and of the gates, for they had all been shut, and the Trojans stood beside them, and strove by force to break them, and enter in. Swiftly then to Aias he sent the herald Thoötes: "Go, noble Thoötes, and run, and call Aias: or rather the twain, for that will be far the best of all, since quickly here will there be wrought utter ruin. For hereby press the leaders of the Lykians, who of old are fierce in strong battle. But if beside them too war and toil arise, yet at least let the strong Telamonian Aias come alone, and let Teukros the skilled bowman follow with him."

So spake he, and the herald listened and disobeyed him

not, but started and ran by the wall of the mail-clad Achaians, and came, and stood by the Aiantes, and straightway spake: "Ye twain Aiantes, leaders of the mail-clad Achaians, the dear son of Peteos, fosterling of Zeus, biddeth you go thither, that, if it be but for a little while, ye may take your part in battle: both of you he more desireth, for that will be far the best of all, since quickly there will there be wrought utter ruin. For thereby press the leaders of the Lykians, who of old are fierce in strong battle. But if beside you too war and toil arise, yet at least let the strong Telamonian Aias come alone, and let Teukros the skilled bowman follow with him."

So spake he, nor did the strong Telamonian Aias disobey, but instantly spake winged words to the son of Oileus: "Aias, do ye twain stand here, thyself and strong Lykomedes, and urge the Danaans to war with all their might; but I go thither, to take my part in battle, and quickly will I come again, when I have well aided them."

So spake Telamonian Aias and departed, and Teukros went with him, his brother by the same father, and with them Pandion bare the bended bow of Teukros.

Now when they came to the tower of great-hearted Menestheus, passing within the wall,—and to men sore pressed they came,—the foe were climbing upon the battlements, like a dark whirlwind, even the strong leaders and counsellors of the Lykians; and they hurled together into the war and the battle-cry arose. Now first did Aias Telamon's son slay a man, Epikles great of heart, the comrade of Sarpedon. With a jagged stone he smote him, a great stone that lay uppermost within the wall, by the battlements. Not lightly could a man hold it in both hands, however strong in his youth, of such mortals as now are, but Aias lifted it, and cast it from above, and shattered the helm of fourfold crest, and all to-brake the bones of the head, and he fell like a diver from the lofty tower, and his life left his bones. And Teukros smote Glaukos, the strong son of

Hippolochos, as he came on, with an arrow from the lofty wall; even where he saw his shoulder bare he smote him, and made him cease from delight in battle. Back from the wall he leapt secretly, lest any of the Achaians should see him smitten, and speak boastfully. But sorrow came on Sarpedon when Glaukos departed, so soon as he was aware thereof, but he forgot not the joy of battle. He aimed at Alkmaon, son of Thestor, with the spear, and smote him, and drew out the spear. And Alkmaon following the spear fell prone, and his bronze-dight arms rang round him. Then Sarpedon seized with strong hands the battlement, and dragged, and it all gave way together, while above the wall was stripped bare, and made a path for many.

Then Aias and Teukros did encounter him: Teukros smote him with an arrow, on the bright baldric of his covering shield, about the breast, but Zeus warded off the Fates from his son, that he should not be overcome beside the ships' sterns. Then Aias leaped on and smote his shield, nor did the spear pass clean through, yet shook he Sarpedon in his eagerness. He gave ground a little way from the battlement, yet retreated not wholly, since his heart hoped to win renown. Then he turned and cried to the godlike Lykians: "O Lykians, wherefore thus are ye slack in impetuous valour. Hard it is for me, stalwart as I am, alone to break through, and make a path to the ships, nay, follow hard after me, for the more men, the better work."

So spake he, and they, dreading the rebuke of their king, pressed on the harder around the counsellor and king. And the Argives on the other side made strong their battalions within the wall, and mighty toil began for them. For neither could the strong Lykians burst through the wall of the Danaans, and make a way to the ships, nor could the warlike Danaans drive back the Lykians from the wall, when once they had drawn near thereto. But as two men contend about the marches of their land, with measuring rods in their hands, in a common field, when in narrow space they strive for equal shares, even so the battlements divided them, and over those they smote the round shields of ox hide about the breasts of either side, and the fluttering bucklers. And many were wounded in the flesh with the ruthless bronze, whensoever the back of any of the warriors was laid bare as he turned, ay, and many clean through the very shield. Yea, everywhere the towers and battlements swam with the blood of men shed on either side, by Trojans and Achaians. But even so they could not put the Argives to rout, but they held their ground, as an honest woman that laboureth with her hands holds the balance, and raises the weight and the wool together, balancing them, that she may win scant wages for her children; so evenly was strained their war and battle, till the moment when Zeus gave the greater renown to Hector, son of Priam, who was the first to leap within the wall of the Achaians. In a piercing voice he cried aloud to the Trojans: "Rise, ye horse-taming Trojans, break the wall of the Argives, and cast among the ships fierce blazing fire."

So spake he, spurring them on, and they all heard him with their ears, and in one mass rushed straight against the wall, and with sharp spears in their hands climbed upon the machicolations of the towers. And Hector seized and carried a stone that lay in front of the gates, thick in the hinder part, but sharp at point: a stone that not the two best men of the people, such as mortals now are, could lightly lift from the ground on to a wain, but easily he wielded it alone, for the son of crooked-counselling Kronos made it light for him. And as when a shepherd lightly beareth the fleece of a ram, taking it in one hand, and little doth it burden him, so Hector lifted the stone, and bare it straight against the doors that closely guarded the stubborn-set portals, double gates and tall, and two cross bars held them within, and one bolt fastened them. And he came, and stood hard by, and firmly planted himself, and smote them in the midst, setting his legs well apart, that his cast might lack no strength. And he brake both the hinges, and the stone fell within by reason of its weight, and the gates rang loud around, and the bars held not, and the doors burst this way and that beneath the rush of the stone. Then glorious Hector leaped in, with face like the sudden night, shining in wondrous mail that was clad about his body, and with two spears in his hands. No man that met him could have held him back when once he leaped within the gates: none but the gods, and his eyes shone with fire. Turning towards the throng he cried to the Trojans to overleap the wall, and they obeyed his summons, and speedily some overleaped the wall, and some poured into the fair-wrought gateways, and the Danaans fled in fear among the hollow ships, and a ceaseless clamour arose.

BOOK XIII

Poseidon stirreth up the Achaians to defend the ships. The valour of Idomeneus.

Now Zeus, after that he had brought the Trojans and Hector to the ships, left them to their toil and endless labour there, but otherwise again he turned his shining eyes, and looked upon the land of the Thracian horsebreeders, and the Mysians, fierce fighters hand to hand, and the proud Hippemolgoi that drink mare's milk, and the Abioi, the most righteous of men. To Troy no more at all he turned his shining eyes, for he deemed in his heart that not one of the Immortals would draw near, to help either Trojans or Danaans.

But the mighty Earth-shaker held no blind watch, who sat and marvelled on the war and strife, high on the topmost crest of wooded Samothrace, for thence all Ida was plain to see; and plain to see were the city of Priam, and the ships of the Achaians. Thither did he go from the sea and sate him down, and he had pity on the Achaians, that they were subdued to the Trojans, and strong was his anger against Zeus.

Then forthwith he went down from the rugged hill, faring with swift steps, and the high hills trembled, and the woodland, beneath the immortal footsteps of Poseidon as he moved. Three strides he made, and with the fourth he reached his goal, even Aigae, and there was his famous palace in the deeps of the mere, his glistering golden mansions builded, imperishable for ever. Thither went he, and let harness to the car his bronze-hooved horses, swift of flight, clothed with their golden manes. He girt his own golden array about his body, and seized the well-wrought lash of gold, and mounted his chariot, and forth he drove across the waves. And the sea beasts frolicked beneath him, on all sides out of the deeps, for well they knew their lord, and with gladness the sea stood asunder, and swiftly they sped, and the axle of bronze was not wetted beneath, and the bounding steeds bare him on to the ships of the Achaians.

Now there is a spacious cave in the depths of the deep mere, between Tenedos and rugged Imbros; there did Poseidon, the Shaker of the earth, stay his horses, and loosed them out of the chariot, and cast before them ambrosial food to graze withal, and golden tethers he bound about their hooves, tethers neither to be broken nor loosed, that there the horses might continually await their lord's return. And he went to the host of the Achaians.

Now the Trojans like flame or storm-wind were following in close array, with fierce intent, after Hector, son of Priam. With shouts and cries they came, and thought to take the ships of the Achaians, and to slay thereby all the bravest of the host. But Poseidon, that girdleth the world, the Shaker of the earth, was urging on the Argives, and forth he came from the deep salt sea, in form and untiring voice like unto Kalchas. First he spake to the two Aiantes, that themselves were eager for battle: "Ye Aiantes twain, ye shall save the people of the Achaians, if ye are mindful of your might, and reckless of chill fear. For verily I do not otherwhere dread the invincible hands of the Trojans, that have climbed the great wall in their multitude, nay, the well-greaved Achaians will hold them all at bay; but hereby verily do I greatly dread lest some evil befall us, even here where that furious one is leading like a flame of fire, Hector, who boasts him to be son of mighty Zeus. Nay, but here may some god put it into the hearts of you twain, to stand sturdily yourselves, and urge others to do the like; thereby might ye drive him from the fleet-faring ships, despite his eagerness, yea, even if the Olympian himself is rousing him to war."

Therewith the Shaker of the world, the girdler of the earth, struck the twain with his staff, and filled them with strong courage, and their limbs he made light, and their feet, and their hands withal. Then, even as a swift-winged hawk speeds forth to fly, poised high above a tall sheer rock, and swoops to chase some other bird across the plain, even so Poseidon sped from them, the Shaker of the world. And of the twain Oileus' son, the swift-footed Aias, was the first to know the god, and instantly he spake to Aias, son of Telamon: "Aias, since it is one of the gods who hold Olympus, that in the semblance of a seer commands us now to fight beside the ships—not Kalchas is he, the prophet and soothsayer, for easily I knew the tokens of his feet and knees as he turned away, and the gods are easy to discern—lo, then mine own heart within my breast is more eagerly set on war and battle, and my feet beneath and my hands above are lusting for the fight."

Then Aias, son of Telamon, answered him saying: "Even so, too, my hands invincible now rage about the spear-shaft, and wrath has risen within me, and both my feet are swift beneath me; yea, I am keen to meet, even in single fight, the ceaseless rage of Hector son of Priam."

So they spake to each other, rejoicing in the delight of battle, which the god put in their heart. Then the girdler of the earth stirred up the Achaians that were in the rear and were renewing their strength beside the swift ships. Their limbs were loosened by their grievous toil, yea, and their souls filled with sorrow at the sight of the Trojans, that had climbed over the great wall in their multitude. And they looked on them, and shed tears beneath their brows, thinking that never would they escape destruction. But the Shaker of the earth right easily came among them, and urged on the strong battalions of warriors. Teukros first he came and summoned, and Leïtos, and the hero

Peneleos, and Thoas, and Deïpyros, and Meriones, and Antilochos, lords of the war-cry, all these he spurred on with winged words: "Shame on you, Argives, shame, ye striplings, in your battle had I trusted for the salvation of our ships. But if you are to withdraw from grievous war, now indeed the day doth shine that shall see us conquered by the Trojans. Out on it, for verily a great marvel is this that mine eyes behold, a terrible thing that methought should never come to pass, the Trojans advancing against our ships! Of yore they were like fleeting hinds, that in the wild wood are the prey of jackals, and pards, and wolves, and wander helpless, strengthless, empty of the joy of battle. Even so the Trojans of old cared never to wait and face the wrath and the hands of the Achaians, not for a moment. But now they are fighting far from the town, by the hollow ships, all through the baseness of our leader and the remissness of the people, who, being at strife with the chief, have no heart to defend the swift-faring ships, nay, thereby they are slain. But if indeed and in truth tne hero Agamemnon, the wide-ruling son of Atreus, is the very cause of all, for that he did dishonour the swift-footed son of Peleus, not even so may we refrain in any wise from war. Nay, let us right our fault with speech, for easily righted are the hearts of the brave. No longer do ye well to refrain from impetuous might, all ye that are the best men of the host. I myself would not quarrel with one that, being a weakling, abstained from war, but with you I am heartily wroth. Ah, friends, soon shall ye make the mischief more through this remissness,—but let each man conceive shame in his heart, and indignation, for verily great is the strife that hath arisen. Lo, the mighty Hector of the loud war-cry is fighting at the ships, and the gates and the long bar he hath burst in sunder."

On this wise did the Earth-enfolder call to and spur on the Achaians. And straightway they made a stand around the two Aiantes, strong bands that Ares himself could not enter and make light of, nor Athene that marshals the host. Yea, they were the chosen best that abode the Trojans and goodly Hector, and spear on spear made close-set fence, and shield on serried shield, buckler pressed on buckler, and helm on helm, and man on man. The horse-hair crests on the bright helmet-ridges touched each other as they nodded, so close they stood each by other, and spears brandished in bold hands were interlaced; and their hearts were steadfast and lusted for battle.

Then the Trojans drave forward in close array, and Hector led them, pressing straight onwards, like a rolling rock from a cliff, that the winter-swollen water thrusteth from the crest of a hill, having broken the foundations of the stubborn rock with its wondrous flood; leaping aloft it flies, and the wood echoes under it, and unstayed it runs its course, till it reaches the level plain, and then it rolls no more for all its eagerness,—even so Hector for a while threatened lightly to win to the sea through the huts and the ships of the Achaians, slaying as he came, but when he encountered the serried battalions, he was stayed when he drew near against them. But they of the other part, the sons of the Achaians, thrust with their swords and double-pointed spears, and drave him forth from them, that he gave ground and reeled backward. Then he cried with a piercing voice, calling on the Trojans: "Trojans, and Lykians, and close-fighting Dardanians, hold your ground, for the Achaians will not long ward me off, nay, though they have arrayed themselves in fashion like a tower. Rather, methinks, they will flee back before the spear, if verily the chief of gods has set me on, the loud-thundering lord of Hera."

Therewith he spurred on the heart and spirit of each man; and Deiphobos, the son of Priam, strode among them with high thoughts, and held in front of him the circle of his shield, and lightly he stepped with his feet, advancing beneath the cover of his shield. Then Meriones aimed at him with a shining spear, and struck, and missed not, but smote the circle of the bulls'-hide shield, yet no whit did he pierce it; nay, well ere that might be, the long spear-shaft snapped in the socket. Now Deiphobos was holding off from him the bulls'-hide shield, and his heart feared the lance of wise Meriones, but that hero shrunk back among the throng of his comrades, greatly in wrath both for the loss of victory, and of his spear, that he had shivered. So he set forth to go to the huts and the ships of the Achaians, to bring a long spear, that he had left in his hut.

Meanwhile the others were fighting on, and there arose an inextinguishable cry. First Teukros, son of Telamon, slew a man, the spearman Imbrios, the son of Mentor rich in horses. In Pedaion he dwelt, before the coming of the sons of the Achaians, and he had for wife a daughter of Priam, born out of wedlock, Medesikaste; but when the curved ships of the Danaans came, he returned again to Ilios, and was pre-eminent among the Trojans, and dwelt with Priam, who honoured him like his own children. Him the son of Telamon pierced below the ear with his long lance, and plucked back the spear. Then he fell like an ash that on the crest of a far-seen hill is smitten with the axe of bronze, and brings its delicate foliage to the ground; even so he fell, and round him rang his armour bedight with bronze. Then Teukros rushed forth, most eager to strip his armour, and Hector cast at him as he came with his shining spear. But Teukros, steadily regarding him, avoided by a little the spear of bronze; so Hector struck Amphimachos, son of Kteatos, son of Aktor, in the breast with the spear, as he was returning to the battle. With a crash he fell, and his armour rang upon him.

Then Hector sped forth to tear from the head of great-hearted Amphimachos the helmet closely fitted to his temples, but Aias aimed at Hector as he came, with a shining spear, yet in no wise touched his body, for he was all clad in dread armour of bronze; but he smote the boss of his shield, and drave him back by main force, and he gave place from behind the two dead men, and the Achaians drew them out of the battle. So Stichios and goodly Menestheus, leaders of the Athenians, conveyed Amphimachos back among the host of the Achaians, but Imbrios the two Aiantes carried, with hearts full of impetuous might. And as when two lions have snatched away a goat from sharp-toothed hounds, and carry it through the deep thicket, holding the body on high above the ground in their jaws, so the two warrior Aiantes held Imbrios aloft and spoiled his arms. Then the son of Oileus cut his head from his delicate neck, in wrath for the sake of Amphimachos, and sent it rolling like a ball through the throng, and it dropped in the dust before the feet of Hector.

Then verily was Poseidon wroth at heart, when his son's son fell in the terrible fray. So he set forth to go by the huts and the ships of the Achaians, to spur on the Danaans, and sorrows he was contriving for the Trojans. Then Idomeneus, spearman renowned, met him on his way from his comrade that had but newly returned to him out of the battle, wounded on the knee with the sharp bronze. Him his comrades carried forth, and Idomeneus gave charge to the leeches, and so went on to his hut, for he still was eager to face the war. Then the mighty Shaker of the earth addressed him, in the voice of Thoas, son of Andraimon, that ruled over the Aitolians in all Pleuron, and mountainous Kalydon, and was honoured like a god by the people: "Idomeneus, thou counsellor of the Cretans, say, whither have thy threats fared, wherewith the sons of the Achaians threatened the Trojans?"

Then Idomeneus, leader of the Cretans, answered him again: "O Thoas, now is there no man to blame, that I wot of, for we all are skilled in war. Neither is there any man that spiritless fear holds aloof, nor any that gives place to cowardice, and shuns the cruel war, nay, but even thus, methinks, must it have seemed good to almighty Kronion, even that the Achaians should perish nameless here, far away from Argos. But Thoas, seeing that of old thou wert staunch, and dost spur on some other man, wheresoever thou mayst see any give ground, therefore slacken not now, but call aloud to every warrior."

Then Poseidon, the Shaker of the earth, answered him again: "Idomeneus, never may that man go forth out of Troy-land, but here may he be the sport of dogs, who this day wilfully is slack in battle. Nay, come, take thy weapons and away: herein we must play the man together, if any avail there may be, though we are no more than two. Ay, and very cowards get courage from company, but we twain know well how to battle even with the brave."

Therewith the god went back again into the strife of men, but Idomeneus, so soon as he came to his well-builded hut, did on his fair armour about his body, and grasped two spears, and set forth like the lightning that Kronion seizes in his hand and brandishes from radiant Olympus, showing forth a sign to mortal men, and far seen are the flames thereof. Even so shone the bronze about the breast of Idomeneus as he ran, and Meriones, his good squire, met him, while he was still near his hut,—he was going to bring his spear of bronze,—and mighty Idomeneus spake to him: "Meriones son of Molos, fleet of foot, dearest of my company, wherefore hast thou come hither and left the war and strife? Art thou wounded at all, and vexed by a dart's point, or dost thou come with a message for me concerning aught? Verily I myself have no desire to sit in the huts, but to fight."

Then wise Meriones answered him again, saying: "[Idomeneus, thou counsellor of the mail-clad Cretans,] I have come to fetch a spear, if perchance thou hast one left in the huts, for that which before I have shivered in casting at the shield of proud Deiphobos."

Then Idomeneus, leader of the Cretans, answered him again: "Spears, if thou wilt, thou shalt find, one, ay, and twenty, standing in the hut, against the shining side walls, spears of the Trojans whereof I have spoiled their slain. Yea, it is not my mood to stand and fight with foemen from afar, wherefore I have spears, and bossy shields, and helms, and corslets of splendid sheen."

Then wise Meriones answered him again: "Yea, and in mine own hut and my black ship are many spoils of the Trojans, but not ready to my hand. Nay, for methinks that neither am I forgetful of valour; but stand forth among the foremost to face the glorious war, whensoever ariseth the strife of battle. Any other, methinks, of the mail-clad Achaians should sooner forget my prowess, but thou art he that knoweth it."

Then Idomeneus, leader of the Cretans, answered him again: "I know what a man of valour thou art, wherefore shouldst thou tell me thereof? Nay, if now beside the ships all the best of us were being chosen for an ambush—wherein the valour of men is best discerned; there the coward, and the brave man most plainly declare themselves: for the colour of the coward changes often, and his spirit cannot abide firm within him, but now he kneels on one knee, now on the other, and rests on either foot, and his heart beats noisily in his breast, as he thinks of doom, and his teeth chatter loudly. But the colour of the brave man does not change, nor is he greatly afraid, from the moment that he enters the ambush of heroes, but his prayer is to mingle instantly in woful war. Were we being chosen for such ambush, I say, not even then would any man reckon lightly of thy courage and thy strength. Nay, and even if thou wert stricken in battle from afar, or smitten in close fight, the dart would not strike thee in the hinder part of the neck, nor in the back, but would encounter thy breast or belly, as thou dost press on, towards the gathering of the foremost fighters. But come, no more let us talk thus, like children, loitering here, lest any man be vehemently wroth, but go thou to the hut, and bring the strong spear."

Thus he spake, and Meriones, the peer of swift Ares, quickly bare the spear of bronze from the hut, and went after Idomeneus, with high thoughts of battle. And even as Ares, the bane of men, goes forth into the war, and with him follows his dear son Panic, stark and fearless, that terrifies even the hardy warrior; and these twain leave Thrace, and harness them for fight with the Ephyri, or the great-hearted Phlegyans, yet hearken not to both peoples, but give honour to one only; like these gods did Meriones and Idomeneus, leaders of men, set forth into the fight, harnessed in gleaming bronze. And Meriones spake first to Idomeneus saying: "Child of Deukalion, whither art thou eager to enter into the throng: on the right of all the host, or in the centre, or on the left? Ay, and no other where, methinks, are the flowing-haired Achaians so like to fail in fight."

Then Idomeneus, the leader of the Cretans, answered him again: "In the centre of the ships there are others to bear the brunt, the two Aiantes, and Teukros, the best bowman of the Achaians, ay, and a good man in close fight; these will give Hector Priam's son toil enough, howsoever keen he be for battle; yea, though he be exceeding stalwart. Hard will he find it, with all his lust for war, to overcome their strength and their hands invincible, and to fire the ships, unless Kronion himself send down on the swift ships a burning brand. But not to a man would he yield, the great Telamonian Aias, to a man that is mortal and eateth Demeter's grain, and may be cloven with the sword of bronze, and with hurling of great stones. Nay, not even to Achilles the breaker of the ranks of men would he give way, not in close fight; but for speed of foot none may in any wise strive with Achilles. But guide us twain, as thou sayest, to the left hand of the host, that speedily we may learn whether we are to win glory from others, or other men from us."

So he spake, and Meriones, the peer of swift Ares, led the way, till they came to the host, in that place whither he bade him go.

And when the Trojans saw Idomeneus, strong as flame, and his squire with him, and their glorious armour, they all shouted and made for him through the press. Then their mellay began, by the sterns of the ships. And as the gusts speed on, when shrill winds blow, on a day when dust lies thickest on the roads, and the winds raise together a great cloud of dust, even so their battle clashed together, and all were fain of heart to slay each other in the press with the keen bronze. And the battle, the bane of men, bristled with the long spears, the piercing spears they grasped, and the glitter of bronze from gleaming helmets dazzled the eyes, and the sheen of new-burnished corslets, and shining shields, as the men thronged all together. Right hardy of heart would he have been that joyed and sorrowed not at the sight of this labour of battle.

Thus the two mighty sons of Kronos, with contending will, were contriving sorrow and anguish for the heroes. Zeus desired victory for the Trojans and Hector, giving glory to swift-footed Achilles; yet he did not wish the Achaian host to perish utterly before Ilios, but only to give renown to Thetis and her strong-hearted son. But Poseidon went among the Argives and stirred them to war, stealing secretly forth from the grey salt sea: for he was sore vexed that they were overcome by the Trojans, and was greatly in wrath against Zeus. Verily both were of the same lineage and the same place of birth, but Zeus was the elder and the wiser. Therefore also Poseidon avoided to give open aid, but secretly ever he spurred them on, throughout the host, in the likeness of a man. These twain had strained the ends of the cords of strong strife and equal war, and had stretched them over both Trojans and Achaians, a knot that none might break nor undo, for the loosening of the knees of many.

Even then Idomeneus, though his hair was flecked with grey, called on the Danaans, and leaping among the Trojans, roused their terror. For he slew Othryoneus of Kabesos, a sojourner there, who but lately had followed after the rumour of war, and asked in marriage the fairest of the daughters of Priam, Kassandra, without gifts of wooing, but with promise of a mighty deed, namely that he would drive perforce out of Troy-land the sons of the Achaians. To him the old man Priam promised and appointed that he would give her, so he fought trusting in his promises. And Idomeneus aimed at him with a bright spear, and cast and smote him as he came proudly striding on, and the corslet of bronze that he wore availed not, but the lance stuck in the midst of his belly. And he fell with a crash, and Idomeneus boasted over him, and lifted up his voice, saying: "Othryoneus, verily I praise thee above all mortal men, if indeed thou shalt accomplish all that thou hast promised to Priam, son of Dardanos, that promised thee again his own daughter. Yea, and we likewise would promise as much to thee, and fulfil it, and would give thee the fairest daughter of the son of Atreus, and bring her from Argos, and wed her to thee, if only thou wilt aid us to take the fair-set citadel of Ilios. Nay, follow us that we may make a covenant of marriage by the seafaring ships, for we are no hard exacters of gifts of wooing."

Therewith the hero Idomeneus dragged him by the foot across the fierce mellay. But Asios came to his aid, on foot before his horses that the charioteer guided so that still their breath touched the shoulders of Asios. And the desire of his heart was to cast at Idomeneus, who was beforehand with him, and smote him with the spear in the throat, below the chin, and drove the point straight through. And he fell as an oak falls, or a poplar, or tall pine-tree, that craftsmen have felled on the hills with new whetted axes, to be a ship's timber, even so he lay stretched out before the horses and the chariot, groaning, and clutching the bloody dust. And the charioteer was amazed, and kept not his wits, as of old, and dared not turn his horses and avoid out of the hands of foemen; and Antilochos the steadfast in war smote him, and pierced the middle of his body with a spear. Nothing availed the corslet of bronze he was wont to wear, but he planted the spear fast in the midst of his belly. Therewith he fell gasping from the well-wrought chariot, and Antilochos, the son of great-hearted Nestor, drave the horses out from the Trojans, among the well-greaved Achaians. Then Deiphobos, in sorrow for Asios, drew very nigh Idomeneus, and cast at him with his shining spear. But Idomeneus steadily watching him, avoided the spear of bronze, being hidden beneath the circle of his shield, the shield covered about with ox-hide and gleaming bronze, that he always bore, fitted with two arm-rods: under this he crouched together, and the spear of bronze flew over. And his shield rang sharply, as the spear grazed thereon. Yet it flew not vainly from the heavy hand of Deiphobos, but smote Hypsenor, son of Hippasos, the shepherd of the hosts, in the liver, beneath the midriff, and instantly unstrung his knees. And Deiphobos boasted over him terribly, crying aloud: "Ah, verily, not unavenged lies Asios, nay, methinks, that even on his road to Hades, strong Warden of the gate, he will rejoice at heart, since, lo, I have sent him escort for the way!"

So spake he, but grief came on the Argives by reason of his boast, and stirred above all the soul of the wise-hearted Antilochos, yet, despite his sorrow, he was not heedless of his dear comrade, but ran and stood over him, and covered him with his buckler. Then two trusty companions, Mekisteus, son of Echios, and goodly Alastor, stooped down and lifted him, and with heavy groaning bare him to the hollow ships.

And Idomeneus relaxed not his mighty force, but ever was striving, either to cover some one of the Trojans with black night, or himself to fall in warding off death from the Achaians. There the dear son of Aisyetes, fosterling of Zeus, even the hero Alkathoos, was slain, who was son-in-law of Anchises, and had married the eldest of his daughters, Hippodameia, whom her father and her lady mother dearly loved in the halls, for she excelled all the maidens of her age in beauty, and skill, and in wisdom, wherefore the best man in wide Troy took her to wife. This Alkathoos did Poseidon subdue to Idomeneus, throwing a spell over his shining eyes, and snaring his glorious limbs; so that he might neither flee backwards, nor avoid the stroke, but stood steady as a pillar, or a tree with lofty crown of leaves, when the hero Idomeneus smote him in the midst of the breast with the spear, and rent the coat of bronze about him, that aforetime warded death from his body, but now rang harsh as it was rent by the spear. And he fell with a crash, and the lance fixed in his heart, that, still beating, shook the butt-end of the spear. Then at length mighty Ares spent its fury there; but Idomeneus boasted terribly, and cried aloud: "Deiphobos, are we to deem it fair acquittal that we have slain three men for one, since thou boastest thus? Nay, sir, but stand thou up also thyself against me, that thou mayst know what manner of son of Zeus am I that have come hither! For Zeus first begat Minos, the warden of Crete, and Minos got him a son, the noble Deukalion, and Deukalion begat me, a prince over many men in wide Crete, and now have the ships brought me hither, a bane to thee and thy father, and all the Trojans."

Thus he spake, but the thoughts of Deiphobos were divided, whether he should retreat, and call to his aid some one of the great-hearted Trojans, or should try the adventure alone. And on this wise to his mind it seemed the better, to go after Aineias, whom he found standing the last in the press, for Aineias was ever wroth against goodly Priam, for that Priam gave him no honour, despite his valour among men. So Deiphobos stood by him, and spake winged words to him: "Aineias, thou counsellor of the Trojans, now verily there is great need that thou shouldst succour thy sister's husband, if any care for kin doth touch thee. Nay follow, let us succour Alkathoos, thy sister's husband, who of old did cherish thee in his hall, while thou wert but a little one, and now, lo, spear-famed Idomeneus hath stripped him of his arms!"

So he spake, and roused the spirit in the breast of Aineias, who went to seek Idomeneus, with high thoughts of war. But fear took not hold upon Idomeneus, as though he had been some tender boy, but he stood at bay, like a boar on the hills that trusteth to his strength, and abides the great assailing throng of men in a lonely place, and he bristles up his back, and his eyes shine with fire, while he whets his tusks, and is right eager to keep at bay both men and hounds. Even so stood spear-famed Idomeneus at bay against Aineias, that came to the rescue, and gave ground no whit, but called on his comrades, glancing to Askalaphos, and Aphareus, and Deipyros, and Meriones, and Antilochos, all masters of the war-cry; them he spurred up to battle, and spake winged words: "Hither, friends, and rescue me, all alone as I am, and terribly I dread the onslaught of swift-footed Aineias, that is assailing me; for he is right strong to destroy men in battle, and he hath the flower of youth, the greatest avail that may be. Yea, if he and I were of like age, and in this spirit whereof now we are, speedily should he or I achieve high victory."

So he spake, and they all, being of one spirit in their hearts, stood hard by each other, with buckler laid on shoulder. But Aineias, on the other side, cried to his comrades, glancing to Deiphobos, and Paris, and noble Agenor, that with him were leaders of the Trojans; and then the hosts followed them, as sheep follow their leader to the water from the pasture, and the shepherd is glad at heart; even so the heart of Aineias was glad in his breast, when he saw the hosts of the people following to aid him.

Then they rushed in close fight around Alkathoos with their long spears, and round their breasts the bronze rang terribly, as they aimed at each other in the press, while two men of war beyond the rest, Aineias and Idomeneus, the peers of Ares, were each striving to hew the flesh of the other with the pitiless bronze. Now Aineias first cast at Idomeneus, who steadily watching him avoided the spear of bronze, and the point of Aineias went quivering in the earth, since vainly it had flown from his stalwart hand. But Idomeneus smote Oinomaos in the midst of the belly, and brake the plate of his corslet, and the bronze let forth the bowels through the corslet, and he fell in the dust and clutched the earth in his palms. And Idomeneus drew forth the far-shadowing spear from the dead, but could not avail to strip the rest of the fair armour from his shoulders, for the darts pressed hard on him. Nay, and his feet no longer served him firmly in a charge, nor could he rush after his own spear, nor avoid the foe. Wherefore in close fight he still held off the pitiless day of destiny, but in retreat his feet no longer bore him swiftly from the battle. And as he was slowly departing, Deiphobos aimed at him with his shining spear, for, verily he ever cherished a steadfast hatred against Idomeneus. But this time, too, he missed him, and smote Askalaphos, the son of Enyalios, with his dart, and the strong spear passed through his shoulder, and he fell in the dust, and clutched the earth in his outstretched hand. But loud-voiced awful Ares was not yet aware at all that his son had fallen in strong battle, but he was reclining on the peak of Olympus, beneath the golden clouds, being held there by the design of Zeus, where also were the other deathless gods, restrained from the war.

Now the people rushed in close fight around Askalaphos, and Deiphobos tore from Askalaphos his shining helm, but

Meriones, the peer of swift Ares, leaped forward and smote the arm of Deiphobos with his spear, and from his hand the vizored casque fell clanging to the ground. And Meriones sprang forth instantly, like a vulture, and drew the strong spear from the shoulder of Deiphobos, and fell back among the throng of his comrades. But the own brother of Deiphobos, Polites, stretched his hands round his waist, and led him forth from the evil din of war, even till he came to the swift horses, that waited for him behind the battle and the fight, with their charioteer, and well-dight chariot. These bore him heavily groaning to the city, worn with his hurt, and the blood ran down from his newly wounded arm.

But the rest still were fighting, and the war-cry rose unquenched. There Aineias rushed on Aphareus, son of Kaletor, and struck his throat, that chanced to be turned to him, with the keen spear, and his head dropped down and his shield and helm fell with him, and death that slays the spirit overwhelmed him. And Antilochos watched Thoon as he turned the other way, and leaped on him, and wounded him, severing all the vein that runs up the back till it reaches the neck; this he severed clean, and Thoon fell on his back in the dust, stretching out both his hands to his comrades dear. Then Antilochos rushed on, and stripped the armour from his shoulders, glancing around while the Trojans gathered from here and there, and smote his wide shining shield, yet did not avail to graze, behind the shield, the delicate flesh of Antilochos with the pitiless bronze. For verily Poseidon, the Shaker of the earth, did guard on every side the son of Nestor, even in the midst of the javelins. And never did Antilochos get free of the foe, but turned him about among them, nor ever was his spear at rest, but always brandished and shaken, and the aim of his heart was to smite a foeman from afar, or to set on him at close quarters. But as he was aiming through the crowd, he escaped not the ken of Adamas, son of Asios, who smote the midst of his shield with the sharp bronze, setting on nigh at hand; but Poseidon of the dark locks made his shaft of no avail, grudging him the life of Antilochos. And part of the spear abode there, like a burned stake, in the shield of Antilochos, and half way lay on the earth, and back retreated Adamas to the ranks of his comrades, avoiding Fate. But Meriones following after him as he departed, smote him with a spear between the privy parts and the navel, where a wound is most baneful to wretched mortals. Even there he fixed the spear in him and he fell, and writhed about the spear, even as a bull that herdsmen on the hills drag along perforce when they have bound him with withes, so he when he was smitten writhed for a moment, not for long, till the hero Meriones came near, and drew the spear out of his body. And darkness covered his eyes.

And Helenos in close fight smote Deipyros on the temple, with a great Thracian sword, and tore away the helm, and the helm, being dislodged, fell on the ground, and one of the Achaians in the fight picked it up as it rolled between his feet. But dark night covered the eyes of Deipyros.

Then grief took hold of the son of Atreus, Menelaos of the loud war-cry, and he went with a threat against the warrior Helenos, the prince, shaking his sharp spear, while the other drew the centre-piece of his bow. And both at once were making ready to let fly, one with his sharp spear, the other with the arrow from the string. Then the son of Priam smote Menelaos on the breast with his arrow, on the plate of the corslet, and off flew the bitter arrow. Even as from a broad shovel in a great threshing floor, fly the black-skinned beans and pulse, before the whistling wind, and the stress of the winnower's shovel, even so from the corslet of renowned Menelaos flew glancing far aside the bitter arrow. But the son of Atreus, Menelaos of the loud war-cry, smote the hand of Helenos wherein he held the polished bow, and into the bow, clean through the hand, was driven the spear of bronze. Back he withdrew to the ranks of his comrades, avoiding Fate, with his hand hanging down at his side, for the ashen spear dragged after him. And the great-hearted Agenor drew the spear from his hand, and himself bound up the hand with a band of twisted sheep's-wool, a sling that a squire carried for him, the shepherd of the host.

Then Peisandros made straight for renowned Menelaos, but an evil Fate was leading him to the end of Death; by thee, Menelaos, to be overcome in the dread strife of battle. Now when the twain had come nigh in onset upon each other, the son of Atreus missed, and his spear was turned aside, but Peisandros smote the shield of renowned Menelaos, yet availed not to drive the bronze clean through, for the wide shield caught it, and the spear brake in the socket, yet Peisandros rejoiced in his heart, and hoped for the victory. But the son of Atreus drew his silver-studded sword, and leaped upon Peisandros. And Peisandros, under his shield, clutched his goodly axe of fine bronze, with long and polished haft of olive-wood, and the twain set upon each other. Then Peisandros smote the crest of the helmet shaded with horse hair, close below the very plume, but Menelaos struck the other, as he came forward, on the brow, above the base of the nose, and the bones cracked, and the eyes, all bloody, fell at his feet in the dust. Then he bowed and fell, and Menelaos set his foot on his breast, and stripped him of his arms, and triumphed, saying: "Even thus then surely, ye will leave the ships of the Danaans of the swift steeds, ye Trojans overweening, insatiate of the dread din of war. Yea, and ye shall not lack all other reproof and shame, wherewith ye made me ashamed, ye hounds of evil, having no fear in your hearts of the strong wrath of loud-thundering Zeus, the god of guest and host, who one day will destroy your steep citadel. O ye that wantonly carried away my wedded wife and many of my possessions, when ye were entertained by her, now again ye are fain to throw ruinous fire on the seafaring ships, and to slay the Achaian heroes. Nay, but ye will yet refrain you from battle, for as eager as ye be. O father Zeus, verily they say that thou dost excel in wisdom all others, both gods and men, and all these things are from thee. How wondrously art thou favouring men of violence, even the Trojans, whose might is ever iniquitous, nor can they have their fill of the din of equal war. Of all things there is satiety, yea, even of love and sleep, and of sweet song, and dance delectable, whereof a man would sooner have his fill than of war, but the Trojans are insatiable of battle."

Thus noble Menelaos spake, and stripped the bloody arms from the body, and gave them to his comrades, and instantly himself went forth again, and mingled in the forefront of the battle. Then Harpalion, the son of king Pylaimenes, leaped out against him, Harpalion that followed his dear father to Troy, to the war, nor ever came again to his own country. He then smote the middle of the shield of Atreus' son with his spear, in close fight, yet availed not to drive the bronze clean through, but fell back into the host of his comrades, avoiding Fate, glancing round every way, lest one should wound his flesh with the bronze. But Meriones shot at him as he retreated with a bronze-shod arrow, and smote him in the right buttock, and the arrow went right through the bladder and came out under the bone. And sitting down, even there, in the arms of his dear comrades, he breathed away his soul, lying stretched like a worm on the earth, and out flowed the black blood, and wetted the ground. And the Paphlagonians great of heart, tended him busily, and set him in a chariot, and drove him to sacred Ilios sorrowing, and with them went his father, shedding tears, and there was no atonement for his dead son.

Now Paris was very wroth at heart by reason of his slaying, for he had been his host among the many Paphlagonians, wherefore, in wrath for his sake, he let fly a bronze-shod arrow. Now there was a certain Euchenor, the son of Polyidos the seer, a rich man and a good, whose dwelling was in Corinth. And well he knew his own ruinous fate, when he went on ship-board, for often would the old man, the good Polyidos, tell him, that he must either perish of a sore disease in his halls, or go with the ships of the Achaians, and be overcome by the Trojans. Wherefore he avoided at once the heavy war-fine of the Achaians, and the hateful disease, that so he might not know any anguish. This man did Paris smite beneath the jaw and under the ear, and swiftly his spirit departed from his limbs, and, lo, dread darkness overshadowed him.

So they fought like flaming fire, but Hector, beloved of Zeus, had not heard nor knew at all that, on the left of the ships, his host was being subdued by the Argives, and soon would the Achaians have won renown, so mighty was the Holder and Shaker of the earth that urged on the Argives; yea, and himself mightily defended them. But Hector kept where at first he had leaped within the walls and the gate, and broken the serried ranks of shield-bearing Danaans, even where were the ships of Aias and Protesilaos, drawn up on the beach of the hoary sea, while above the wall was builded lowest, and thereby chiefly the heroes and their horses were raging in battle.

There the Boiotians, and Ionians with trailing tunics, and Lokrians and Phthians and illustrious Epeians scarcely availed to stay his onslaught on the ships, nor yet could they drive back from them noble Hector, like a flame of fire. And there were the picked men of the Athenians; among them Menestheus son of Peteos was the leader; and there followed with him Pheidas and Stichios, and brave Bias, while the Epeians were led by Meges, son of Phyleus, and Amphion and Drakios, and in front of the Phthians were Medon, and Podarkes resolute in war. Now the one, Medon, was the bastard son of noble Oileus, and brother of Aias, and he dwelt in Phylake, far from his own country, for that he had slain a man, the brother of his stepmother Eriopis, wife of Oileus. But the other, Podarkes, was the son of Iphiklos son of Phylakos, and they in their armour, in the van of the great-hearted Phthians, were defending the ships, and fighting among the Boiotians.

Now never at all did Aias, the swift son of Oileus, depart from the side of Aias, son of Telamon, nay, not for an instant, but even as in fallow land two wine-dark oxen with equal heart strain at the shapen plough, and round the roots of their horns springeth up abundant sweat, and nought sunders them but the polished yoke, as they labour through the furrow, till the end of the furrow brings them up, so stood the two Aiantes close by each other. Now verily did many and noble hosts of his comrades follow with the son of Telamon, and bore his shield when labour and sweat came upon his limbs. But the Lokrians followed not with the high-hearted son of Oileus, for their hearts were not steadfast in close brunt of battle, seeing that they had no helmets of bronze, shadowy with horse-hair plumes, nor round shields, nor ashen spears, but trusting in bows and well-twisted slings of sheep's wool, they followed with him to Ilios. Therewith, in the war, they shot thick and fast, and brake the ranks of the Trojans. So the one party in front, with their well-dight arms contended with the Trojans, and with Hector arrayed in bronze, while the others from behind kept shooting from their ambush, and the Trojans lost all memory of the joy of battle, for the arrows confounded them.

There then right ruefully from the ships and the huts would the Trojans have withdrawn to windy Ilios, had not Polydamas come near valiant Hector and said: "Hector, thou art hard to be persuaded by them that would counsel thee; for that god has given thee excellence in the works of war, therefore in council also thou art fain to excel other men in knowledge. But in no wise wilt thou be able to take everything on thyself. For to one man has god given for his portion the works of war, [to another the dance, to another the lute and song,] but in the heart of yet another hath far-seeing Zeus placed an excellent understanding, whereof many men get gain, yea he saveth many an one, and himself best knoweth it. But, lo, I will speak even as it seemeth best to me. Behold all about thee the circle of war is blazing, but the great-hearted Trojans, now that they have got down the wall, are some with their arms standing aloof and some are fighting, few men against a host, being scattered among the ships. Nay, withdraw thee, and call hither all the best of the warriors. Thereafter shall we take all counsel carefully, whether we should fall on the ships of many benches, if indeed god willeth to give us victory, or after counsel held, should return unharmed from the ships. For verily I fear lest the Achaians repay their debt of yesterday, since by the ships there tarrieth a man insatiate of war, and never, methinks, will he wholly stand aloof from battle."

So spake Polydamas, and his safe counsel pleased Hector well, who [straightway sprang to earth from the chariot with his arms, and] spake to him winged words and said: "Polydamas, do thou stay here all the best of the host, but I will go thither to face the war, and swiftly will return again, when I have straitly laid on them my commands."

So he spake, and set forth, in semblance like a snowy mountain, and shouting aloud he flew through the Trojans and allies. And they all sped to Polydamas, the kindly son of Panthoos, when they heard the voice of Hector. But he went seeking Deiphobos, and the strong prince Helenos, and Adamas son of Asios, and Asios son of Hyrtakos, among the warriors in the foremost line, if anywhere he might find them. But them he found not at all unharmed, nor free of bane, but, lo, some among the sterns of the ships of the Achaians lay lifeless, slain by the hands of the Argives, and some were within the wall wounded by thrust or cast. But one he readily found, on the left of the dolorous battle, goodly Alexandros, the lord of fair-tressed Helen, heartening his comrades and speeding them to war. And he drew near to him, and addressed him with words of shame:

"Thou evil Paris, fairest of face, thou that lustest for women, thou seducer, where, prithee, are Deiphobos, and the strong prince Helenos, and Adamas son of Asios, and Asios son of Hyrtakos, and where is Othryoneus? Now hath all high Ilios perished utterly. Now, too, thou seest, is sheer destruction sure."

Then godlike Alexandros answered him again saying: "Hector, since thy mind is to blame one that is blameless, some other day might I rather withdraw me from the war, since my mother bare not even me wholly a coward. For from the time that thou didst gather the battle of thy comrades about the ships, from that hour do we abide here, and war with the Danaans ceaselessly; and our comrades concerning whom thou inquirest are slain. Only Deiphobos and the strong prince Helenos have both withdrawn, both of them being wounded in the hand with long spears, for Kronion kept death away from them. But now lead on, wheresoever thy heart and spirit bid thee, and we will follow with thee eagerly, nor methinks shall we lack for valour, as far as we have strength; but beyond his strength may no man fight, howsoever eager he be."

So spake the hero, and persuaded his brother's heart, and they went forth where the war and din were thickest, round Kebriones, and noble Polydamas, and Phalkes, and Orthaios, and godlike Polyphetes, and Palmys, and Askanios, and Morys, son of Hippotion, who had come in their turn, out of deep-soiled Askanie, on the morn before, and now Zeus urged them to fight. And these set forth like the blast of violent winds, that rushes earthward beneath the thunder of father Zeus, and with marvellous din doth mingle with the salt sea, and therein are many swelling waves of the loud roaring sea, arched over and white with foam, some vanward, others in the rear; even so the Trojans arrayed in van and rear and shining with bronze, followed after their leaders. And Hector son of Priam was leading them, the peer of Ares, the bane of men. In front he held the circle of his shield, thick with hides, and plates of beaten bronze, and on his temples swayed his shining helm. And everywhere he went in advance and made trial of the ranks, if perchance they would yield to him as he charged under cover of his shield. But he could not confound the heart within the breast of the Achaians. And Aias, stalking with long strides, challenged him first: "Sir, draw nigh, wherefore dost thou vainly try to dismay the Argives? We are in no wise ignorant of war, but by the cruel scourge of Zeus are we Achaians vanquished. Surely now thy heart hopes utterly to spoil the ships, but we too have hands presently to hold our own. Verily your peopled city will long ere that beneath our hands be taken and sacked. But for thee, I tell thee that the time is at hand, when thou shalt pray in thy flight to father Zeus, and the other immortal gods, that thy fair-maned steeds may be fleeter than falcons: thy steeds that are to bear thee to the city, as they storm in dust across the plain."

And even as he spake, a bird flew forth on the right hand, an eagle of lofty flight, and the host of the Achaians shouted thereat, encouraged by the omen, but renowned Hector answered: "Aias, thou blundering boaster, what sayest thou! Would that indeed I were for ever as surely the son of aegis-bearing Zeus, and that my mother were lady Hera, and that I were held in such honour as Apollo and Athene, as verily this day is to bring utter evil on all the Argives! And thou among them shalt be slain, if thou hast the heart to await my long spear, which shall rend thy lily skin, and thou shalt glut with thy fat and flesh the birds and dogs of the Trojans, falling among the ships of the Achaians."

So he spake and led the way, and they followed with wondrous din, and the whole host shouted behind. And the Argives on the other side answered with a shout, and forgot not their valiance, but abode the onslaught of the bravest of the Trojans. And the cry of the two hosts went up through the higher air, to the splendour of Zeus.

BOOK XIV

How Sleep and Hera beguiled Zeus to slumber on the heights of Ida, and Poseidon spurred on the Achaians to resist Hector, and how Hector was wounded.

YET the cry of battle escaped not Nestor, albeit at his wine, but he spake winged words to the son of Asklepios: "Bethink thee, noble Machaon, what had best be done; lo, louder waxes the cry of the strong warriors by the ships. Nay, now sit where thou art, and drink the bright wine, till Hekamede of the fair tresses shall heat warm water for the bath, and wash away the clotted blood, but I will speedily go forth and come to a place of outlook."

Therewith he took the well-wrought shield of his son, horse-taming Thrasymedes, which was lying in the hut, all glistering with bronze, for the son had the shield of his father. And he seized a strong spear, with a point of keen bronze, and stood outside the hut, and straightway beheld a deed of shame, the Achaians fleeing in rout, and the high-hearted Trojans driving them, and the wall of the Achaians was overthrown. And as when the great sea is troubled with a dumb wave, and dimly bodes the sudden paths of the shrill winds, but is still unmoved nor yet rolled forward or to either side, until some steady gale comes down from Zeus, even so the old man pondered,—his mind divided this way and that,—whether he should fare into the press of the Danaans of the swift steeds, or go after Agamemnon, son of Atreus, shepherd of the host. And thus as he pondered, it seemed to him the better counsel to go to the son of Atreus. Meanwhile they were warring and slaying each other, and the stout bronze rang about their bodies as they were thrust with swords and double-pointed spears.

Now the kings, the fosterlings of Zeus, encountered Nestor, as they went up from the ships, even they that were wounded with the bronze, Tydeus' son, and Odysseus, and Agamemnon, son of Atreus. For far apart from the battle were their ships drawn up, on the shore of the grey sea, for these were the first they had drawn up to the plain, but had builded the wall in front of the hindmost. For in no wise might the beach, for as wide as it was, hold all the ships, and the host was straitened. Wherefore they drew up the ships row within row, and filled up the wide mouth of all the shore that the headlands held between them. Therefore the kings were going together, leaning on their spears, to look on the war and fray, and the heart of each was sore within his breast. And the old man met them, even Nestor, and caused the spirit to fail within the breasts of the Achaians.

And mighty Agamemnon spake and accosted him: "O Nestor, son of Neleus, great glory of the Achaians, wherefore dost thou come hither and hast deserted the war, the bane of men? Lo, I fear the accomplishment of the word that dread Hector spake, and the threat wherewith he threatened us, speaking in the assembly of the Trojans, namely, that never would he return to Ilios from the ships, till he had burned the ships with fire, and slain the men. Even so he spake, and, lo, now all these things are being fulfilled. Alas, surely even the other well-greaved Achaians store wrath against me in their hearts, like Achilles, and have no desire to fight by the rearmost ships."

Then Nestor of Gerenia the knight answered him saying: "Verily these things are now at hand, and being accomplished, nor otherwise could Zeus himself contrive them, he that thundereth on high. For, lo, the wall is overthrown, wherein we trusted that it should be an unbroken bulwark of the ships and of our own bodies. And these men by the swift ships have endless battle without sparing, and no more couldst thou tell, howsoever closely thou mightst spy, from what side the Achaians are driven in rout, so confusedly are they slain, and the cry of battle goeth up to heaven. But let us take counsel, how these things may best be done, if wit may do aught: but into the war I counsel not that we should go down, for in no wise may a wounded man do battle."

Then Agamemnon king of men answered him again: "Nestor, for that they are warring by the rearmost ships, and the well-builded wall hath availed not, nor the trench, whereat the Achaians endured so much labour, hoping in their hearts that it should be the unbroken bulwark of the ships, and of their own bodies—such it seemeth must be the will of Zeus supreme, [that the Achaians should perish here nameless far from Argos]. For I knew it when he was forward to aid the Danaans, and now I know that he is giving to the Trojans glory like that of the blessed gods, and hath bound our hands and our strength. But come, as I declare, let us all obey. Let us drag down the ships that are drawn up in the first line near to the sea, and speed them all forth to the salt sea divine, and moor them far out with stones, till the divine night comes, if even at night the Trojans will refrain from war, and then might we drag down all the ships. For there is no shame in fleeing from ruin, yea, even in the night. Better doth he fare who flees from trouble, than he that is overtaken."

Then, looking on him sternly, spake Odysseus of many counsels: "Atreus' son, what word hath passed the door of thy lips? Man of mischief, sure thou shouldst lead some other inglorious army, not be king among us, to whom Zeus hath given it, from youth even unto age, to wind the skein of grievous wars, till every man of us perish. Art thou indeed so eager to leave the wide-wayed city of the Trojans, the city for which we endure with sorrow so many evils? Be silent, lest some other of the Achaians hear this word, that no man should so much as suffer to pass through his mouth, none that understandeth in his heart how to speak fit counsel, none that is a sceptred king, and hath hosts obeying him so many as the Argives over whom thou reignest. And now I wholly scorn thy thoughts, such a word as thou hast uttered, thou that, in the midst of war and battle, dost bid us draw down the well-timbered ships to the sea, that even more than ever the Trojans may possess their desire, albeit they win the mastery even now, and sheer destruction fall upon us. For the Achaians will not make good the war, when the ships are drawn down to the salt sea, but will look round about to flee, and withdraw from battle. There will thy counsel work a mischief, O marshal of the host!"

Then the king of men, Agamemnon, answered him: "Odysseus, right sharply hast thou touched my heart with thy stern reproof: nay, I do not bid the sons of the Achaians to drag, against their will, the well-timbered ships to the salt sea. Now perchance there may be one who will utter a wiser counsel than this of mine,—a young man or an old,—welcome would it be to me."

Then Diomedes of the loud war-cry spake also among them: "The man is near,—not long shall we seek him, if ye be willing to be persuaded of me, and each of you be not resentful at all, because in years I am the youngest among you. Nay, but I too boast me to come by lineage of a noble sire, Tydeus, whom in Thebes the piled-up earth doth cover. For Portheus had three well-born children, and they dwelt in Pleuron, and steep Kalydon, even Agrios and Melas, and the third was Oineus the knight, the father of my father, and in valour he excelled the others. And there he abode, but my father dwelt at Argos, whither he had wandered, for so Zeus and the other gods willed that it should be. And he wedded one of the daughters of Adrastos, and dwelt in a house full of livelihood, and had wheat-bearing fields enow, and many orchards of trees apart, and many sheep were his, and in skill with the spear he excelled all the

Achaians: these things ye must have heard, if I speak sooth. Therefore ye could not say that I am weak and a coward by lineage, and so dishonour my spoken counsel, that well I may speak. Let us go down to the battle, wounded as we are, since we needs must; and then might we hold ourselves aloof from the battle, beyond the range of darts, lest any take wound upon wound; but the others will we spur on, even them that aforetime gave place to their passion, and stand apart, and fight not."

So he spake, and they all heard him readily, and obeyed him. And they set forth, led by Agamemnon the king of men.

Now the renowned Earth-shaker held no vain watch, but went with them in the guise of an ancient man, and he seized the right hand of Agamemnon, Atreus' son, and uttering winged words he spake to him, saying: "Atreides, now methinks the ruinous heart of Achilles rejoices in his breast, as he beholds the slaughter and flight of the Achaians, since he hath no wisdom, not a grain. Nay, even so may he perish likewise, and god mar him. But with thee the blessed gods are not utterly wroth, nay, even yet methinks the leaders and rulers of the Trojans will cover the wide plain with dust, and thyself shalt see them fleeing to the city from the ships and the huts."

So spake he, and shouted mightily, as he sped over the plain. And loud as nine thousand men, or ten thousand cry in battle, when they join the strife of war, so mighty was the cry that the strong Shaker of the earth sent forth from his breast, and great strength he put into the heart of each of the Achaians, to strive and war unceasingly.

Now Hera of the golden throne stood on the peak of Olympus, and saw with her eyes, and anon knew him that was her brother and her lord's going to and fro through the glorious fight, and she rejoiced in her heart. And she beheld Zeus sitting on the topmost crest of many-fountained Ida, and to her heart he was hateful. Then she took thought, the ox-eyed lady Hera, how she might beguile the mind of aegis-bearing Zeus. And this seemed to her in her heart to be the best counsel, namely to fare to Ida, when she had well adorned herself, if perchance he would desire to sleep beside her and embrace her body in love, and a sweet sleep and a kindly she could pour on his eyelids and his crafty wits. And she set forth to her bower, that her dear son Hephaistos had fashioned, and therein had made fast strong doors on the pillars, with a secret bolt, that no other god might open. There did she enter in and closed the shining doors. With ambrosia first did she cleanse every stain from her winsome body, and anointed her with olive oil, ambrosial, soft, and of a sweet savour; if it were but shaken in the bronze-floored mansion of Zeus, the savour thereof went right forth to earth and heaven. Therewith she anointed her fair body, and combed her hair, and with her hands plaited her shining tresses, fair and ambrosial, flowing from her immortal head. Then she clad her in her fragrant robe that Athene wrought delicately for her, and therein set many things beautifully made, and fastened it over her breast with clasps of gold. And she girdled it with a girdle arrayed with a hundred tassels, and she set earrings in her pierced ears, earrings of three drops, and glistering, therefrom shone grace abundantly. And with a veil over all the peerless goddess veiled herself, a fair new veil, bright as the sun, and beneath her shining feet she bound goodly sandals. But when she had adorned her body with all her array, she went forth from her bower, and called Aphrodite apart from the other gods, and spake to her saying: "Wilt thou obey me, dear child, in that which I shall tell thee? or wilt thou refuse, with a grudge in thy heart, because I succour the Danaans, and thou the Trojans?"

Then Aphrodite the daughter of Zeus answered her: "Hera, goddess queen, daughter of mighty Kronos, say the thing that is in thy mind, my heart bids me fulfil it, if fulfil it I may, and if it may be accomplished."

Then with crafty purpose the lady Hera answered her: "Give me now Love and Desire wherewith thou dost overcome all the Immortals, and mortal men. For I am going to visit the limits of the bountiful Earth, and Okeanos, father of the gods, and mother Tethys, who reared me well and nourished me in their halls, having taken me from Rhea, when far-seeing Zeus imprisoned Kronos beneath the earth and the unvintaged sea. Them am I going to visit, and their endless strife will I loose, for already this long time they hold apart from each other, apart from love and the marriage bed, since wrath had settled in their hearts. If with words I might persuade their hearts, and bring them back to love and the marriage bed, ever should I be called dear to them and worshipful."

Then laughter-loving Aphrodite answered her again: "It may not be, nor seemly were it to deny that thou askest, for thou sleepest in the arms of Zeus, the chief of gods."

Therewith from her breast she loosed the broidered girdle, fair-wrought, wherein are all her enchantments; therein are love, and desire, and loving converse, that steals the wits even of the wise. This girdle she laid in her hands, and spake, and said: "Lo now, take this girdle and lay it up in thy bosom, this fair-wrought girdle, wherein all things are fashioned; methinks thou wilt not return with that unaccomplished, which in thy heart thou desirest."

So spake she, and the ox-eyed lady Hera smiled, and smiling laid up the zone within her breast.

Then the daughter of Zeus, Aphrodite, went to her house, and Hera, rushing down, left the peak of Olympus, and touched on Pieria and pleasant Emathia, and sped over the snowy hills of the Thracian horsemen, even over the topmost crests, nor grazed the ground with her feet, and from Athos she fared across the foaming sea, and came to Lemnos, the city of godlike Thoas. There she met Sleep, the brother of Death, and clasped her hand in his, and spake and called him by name: "Sleep, lord of all gods and of all men, if ever thou didst hear my word, obey me again even now, and I will be grateful to thee always. Lull me, I pray thee, the shining eyes of Zeus beneath his brows, so soon as I have laid me down by him in love. And gifts I will give to thee, even a fair throne, imperishable for ever, a golden throne, that Hephaistos the Lame, mine own child, shall fashion skilfully, and will set beneath it a footstool for the feet, for thee to set thy shining feet upon, when thou art at a festival."

Then sweet Sleep answered her and said: "Hera, goddess and queen, daughter of mighty Kronos, another of the eternal gods might I lightly lull to slumber, yea, were it the streams of Okeanos himself, that is the father of them all. But to Zeus the son of Kronos might I not draw near, nor lull him to slumber, unless himself commanded it. For ere now did a behest of thine teach me a lesson, on the day when that famed high-hearted son of Zeus sailed from Ilios, when he had sacked the city of the Trojans. Then verily I lulled the soul of aegis-bearing Zeus, with my sweet influence poured about him, and thou didst contrive evil against him in thy heart, and didst rouse over the sea the blasts of violent winds, and Herakles thou then didst bear to well-peopled Kos, far from all his friends. But Zeus, when he wakened, was wrathful, and dashed the gods about his mansion, and me above all he sought, and he would have cast me from the upper air to perish in the deep, if Night had not saved me, Night, that subdues both gods and men. To her I came as a suppliant in my flight, and he ceased from pursuing, wrathful as he was, for he was in awe of doing aught displeasing to swift Night. And now again thou biddest me accomplish this other task that may not be accomplished."

Then the ox-eyed lady Hera answered him again: "Sleep, wherefore dost thou consider these things in thy heart? dost thou deem that Zeus of the far-borne voice will succour the Trojans even as he was wroth for the sake of Herakles, his own child? Nay come, and I will give thee one of the younger of the Graces, to wed and to be called thy wife [even Pasithea, that ever thou longest for all thy days]."

So she spake, and Sleep was glad, and answered and said: "Come now, swear to me by the inviolable water of Styx, and with one of thy hands grasp the bounteous earth, and with the other the shining sea, that all may be witnesses to us, even all the gods below that are with Kronos, that verily thou wilt give me one of the younger of the Graces, even Pasithea, that myself do long for all my days."

So spake he, nor did she disobey, the white-armed goddess Hera; she sware as he bade her, and called all the gods by name, even those below Tartaros that are called Titans. But when she had sworn and ended that oath, the twain left the citadel of Lemnos, and of Imbros, clothed on in mist, and swiftly they accomplished the way. To many-fountained Ida they came, the mother of wild beasts, to Lekton, where first they left the sea, and they twain fared above the dry land, and the topmost forest waveth beneath their feet. There Sleep halted, ere the eyes of Zeus beheld him, and alighted on a tall pine-tree, the loftiest pine that then in all Ida rose through the nether to the upper air. Therein sat he, hidden by the branches of the pine, in the likeness of the shrill bird that on the mountains the gods call *chalkis*, but men *kymindis*. But Hera swiftly drew nigh to topmost Gargaros, the highest crest of Ida, and Zeus the cloud-gatherer beheld her. And as he saw her, so love came over his deep heart, even as when first they mingled with each other in delight, and went together to the couch, their dear parents knowing it not. And he stood before her, and spoke, and said: "Hera, with what desire comest thou thus hither from Olympus, and thy horses and chariot are not here, whereon thou mightst ascend?"

Then with crafty purpose lady Hera answered him: "I am going to visit the limits of the bountiful earth, and Okeanos, father of the gods, and mother Tethys, who reared me well and cherished me in their halls. Them am I going to visit, and their endless strife will I loose, for already this long time they hold apart from each other, from love and the marriage bed, since wrath hath settled in their hearts. But my horses are standing at the foot of many-fountained Ida, my horses that shall bear me over wet and dry. And now it is because of thee that I am thus come hither, down from Olympus, lest perchance thou mightest be wroth with me hereafter, if silently I were gone to the mansion of deep-flowing Okeanos."

Then Zeus, the gatherer of the clouds, answered her and said: "Hera, thither mayst thou go on a later day. But come let us twain take pleasure in the bed of love. For never once as thus did the love of goddess or woman so mightily overflow and conquer the heart within my breast. Not when I loved the wife of Ixion, who bore Pirithoos, the peer of gods in counsel, nor when I loved Danae of the fair ankles, daughter of Akrisios, who bore Perseus, most renowned of all men, nor when I loved the famed daughter of Phoinix, who bore me Minos, and godlike Rhadamanthys, nay, nor even when I loved Semele, nor Alkmene in Thebes, and she bore Herakles, a child hardy of heart, but Semele bore Dionysos, a delight to mortals, nay, nor when I loved the fair-tressed queen, Demeter, nor renowned Leto, nay, nor thy very self, as now I love thee, and sweet desire possesses me."

And him the lady Hera answered with crafty purpose: "Most dread son of Kronos, what a word thou hast spoken! If now thou dost long to be couched in love on the crests of Ida, and all stands plain to view, how would it be if some one of the eternal gods should see us slumbering, and go and tell it to all the gods? It is not I that could arise from the couch and go again to thy house, nay, it would be a thing for righteous anger. But if thou wilt, and it is dear to thy heart, thou hast a chamber that thine own son Hephaistos builded, and fastened strong doors to the pillars, thither let us go and lie down, if the couch be thy desire."

Then Zeus the cloud-gatherer answered her and said: "Hera, fear not lest any god, or any man should spy the thing, so great a golden cloud will I cast all over thee. Nay, methinks not even the sun might see through it, the sun, whose light is keenest of all to behold."

So spake he, and the son of Kronos clasped his consort in his arms. And beneath them the divine earth sent forth fresh new grass, and dewy lotus, and crocus, and hyacinth, thick and soft, that raised them aloft from the ground. Therein they lay, and were clad on with a fair golden cloud, whence fell drops of glittering dew.

Thus slept the Father in quiet on the crest of Gargaros, by Sleep and love overcome, with his bedfellow in his arms. But sweet Sleep started and ran to the ships of the Achaians, to tell his tidings to the god that holdeth and shaketh the earth. And he stood near him, and spake winged words: "Eagerly now, Poseidon, do thou aid the Danaans, and give them glory for a little space, while yet Zeus sleepeth, for over him have I shed soft slumber, and Hera hath beguiled him to couch in love."

So he spake, and passed to the renowned tribes of men, and still the more did he set on Poseidon to aid the Danaans, who straightway sprang far afront of the foremost, and called to them: "Argives, are we again to yield the victory to Hector, son of Priam, that he may take our ships and win renown? Nay, even so he saith and declareth that he will do, for that Achilles by the hollow ships abides angered at heart. But for him there will be no such extreme regret, if we spur us on to aid each the other. Nay come, as I command, let us all obey. Let us harness us in the best shields that are in the host, and the greatest, and cover our heads with shining helms, and take the longest spears in our hands, and so go forth. Yea, and I will lead the way, and methinks that Hector, son of Priam, will not long await us, for all his eagerness. And whatsoever man is steadfast in battle, and hath a small buckler on his shoulder, let him give it to a worse man, and harness him in a larger shield."

So spake he, and they heard him eagerly and obeyed him. And them the kings themselves arrayed, wounded as they were, Tydeus' son, and Odysseus, and Agamemnon, son of Atreus. They went through all the host, and made exchange of weapons of war. The good arms did the good warrior harness him in, the worse he gave to the worse. But when they had done on the shining bronze about their bodies, they started on the march, and Poseidon led them, the Shaker of the earth, with a dread sword of fine edge in his strong hand, like unto lightning; wherewith it is not permitted that any should mingle in woful war, but fear holds men afar therefrom. But the Trojans on the other side was renowned Hector arraying. Then did they now strain the fiercest strife of war, even dark-haired Poseidon and glorious Hector, one succouring the Trojans, the other with the Argives. And the sea washed up to the huts and ships of the Argives, and they gathered together with a mighty cry. Not so loudly bellows the wave of the sea against the land, stirred up from the deep by the harsh breath of the north wind, nor so loud is the roar of burning fire in the glades of a mountain, when it springs to burn up the forest, nor calls the wind so loudly in the high leafy tresses of the trees, when it rages and roars its loudest, as then was the cry of the Trojans and Achaians, shouting dreadfully as they rushed upon each other.

First glorious Hector cast with his spear at Aias, who was facing him full, and did not miss, striking him where two belts were stretched across his breast, the belt of his shield, and of his silver-studded sword; these guarded his tender flesh. And Hector was enraged because his swift spear had flown vainly from his hand, and he retreated into the throng of his fellows, avoiding Fate.

Then as he was departing the great Telamonian Aias smote him with a huge stone; for many stones, the props of swift ships, were rolled among the feet of the fighters; one of these he lifted, and smote Hector on the breast, over the shield-rim, near the neck, and made him spin like a top with the blow, that he reeled round and round. And even as when an oak falls uprooted beneath the stroke of father Zeus, and a dread savour of brimstone arises therefrom, and whoso stands near and beholds it has no more courage, for dread is the bolt of great Zeus, even so fell mighty Hector straightway in the dust. And the spear fell from his hand, but his shield and helm were made fast to him, and round him rang his arms adorned with bronze.

Then with a loud cry they ran up, the sons of the Achaians, hoping to drag him away, and they cast showers of darts. But not one availed to wound or smite the shepherd of the host; before that might be the bravest gathered about him, Polydamas, and Aineias, and goodly Agenor, and Sarpedon, leader of the Lykians, and noble Glaukos, and of the rest not one was heedless of him, but they held their round shields in front of him, and his comrades lifted him in their arms, and bare him out of the battle, till he reached his swift horses that were standing waiting for him, with the charioteer and the fair-dight chariot at the rear of the combat and the war. These toward the city bore him heavily moaning. Now when they came to the ford of the fair-flowing river, of eddying Xanthos, that immortal Zeus begat, there they lifted him from the chariot to the ground, and poured water over him, and he gat back his breath, and looked up with his eyes, and sitting on his heels kneeling, he vomited black blood. Then again he sank back on the ground, and black night covered his eyes, the stroke still conquering his spirit.

Now the Argives when they saw Hector departed rushed yet the more upon the Trojans, and were mindful of the delight of battle. There far the foremost did swift Aias, son of Oileus, leap on Satnios, son of Enops, and wounded him with his sharp spear; Satnios whom the fair Naiad-nymph bore to Enops as he herded his flocks by the banks of Satnioeis. Him did the spear-famed son of Oileus draw nigh, and wounded him on the flank, and he fell, and round him did Trojans and Danaans join in strong battle. Then to his aid came Polydamas, the wielder of the spear, son of Panthoos, and smote Prothoenor on the right shoulder, Prothoenor, son of Areïlykos, and through his shoulder went the mighty spear, and he fell in the dust, and clutched the earth with his palm. And Polydamas boasted over him terribly, crying aloud: "Verily methinks that again from the strong hand of the high-hearted son of Panthoos, the spear hath not leaped in vain. Nay, one of the Argives hath caught it in his flesh, and leaning thereon for a staff, methinks that he will go down within the house of Hades."

So spake he, and sorrow came on the Argives by reason of his boasting. And chiefly he roused the wrath of the wise son of Telamon, Aias, for the man fell close by him. Swiftly he cast at the other, as he departed, with his shining spear. And Polydamas himself avoided black Fate, starting to one side, but Archelochos, son of Antenor, received the spear, for the gods had willed his death. Him the spear struck at the meeting of the head and neck, on the last joint of the spine, and cut in twain both the tendons. And his head, and mouth, and nose, as he fell, reached the earth long before his legs and knees, and Aias again shouted to noble Polydamas: "Consider, Polydamas, and tell me truly, whether thou sayst not that this man is worth slaying in place of Prothoenor: he seems to me no coward, nor born of cowards, but a brother of horse-taming Antenor, or a child, for he most closely favoureth his house."

So he spake, knowing the truth right well, and sorrow seized the hearts of the Trojans. Then Akamas wounded Promachos the Boiotian with his spear, from where he stood above his brother, that Promachos was dragging away by the feet. Over him Akamas boasted terribly, shouting aloud: "Ye Argive bowmen, insatiate of threats, verily not for us alone shall there be struggle and toil, nay, but even as we shall ye likewise perish. Consider how your Promachos sleepeth, vanquished by my spear, that my brother's blood-price may not be long unpaid. Even for this it is that a man may well pray to leave some kinsman in his halls, that will avenge his fall."

So he spake, and sorrow came on the Argives at his boast. And chiefly he stirred the heart of the wise Peneleos, who made for Akamas, and Akamas abode not the onset of the prince Peneleos. But Peneleos wounded Ilioneus, the son of Phorbas, rich in herds, that Hermes loved most dearly of all the Trojans, and gave him wealth. Now his mother bare Ilioneus, an only child, to Phorbas. Him did Peneleos wound beneath the brows, at the bases of the eye, and drave out the eyeball, and the spear went clean through the eye and through the nape of the neck, and he fell back, stretching out both his hands. And Peneleos, drawing forth his sharp sword, smote him on the middle of the neck, and smote off even to the ground the head with the helmet, and still the strong spear stood in the eye, and lifting it up like a poppy head, he showed it to the Trojans, and spoke his boastful words: "Ye Trojans, I pray you bid the dear father and the mother of proud Ilioneus to wail in their halls, for neither will the wife of Promachos, son of Alegenor, rejoice in her dear husband's coming, in that hour when we youths of the Achaians return with our ships out of Troy-land."

So he spake, and fear fell on the limbs of all of them; and each man looked about to see where he might flee sheer destruction.

Tell me now, ye Muses, that dwell in the mansions of Olympus, who was the first of the Achaians to lift the bloody spoils, when once the renowned Shaker of the earth turned the battle.

Verily it was Aias, son of Telamon, that first wounded Hyrtios, the son of Gyrtias, the leader of the Mysians strong of heart, and Antilochos stripped the spoils from Phalkes and Mermeros, and Meriones slew Morys and Hippotion, and Teukros slew Prothoon and Periphetes, and next Atreus' son wounded in the flank Hyperenor, the shepherd of the host, and the bronze point tore through and let out the entrails, and the soul through the stricken wound fled hastily, and darkness covered his eyes. But most men did Aias slay, the swift-footed son of Oileus, for there was none so speedy of foot as he, to follow when men fled, when Zeus sent terror among them.

BOOK XV

Zeus awakening, biddeth Apollo revive Hector, and restore the fortunes of the Trojans. Fire is thrown on the ship of Protesilaos.

Now when they had sped in flight across the palisade and trench, and many were overcome at the hands of the Danaans, the rest were stayed, and abode beside the chariots in confusion, and pale with terror, and Zeus awoke, on the peaks of Ida, beside Hera of the golden throne. Then he leaped up, and stood, and beheld the Trojans and Achaians, those in flight, and these driving them on from the rear, even the Argives, and among them the prince Poseidon. And Hector he saw lying on the plain, and around him sat his comrades, and he was gasping with difficult breath, and his mind wandering, and was vomiting blood, for it was not the weakest of the Achaians that had smitten him. Beholding him, the father of men and gods had pity on him, and terribly he spoke to Hera, with fierce look: "O thou ill to deal with, Hera, verily it is thy crafty wile that has made noble Hector cease from the fight, and has terrified the host. Nay, but yet I know not whether thou mayst not be the first to reap the fruits of thy cruel treason, and I beat thee with stripes. Dost thou not remember, when thou wert hung from on high, and from thy feet I suspended two anvils, and round thy hands fastened a golden bond that might not be broken? And thou didst hang in the clear air and the clouds, and the gods were wroth in high Olympus, but they could not come round and unloose thee. Nay, whomsoever I might take, I would clutch, and throw from the threshold, to come fainting to the earth, yet verily not even so did the ceaseless sorrow leave my soul free: sorrow for godlike Herakles. Him didst thou drive, when thou hadst suborned the tempest, with the help of the North Wind, over the unvintaged deep, out of thine evil counsel, and then didst carry him away to well-peopled Kos. Him did I rescue thence, and lead again to Argos, the pasture-land of horses, after his much labour. Of these things will I mind thee again, that thou mayst cease from thy wiles, that thou mayst know if it profit thee at all, the dalliance and the love, wherein thou didst lie with me, when thou hadst come from among the gods, and didst beguile me."

So spake he, and the ox-eyed lady Hera shuddered, and spake unto him winged words, saying: "Let earth now be witness hereto, and wide heaven above, and that falling water of Styx, the greatest oath and the most terrible to the blessed gods, and thine own sacred head, and our own bridal bed, whereby never would I forswear myself, that not by my will does earth-shaking Poseidon trouble the Trojans and Hector, and succour them of the other part. Nay, it is his own soul that urgeth and commandeth him, and he had pity on the Achaians, when he beheld them hard pressed beside the ships. I would even counsel him also to go even where thou, lord of the storm-cloud, mayst lead him."

So spake she, and the father of gods and men smiled, and answering her he spake winged words: "If thou, of a truth, O ox-eyed lady Hera, wouldst hereafter abide of one mind with me among the immortal gods, thereon would Poseidon, howsoever much his wish be contrariwise, quickly turn his mind otherwhere, after thy heart and mine. But if indeed thou speakest the truth and soothly, go thou now among the tribes of the gods, and call Iris to come hither, and Apollo, the renowned archer, that Iris may go among the host of mail-clad Achaians and tell Poseidon the prince to cease from the war, and get him unto his own house. But let Phoebus Apollo spur Hector on to the war, and breathe strength into him again, and make him forget his anguish, that now wears down his heart, and drive the Achaians back again, when he hath stirred in them craven fear. Let them flee and fall among the many-benched ships of Achilles son of Peleus, and he shall rouse his own comrade, Patroklos; and him shall renowned Hector slay with the spear, in front of Ilios, after that he has slain many other youths, and among them my son, noble Sarpedon. In wrath therefor shall goodly Achilles slay Hector. From that hour verily will I cause a new pursuit from the ships, that shall endure continually, even until the Achaians take steep Ilios, through the counsels of Athene. But before that hour neither do I cease in my wrath, nor will I suffer any other of the Immortals to help the Danaans there, before I accomplish that desire of the son of Peleus, as I promised him at the first, and confirmed the same with a nod of my head, on that day when the goddess Thetis clasped my knees, imploring me to honour Achilles, the sacker of cities."

So spake he, nor did the white-armed goddess Hera disobey him, and she sped down from the hills of Ida to high Olympus. And even as when the mind of a man darts speedily, of one that hath travelled over far lands, and considers in his wise heart, "Would that I were here or there," and he thinketh him of many things, so swiftly fled she in her eagerness, the lady Hera, and came to steep Olympus, and went among the gathering of the immortal gods in the house of Zeus, and when they beheld her they all rose up together, and held out their cups to her in welcome. The others she left alone, but took the cup of Themis of the fair cheeks, for she was the first that came running to meet her, and speaking winged words accosted her: "Hera, wherefore hast thou come? thou seemest like one confounded; verily the son of Kronos hath made thee adread, thine own husband."

Then the white-armed goddess Hera answered her, saying: "Ask me not concerning this, O goddess Themis;

thyself knowest it, how overweening is his heart, and unyielding. But do thou begin the equal banquet of the gods in the halls, and thus shalt thou hear among all the Immortals, even what evil deeds Zeus declareth. Nay, methinks, not equally will it delight the minds of all, neither of gods nor morals, if even now any still sit with pleasure at the feast."

So spake the lady Hera, and sat her down, while the gods were heavy at heart in the hall of Zeus. And she laughed with her lips, but her forehead above her dark brows was not gladdened, and indignantly she spake among them all: "Witless that we are to be wroth in our folly against Zeus! Even still we are eager to draw nigh to him, and let him from his will, by word or deed, but he sits apart and careth not, nor takes any thought thereof, for he deems that among the immortal gods he is manifestly pre-eminent in force and might. Wherefore do ye content yourselves with whatsoever sorrow he sends on each of you. Already, methinks, has sorrow been wrought for Ares, for his son has fallen in the fight, even the dearest of men, Askalaphos, that dread Ares deemeth to be verily his own."

So spake she, but Ares smote his strong thighs with his hands flatlings, and sorrowing he spake: "Hold me not now to blame, ye that keep the mansions of Olympus, if I avenge the slaying of my son, and go to the ships of the Achaians, even if it be my doom to be smitten with the bolt of Zeus, and lie among the dead, in the dust and blood."

So spake he, and bade yoke his horses, Fear and Dread, and himself did on his shining harness. Thereby would yet a greater and more implacable wrath and anger have been caused between Zeus and the Immortals, had not Athene, in terror for the sake of all the gods, leaped out through the doorway, and left the throne wherein she sat, and taken from Ares' head the helmet, and the shield from his shoulders, and drawn the spear of bronze from his stalwart hand, and set it apart, and then with words she rebuked the impetuous Ares: "Mad that thou art, and distraught of wit—this is thy bane! Verily thou hast ears and hearest not, and perished have thine understanding and thine awe. Hearest thou not what she saith, the white-armed goddess Hera, that even now is come from Olympian Zeus? Dost thou wish both thyself to fill up the measure of mischief and so return to Olympus ruefully, of necessity, and for all the other gods to sow the seed of a great wrong? For straightway will he leave the high-hearted Trojans and the Achaians, and to us will he come to make tumult in Olympus: and he will clutch us each in turn, the blameless with the guilty. Wherefore now again I bid thee to abate thine anger for thy son, for already many a man stronger than he, and more hardy of his hands, has fallen, or yet will fall; and a hard thing it is to save the lineage and offspring of all men."

So spake she, and made impetuous Ares sit down on his throne. But Hera called Apollo without the hall, and Iris, that is the messenger of the immortal gods, and she spake winged words, and addressed them, saying: "Zeus bids you go to Ida as swiftly as may be, and when ye have gone, and looked on the face of Zeus, do ye whatsoever he shall order and command."

So spake she, and returned again, the lady Hera, and sat down on her throne, and they flew forward speedily, and came to many-fountained Ida, mother of wild beasts, and found far-seeing Zeus seated on topmost Gargaros, and round him a fragrant cloud was circled like a crown. And these twain came before the face of Zeus the cloud-gatherer, and stood there, and he was no wise displeased at heart when he beheld them, for that speedily they had obeyed the words of his dear wife. And to Iris first he spake winged words: "Go, get thee, swift Iris, to the prince Poseidon, and tell him all these things, nor be a false messenger. Command him to cease from war and battle, and to go among the tribes of the gods, or into the bright sea. But if he will not obey my words, but will hold me in no regard, then let him consider in his heart and mind, lest he dare not for all his strength to abide me when I come against him, since I deem me to be far mightier than he, and elder born. But this his heart feareth not,—to call himself the peer of me whom even the other gods do hold in dread."

So spake he, nor did the wind-footed fleet Iris disobey him, but went down the hills of Ida to sacred Ilios. And as when snow or chill hail fleets from the clouds beneath the stress of the North Wind born in the clear air, so fleetly she fled in her eagerness, swift Iris, and drew near the renowned Earth-shaker and spake to him, saying: "A certain message to thee, O dark-haired embracer of the earth, have I come hither to bring from aegis-bearing Zeus. He biddeth thee cease from the battle and war, and go among the tribes of the gods, or into the bright sea. And if thou wilt not obey his word, but wilt hold him in no regard, he threatens that even himself will come hither against thee in battle, and he biddeth thee avoid thee out of his hands, since he deemeth him far mightier than thou, and elder born, but thy heart feareth not to call thyself the peer of him whom even the other gods do hold in dread."

Then, in great displeasure the renowned Shaker of the earth answered her: "Out on it, verily now, for as strong as he is, he hath spoken over-haughtily, if indeed he will subdue by force, against my will, me that am his equal in honour. For three brethren are we, and sons of Kronos, whom Rhea bare, Zeus, and myself, and Hades is the third, the ruler of the folk in the under-world. And in three lots are all things divided, and each drew a domain of his own, and to me fell the hoary sea, to be my habitation for ever, when we shook the lots: and Hades drew the murky darkness, and Zeus the wide heaven, in clear air and clouds, but the earth and high Olympus are yet common to all. Wherefore no whit will I walk after the will of Zeus, but quietly let him abide, for all his strength, in his third portion. And with the might of his hands let him not strive to terrify me withal, as if I were a coward. Better for him were it to threaten with terrible words his daughters and his sons, that himself begat, who will perforce listen to whatso he enjoins."

Then the fleet wind-footed Iris answered him: "Is it indeed thy will, O dark-haired embracer of the earth, that even thus I shall carry to Zeus this message, hard and froward, or wilt thou turn thee at all, for the hearts of the good may be turned? Thou knowest how the Erinyes do always follow to aid the elder-born."

Then he answered her again, Poseidon, the Shaker of the earth: "Goddess Iris, most duly hast thou spoken this word. Yea, an excellent thing is this, when the bearer of a message has a prudent wit. Yet this is a terrible grief that cometh on heart and spirit, whenso any desireth to upbraid with angry words his peer to whom fate hath assigned an equal share with himself. But verily now will I yield, for all mine anger; but another thing will I tell thee, and make this threat in my heart, that if against my will, and the will of Athene, the driver of the prey, and of Hera and Hermes, and prince Hephaistos, Zeus shall spare steep Ilios, nor choose utterly to destroy it, and give great might to the Argives, let him know this, that our wrath will be inappeasable."

So spake the Shaker of the earth, and left the host of the Achaians, and passed to the sea, and sank, and sorely they missed him, the heroes of the Achaians.

Then Zeus, the gatherer of the clouds, spake to Apollo, saying: "Go now, dear Phoebus, to Hector of the helm of bronze, for, lo, already the embracer of the world, the Earth-shaker, is gone to the bright sea, shunning our utter wrath, ay, and had he not done so, even the others would have heard of our strife, even the gods of the nether world, that are with Kronos. But better far is this, both for me, and for him, that, despite his wrath, he should yield to my hands, for not without sweat would this strife have been accomplished. But do thou take in thy hands the tasselled aegis, and shake it fiercely and affright the Achaian heroes. But, thou Archer-God, let glorious Hector be thy care, and rouse in him great wrath even till the Achaians come in their flight to the ships, and the Hellespont. And from that moment will I devise word and deed wherewithal the Achaians may take breath again from their toil."

So spake he, nor was Apollo deaf to the word of the Father, but he went down the hills of Ida like a fleet falcon, the bane of doves, that is the swiftest of flying things. And he found the son of wise-hearted Priam, noble Hector, sitting up, no longer lying, for he had but late got back his life, and knew the comrades around him, and his gasping and his sweat had ceased, from the moment when the will of aegis-bearing Zeus began to revive him. Then far-darting Apollo stood near him, and spake to him: "Hector, son of Priam, why dost thou sit fainting apart from the others? Is it perchance that some trouble cometh upon thee?"

Then, with faint breath answered him Hector of the glancing helm: "Nay, but who art thou, best of the gods, who inquirest of me face to face? Dost thou not know that by the hindmost row of the ships of the Achaians, Aias of the loud war-cry smote me on the breast with a stone, as I was slaying his comrades, and made me cease from mine impetuous might? And verily I deemed that this very day I should pass to the dead, and the house of Hades, when I had gasped my life away."

Then prince Apollo the Far-darter answered him again: "Take courage now, so great an ally hath the son of Kronos sent thee out of Ida, to stand by thee and defend thee, even Phoebus Apollo of the golden sword, me who of old defend thee, thyself and the steep citadel. But come now bid thy many charioteers drive their swift steeds against the hollow ships, and I will go before and make smooth all the way for the chariots, and will put to flight the Achaian heroes."

So he spake, and breathed great might into the shepherd of the host, and even as when a stalled horse, full fed at the manger, breaks his tether and speedeth at the gallop over the plain exultingly, being wont to bathe in the fair-flowing stream, and holds his head on high, and the mane floweth about his shoulders, and he trusteth in his glory, and nimbly his knees bear him to the haunts and pasture of the mares, even so Hector lightly moved his feet and knees, urging on his horsemen, when he heard the voice of the god. But as when hounds and country folk pursue a horned stag, or a wild goat, that steep rock and shady wood save from them, nor is it their lot to find him, but at their clamour a bearded lion hath shown himself on the way, and lightly turned them all despite their eagerness, even so the Danaans for a while followed on always in their companies, smiting with swords and double-pointed spears, but when they saw Hector going up and down the ranks of men, then were they afraid, and the hearts of all fell to their feet.

Then to them spake Thoas, son of Andraimon, far the best of the Aitolians, skilled in throwing the dart, and good in close fight, and in council did few of the Achaians surpass him, when the young men were striving in debate; with good intent he made harangue and spake among them: "Alas, and verily a great marvel is this I behold with mine eyes, how he hath again arisen, and hath avoided the Fates, even Hector. Surely each of us hoped in his heart, that he had died beneath the hand of Aias, son of Telamon. But some one of the gods again hath delivered and saved Hector, who verily hath loosened the knees of many of the Danaans, as methinks will befall even now, for not without the will of loud-thundering Zeus doth he rise in the front ranks, thus eager for battle. But come, as I declare let us all obey. Let us bid the throng turn back to the ships, but let us as many as avow us to be the best in the host, take our stand, if perchance first we may meet him, and hold him off with outstretched spears, and he, methinks, for all his eagerness, will fear at heart to enter into the press of the Danaans."

So spake he, and they heard him eagerly, and obeyed him. They that were with Aias and the prince Idomeneus, and Teukros, and Meriones, and Meges the peer of Ares, called to all the best of the warriors and sustained the fight with Hector and the Trojans, but behind them the multitude returned to the ships of the Achaians.

Now the Trojans drave forward in close ranks, and with long strides Hector led them, while in front of him went Phoebus Apollo, his shoulders wrapped in cloud, and still he held the fell aegis, dread, circled with a shaggy fringe, and gleaming, that Hephaistos the smith gave to Zeus, to bear for the terror of men; with this in his hands did he lead the host.

Now the Argives abode them in close ranks, and shrill the cry arose on both sides, and the arrows leaped from the bow-strings, and many spears from stalwart hands, whereof some stood fast in the flesh of young men swift in fight, but many halfway, ere ever they reached the white flesh, stuck in the ground, longing to glut themselves with flesh. Now so long as Phoebus Apollo held the aegis unmoved in his hands, so long the darts smote either side amain, and the folk fell. But when he looked face to face on the Danaans of the swift steeds, and shook the aegis, and himself shouted mightily, he quelled their heart in their breast, and they forgot their impetuous valour. And as when two wild beasts drive in confusion a herd of kine, or a great flock of sheep, in the dark hour of black night, coming swiftly on them when the herdsman is not by, even so were the Achaians terror-stricken and strengthless, for Apollo sent a panic among them, but still gave renown to the Trojans and Hector.

Then man fell upon man, when the close fight was scattered. Hector slew Stichios, and Arkesilaos, one a leader of the mail-clad Boiotians, the other the true comrade of great-hearted Menestheus. And Aineias slew Medon and Iasos, whereof one was the bastard son of divine Oileus, even Medon, brother of Aias, but he dwelt in Phylake, far from his own country, for that he had slain a man the brother of his stepmother Eriopis, the wife of Oileus. But Iasos was a leader of the Athenians, and was called the son of Sphelos, the son of Boukolos. And Polydamas slew Mekisteus, and Polites Echios in the forefront of the battle, and noble Agenor overcame Klonis. And Deïochos as he was flying among the fighters in the foremost rank Paris smote behind the lower part of the shoulder, and drave the bronze clean through.

Now while they were stripping the spoil from these, even then the Achaians were dashing into the delved fosse, and against the palisade, fleeing hither and thither in their terror, and were driven perforce within the wall, but Hector called with a loud shout to the Trojans: "Make ye against the ships, and leave the bloody spoils. Whomsoever I shall see apart from the ships on the other side, his death will I there devise, nor forthwith shall his kinsmen and kinswomen lay him dead on the funeral fire, but dogs shall tear him in front of our citadel."

So speaking he smote his horses on the shoulder with the lash, and called aloud on the Trojans along the ranks. And they all cried out, and level with his held the steeds that drew their chariots, with a marvellous din, and in front of them Phoebus Apollo lightly dashed down with his feet the banks of the deep ditch, and cast them into the midst thereof, making a bridgeway long and wide as is a spear-cast, when a man throws to make trial of his strength. Thereby the Trojans poured forward in their battalions, while in their van Apollo held the splendid aegis. And most easily did he cast down the wall of the Achaians, as when a boy scatters the sand beside the sea, first making sand buildings for sport in his childishness, and then again, in his sport, confounding them with his feet and hands; even so didst thou, archer Apollo, confound the long toil and labour of the Argives, and among them rouse a panic fear.

So they were halting, and abiding by the ships, calling each to other; and lifting their hands to all the gods did each man pray vehemently, and chiefly prayed Gerenian Nestor, the Warden of the Achaians, stretching his hand towards the starry heaven: "O father Zeus, if ever any one of us in wheat-bearing Argos did burn to thee fat thighs of bull or sheep, and prayed that he might return, and thou didst promise and assent thereto, of these things be thou mindful, and avert, Olympian, the pitiless day, nor suffer the Trojans thus to overcome the Achaians."

So spake he in his prayer, and Zeus, the Lord of counsel, thundered loudly, hearing the prayers of the ancient son of Neleus.

But the Trojans, when they heard the thunder of aegis-bearing Zeus, rushed yet the more eagerly upon the Argives, and were mindful of the joy of battle. And as when a great wave of the wide sea sweeps over the bulwarks of a ship, the might of the wind constraining it, which chiefly swells the waves, even so did the Trojans with a great cry bound over the wall, and drave their horses on, and at the hindmost row of the ships were fighting hand to hand with double-pointed spears, the Trojans from the chariots, but the Achaians climbing up aloft, from the black ships with long pikes that they had lying in the ships for battle at sea, jointed pikes shod at the head with bronze.

Now Patroklos, as long as the Achaians and Trojans were fighting about the wall, without the swift ships, sat in the hut of kindly Eurypylos, and was making him glad with talk, and on his cruel wound was laying herbs, to medicine his dark pain. But when he perceived the Trojans rushing over the wall, and the din and flight of the Danaans began, then did he groan, and smote his two thighs with his hands flatlings, and sorrowing he spake: "Eurypylos, no longer at all may I abide with thee here, though great thy need, for verily a great strife has arisen. But thee let thy squire comfort, while I hasten to Achilles, that I may urge him to join the battle. Who knows but with god's help I may arouse his spirit with my persuasion? and a good thing is the persuasion of a friend."

Even as he spake, his feet were bearing him away, but the Achaians abode the onset of the Trojans steadfastly, yet availed not to drive them, though fewer they were, from the ships: neither at all could the Trojans break the ranks of the Danaans and pour among the huts and the ships. But even as the carpenter's line doth straighten the timber of a ship, in the hands of a cunning shipwright that is well skilled in all craft, by the inspiration of Athene, so equally was strained their war and battle, and divers of them were fighting about divers ships. Now Hector made for renowned Aias, and they twain were warring about the same ship, nor could the one drive back the other and set fire to the ship, nor could the other thrust him away, since the god urged him on. There did glorious Aias smite Kaletor son of Klytios in the breast with a spear, as he was carrying fire against the ship, and he fell with a crash, and the torch dropped from his hand. But Hector, when he beheld with his eyes his cousin fallen in the dust, in front of the black ship, called with a loud cry to the Trojans and Lykians: "Ye Trojans, and Lykians, and Dardanians that fight hand to hand, slacken not at all from the battle in this strait, but save the son of Klytios; lest the Achaians spoil him of his harness, now that he hath fallen in the precinct of the ships."

So spake he, and hurled at Aias with a shining spear: and Aias he missed, but Lykophron, the son of Mastor, the Kytherian squire of Aias, who dwelt with him, having slain a man in divine Kythera, him Hector smote on the head above the ear with the sharp bronze, even as he stood near Aias; and backward in the dust he fell to earth from the stern of the ship, and his limbs were loosened. And Aias shuddered, and spake to his brother: "Dear Teukros, lo our true comrade hath been slain, even the son of Mastor out of Kythera whom we honoured at home in the halls like our own parents. Him hath great-hearted Hector slain. Where now are thy swift shafts of doom, and the bow that Phoebus Apollo gave thee?"

So spake he, and the other marked him, and ran, and came and stood close by him, with the bended bow in his hand, and the quiver with the arrows, and right swiftly he showered his shafts upon the Trojans. And he smote Kleitos, the splendid son of Peisenor, the comrade of Polydamas, the haughty son of Panthoos, with the reins in his hand, as he was busy with the horses, for thither was he driving them where far the most of the companies were broken in confusion, and he was showing a favour to Hector and the Trojans. But swiftly on himself came his bane, that not one of them could ward off from him, despite their desire. For the woful arrow lighted on the back of his neck, and he fell from the chariot, and back started his horses, shaking the empty car. But straightway the prince Polydamas beheld it, and was the first to come over against the horses. Them he gave to Astynoos, the son of Protiaon, and enjoined him straitly to hold the horses close at hand, and look on, and himself went back, and mingled with the foremost fighters. Then Teukros aimed another shaft against Hector of the helm of bronze, and would have made cease the battle by the ships of the Achaians, if he had smitten him in his prowess and taken his life away. But he escaped not the wise mind of Zeus, who guarded Hector, but took away the praise from Teukros son of Telamon, for he brake the well-twisted string on the goodly bow, even as Teukros was aiming at Hector, and his arrow weighted with bronze wandered otherwhere, and the bow fell from his hands. But Teukros shuddered, and spake to his brother saying: "Alas, now verily the god breaks altogether the purpose of our battle, in that he hath cast the bow from my hand, and hath broken the newly twisted cord, which I bound on but this morning, that it might sustain the many shafts that should leap from the bow."

Then the great Aias son of Telamon answered him saying: "Yea, friend, but let the bow and the many arrows lie, even so, since the god had confounded them, being jealous of the Danaans, but take in thy hands a long spear, and a shield on thy shoulder, and war with the Trojans, and arouse the rest of the host. Verily not without labour, for all their victory, let them take the well-timbered ships; nay, let us be mindful of the delight of battle."

So spake he, and Teukros set the bow within the huts again, but round his shoulder he set a fourfold shield, and on his mighty head a well-wrought helmet, [with a horse-hair plume, and terribly the crest nodded above.] And he seized a strong spear, shod with sharp bronze, and started on his way, and started and running right speedily stood beside Aias.

But when Hector saw the artillery of Teukros harmed, he cried, with a mighty shout, to the Trojans and Lykians: "Trojans, and Lykians, and Dardanians that love close fight, play the man, my friends, and be mindful of impetuous valour, here by the hollow ships, for I have seen with mine eyes, how the artillery of the bravest warrior was harmed by Zeus. And most easily discerned is the aid of Zeus to men, both to whomso he gives the meed of the greater honour, and whom he would minish and hath no will to aid, as even now he minisheth the strength of the Argives, but us he aideth. But fight in your firm companies at the ships, and whosoever of you be smitten by dart or blow and meeteth death and fate, so let him die. Lo, it is no dishonourable thing for him to fall fighting for his country, but his wife and his children after him are safe, and his house unharmed, and his lot of land, if but the Achaians fare with their ships to their dear native land."

So spake he and aroused the might and the spirit of every man.

But Aias again, on the other side, called unto his comrades: "Shame on you, Argives: now is one thing sure, either that we must perish utterly, or be saved and drive the peril from the ships. Think ye that if Hector of the glancing helm take the ships, ye will come by dry land each to his own country? Hear ye not Hector exhorting all the host, so eager, verily, is he to burn the ships? Truly he bids not men to the dance but to battle. And for us there is no better counsel nor device, but to put forth our hands and all our might in close combat. Better it were to risk life or death, once for all, than long to be straitened in the dread stress of battle, thus vainly by the ships, at the hands of worse men than we be."

So spake he, and aroused the might and the spirit of every man. Then Hector slew Schedios, the son of Perimedes, a leader of the Phokians, while Aias slew Laodamas, the leader of the foot-men, the noble son of Antenor, and Polydamas slew Otos, of Kyllene, comrade of Phyleides, a chief of the high-hearted Epeians. And Meges, when he beheld it rushed on him, but Polydamas stooped downwards, and him Meges missed,—for Apollo suffered not the son of Panthoos to be smitten among the foremost fighters,—but he wounded Kroismos in the midst of the breast with his spear. And he fell with a crash, and the other set to stripping the harness from his shoulders. Then Dolops rose against him, a warrior skilled, Dolops son of Lampos, whom Lampos Laomedon's son begat, his bravest son, well skilled in impetuous valour; who then smote the midst of the shield of Phyleus' son, setting on him at close quarters. But his well-wrought corslet guarded him, the corslet that he wore, fashioned of plates of mail. This corslet did Phyleus once bear out of Ephyre, from the river Selleëis. For a guest friend of his had given him the same, even Euphetes, king of men, that he might bear it in war, a defence against foemen; and now from his son's flesh too it warded off his bane. Now Meges smote with sharpened spear at the topmost crest of his helmet of bronze with horse-hair plume, and brake off his plume of horse-hair, and it all fell earthward in the dust, shining with its new scarlet dye. Now while he abode, and fought, and yet hoped for victory, there came against him to the rescue warlike Menelaos, and stood unmarked on his flank with his spear, and smote him on the shoulder from behind, and the eager spear rushed through his breast, in forward flight, and then fell he forward. Then the twain made for him to strip from his shoulders his harness of bronze. But Hector called to all his kinsmen, and first he chid the son of Hiketaon, the strong Melanippos. Now till then was Melanippos wont to feed his kine of trailing gait in Perkote, far off from hostile men, but when the curved ships of the Danaans came, he returned to Ilios, and excelled among the Trojans, and dwelt hard by Priam, who honoured him equally with his own children. Him did Hector chide, and spake out, and called him by name: "Melanippos, are we to be thus slack? Is thy heart not moved at all, at sight of thy kinsman slain? Seest thou not how they are busied about the harness of Dolops? nay, follow on, for no longer may we fight with the Argives from afar, till either we slay them, or they utterly take steep Ilios, and slay her people."

So spake he, and led on, while the other followed him, a godlike man. But the great Aias, son of Telamon, exhorted the Argives, saying: "O friends, play the man, and take shame in your hearts; yea, have shame each of the other's contempt, in the strong battle. For of men thus shamefast more escape than fall, but of men that flee cometh neither glory, nor any avail."

So spake he, and they likewise themselves were eager to drive off the others, and laid up his word in their hearts, and begirt the ships with a ring of bronze, while Zeus urged on the Trojans. Then Menelaos of the loud war-cry exhorted Antilochos, "Antilochos, not one of the Achaians is younger than thou, nor swifter of foot, nor strong as art thou in fight; see now if thou canst leap out, and smite some man of the Trojans."

So spake he, and hasted back again, having heartened the other, and forth Antilochos leaped from the foremost ranks, and cast his shining spear, glancing all around him, and the Trojans gave ground before him when he threw. And no vain dart threw he, but smote Melanippos, the proud son of Hiketaon, as he was returning to the combat; on the breast hard by the nipple he smote him. And he fell with a crash, and darkness covered his eyes. And Antilochos set on like a hound that rushes upon a wounded fawn, that the hunter hath aimed at and smitten as it leaped from its lair, and hath loosened all its limbs. Even so upon thee, Melanippos, leaped Antilochos steadfast in battle, to spoil thy harness. But noble Hector marked him, and came running against him through the battle. But Antilochos abode not his onset, swift warrior though he was, but he fled, like a wild beast that hath done some evil thing, having slain a dog, or a herdsman by the kine, and flees, before the press of men can gather; even so fled the son of Nestor. Now the Trojans and Hector, with wonderful clamour, showered upon him their dolorous darts, but he turned, and stood, when he had reached the host of his comrades.

Now the Trojans, like ravening lions, rushed upon the ships, fulfilling the behests of Zeus, that ever was rousing their great wrath, but softened the temper of the Argives, and took away their glory, while he spurred on the others. For the heart of Zeus was set on giving glory to Hector, the son of Priam, that withal he might cast fierce-blazing fire, unwearied, upon the beaked ships, and so fulfil all the presumptuous prayer of Thetis; wherefore wise-counselling Zeus awaited, till his eyes should see the glare of a burning ship. For even from that hour was he to ordain the backward chase of the Trojans from the ships, and to give glory to the Danaans. With this design was he rousing Hector, Priam's son, that himself was right eager, against the hollow ships. And he was raging, like Ares, the brandisher of the spear, or as when ruinous fire rages on the hills, in the folds of a deep woodland; and foam grew about his mouth, and his eyes shone beneath his dreadful brows, and around the temples of Hector as he fought his helm shook terribly. For Zeus out of heaven was his ally, and gave him honour and renown, he being but one man against so many. For short of life was he to be, yea, and already Pallas Athene was urging against him the day of destiny, at the hand of the son of Peleus. And fain he was to break the ranks of men, trying them wheresoever he saw the thickest press, and the goodliest harness. Yet not even so might he break them for all his eagerness. Nay, they stood firm, and embattled like a steep rock and a great, hard by the hoary sea, a rock that abides the swift paths of the shrill winds, and the swelling waves that roar against it. Even so the Danaans steadfastly abode the Trojans, and fled not away. But Hector shining with fire on all sides leaped on the throng, and fell upon them, as when beneath the storm-clouds a fleet wave reared of the winds falls on a swift ship, and she is all hidden with foam, and the dread blast of the wind roars against the sail, and the sailors fear, and tremble in their hearts, for by but a little way are they borne forth from death, even so the spirit was torn in the breasts of the Achaians. But he came on like a ravening lion making against the kine, that are feeding innumerable in the low-lying land of a great marsh, and among them is a herdsman that as yet knoweth not well how to fight with a wild beast concerning the slaughter of the kine of crooked horn, and ever he paces abreast with the rear or the van of the cattle, but the lion leaps into the midst, and devours a cow, and they all tremble for fear, even so the Achaians all were made terribly adread by Hector and father Zeus. But Hector slew Periphetes of Mykene only, the dear son of Kopreus, that was wont to go on the errands of Eurystheus, to the mighty Herakles. From him, a far baser father, was born a better son, in all manner of excellence, in fleetness of foot, and in war, and of mind he was wise among the first of the Mykenaeans. He thus then yielded Hector the greater glory. For as he turned back, he tripped against the rim of his shield which he was wont to bear, a shield that reached to the feet, a fence against javelins—thereon he stumbled, and fell back, and his helm rang wondrously around his temples as he fell. And Hector quickly spied it, and ran up swiftly and stood by him, and fixed a spear in his breast, and slew him hard by his dear comrades that could not aid him, despite all their sorrow for their friend, for themselves greatly dreaded noble Hector.

Now were they come between the ships, and the prows protected them, the prows of the ships drawn up in the first line, but the Trojans rushed in after them. And the Argives were compelled even of necessity to give back from the foremost ships, yet there they abode in close rank beside the huts, and did not scatter throughout the camp. For shame and fear restrained them and ceaselessly they kept shouting each to other. Now Gerenian Nestor above all, the Warden of the Achaians, implored each man by the memory of them that begat him, and spake beseechingly: "O friends, play the man, and set shame of other men's contempt in your hearts. Let each also be mindful of children and wives, and of his possessions, and of them that begat him, whether any have parents yet alive or they be already dead. For their sake do I here beseech you, for the sake of them that are not with us, to stand stoutly, nor turn to flight."

So spake he, and roused each man's courage and might, and from their eyes Athene lifted the wondrous cloud of mist, and light came mightily upon them from either side, both from the side of the ships, and from the quarter of even-balanced war. And they beheld Hector of the loud war-cry, and his comrades, both them that stood in the rear and were not fighting, and all them that fought in the battle by the swift ships.

Nor yet did it please the spirit of high-hearted Aias, to stand in the place whereto the other sons of the Achaians had withdrawn, but he kept faring with long strides, up and down the decks of the ships, and he wielded in his hands a great pike for sea-battles, jointed with rings, two and twenty cubits in length. And even as a man right well skilled in horsemanship that couples four horses out of many, and hurrying them from the plain towards a great city, drives along the public way, many men and women marvelling on him, and firmly ever he leaps, and changes his stand from horse to horse, while they fly along, even so Aias went with long strides, over many a deck of the swift ships, and his voice went up unto heaven. And always with terrible cries he summoned the Danaans to defend the ships and the huts. Nor did Hector abide in the throng of well-armed Trojans, but even as a tawny eagle rushes on a flock of winged fowl, that are feeding by a riverside, a flock of geese, or cranes, or long-necked swans, even so Hector made straight for a black-beaked ship, rushing right on it, and mightily Zeus urged him on from behind with his strong hand, and roused on the host along with him.

So again keen battle was set by the ships. Thou wouldst deem that unwearied and unworn they met each other in war, so eagerly they fought. And in their striving they were minded thus; the Achaians verily deemed that never would they flee from the danger, but perish there, but the heart of each Trojan hoped in his breast, that they should fire the ships, and slay the heroes of the Achaians. With these imaginations they stood to each other, and Hector seized the stern of a seafaring ship, a fair ship, swift on the brine, that had borne Protesilaos to Troia, but brought him not back again to his own country. Now round his ship the Achaians and Trojans warred on each other hand to hand, nor far apart did they endure the flights of arrows, nor of darts, but standing hard each by other, with one heart, with sharp axes and hatchets they fought, and with great swords, and double-pointed spears. And many fair brands, dark-scabbarded and hilted, fell to the ground, some from the hands, some from off the shoulders of warring men, and the black earth ran with blood. But Hector, after that once he had seized the ship's stern, left not his hold, keeping the ensign in his hands, and he called to the Trojans: "Bring fire, and all with one voice do ye raise the war-cry; now hath Zeus given us the dearest day of all,—to take the ships that came hither against the will of the gods, and brought many woes upon us, by the cowardice of the elders, who withheld me when I was eager to fight at the sterns of the ships, and kept back the host. But if even then far-seeing Zeus did harm our wits, now he himself doth urge and command us onwards."

So spake he, and they set yet the fiercer on the Argives. And Aias no longer abode their onset, for he was driven back by the darts, but he withdrew a little,—thinking that now he should die,—onto the oarsmen's bench of seven feet long, and he left the decks of the trim ship. There then he stood on the watch, and with his spear he ever drave the Trojans from the ships, whosoever brought unwearied fire, and ever he shouted terribly, calling to the Danaans: "O friends, Danaan heroes, men of Ares' company, play the man, my friends, and be mindful of impetuous valour. Do we deem that there be allies at our backs, or some wall stronger than this to ward off death from men? Verily there is not hard by any city arrayed with towers, whereby we might defend ourselves, having a host that could turn the balance of battle. Nay, but we are set down in the plain of the mailed men of Troy, with our backs against the sea, and far off from our own land. Therefore is safety in battle, and not in slackening from the fight."

So spake he, and rushed on ravening for battle, with his keen spear. And whosoever of the Trojans was coming against the ship with blazing fire, to pleasure Hector at his urging, him would Aias wound, awaiting him with his long spear, and twelve men in front of the ships at close quarters did he wound.

BOOK XVI

How Patroklos fought in the armour of Achilles, and drove the Trojans from the ships, but was slain at last by Hector.

So they were warring round the well-timbered ship, but Patroklos drew near Achilles, shepherd of the host, and he shed warm tears, even as a fountain of dark water that down a steep cliff pours its cloudy stream. And noble swift-footed Achilles when he beheld him was grieved for his sake, and accosted him, and spake winged words, saying: "Wherefore weepest thou, Patroklos, like a fond little maid, that runs by her mother's side, and bids her mother take her up, snatching at her gown, and hinders her in her going, and tearfully looks at her, till the mother takes her up? like her, Patroklos, dost thou let fall soft tears. Hast thou aught to tell to the Myrmidons, or to me myself, or is it some tidings out of Phthia that thou alone hast heard? They say that Menoitios son of Aktor still lives: and Peleus son of Aiakos lives yet among the Myrmidons, for which twain, were they dead, right sore would we sorrow. Or dost thou lament for the sake of the Argives,—how they perish by the hollow ships through their own transgression? Speak out, and hide it not within thy spirit, that we may both know all."

But with a heavy groan didst thou speak unto him, O knight Patroklos: "O Achilles, son of Peleus, far the bravest of the Achaians, be not wroth, seeing that so great calamity has beset the Achaians. For verily all of them that aforetime were the best are lying among the ships, smitten and wounded. Smitten is the son of Tydeus, strong

Diomedes, and wounded is Odysseus, spearman renowned, and Agamemnon; and smitten is Eurypylos on the thigh with an arrow. And about them the leeches skilled in medicines are busy, healing their wounds, but thou art hard to reconcile, Achilles. Never then may such wrath take hold of me as that thou nursest; thou brave to the hurting of others. What other man later born shall have profit of thee, if thou dost not ward off base ruin from the Argives? Pitiless that thou art, the knight Peleus was not then thy father, nor Thetis thy mother, but the grey sea bare thee, and the sheer cliffs, so untoward is thy spirit. But if in thy heart thou art shunning some oracle, and thy lady mother hath told thee somewhat from Zeus, yet me do thou send forth quickly, and make the rest of the host of the Myrmidons follow me, if yet any light may arise from me to the Danaans. And give me thy harness to buckle about my shoulders, if perchance the Trojans may take me for thee, and so abstain from battle, and the warlike sons of the Achaians may take breath, wearied as they be, for brief is the breathing in war. And lightly might we that are fresh drive men wearied with the battle back to the citadel, away from the ships and the huts."

So he spake and besought him, in his unwittingness, for truly it was to be his own evil death and fate that he prayed for. Then to him in great heaviness spake swift-footed Achilles: "Ah me, Patroklos of the seed of Zeus, what word hast thou spoken? Neither take I heed of any oracle that I wot of, nor yet has my lady mother told me somewhat from Zeus, but this dread sorrow comes upon my heart and spirit, from the hour that a man wishes to rob me who am his equal, and to take away my prize, for that he excels me in power. A dread sorrow to me is this, after all the toils that my heart hath endured. The maiden that the sons of the Achaians chose out for me as my prize, and that I won with my spear when I sacked a well-walled city, her has mighty Agamemnon the son of Atreus taken back out of my hands, as though I were but some sojourner dishonourable. But we will let bygones be bygones. No man may be angry of heart for ever, yet verily I said that I would not cease from my wrath, until that time when to mine own ships should come the war-cry and the battle. But do thou on thy shoulders my famous harness, and lead the war-loving Myrmidons to the fight, if indeed the dark cloud of the Trojans hath mightily surrounded the ships, and if the Argives are given back to the shore of the sea, holding but a narrow space of land, and the whole town of Troy hath come boldly against them. Yea, for they behold not the vizor of my helm shining hard at hand; swiftly would they flee, and fill the watercourses with dead, if mighty Agamemnon had been but kindly to me,—but now are they warring round the camp. For not in the hands of Diomedes, the son of Tydeus, rageth the spear, to ward off destruction from the Danaans. Neither as yet have I heard the voice of the son of Atreus, shouting out of his hated mouth, but of Hector the slayer of men doth the voice burst around me, as he calls on the Trojans, and they with their cries fill all the plain, overcoming the Achaians in the battle. But even so, Patroklos, to ward off destruction from the ships, do thou fall on mightily, lest they even burn the ships with blazing fire, and take away our desired return. But do thou obey, even as I shall put into thy mind the end of my commandment, that in my sight thou mayst win great honour and fame of all the Danaans, and they may give me back again the fairest maiden, and thereto add splendid gifts. When thou hast driven them from the ships, return, and even if the loud-thundering lord of Hera grant thee to win glory, yet long not thou apart from me to fight with the war-loving Trojans; thereby wilt thou minish mine honour. Neither do thou, exulting in war and strife, and slaying the Trojans, lead on toward Ilios, lest one of the eternal gods from Olympus come against thee; right dearly doth Apollo the

Far-darter love them. Nay, return back when thou hast brought safety to the ships, and suffer the rest to fight along the plain. For would, O father Zeus, and Athene, and Apollo, would that not one of all the Trojans might escape death, nor one of the Argives, but that we twain might avoid destruction, that alone we might undo the sacred coronal of Troy."

So spake they each to other, but Aias no longer abode the onset, for he was overpowered by darts; the counsel of Zeus was subduing him, and the shafts of the proud Trojans; and his bright helmet, being smitten, kept ringing terribly about his temples: for always it was smitten upon the fair-wrought cheek-pieces. Moreover his left shoulder was wearied, as steadfastly he held up his glittering shield, nor yet could they make him give ground, as they pressed on with their darts around him. And ever he was worn out with difficult breath, and much sweat kept running from all his limbs, nor had he a moment to draw breath, so on all sides was evil heaped on evil.

Tell me now, ye Muses that have mansions in Olympus, how first fire fell on the ships of the Achaians. Hector drew near, and the ashen spear of Aias he smote with his great sword, hard by the socket, behind the point, and shore it clean away, and the son of Telamon brandished in his hand no more than a pointless spear, and far from him the head of bronze fell ringing on the ground.

And Aias knew in his noble heart, and shuddered at the deeds of the gods, even how Zeus that thundereth on high did utterly cut off from him avail in war, and desired victory for the Trojans. Then Aias gave back out of the darts. But the Trojans cast on the swift ship unwearying fire, and instantly the inextinguishable flame streamed over her: so the fire begirt the stern, whereon Achilles smote his thighs, and spake to Patroklos: "Arise, Patroklos of the seed of Zeus, commander of the horsemen, for truly I see by the ships the rush of the consuming fire. Up then, lest they take the ships, and there be no more retreat; do on thy harness speedily, and I will summon the host."

So spake he, while Patroklos was harnessing him in shining bronze. His goodly greaves, fitted with silver clasps, he first girt round his legs, and next did on around his breast the well-dight starry corslet of the swift-footed son of Aiakos. And round his shoulders he cast a sword of bronze, with studs of silver, and next took the great and mighty shield, and on his proud head set a well-wrought helm with a horse-hair crest, and terribly nodded the crest from above. Then seized he two strong lances that fitted his grasp, only he took not the spear of the noble son of Aiakos, heavy, and huge, and stalwart, that none other of the Achaians could wield, but Achilles alone availed to wield it: even the ashen Pelian spear that Cheiron gave to his father dear, from a peak of Pelion, to be the death of warriors. And Patroklos bade Automedon to yoke the horses speedily, even Automedon whom most he honoured after Achilles, the breaker of the ranks of men, and whom he held trustiest in battle to abide his call. And for him Automedon led beneath the yoke the swift horses, Xanthos and Balios, that fly as swift as the winds, the horses that the harpy Podarge bare to the West Wind, as she grazed on the meadow by the stream of Okeanos. And in the side-traces he put the goodly Pedasos, that Achilles carried away, when he took the city of Eetion; and being but a mortal steed, he followed with the immortal horses.

Meanwhile Achilles went and harnessed all the Myrmidons in the huts with armour, and they gathered like ravening wolves with strength in their hearts unspeakable, that have slain a great horned stag in the hills and rend him piecemeal; and all their jaws are red with blood, and in a herd they go, to lap with their thin tongues the surface of the dark water in a dusky well, belching out the blood of the slaughter, their heart steadfast within their breasts, and their bellies swollen, even so hastened the leaders and chiefs of the Myrmidons around the good squire of swift-footed Achilles. And among them all stood warlike Achilles, urging on the horses and the targeteers.

Fifty were the swift ships which Achilles, beloved of Zeus, led to Troia, and in each ship on the benches sat fifty men his comrades, and five leaders he made, wherein he trusted to give command, and himself with great lordship was chief of them all. One rank led Menesthios of the shining corslet, the son of Spercheios, the River that falleth from Zeus. Him did the daughter of Peleus bear, beautiful Polydora, to tireless Spercheios, a woman couched with a god. But by name was he the son of Boros, Perieres' son, who openly wedded her, giving countless gifts of wooing. And the next company did warlike Eudoros lead, the son of an unwedded girl, and him bare Polymele, fair in the dance, the daughter of Phylas. Her did the strong slayer of Argus love, when he had beheld her with his eyes among the singing maidens, in the choir of Artemis, the swift-rushing goddess of the golden arrows. Then straightway he went up into her upper chamber, and lay with her secretly, even Hermes the bearer of all things good, and gat by her a glorious son, Eudoros, swift of foot and a man of war. But when Eilithyia, goddess of the pains of travail, had brought him to the light, and he saw the rays of the sun, then the strong Echekles, son of Aktor, led Polymele to his halls, after he had given countless gifts of wooing, but Eudoros did the old Phylas rear well and nourish tenderly, loving him dearly as he had been his own son.

And the third company led warlike Peisandros, the son of Maimalos, most excellent among the Myrmidons in fighting with the spear, after the comrade of the son of Peleus. And the ancient knight Phoinix led the fourth company, and the fifth Alkimedon the noble son of Laerkes led. But when Achilles had stationed them all, and arrayed them well with their leaders, he laid on them a strong command: "Myrmidons, let me find none of you forgetful of the threats wherewith by the swift ships ye threatened the Trojans, through all the time of my wrath, and ye did each accuse me, saying, 'Hard-hearted son of Peleus, surely on gall thy mother reared thee, thou pitiless one that restrainest thy comrades at the ships, against their will. Nay, homewards let us return again with our seafaring ships, since such an evil wrath has sunk into thy heart.' Even thus did ye often clamour against me in your gatherings, but now hath appeared the mighty work of war, wherewith in time past ye were in love. Therefore let each man keep a stout heart in the battle with the Trojans."

So spake he, and aroused the heart and valour of each of them, and the ranks were yet the closer serried when they heard the prince. And as when a man builds the wall of a high house with close-set stones, to avoid the might of the winds, even so close were arrayed the helmets and bossy shields, and shield pressed on shield, helm on helm, and man on man, and the horse-hair crests on the bright helmet-ridges touched each other when they nodded, so close they stood by each other.

But in front of them all were two men harnessed, Patroklos and Automedon, both of one heart, to war in the van of the Myrmidons. But Achilles went into his hut, and opened the lid of a fair and well-wrought coffer, that silver-footed Thetis placed on board his ship to carry with him, and filled it well with doublets, and cloaks to keep the wind away, and thick carpets. Therein had he a fair-fashioned cup, and neither was any other man wont to drink therefrom the bright wine, nor to any other god was he wont to do libation therewith, save to Zeus the Father only. This cup he took from the coffer, and first purified it with brimstone, and then washed it in fair streams of water, and himself washed his hands, and drew bright wine. Then prayed he, standing in the mid-court, and poured forth the wine, looking up to heaven, and Zeus that hath joy of the thunder was ware of him: "King Zeus, Dodonaean, Pelasgian, thou that dwellest afar, ruling over wintry Dodona—and around thee dwell the Selloi, thy prophets, with unwashen feet, and couching on the ground,—even as once thou didst hear my voice in prayer, and didst honour me, and mightily afflict the host of the Achaians, even now too fulfil for me this my desire. For I myself will abide in the gathering of the ships, but my comrade I send with many Myrmidons to war: to him do thou speed the victory, O far-seeing Zeus, and strengthen his heart within him, that Hector too may know whether my squire hath skill to war even alone,—or whether his hands invincible rage only when I enter the moil of war. But when he has driven from the ships the war and din of battle, scathless then let him return to me at the swift ships with all his arms, and his comrades that fight hand to hand."

So spake he in his prayer, and wise-counselling Zeus heard him, and the Father granted part to him, and part he denied. He granted him that Patroklos should drive the war and the fight from the ships, but denied him to return safe out of the fight. Then Achilles, having made libation and prayer to father Zeus, went back into his hut, and placed the cup in the coffer again, and came forth and stood in front of his hut, for still his heart desired to see the dread strife of the Trojans and Achaians.

But they that were armed about the high-hearted Patroklos marched forward till they rushed in their pride on the Trojans. And straightway they poured forth like wasps that have their dwelling by the wayside, and that boys are ever wont to vex, always tormenting them in their nests beside the way in childish sport, and a common evil they make for many. And they, if ever some wayfaring man passing by stir them unwittingly, fly forth every one of them, with a heart of valour, and each defends his children; with heart and spirit like theirs the Myrmidons poured out now from the ships, and a cry arose unquenchable, and Patroklos called on his comrades, shouting alouu: "Myrmidons, ye comrades of Achilles son of Peleus, be men, my friends, and be mindful of your impetuous valour, that so we may win honour for the son of Peleus, that is far the bravest of the Argives by the ships, and whose close-fighting squires are the best. And let wide-ruling Agamemnon the son of Atreus learn his own blindness of heart, in that he nothing honoured the best of the Achaians."

So spake he, and aroused each man's heart and courage, and all in a mass they fell on the Trojans, and the ships around echoed wondrously to the cry of the Achaians. But when the Trojans beheld the strong son of Menoitios, himself and his squire, shining in their armour, the heart was stirred in all of them, and the companies wavered, for they deemed that by the ships the swift-footed son of Peleus had cast away his wrath, and chosen reconcilement: then each man glanced round, to see where he might flee sheer destruction.

But Patroklos first with a shining spear cast straight into the press, where most men were thronging, even by the stern of the ship of great-hearted Protesilaos, and he smote Pyraichmes, who led his Paionian horsemen out of Amydon, from the wide water of Axios; him he smote on the right shoulder, and he fell on his back in the dust with a groan, and his comrades around him, the Paionians, were afraid, for Patroklos sent fear among them all, when he slew their leader that was ever the best in fight. Then he drove them out from the ships, and quenched the burning fire. And the half-burnt ship was left there, and the Trojans fled, with a marvellous din, and the Danaans poured in among the hollow ships, and ceaseless was the shouting. And as when from the high crest of a great hill Zeus, the gatherer of the lightning, hath stirred a dense cloud, and forth shine all the peaks, and sharp promontories, and glades, and from heaven the infinite air breaks open, even so the Danaans, having driven the blazing fire from the ships, for a little while took breath, but there was no pause in the battle. For not yet were the Trojans driven in utter rout by the Achaians, dear to Ares, from the black ships, but they still stood up against them, and only perforce gave ground from the ships.

Then man slew man of the chieftains, in the scattered fight. First the strong son of Menoitios smote the thigh of Areïlykos, at the moment when he turned, with a sharp spear, and drave the bronze clean through, and the spear brake the bone, and he fell on his face, on the ground. Meanwhile warlike Menelaos wounded Thoas on his breast where it was left uncovered, by the edge of the shield, and loosened his limbs. And Phyleides watched Amphiklos as he set on, and was beforehand with him, stretching forward at the thigh, where a man's muscle is thickest, and the sinews were rent with the point of the spear, and darkness covered his eyes. And as for the sons of Nestor, one of them, Antilochos, smote Atymnios with the sharp spear, and drave the spear of bronze through his flank, and he fell forward. But hard at hand Maris rushed on Antilochos with the spear, in wrath for his brother's sake, and stood in front of the dead; but godlike Thrasymedes was beforehand with him, and smote forward instantly at his shoulder ere he could deal a wound, and missed not, for the point of the spear rent the root of the arm from the muscles, and tore it to the bone. Then fell he with a crash, and darkness covered his eyes. So these twain, subdued by the two brothers, went to Erebos, even the noble comrades of Sarpedon, the warrior sons of Amisodaros, that reared the invincible Chimaira, the bane of many a man. But Aias son of Oileus rushed on Cleoboulos, and took him alive, entangled in the press; so even there he loosened his might, and smote him on the neck with the hilted sword. And all the blade was warm with his blood, and dark death closed his eyes, and mighty Fate.

Then Peneleos and Lykon ran together, for with their spears they missed each other, yea, both had cast in vain, and instantly they ran together with their swords. There Lykon smote the socket of the horse-hair crest, and his sword brake at the hilt, but Peneleos smote his neck behind the ear, and all the blade sank in, and naught but the skin held, and the head hung slack, and loosened were his limbs.

Now Meriones overtook Akamas with swift strides, and smote him on the right shoulder, as he went up into his chariot, and he slipped out of his chariot, and mist was poured over his eyes. And Idomeneus wounded Erymas on the mouth with the pitiless bronze, and the spear of bronze went clean through below, beneath the brain, and shattered his white bones, and his teeth were shaken out, and both his eyes were filled with blood, and he blew blood up through mouth and nostrils as he gaped, and the black cloud of death covered him about.

Thus those leaders of the Danaans slew each his man. But even as robber wolves fall on the lambs or kids, choosing them out of the herds, when they are scattered on hills by the witlessness of the shepherd, and the wolves behold it, and speedily harry the younglings that have no heart of courage,—even so the Danaans fell on the Trojans, and they were mindful of ill-sounding flight, and forgot their impetuous valour.

But that great Aias ever was fain to cast his spear at Hector of the helm of bronze, but he, in his cunning of war, covered his broad shoulders with his shield of bulls' hide, and watched the hurtling of the arrows, and the noise of spears. And verily well he knew the change in the mastery of war, but even so he abode, and was striving to rescue his trusty comrades.

And as when from Olympus a cloud fares into heaven, from the sacred air, when Zeus spreadeth forth the tempest, even so from the ships came the war-cry and the rout, nor in order due did they cross the ditch again. But his swift-footed horses bare Hector forth with his arms, and he left the host of Troy, whom the delved trench restrained against their will. And in the trench did many swift steeds that draw the car break the fore-part of the pole, and leave the chariots of their masters.

But Patroklos followed after, crying fiercely to the Danaans, and full of evil will against the Trojans, while they with cries and flight filled all the ways, for they were scattered, and on high the storm of dust was scattered below the clouds, and the whole-hooved horses strained back towards the city, away from the ships and the huts.

But even where Patroklos saw the folk thickest in the rout, thither did he guide his horses with a cry, and under his axle-trees men fell prone from their chariots, and the cars were overturned with a din of shattering. But straight over the ditch, in forward flight, leaped the swift [immortal] horses [that the gods gave for glorious gifts to Peleus]. And the heart of Patroklos urged him against Hector, for he was eager to smite him, but his swift steeds bore Hector forth and away. And even as beneath a tempest the whole black earth is oppressed, on an autumn day, when Zeus pours forth rain most vehemently, being in wrath and anger against men, who judge crooked judgments forcefully in the assembly, and drive justice out, and reck not of the vengeance of the gods, and all their rivers run full, and many a scaur the torrents tear away, and down to the dark sea they rush headlong from the hills, roaring mightily, and minished are the works of men, even so mighty was the roar of the Trojan horses as they ran.

Now Patroklos when he had cloven the nearest companies, drave them backward again to the ships, nor suffered them to approach the city, despite their desire, but between the ships, and the river, and the lofty wall, he rushed on them, and slew them, and avenged many a comrade slain. There first he smote Pronoos with a shining spear, where the shield left bare the breast, and loosened his limbs, and he fell with a crash. Then Thestor the son of Enops he next assailed, as he sat crouching in the polished chariot, for he was struck distraught, and the reins flew from his hands. Him he drew near, and smote with the lance on the right jaw, and clean pierced through his teeth. And Patroklos caught hold of the spear and dragged him over the rim of the car, as when a man sits on a jutting rock, and drags a sacred fish forth from the sea, with line and glittering hook of bronze; so on the bright spear dragged he Thestor gaping from the chariot, and cast him down on his face, and life left him as he fell. Next, as Euryalos came on, he smote him on the midst of the head with a stone, and all his head was shattered within the strong helmet, and prone on the earth he fell, and death that slayeth the spirit overwhelmed him. Next Erymas, and Amphoteros, and Epaltes and Tlepolemos son of Damastor, and Echios and Pyris, and Ipheus and Euippos, and Polymelos son of Argeas, all these in turn he brought low to the bounteous earth. But when Sarpedon beheld his comrades with ungirdled doublets, subdued beneath the hands of Patroklos son of Menoitios, he cried aloud, upbraiding the godlike Lykians: "Shame, ye Lykians, whither do ye flee? Now be ye strong, for I will encounter this man that I may know who he is that conquers here, and verily many evils hath he wrought the Trojans, in that he hath loosened the knees of many men and noble."

So spake he, and leaped with his arms from the chariot to the ground. But Patroklos, on the other side, when he beheld him leaped from his chariot. And they, like vultures of crooked talons and curved beaks, that war with loud yells on some high cliff, even so they rushed with cries against each other. And beholding then the son of Kronos of the crooked counsels took pity on them, and he spake to Hera, his sister and wife: "Ah woe is me for that it is fated that Sarpedon, the best-beloved of men to me, shall be subdued under Patroklos son of Menoitios. And in two ways my heart within my breast is divided, as I ponder whether I should catch him up alive out of the tearful war, and set him down in the rich land of Lykia, or whether I should now subdue him beneath the hands of the son of Menoitios."

Then the ox-eyed lady Hera made answer to him: "Most dread son of Kronos, what word is this thou hast spoken? A mortal man long doomed to fate dost thou desire to deliver again from death of evil name? Work thy will, but all we other gods will in no wise praise thee. And another thing I will tell thee, and do thou lay it up in thy heart; if thou dost send Sarpedon living to his own house, consider lest thereon some other god likewise desire to send his own dear son away out of the strong battle. For round the great citadel of Priam war many sons of the Immortals, and among the Immortals wilt thou send terrible wrath. But if he be dear to thee, and thy heart mourns for him, truly then suffer him to be subdued in the strong battle beneath the hands of Patroklos son of Menoitios, but when his soul and life leave that warrior, send Death and sweet Sleep to bear him, even till they come to the land of wide Lykia, there will his kindred and friends bury him, with a barrow and a pillar, for this is the due of the dead."

So spake she, nor did the father of gods and men disregard her. But he shed bloody raindrops on the earth, honouring his dear son, that Patroklos was about to slay in the deep-soiled land of Troia, far off from his own country. Now when they were come near each other in onset, there verily did Patroklos smite the renowned Thrasymelos, the good squire of the prince Sarpedon, on the lower part of the belly, and loosened his limbs. But Sarpedon missed him with his shining javelin, as he in turn rushed on, but wounded the horse Pedasos on the right shoulder with the spear, and he shrieked as he breathed his life away, and fell crying in the dust, and his spirit fled from him. But the other twain reared this way and that, and the yoke creaked, and the reins were confused on them, when their trace-horse lay in the dust. But thereof did Automedon, the spearman renowned, find a remedy, and drawing his long-edged sword from his stout thigh, he leaped forth, and cut adrift the horse, with no delay, and the pair righted themselves, and strained in the reins, and they met again in life-devouring war.

Then again Sarpedon missed with his shining dart, and the point of the spear flew over the left shoulder of Patroklos and smote him not, but he in turn arose with the bronze, and his javelin flew not vainly from his hand, but struck Sarpedon even where the midriff clasps the beating heart. And he fell as falls an oak, or a silver poplar, or a slim pine-tree, that on the hills the shipwrights fell with whetted axes, to be timber for shipbuilding; even so before the horses and chariot he lay at length, moaning aloud, and clutching at the bloody dust. And as when a lion hath fallen on a herd, and slain a bull, tawny and high of heart, among the kine of trailing gait, and he perishes groaning beneath the claws of the lion, even so under Patroklos did the leader of the Lykian shieldmen rage, even in death, and he called to his dear comrade: "Dear Glaukos, warrior among warlike men, now most doth it behove thee to be a spearman, and a hardy fighter: now let baneful war be dear to thee, if indeed thou art a man of might. First fare all about and urge on the heroes that be leaders of the Lykians, to fight for Sarpedon, and thereafter thyself do battle for me with the sword. For to thee even in time to come shall I be shame and disgrace for ever, all thy days, if the Achaians strip me of mine armour, fallen in the gathering of the ships. Nay, hold out manfully, and spur on all the host."

Even as he spake thus, the end of death veiled over his eyes and his nostrils, but Patroklos, setting foot on his breast, drew the spear out of his flesh, and the midriff followed with the spear, so that he drew forth together the spear point, and the soul of Sarpedon; and the Myrmidons held there his panting steeds, eager to fly afar, since the chariot was reft of its lords.

Then dread sorrow came on Glaukos, when he heard the voice of Sarpedon, and his heart was stirred, that he availed not to succour him. And with his hand he caught and held his arm, for the wound galled him, the wound of the arrow wherewith, as he pressed on towards the lofty wall, Teukros had smitten him, warding off destruction from his fellows. Then in prayer spake Glaukos to far-darting Apollo: "Hear, O Prince that art somewhere in the rich land of Lykia, or in Troia, for thou canst listen everywhere to the man that is in need, as even now need cometh upon me. For I have this stark wound, and mine arm is thoroughly pierced with sharp pains, nor can my blood be stanched, and by the wound is my shoulder burdened, and I cannot hold my spear firm, nor go and fight against the enemy. And the best of men has perished, Sarpedon, the son of Zeus, and he succours not even his own child. But do thou, O Prince, heal me this stark wound, and lull my pains, and give me strength, that I may call on my Lykian kinsmen, and spur them to the war, and myself may fight about the dead man fallen."

So spake he in his prayer, and Phoebus Apollo heard him. Straightway he made his pains to cease, and in the previous wound stanched the black blood, and put courage into his heart. And Glaukos knew it within him, and was glad, for that the great god speedily heard his prayer. First went he all about and urged on them that were leaders of the Lykians to fight around Sarpedon, and thereafter he went with long strides among the Trojans, to Polydamas son of Panthoos and noble Agenor, and he went after Aineias, and Hector of the helm of bronze, and standing by them spake winged words: "Hector, now surely art thou utterly forgetful of the allies, that for thy sake far from their friends and their own country, breathe their lives away! but thou carest not to aid them! Sarpedon lies low, the leader of the Lykian shieldmen, he that defended Lykia by his dooms and his might, yea him hath mailed Ares subdued beneath the spear of Patroklos. But, friends, stand by him, and be angry in your hearts lest the Myrmidons strip him of his harness, and dishonour the dead, in wrath for the sake of the Danaans, even them that perished, whom we slew with spears by the swift ships."

So spake he, and sorrow seized the Trojans utterly, ungovernable and not to be borne; for Sarpedon was ever the stay of their city, all a stranger as he was, for many people followed with him, and himself the best warrior of them all. Then they made straight for the Danaans eagerly, and Hector led them, being wroth for Sarpedon's sake. But the fierce heart of Patroklos son of Menoitios urged on the Achaians. And he spake first to the twain Aiantes that themselves were right eager: "Aiantes, now let defence be your desire, and be such as afore ye were among men, or even braver yet. That man lies low who first leaped on to the wall of the Achaians, even Sarpedon. Nay, let us strive to take him, and work his body shame, and strip the harness from his shoulders, and many a one of his comrades fighting for his sake let us subdue with the pitiless bronze."

So spake he, and they themselves were eager in defence. So on both sides they strengthened the companies, Trojans and Lykians, Myrmidons and Achaians, and they joined battle to fight around the dead man fallen; terribly they shouted, and loud rang the harness of men. But Zeus drew baneful night above the strong battle, that round his dear son might be the woful toil of war. Now first the Trojans drove back the bright-eyed Achaians, for a man in no wise the worst among the Myrmidons was smitten, the son of great-hearted Agakles, goodly Epeigeus, who ruled fair-set Boudeion of old, but when he had slain a good man of his kin, to Peleus he came as a suppliant, and to silver-footed Thetis. And they sent him to follow with Achilles, the breaker of the ranks of men, to Ilios of the goodly steeds, to war with the Trojans. Then him, as he was laying hold of the dead man, did renowned Hector smite on the head with a stone, and all his head was broken in twain within the strong helm, and prone on the dead he fell, and round him was poured death that slayeth the spirit. Then grief came on Patroklos for his comrade slain, and he rushed through the foremost fighters, like to a falcon swift of flight, that scareth daws and starlings, even so against the Lykians, O Patroklos, warrior-charioteer, and against the Trojans didst thou rush, being wroth at heart for thy comrade's sake. And he smote Sthenelaos, the dear son of Ithaimenes, on the neck, with a stone, and brake away his sinews. Then back drew the foremost fighters, and renowned Hector. And as far as is the flight of a long javelin, that a man casts, making trial of his skill, either in a contest for a prize, or in war, being pressed by deadly foemen, so far did the Trojans draw back, and the Achaians drave them. And Glaukos first, the leader of the Lykian shieldmen, turned him about, and slew Bathykles great of heart, the dear son of Chalkon, that dwelt in his home in Hellas, and for wealth and riches was pre-eminent among the Myrmidons. Him did Glaukos wound in the mid-breast with a spear, turning suddenly about, when Bathykles was about to seize him as he followed hard after him. With a crash he fell, and great woe came on the Achaians, that a good man was down, but mightily did the Trojans rejoice. And they all thronged around him and stood firm, nor did the Achaians forget their valour, but bare their might straight down on them. There likewise Meriones slew a mailed warrior of the Trojans, Laogonos, the bold son of Onetor, that was priest of Idaean Zeus, and as a god was honoured by the people, —him he smote beneath the jaw and the ear, and swiftly his spirit departed from his limbs, and so loathly darkness gat hold on him. And Aineias cast against Meriones his spear of bronze, for he hoped to smite him as he came on beneath the shield. But he kept a forward watch, and avoided the spear of bronze, stooping forward, and behind him the long dart stood fast in the ground, but the butt of the spear quivered, and there then strong Ares took its strength away. [And the spear of Aineias sunk quivering into the earth, since vainly it had sped from his strong hand]. But Aineias was wroth at heart, and spake aloud: "Meriones, swiftly should my spear have stopped thy dancing for ever, good dancer as thou art, if I had but struck thee."

But to him again Meriones, spearman renowned, replied: "Aineias, it is hard for thee, strong as thou art, to quench the might of every man that cometh against thee in battle. Yea, thou too art a mortal. And if ever I should cast at thee and strike thee in the midst with the sharp bronze, quickly shouldst thou for all thy valour and trust in thy hands give glory to me, and thy soul to Hades of the famous steeds."

So spake he, but him did the strong son of Menoitios rebuke: "Meriones, why speakest thou thus, thou that art a man of valour? O my friend, not for railing words will the Trojans draw back from the dead, the earth must hold some fast ere that may be. For in the hands of men is the end of war, but of words the end is in council, wherefore in no wise should we multiply words, but do battle."

So speaking, he began, and the other followed him, a godlike man. And as the din ariseth of woodcutters in the glades of a mountain, and the sound thereof is heard far away, so rose the din of them from the wide-wayed earth, the noise of bronze and of well-tanned bulls' hides smitten with swords and double-pointed spears. And now not even a clear-sighted man could any longer have known noble Sarpedon, for with darts and blood and dust was he covered wholly from head to foot. And ever men thronged about the dead, as in a steading flies buzz around the full milk-pails, in the season of spring, when the milk drenches the bowls, even so thronged they about the dead. Nor ever did Zeus turn from the strong fight his shining eyes, but ever looked down on them, and much in his heart he debated of the slaying of Patroklos, whether there and then above divine Sarpedon glorious Hector should slay him likewise in strong battle with the sword, and strip his harness from his shoulders, or whether to more men yet he should deal sheer labour of war. And thus to him as he pondered it seemed the better way, that the gallant squire of Achilles, Peleus' son, should straightway drive the Trojans and Hector of the helm of bronze towards the city, and should rob many of their life. And in Hector first he put a weakling heart, and leaping into his car Hector turned in flight, and cried on the rest of the Trojans to flee, for he knew the turning of the sacred scales of Zeus. Thereon neither did the strong Lykians abide, but fled all in fear, when they beheld their king stricken to the heart, lying in the company of the dead, for many had fallen above him, when Kronion made fierce the fight. Then the others stripped from the shoulders of Sarpedon his shining arms of bronze, and these the strong son of Menoitios gave to his comrades to bear to the hollow ships. Then Zeus that gathered the clouds spake to Apollo: "Prithee, dear Phoebus, go take Sarpedon out of range of darts, and cleanse the black blood from him, and thereafter bear him far away, and bathe him in the streams of the river, and anoint him with ambrosia, and clothe him in garments that wax not old, and send him to be wafted by fleet convoy, by the twin brethren Sleep and Death, that quickly will set him in the rich land of wide Lykia. There will his kinsmen and clansmen give him burial, with barrow and pillar, for such is the due of the dead."

So spake he, nor was Apollo disobedient to his father. He went down the hills of Ida to the dread battle-din, and straightway bore goodly Sarpedon out of the darts, and carried him far away, and bathed him in the streams of the river, and anointed him with ambrosia, and clad him in garments that wax not old, and sent him to be wafted by fleet convoy, the twin brethren Sleep and Death, that swiftly set him down in the rich land of wide Lykia. But Patroklos cried to his horses and Automedon, and after the Trojans and Lykians went he, and so was blindly forgetful, in his witlessness, for if he had kept the saying of the son of Peleus, verily he should have escaped the evil fate of black death. But ever is the wit of Zeus stronger than the wit of men, [for he driveth the valiant man in flight, and easily taketh away the victory, and then again himself rouseth men to fight], so now he roused the spirit of Patroklos in his breast. There whom first, whom last didst thou slay, Patroklos, when the gods called thee deathward? Adrestos first, and Autonoos, and Echeklos, and Perimos, son of Megas, and Epistor, and Melanippos, and thereafter Elasos, and Moulios, and Pylartes; these he slew, but the others were each man of them fain of flight. Then would the sons of the Achaians have taken high-gated Troy, by the hands of Patroklos, for around and before him he raged with the spear, but that Phoebus Apollo stood on the well-builded wall, with baneful thoughts towards Patroklos, and succouring the Trojans. Thrice clomb Patroklos on the corner of the lofty wall, and thrice did Apollo force him back and smote the shining shield with his immortal hands. But when for the fourth time he came on like a god, then cried far-darting Apollo terribly, and spake winged words: "Give back, Patroklos of the seed of Zeus! Not beneath thy spear is it fated that the city of the valiant Trojans shall fall, nay nor beneath Achilles, a man far better than thou."

So spake he, and Patroklos retreated far back, avoiding the wrath of far-darting Apollo. But Hector within the Skaian gates was restraining his whole-hooved horses, pondering whether he should drive again into the din and fight, or should call unto the host to gather to the wall. While thus he was thinking, Phoebus Apollo stood by him in the guise of a young man and a strong, Asios, who was the mother's brother of horse-taming Hector, being own brother of Hekabe, and son of Dymas, who dwelt in Phrygia, on the streams of Sangarios. In his guise spake Apollo, son of Zeus, to Hector: "Hector, wherefore dost thou cease from fight? It doth not behove thee. Would that I were as much stronger than thou as I am weaker, thereon quickly shouldst thou stand aloof from war to thy hurt. But come turn against Patroklos thy strong-hooved horses, if perchance thou mayst slay him, and Apollo give thee glory."

So spake the god, and went back again into the moil of men. But renowned Hector bade wise-hearted Kebriones to lash his horses into the war. Then Apollo went and passed into the press, and sent a dread panic among the Argives, but to the Trojans and Hector gave he renown. And Hector let the other Argives be, and slew none of them, but against Patroklos he turned his strong-hooved horses, and Patroklos on the other side leaped from his chariot to the ground, with a spear in his left hand, and in his other hand grasped a shining jagged stone, that his hand covered. Firmly he planted himself and hurled it, nor long did he shrink from his foe, nor was his cast in vain, but he struck Kebriones the charioteer of Hector, the bastard son of renowned Priam, on the brow with the sharp stone, as he held the reins of the horses. Both his brows the stone drave together, and his bone held not, but his eyes fell to the ground in the dust, there, in front of his feet. Then he, like a diver, fell from the well-wrought car, and his spirit left his bones. Then taunting him didst thou address him, knightly Patroklos: "Out on it, how nimble a man, how lively he diveth! Yea, if perchance he were on the teeming deep, this man would satisfy many by seeking for oysters, leaping from the ship, even if it were stormy weather, so lightly now he diveth from the chariot into the plain. Verily among the Trojans too there be diving men."

So speaking he set on the hero Kebriones with the rush of a lion, that while wasting the cattle-pens is smitten in the breast, and his own valour is his bane, even so against Kebriones, Patroklos, didst thou leap furiously. But Hector, on the other side, leaped from his chariot to the ground. And these twain strove for Kebriones like lions, that on the mountain peaks fight, both hungering, both high of heart, for a slain hind. Even so for Kebriones' sake these two masters of the war-cry, Patroklos son of Menoitios, and renowned Hector, were eager each to hew the other's flesh with the ruthless bronze.

Hector then seized him by the head, and slackened not hold, while Patroklos on the other side grasped him by the foot, and thereon the others, Trojans and Danaans, joined strong battle. And as the East wind and the South contend with one another in shaking a deep wood in the dells of a mountain, shaking beech, and ash, and smooth-barked cornel tree, that clash against each other their long boughs with marvellous din, and a noise of branches broken, so the Trojans and Achaians were leaping on each other and slaying, nor had either side any thought of ruinous flight. And many sharp darts were fixed around Kebriones, and winged arrows leaping from the bow-string, and many mighty stones smote the shields of them that fought around him. But he in the whirl of dust lay mighty and mightily fallen, forgetful of his chivalry.

Now while the sun was going about mid-heaven, so long the darts smote either side, and the host fell, but when the sun turned to the time of the loosing of oxen, lo, then beyond their doom the Achaians proved the better. The hero Kebriones drew they forth from the darts, out of the tumult of the Trojans, and stripped the harness from his shoulders, and with ill design against the Trojans, Patroklos rushed upon them. Three times then rushed he on, peer of swift Ares, shouting terribly, and thrice he slew nine men. But when the fourth time he sped on like a god, thereon to thee, Patroklos, did the end of life appear, for Phoebus met thee in the strong battle, in dreadful wise. And Patroklos was not ware of him coming through the press, for hidden in thick mist did he meet him, and stood behind him, and smote his back and broad shoulders with a down-stroke of his hand, and his eyes were dazed. And from his head Phoebus Apollo smote the helmet that rolled rattling away with a din beneath the hooves of the horses, the helm with upright socket, and the crests were defiled with blood and dust. Not of old was it suffered that the helm with horse-hair crest should be defiled with dust, nay, but it kept the head and beautiful face of a man divine, even of Achilles. But as then Zeus gave it to Hector, to bear on his head, yet was destruction near him. And all the long-shadowed spear was shattered in the hands of Patroklos, the spear great and heavy and strong, and sharp, while from his shoulders the tasselled shield with the baldric fell to the ground.

And the prince Apollo, son of Zeus, loosed his corslet, and blindness seized his heart and his shining limbs were unstrung, and he stood in amaze, and at close quarters from behind a Dardanian smote him on the back, between the shoulders, with a sharp spear, even Euphorbos, son of Panthoös, who excelled them of his age in casting the spear, and in horsemanship, and in speed of foot. Even thus, verily, had he cast down twenty men from their chariots, though then first had he come with his car to learn the lesson of war. He it was that first smote a dart into thee, knightly Patroklos, nor overcame thee, but ran back again and mingled with the throng, first drawing forth from the flesh his ashen spear, nor did he abide the onset of Patroklos, unarmed as he was, in the strife. But Patroklos, being overcome by the stroke of the god, and by the spear, gave ground, and retreated to the host of his comrades, avoiding Fate. But Hector, when he beheld great-hearted Patroklos give ground, being smitten with the keen bronze, came nigh unto him through the ranks, and wounded him with a spear, in the lowermost part of the belly, and drave the bronze clean through. And he fell with a crash, and sorely grieved the host of Achaians. And as when a lion hath overcome in battle an untiring boar, they twain fighting with high heart on the crests of a hill, about a little well, and both are desirous to drink, and the lion hath by force overcome the boar that draweth difficult breath; so after that he had slain many did Hector son of Priam take the life away from the strong son of Menoitios, smiting him at close quarters with the spear; and boasting over him he spake winged words: "Patroklos, surely thou saidst that thou wouldst sack my town, and from Trojan women take away the day of freedom, and bring them in ships to thine own dear country: fool! nay, in front of these were the swift horses of Hector straining their speed for the fight; and myself in wielding the spear excel among the war-loving Trojans, even I who ward from them the day of destiny: but thee shall vultures here devour. Ah, wretch, surely Achilles for all his valour, availed thee not, who straitly charged thee as thou camest, he abiding there, saying, 'Come not to me, Patroklos lord of steeds, to the hollow ships, till thou hast torn the gory doublet of man-slaying Hector about his breast;' so, surely, he spake to thee, and persuaded the wits of thee in thy witlessness."

Then faintly didst thou answer him, knightly Patroklos: "Boast greatly, as now, Hector, for to thee have Zeus, son of Kronos, and Apollo given the victory, who lightly have subdued me; for themselves stripped my harness from my shoulders. But if twenty such as thou had encountered me, here had they all perished, subdued beneath my spear. But me had ruinous Fate and the son of Leto slain, and of men Euphorbos, but thou art the third in my slaying. But another thing will I tell thee, and do thou lay it up in thy heart; verily thou thyself art not long to live, but already doth Death stand hard by thee, and strong Fate, that thou art to be subdued by the hands of noble Achilles, of the seed of Aiakos."

Even as so he spake the end of death overshadowed him. And his soul, fleeting from his limbs, went down to the house of Hades, wailing its own doom, leaving manhood and youth.

Then renowned Hector spake to him even in his death: "Patroklos, wherefore to me dost thou prophesy sheer destruction? who knows but that Achilles, the child of fair-tressed Thetis, will first be smitten by my spear, and lose his life?"

So spake he, and drew the spear of bronze from the wound, setting his foot on the dead, and cast him off on his back from the spear. And straightway with the spear he went after Automedon, the godlike squire of the swift-footed Aikides, for he was eager to smite him; but his swift-footed immortal horses bare him out of the battle, horses that the gods gave to Peleus a splendid gift.

BOOK XVII

Of the battle around the body of Patroklos.

But Atreus' son, Menelaos dear to Ares, was not unaware of the slaying of Patroklos by the Trojans in the fray. He went up through the front of the fight harnessed in flashing bronze, and strode over the body as above a first-born calf standeth lowing its mother, ere then unused to motherhood. Thus above Patroklos strode fair-haired Menelaos, and before him held his spear and the circle of his shield, eager to slay whoever should encounter him. Then was Panthoös' son of the stout ashen spear not heedless of noble Patroklos as he lay, and he stood anigh him and spake to Menelaos dear to Ares: "Atreus' son Menelaos, Zeus-fostered, captain of the host, give back and leave the body and yield the bloody spoils; for before me was there none of the Trojans and their famed allies who smote Patroklos with the spear in the stress of fight; wherefore yield me this fair glory to win among the Trojans, lest I hurl and smite thee, and bereave thee of sweet life."

Then sorely wroth spake unto him fair-haired Menelaos: "O father Zeus, no seemly thing is it to boast above measure. Verily neither is spirit of pard or of lion or of cruel wild boar, in the strength of whose breast rageth fury fiercest of all, so high as those proud spirits of Panthoös' sons of the good ashen spear. Yet had the mighty Hyperenor, tamer of horses, no profit of his youth when he reviled me and abode my onset and deemed that I was the meanest warrior among the Danaans; not on his own feet, I ween, did he fare home to gladden his dear wife and his good parents. Thus, methinketh, will I quench thy spirit also, if thou stand up against me; rather I bid thee get thee back into the throng nor stand to encounter me, or ever some ill thing befall thee; by the event is even a fool made wise."

Thus he said, but persuaded not the other, but he spake to him in answer: "Now therefore, Zeus-fostered Menelaos, thou shalt in very deed pay for my brother whom thou slewest and boasted over, and therewithal didst leave his wife a widow in her new bridal-chamber afar, and to his parents broughtest lamentation unspeakable and woe. Verily to those hapless twain shall I be for a withstaying of their lamentation, if I shall carry back thy head and armour and lay them in the hands of Panthoös and noble Phrontis. But now no longer shall the struggle be untried or unfought, whether for victory or for rout."

Thus saying he smote on the circle of the shield of Menelaos, but the bronze spear brake it not, but the point was bent back in the stubborn shield. And Menelaos Atreus' son in his turn made at him with his bronze spear, having prayed unto father Zeus, and as he gave back pierced the nether part of his throat, and threw his weight into the stroke, following his heavy hand; and sheer through the tender neck went the point of the spear. And he fell with a crash, and his armour rang upon him. In blood was his hair drenched that was like unto the hair of the Graces, and his tresses closely knit with bands of silver and gold. As when a man reareth some lusty sapling of an olive in a clear space where water springeth plenteously, a goodly shoot fair-growing; and blasts of all winds shake it, yet it bursteth into white blossom; then suddenly cometh the wind of a great hurricane and wresteth it out of its abiding place and stretcheth it out upon the earth: even so lay Panthoös' son Euphorbos of the good ashen spear when Menelaos Atreus' son had slain him, and dispoiled him of his arms.

Now as when some mountain-bred lion, trusting in his might, hath seized the best heifer out of a feeding herd, and first taketh her neck in his strong teeth and breaketh it, and then devoureth fiercely the blood and all the inward parts, while around him hounds and herdsmen clamour loudly afar off yet will not come up against him, for pale fear taketh hold on them,—even so dared not the heart in the breast of any Trojan to come up against glorious Menelaos. Then easily would the son of Atreus have borne off the noble spoils of Panthoös' son, had not Phoebus Apollo grudged it him, and aroused against him Hector peer of swift Ares, putting on the semblance of a man, of Mentes chief of the Kikones. And he spake aloud to him winged words: "Hector, now art thou hasting after things unattainable, even the horses of wise Aiakides; for hard are they to be tamed or driven by mortal man, save only Achilles whom an immortal mother bare. Meanwhile hath warlike Menelaos Atreus' son stridden over Patroklos and slain the best of the Trojans there, even Panthoös' son Euphorbos, and hath stayed him in his impetuous might."

Thus saying the god went back into the strife of men, but dire grief darkened Hector's inmost soul, and then he gazed searchingly along the lines, and straightway was aware of the one man stripping off the noble arms, and the other lying on the earth; and blood was flowing about the gaping wound. Then he went through the front of the fight harnessed in flashing bronze, crying a shrill cry, like unto Hephaistos' flame unquenchable. Not deaf to his shrill cry was Atreus' son, and sore troubled he spake to his great heart: "Ay me, if I shall leave behind me these goodly arms, and Patroklos who here lieth for my vengeance' sake, I fear lest some Danaan beholding it be wroth against me. But if for honour's sake I do battle alone with Hector and the Trojans, I fear lest they come about me many against one; for all the Trojans is bright-helmed Hector leading hither. But wherefore thus debateth my heart? When a man against the power of heaven is fain to fight with another whom God exalteth, then swiftly rolleth on him mighty woe. Therefore shall none of the Danaans be wroth with me though he behold me giving place to Hector, since he warreth with gods upon his side. But if I might somewhere find Aias of the loud war-cry, then both together would we go and be mindful of battle even were it against the power of heaven, if haply we might save his dead for Achilles Peleus' son: that were best among these ills."

While thus he communed with his mind and heart, therewithal the Trojan ranks came onward, and Hector at their head. Then Menelaos gave backward, and left the dead man, turning himself ever about like a deep-maned lion which men and dogs chase from a fold with spears and cries; and his strong heart within him groweth chill, and loth goeth he from the steading; so from Patroklos went fair-haired Menelaos, and turned and stood, when he came to the host of his comrades, searching for mighty Aias Telamon's son. Him very speedily he espied on the left of the whole battle, cheering his comrades and rousing them to fight, for great terror had Phoebus Apollo sent on them; and he hasted him to run, and straightway stood by him and said: "This way, beloved Aias; let us bestir us for the dead Patroklos, if haply his naked corpse at least we may carry to Achilles, though his armour is held by Hector of the glancing helm."

Thus spake he, and aroused the heart of wise Aias. And he went up through the front of the fight, and with him fair-haired Menelaos. Now Hector, when he had stripped from Patroklos his noble armour, was dragging him thence that he might cut off the head from the shoulders with the keen bronze and carry his body to give to the dogs of Troy. But Aias came anigh, and the shield that he bare was as a tower; then Hector gave back into the company of his comrades, and sprang into his chariot; and the goodly armour he gave to the Trojans to carry to the city, to be great glory unto him. But Aias spread his broad shield over the son of Menoitios and stood as it were a lion before his whelps when huntsmen in a forest encounter him as he leadeth his young

—then waxeth he in his strength, and draweth down all his brows to cover his eyes:—so over the hero Patroklos Aias strode. And by his side stood Atreus' son, Menelaos dear to Ares, nursing great sorrow in his breast.

Then Glaukos, Hippolochos' son, chief of the men of Lykia, looked toward Hector with a frown and chode him with rough words: "Hector, in semblance bravest, lo, in battle sorely art thou lacking. Verily in vain doth fair glory rest on thee since thou turnest runagate. Bethink thee now how thou shalt save thy city and home, thou only with the host who were born in Ilios; for of the Lykians at least shall none go up to fight against the Danaans for the city's sake, since no boon, it seemeth, is it to fight unsparingly ever against men of war. How art thou like to bring back safe into thy host any lesser man, thou hard of heart, when Sarpedon that was both guest and friend thou leftest to the Argives to be their prey and spoil, though in his life he aided oftentimes both thy city and thyself? Yet now thou hast not dared to save him from the dogs. Therefore now if any of the men of Lykia will hearken unto me we will go home, and to Troy shall be revealed sheer doom. For if now a spirit of good courage were in the Trojans, a fearless spirit such as entereth into men who for their native land array toil and strife against men that are their enemies, speedily should we drag Patroklos within Ilios' wall. And if this dead man were brought into the great city of king Priam, and we drew him forth from the battle, then speedily would the Argives give back the goodly armour of Sarpedon, and we should bring his body into Ilios; so great is he whose squire is slain, even the man who is far best of the Argives beside the ships—he and his close-fighting squires. But thou endureth not to stand up against great-hearted Aias and to look in his face amid the cry of the men of war, nor to do fair battle with him, since he is a better man than thou."

Then, with a frown, spake unto him Hector of the glancing helm: "Glaukos, wherefore hath such an one as thou spoken thus over measure? Out on it, I verily thought that thou in wisdom wert above all others that dwell in deep-soiled Lykia; but now think I altogether scorn of thy wisdom, since thou speakest thus, and sayest that I dared not to meet the mighty Aias. No terror have I of battle or din of chariots, but the intent of aegis-bearing Zeus is ever strongest, and even a brave man he overaweth and lightly snatcheth from him victory, and yet anon himself arouseth him to fight. Come hither, friend, stand beside me and see my handiwork, whether all this day I shall play the coward, according to thy words, or shall yet stay certain of the Danaans, how fierce soever be their valour, from doing battle for Patroklos' corpse."

Thus saying he called on the Trojans with a mighty shout: "Trojans and Lykians and Dardanians that fight hand to hand, be men, my friends, and bethink you of impetuous valour, until I do on me the goodly arms of noble Achilles that I stripped from brave Patroklos when I slew him."

Thus having spoken went Hector of the glancing helm forth out of the strife of war, and ran and speedily with fleet feet following overtook his comrades, not yet far off, who were bearing to the city Peleides' glorious arms. And standing apart from the dolorous battle he changed his armour; his own he gave the warlike Trojans to carry to sacred Ilios, and he put on the divine arms of Achilles, Peleus' son, which to his dear father the gods who inhabit heaven gave, and Peleus committed them unto his child when old himself; but never in his father's armour did that son grow old.

But when Zeus that gathereth the clouds beheld from afar off Hector arming him in the armour of Peleus' god-like son, he shook his head and spake thus unto his soul: "Ah, hapless man, no thought is in thy heart of death that yet draweth nigh unto thee; thou doest on thee the divine armour of a peerless man before whom the rest have terror. His comrade, gentle and brave, thou hast slain, and unmeetly hast stripped the armour from his head and shoulders; yet now for a while at least I will give into thy hands great might, in recompense for this, even that no wise shalt thou come home out of the battle, for Andromache to receive from thee Peleides' glorious arms."

Thus spake the son of Kronos and bowed his dark brows therewithal.

But the armour fitted itself unto Hector's body, and Ares the dread war-god entered into him, and his limbs were filled within with valour and strength. Then he sped among the noble allies with a mighty cry, and in the flashing of his armour he seemed to all of them like unto Peleus' great-hearted son. And he came to each and encouraged him with his words—Mesthles and Glaukos and Medon and Thersilochos and Asteropaios and Deisenor and Hippothoös and Phorkys and Chromios and the augur Ennomos—these encouraged he and spake to them winged words: "Listen, ye countless tribes of allies that dwell round about. It was not for mere numbers that I sought or longed when I gathered each of you from your cities, but that ye might zealously guard the Trojans' wives and infant little ones from the war-loving Achaians. For this end am I wearying my people by taking gifts and food from them, and nursing thereby the courage of each of you. Now therefore let all turn straight against the foe and live or die, for such is the dalliance of war. And whoso shall drag Patroklos, dead though he be, among the horse-taming men of Troy, and make Aias yield, to him will I award half the spoils and keep half myself; so shall his glory be great as mine."

Thus spake he, and they against the Danaans charged with all their weight, levelling their spears, and their hearts were high of hope to drag the corpse from under Aias, Telamon's son. Fond men! from full many reft he life over that corpse. And then spake Aias to Menelaos of the loud war-cry: "Dear Menelaos, fosterling of Zeus, no longer count I that we two of ourselves shall return home out of the war. Nor have I so much dread for the corpse of Patroklos, that shall soon glut the dogs and birds of the men of Troy, as for thy head and mine lest some evil fall thereon, for all is shrouded by a storm-cloud of war, even by Hector, and sheer doom stareth in our face. But come, call thou to the best men of the Danaans, if haply any hear."

Thus spake he, and Menelaos of the loud war-cry disregarded him not, but shouted unto the Danaans, crying a far-heard cry: "O friends, ye leaders and counsellors of the Argives, who by the side of the sons of Atreus, Agamemnon and Menelaos, drink at the common cost and are all commanders of the host, on whom wait glory and honour from Zeus, hard is it for me to distinguish each chief amid the press—such blaze is there of the strife of war. But let each go forward of himself and be wroth at heart that Patroklos should become a sport among the dogs of Troy."

Thus spake he, and Oileus' son fleet Aias heard him clearly, and was first to run along the mellay to meet him, and after him Idomeneus, and Idomeneus' brother-in-arms, Meriones, peer of the man-slaying war-god. And who shall of his own thought tell the names of the rest, even of all that after these aroused the battle of the Achaians?

Now the Trojans charged forward in close array, and Hector led them. And as when at the mouth of some heaven-born river a mighty wave roareth against the stream, and arouseth the high cliffs' echo as the salt sea belloweth on the beach, so loud was the cry wherewith the Trojans came. But the Achaians stood firm around Menoitios' son with one soul all, walled in with shields of bronze. And over their bright helmets the son of Kronos shed thick darkness, for in the former time was Menoitios' son not unloved of him, while he was yet alive and squire of Aiakides. So was Zeus loth that he should become a prey of the dogs of his enemies at Troy, and stirred his comrades to do battle for him.

Now first the Trojans thrust back the glancing-eyed Achaians, who shrank before them and left the dead, yet the proud Trojans slew not any of them with spears, though they were fain, but set to hale the corpse. But little while would the Achaians hold back therefrom, for very swiftly Aias rallied them, Aias the first in presence and in deeds of all the Danaans after the noble son of Peleus. Right through the fighters in the forefront rushed he like a wild boar in his might that in the mountains when he turneth at bay scattereth lightly dogs and lusty young men through the glades. Thus did proud Telamon's son the glorious Aias press on the Trojan battalions and lightly scatter them, as they had bestrode Patroklos and were full fain to drag him to their city and win renown.

Then Hippothoös, glorious son of Pelasgian Lethos, set to drag him by the foot through the violent fray, binding him by the ankle with a strap around the sinews, to do pleasure to Hector and the Trojans. But an ill thing came swiftly upon him wherefrom none of his comrades, albeit full fain, might help him. For the son of Telamon set on him through the press and smote him hard at hand through the bronze-cheeked helm. And the horse-hair-plumed head-piece brake about the spear point, smitten by the great spear and stalwart arm, and brain and blood spouted from the wound through the vizor. And Hippothoös' strength was unstrung, and from his hands he let great-hearted Patroklos' foot fall to earth, and close thereon fell he prone upon the corpse, far from deep-soiled Larissa, nor repaid his dear parents for his nurture, for short was his span of life as he fell beneath great-hearted Aias' spear. And Hector in his turn hurled at Aias with his bright spear, but the other saw the bronze dart as it came and hardly avoided it; yet Schedios, son of great-hearted Iphitos, the best man of the Phokians who in famous Panopeus had his dwelling and was king over many men—this man Hector smote beneath the midst of his collar-bone, and right through went the point of the bronze spear and stood out beside the nether part of his shoulder. And he fell with a crash, and his armour rang upon him. And Aias in his turn smote Phorkys in the midst of the belly, the wise son of Phainops, as he bestrode Hippothoös, and brake the plate of his corslet, and the bronze let forth his bowels, and he fell in the dust and grasped the earth with his hand. And the front fighters and glorious Hector gave back, and the Argives shouted aloud and haled the dead men, Phorkys and Hippothoös, and did off the armour from their shoulders.

Then would the Trojans in their turn in their weakness overcome have been driven back into Ilios by the Achaians dear to Ares, and the Argives would have won glory even against the appointment of Zeus by their power and might. But Apollo himself aroused Aineias, putting on the semblance of Periphas the herald, the son of Epytos, who grew old with his old father in his heraldship, of friendly thought toward Aineias. In his similitude spake Apollo, son of Zeus: "Aineias, how could ye ever guard high Ilios if it were against the will of God? Other men have I seen that trust in their own might and power and valour, and in their host, even though they have scant folk to lead. But here, albeit Zeus is fainer far to give victory to us than to the Danaans, yet ye are dismayed exceedingly and fight not."

Thus spake he, and Aineias knew far-darting Apollo when he looked upon his face, and spake unto Hector, shouting aloud: "Hector and ye other leaders of the Trojans and their allies, shame were this if in our weakness overcome we were driven back into Ilios by the Achaians dear to Ares. Nay, thus saith a god, who standeth by my side: Zeus, highest Orderer, is our helper in this fight. Therefore let us go right onward against the Danaans. Not easily at least let them take the dead Patroklos to the ships."

Thus spake he, and leapt forth far before the fighters in the front. And the Trojans rallied and stood up against the Achaians. Then Aineias wounded with his spear Leokritos son of Arisbas, Lykomedes' valiant comrade. And as he fell Lykomedes dear to Ares was grieved for him and came hard by him and halted and hurled his bright spear and smote Hippasos' son Apisaon, shepherd of the host, in the liver beneath the midriff and straightway unstrung his knees, Apisaon who had come out of deep-soiled Paionia and after Asteropaios was their best man in fight. And as he fell warlike Asteropaios was grieved for him and made onward full fain to do battle against the Danaans; but that could he nowise any more, for they were fenced on every side with shields as they stood around Patroklos, and held their spears in front of them. For Aias ranged through them all and called on them now and again, and bade that none of the Achaians should give back behind the corpse nor fight in front of the rest but keep close beside the dead and do battle hand to hand. Thus mighty Aias commanded, and the earth was wet with dark blood, and the dead fell thickly both of the Trojans and their brave allies, and likewise of the Danaans, for these too fought no bloodless fight, yet far fewer perished of them, for they were ever mindful to ward sheer death from one another in the press.

Thus strove they as it had been fire, nor wouldst thou have thought there was still sun or moon, for over all the battle where the chiefs stood around the slain son of Menoitios they were shrouded in darkness, while the other Trojans and well-greaved Achaians fought at ease in the clear air, and piercing sunlight was spread over them, and on all the earth and hills there was no cloud seen; and they ceased fighting now and again, avoiding each other's dolorous darts and standing far apart. But they who were in the midst endured affliction of the darkness and the battle, and all the best men of them were wearied by the pitiless weight of their bronze arms. Yet two men, famous warriors, Thrasymedes and Antilochos, knew not yet that noble Patroklos was dead, but deemed that he was yet alive and fighting against the Trojans in the forefront of the press.

So they twain in watch against the death or flight of their comrades were doing battle apart from the rest, since thus had Nestor charged when he roused them forth to the battle from the black ships.

Thus all day long waxed the mighty fray of their sore strife, and unabatingly ever with the sweat of toil were the knees and legs and feet of each man and arms and eyes bedewed as the two hosts did battle around the brave squire of fleet Aiakides. And as when a man giveth the hide of a great bull to his folk to stretch, all soaked in fat, and they take and stretch it standing in a circle, and straightway the moisture thereof departeth and the fat entereth in under the haling of many hands, and it is all stretched throughout,—thus they on both sides haled the dead man this way and that in narrow space, for their hearts were high of hope, the Trojans that they should drag him to Ilios and the Achaians to the hollow ships; and around him the fray waxed wild, nor might Ares rouser of hosts nor Athene despise the sight thereof, albeit their anger were exceeding great.

Such was the grievous travail of men and horses over Patroklos that Zeus on that day wrought. But not as yet knew noble Achilles aught of Patroklos' death, for far away from the swift ships they were fighting beneath the wall of the men of Troy. Therefore never deemed he in his heart that he was dead, but that he should come back alive, after that he had touched the gates; for neither that other thought had he anywise, that Patroklos should sack the stronghold without his aid, nay, nor yet therewithal, for thus had he oft heard from his mother, hearkening to her apart as she brought tidings unto him of the purposes of mighty Zeus. Yet verily then his mother told him not how great an ill was come to pass, that his far dearest comrade was no more.

Now the rest continually around the dead man with their keen spears made onset relentlessly and slew each the other. And thus would one speak among the mail-clad Achaians: "Friends, it were verily not glorious for us to go back to the hollow ships; rather let the black earth yawn for us all beneath our feet. Far better were that straightway for us if we suffer the horse-taming Trojans to hale this man to their city and win renown."

And thus on the other side would one of the great-hearted Trojans say: "Friends, though it were our fate that all together we be slain beside this man, let none yet give backward from the fray."

Thus would one speak, and rouse the spirit of each. So they fought on, and the iron din went up through the high desert air unto the brazen heaven. But the horses of Aiakides that were apart from the battle were weeping, since first they were aware that their charioteer was fallen in the dust beneath the hand of man-slaying Hector. Verily Automedon, Diores' valiant son, plied them oft with blows of the swift lash, and oft with gentle words he spake to them and oft with chiding, yet would they neither go back to the ships at the broad Hellespont nor yet to the battle after the Achaians, but as a pillar abideth firm that standeth on the tomb of a man or woman dead, so abode they immovably with the beautiful chariot, abasing their heads unto the earth. And hot tears flowed from their eyes to the ground as they mourned in sorrow for their charioteer, and their rich manes were soiled as they drooped from beneath the yoke-cushion on both sides beside the yoke. And when the son of Kronos beheld them mourning he had compassion on them, and shook his head and spake to his own heart: "Ah, hapless pair, why gave we you to king Peleus, a mortal man, while ye are deathless and ever young? Was it that ye should suffer sorrows among ill-fated men? For methinketh there is nothing more piteous than a man among all things that breathe and creep upon the earth. But verily Hector Priam's son shall not drive you and your deftly-wrought car; that will I not suffer. Is it a small thing that he holdeth the armour and vaunteth himself vainly thereupon? Nay, I will put courage into your knees and heart that ye may bring Automedon also safe out of the war to the hollow ships. For yet further will I increase victory to the men of Troy, so that they slay until they come unto the well-timbered ships, and the sun set and divine night come down."

Thus saying he breathed good courage into the horses. And they shook to earth the dust from their manes, and lightly bare the swift car amid Trojans and Achaians. And behind them fought Automedon, albeit in grief for his comrade, swooping with his chariot as a vulture on wild geese; for lightly he would flee out of the onset of the Trojans and lightly charge, pursuing them through the thick mellay. Yet could he not slay any man as he hasted to pursue them, for it was impossible that being alone in his sacred car he should at once assail them with the spear and hold his fleet horses. Then at last espied him a comrade, even Alkimedon son of Laerkes, son of Haimon, and he halted behind the car and spake unto Automedon: "Automedon, what god hath put into thy breast unprofitable counsel and taken from thee wisdom, that thus alone thou art fighting against the Trojans in the forefront of the press? Thy comrade even now was slain, and Hector goeth proudly, wearing on his own shoulders the armour of Aiakides."

And Automedon son of Diores answered him, saying: "Alkimedon, what other Achaian hath like skill to guide the spirit of immortal steeds, save only Patroklos, peer of gods in counsel, while he yet lived? but now have death and fate overtaken him. But take thou the lash and shining reins, and I will get me down from my horses, that I may fight."

Thus spake he, and Alkimedon leapt on the fleet war-chariot and swiftly took the lash and reins in his hands, and Automedon leapt down. And noble Hector espied them, and straightway spake unto Aineias as he stood near: "Aineias, counsellor of mail-clad Trojans, I espy here the two horses of fleet Aiakides come forth to battle with feeble charioteers. Therefore might I hope to take them if thou in thy heart art willing, since they would not abide our onset and stand to do battle against us."

Thus spake he, and the brave son of Anchises disregarded him not. And they twain went right onward, their shoulders shielded by ox-hides dried and tough, and bronze thick overlaid. And with them went both Chromios and godlike Aretos, and their hearts were of high hope to slay the men and drive off the strong-necked horses—fond hope, for not without blood lost were they to get them back from Automedon. He praying to father Zeus was filled in his inmost heart with valour and strength. And straightway he spake to Alkimedon, his faithful comrade: "Alkimedon, hold the horses not far from me, but with their very breath upon my back; for I deem that Hector the son of Priam will not refrain him from his fury until he mount behind Achilles' horses of goodly manes after slaying us twain, and dismay the ranks of Argive men, or else himself fall among the foremost."

Thus said he, and called upon the Aiantes and Menelaos: "Aiantes, leaders of the Argives, and Menelaos, lo now, commit ye the corpse unto whoso may best avail to bestride it and resist the ranks of men, and come ye to ward the day of doom from us who are yet alive, for here in the dolorous war are Hector and Aineias, the best men of the Trojans, pressing hard. Yet verily these issues lie in the lap of the gods: I too will cast my spear, and the rest shall Zeus decide."

He said, and poised his far-shadowing spear and hurled it, and smote on the circle of the shield of Aretos, and the shield sustained not the spear, but right through went the bronze, and he forced it into his belly low down through his belt. And as when a strong man with a sharp axe smiting behind the horns of an ox of the homestead cleaveth the sinew asunder, and the ox leapeth forward and falleth, so leapt Aretos forward and fell on his back; and the spear in his entrails very piercingly quivering unstrung his limbs. And

Hector hurled at Automedon with his bright spear, but he looked steadfastly on the bronze javelin as it came at him and avoided it, for he stooped forward, and the long spear fixed itself in the ground behind, and the javelin-butt quivered, and there dread Ares took away its force. And then had they lashed at each other with their swords hand to hand, had not the Aiantes parted them in their fury, when they were come through the mellay at their comrade's call. Before them Hector and Aineias and godlike Chromios shrank backward and gave ground and left Aretos wounded to the death as he lay. And Automedon, peer of swift Ares, stripped off the armour of the dead, and spake exultingly: "Verily, I have a little eased my heart of grief for the death of Menoitios' son, albeit a worse man than him have I slain."

Thus saying he took up the gory spoils and set them in his car, and gat him thereon, with feet and hands all bloody, as a lion that hath devoured a bull.

So again above Patroklos was waged the violent fray, cruel and woful, and Athene roused their strife, from heaven descended, for far-seeing Zeus sent her to urge on the Danaans, for his mind was changed. As Zeus stretcheth forth a gleaming rainbow from heaven to be a sign to mortals whether of war or of chill storm that maketh men to cease from their works upon the face of the earth, and afflicteth flocks, thus Athene clothing her in a gleaming cloud entered the Achaians' host, and roused each man thereof. First to urge Atreus' son, strong Menelaos, for he was nigh to her, she spake to him, making herself like unto Phoinix in shape and unwearying voice: "To thee verily, Menelaos, will be it shame and reproach if beneath the wall of the men of Troy fleet dogs tear the faithful comrade of proud Achilles. Nay, bear thee stoutly up, and urge on all the host."

Then answered her Menelaos of the loud war-cry, saying: "O Phoinix, ancient father of the elder time, would that

Athene may give me strength and keep off the assault of darts. So would I well be fain to stand by Patroklos and to shield him, for his death touched me very close at heart. But Hector hath the terrible fury of fire, neither ceaseth in making havoc with his spear, for to him Zeus giveth glory."

Thus spake he, and the bright-eyed goddess Athene was glad, for that to her first of all gods whatsoever he prayed. And she put force into his shoulders and his knees, and in his breast the boldness of the fly that albeit driven away once and again from the skin of men still is eager to bite, and sweet to it is the blood of mankind—even with such boldness the goddess filled his inmost heart, and he bestrode Patroklos, and hurled with his bright spear. Now among the Trojans was one Podes, son of Eëtion, a rich man and a brave, and Hector honoured him especially among the people for that he was his dear comrade and boon companion. Him smote fair-haired Menelaos in the belt as he started to flee, and drove his spearhead right through, and he fell with a crash, and Menelaos, Atreus' son, haled his body from amid the Trojans among his comrades' company.

But Apollo came and stood near Hector and aroused him, in the semblance of Asios' son Phainops, who of all guest-friends was dearest to him, and had his home in Abydos. [In his likeness spake far-darting Apollo unto Hector]: "Hector, what other of the Achaians will fear thee any more, if now thou hast shrunk from Menelaos who formerly was an unhardy warrior? Now is he gone and alone hath seized a dead Trojan from among our ranks, and hath slain thy faithful comrade, a good man among the fighters in the front, even Podes, son of Eëtion."

Thus spake he, and a black cloud of grief fell on Hector, and he went through the forefront of the battle harnessed in flashing bronze. Then also the son of Kronos took up his tasselled aegis glittering, and shrouded Ida in clouds, and lightened and thundered mightily, and shook the earth;

and he gave victory to the Trojans, and the Achaians he dismayed.

First to set dismay on foot was Peneleos the Boiotian. For he was smitten in the shoulder by a javelin grazingly on the surface, as he kept ever his face to the foe; the spear point of Polydamas scratched the bone, for he cast it from nigh at hand. Then again Hector in close fight wounded Leïtos on the wrist, the son of great-hearted Alektryon, and stayed him from the joy of battle: and he shrank back as he gazed around him, for that he might no longer hope to hold spear in hand to do battle against the men of Troy. Then Idomeneus smote Hector as he pursued after Leïtos on the corslet of his breast beside the nipple, but the long spear brake at the socket and the Trojans shouted. And Hector hurled at Idomeneus son of Deukalion as he had mounted his car, and missed him by a little, but smote Koiranos, Meriones' brother-in-arms and charioteer who from stablished Lyktos followed him—(for on foot came Idomeneus first from the curved ships and would have yielded great triumph to the Trojans had not Koiranos quickly driven up his fleet horses, and thus come as succour to Idomeneus and guarded him from the day of death, but himself lost his life at the hands of man-slaying Hector)—him Hector smote beneath the jaw and ear, and the spear-end dashed out his teeth and clave his tongue asunder in the midst. And he fell forth from the chariot and let fall the reins to the ground. Then Meriones stooped and gathered them in his own hands from the earth and spake unto Idomeneus: "Now lay on, till thou come to the swift ships: thyself too knowest that triumph is no longer with the Achaians."

Thus spake he, and Idomeneus lashed the horses of goodly manes back to the hollow ships; for fear had fallen upon his soul.

Now great-hearted Aias and Menelaos were aware of Zeus how he gave the Trojans their turn of victory. First of these to speak was great Aias son of Telamon: "Ay me, now may any man, even though he be a very fool, know that Father Zeus himself is helping the Trojans. For the darts of all of them strike, whosoever hurleth them, be he good man or bad—Zeus guideth them notwithstanding home: but all our darts only fall idly to the earth. Nay come, let us ourselves devise some excellent means, that we may both hale the corpse away and ourselves return home to the joy of our friends, who grieve as they look hitherward and deem that no longer shall the fury of man-slaying Hector's unapproachable hand refrain itself, but fall upon the black ships. And would there were some comrade to carry tidings with all speed unto the son of Peleus, since I deem that he hath not even heard the grievous tidings, how his dear comrade is slain. But nowhere can I behold such an one among the Achaians, for themselves and their horses likewise are wrapped in darkness. O father Zeus, deliver thou the sons of the Achaians from the darkness, and make clear sky and vouchsafe sight unto our eyes. In the light be it that thou slayest us, since it is thy good pleasure that we die."

Thus spake he, and the Father grieved to see him weep, and straightway scattered the darkness and drave away the mist, and the sun shone out on them, and all the battle was manifest. Then spake Aias to Menelaos of the loud war-cry: "Look forth now, Menelaos fosterling of Zeus, if haply thou mayest see Antilochos yet alive, great-hearted Nestor's son, and rouse him to go with speed to wise Achilles to tell him that his far dearest comrade is slain."

Thus spake he, and Menelaos of the loud war-cry disregarded him not, but went forth as a lion from a steading when he is tired of vexing men and dogs that suffer him not to devour fat oxen and all night keep their watch; but he in hunger for flesh presseth onward yet availeth nought, for thickly fly the javelins against him from hardy hands, with blazing firebrands, wherefrom he shrinketh for all his fury, and in the morning departeth afar with grief at heart:—thus from Patroklos went Menelaos of the loud war-cry, sore loth; for exceedingly he feared lest the Achaians in cruel rout should leave him a prey to the enemy. And straitly charged he Meriones and the Aiantes, saying: "Aiantes leaders of the Argives, and Meriones, now let each remember the loving-kindness of hapless Patroklos, for he would be gentle unto all while he was yet alive: now death and fate have overtaken him."

Thus saying fair-haired Menelaos departed glancing everywhither, as an eagle which men say hath keenest sight of all birds under heaven, and though he be far aloft the fleet-footed hare eludeth him not by crouching beneath a leafy bush, but the eagle swoopeth thereon and swiftly seizeth her and taketh her life. Thus in that hour, Menelaos fosterling of Zeus, ranged thy shining eyes everywhither through the multitude of the host of thy comrades, if haply they might behold Nestor's son yet alive. Him quickly he perceived at the left of the whole battle, heartening his comrades and rousing them to fight. And fair-haired Menelaos came and stood nigh and said unto him:

"Antilochos, fosterling of Zeus, come hither that thou mayest learn woful tidings—would it had never been. Ere now, I ween, thou too hast known by thy beholding that God rolleth mischief upon the Danaans, and with the Trojans is victory. And slain is the best man of the Achaians, Patroklos, and great sorrow is wrought for the Danaans. But run thou to the ships of the Achaians and quickly tell this to Achilles, if haply he may straightway rescue to his ship the naked corpse: but his armour is held by Hector of the glancing helmet."

Thus spake he, and Antilochos had horror of the word he heard. And long time speechlessness possessed him, and his eyes were filled with tears, and his full voice choked. Yet for all this disregarded he not the bidding of Menelaos, but set him to run, when he had given his armour to a noble comrade, Laodokos, who close anigh him was wheeling his whole-hooved horses.

So him his feet bare out of the battle weeping, to Achilles son of Peleus carrying an evil tale. But thy heart, Menelaos fosterling of Zeus, chose not to stay to aid the wearied comrades from whom Antilochos departed, and great sorrow was among the Pylians. But to them Menelaos sent noble Thrasymedes, and himself went again to bestride the hero Patroklos. And he hasted and stood beside the Aiantes and straightway spake to them: "So have I sent that man to the swift ships to go to fleet-footed Achilles. Yet deem I not that he will now come, for all his wrath against noble Hector, for he could not fight unarmed against the men of Troy. But let us ourselves devise some excellent means, both how we may hale the dead away, and how we ourselves may escape death and fate amid the Trojans' battle-cry."

Then answered him great Aias Telamon's son, saying: "All this hast thou said well, most noble Menelaos. But do thou and Meriones put your shoulders beneath the dead and lift him and bear him swiftly out of the fray, while we twain behind you shall do battle with the Trojans and noble Hector, one in heart as we are in name, for from of old time we are wont to await fierce battle side by side."

Thus spake he, and the others took the dead man in their arms and lifted him mightily on high. But the Trojan host behind cried aloud when they saw the Achaians lifting the corpse, and charged like hounds that spring in front of hunter-youths upon a wounded wild boar, and for a while run in in haste to rend him, but when he wheeleth round among them, trusting in his might, then they give ground and shrink back here and there. Thus for a while the Trojans pressed on with all their power, striking with swords and double-headed spears, but when the Aiantes turned about and halted over against them, then they changed colour, and none dared farther onset to do battle around the dead.

Thus were those twain struggling to bear the corpse out of the battle toward the hollow ships, but the stress of war waxed fierce upon them as fire that leapeth on a city of men and bursteth into sudden blaze and houses perish amid the mighty glare, and it roareth beneath the strength of the wind. Thus roared the unceasing din of horses and of fighting men against the bearers as they went. As mules that throw their great strength into the draught and drag out of the mountain down a rugged track some beam or huge ship-timber, and their hearts as they strive are spent with toil and sweat, thus were those twain struggling to bear the corpse. And behind them the two Aiantes held their ground, as a woody ridge that chanceth to stretch all its length across the plain holdeth back a flood and stayeth even the wasting streams of mighty rivers, and turneth all their current wandering into the plain, neither doth the violence of their stream break through it. Thus ever the Aiantes kept back the Trojans' battle, but they pressed hard anigh, and among them twain the first, even Aineias, Anchises' son, and glorious Hector. As flieth a flock of starlings or of daws with confused cries when they see a hawk coming, to small birds bearer of death, thus before Aineias and Hector the Achaian youth confusedly crying fell back, and forgat the joy of battle. And thickly fell the goodly arms about and around the trench, as the Danaans fled, and there was never a pause of fight.

BOOK XVIII

How Achilles grieved for Patroklos, and how Thetis asked for him new armour of Hephaistos; and of the making of the armour.

THUS fought the rest in the likeness of blazing fire, while to Achilles came Antilochos, a messenger fleet of foot. Him found he in front of his ships of upright horns, boding in his soul the things which even now were accomplished. And sore troubled he spake to his great heart: "Ay me, wherefore again are the flowing-haired Achaians flocking to the ships and flying in rout over the plain? May the gods not have wrought against me the grievous fears at my heart, even as my mother revealed and told me that while I am yet alive the best man of the Myrmidons must by deed of the men of Troy forsake the light of the sun. Surely now must Menoitios' valiant son be dead—foolhardy! surely I bade him when he should have beaten off the fire of the foe to come back to the ships nor with Hector fight amain."

While thus he held debate in his heart and soul, there drew nigh unto him noble Nestor's son, shedding hot tears, and spake his grievous tidings: "Ay me, wise Peleus' son, very bitter tidings must thou hear, such as I would had never been. Fallen is Patroklos, and they are fighting around his body, naked, for his armour is held by Hector of the glancing helm."

Thus spake he, and a black cloud of grief enwrapped Achilles, and with both hands he took dark dust and poured it over his head and defiled his comely face, and on his fragrant doublet black ashes fell. And himself in the dust lay mighty and mightily fallen, and with his own hands tore and marred his hair. And the handmaidens, whom Achilles and Patroklos took captive, cried aloud in the grief of their hearts, and ran forth around valiant Achilles, and all beat on their breasts with their hands, and the knees of each of them were unstrung. And Antilochos on the other side wailed and shed tears, holding Achilles' hands while he groaned in his noble heart, for he feared lest he should cleave his throat with the sword. Then terribly moaned Achilles; and his lady mother heard him as she sat in the depths of the sea beside her ancient sire. And thereon she uttered a cry, and the goddesses flocked around her, all the daughters of Nereus that were in the deep of the sea. There were Glauke, and Thaleia, and Kymodoke, Nesaia and Speio and Thoë and ox-eyed Halië and Kymothoë and Aktaie and Limnoreia and Melite and Iaira and Amphithoë and Agauë and Doto and Proto and Pherusa and Dynamene and Dexamene and Amphinome and Kallianeira, Doris and Panope and noble Galateia, and Nemertes, and Apseudes and Kallianassa, and there were Klymene and Ianeira and Ianassa and Maira, and Oreithuia, and fair-tressed Amathyia, and other Nereids that were in the deep of the sea. With these the bright cave was filled, and they all beat together on their breasts, and Thetis led the lament: "Listen, sister Nereids, that ye all hear and know well what sorrows are in my heart. Ay me unhappy, ay me that bare to my sorrow the first of men! For after I had born a son noble and strong, the chief of heroes, and he shot up like a young branch, then when I had reared him as a plant in a very fruitful field I sent him in beaked ships to Ilios to fight against the men of Troy; but never again shall I welcome him back to his home, to the house of Peleus. And while he yet liveth in my sight and beholdeth the light of the sun, he sorroweth, neither can I help him any whit though I go unto him. But I will go, that I may look upon my dear child, and learn what sorrow hath come to him though he abide aloof from the war."

Thus spake she and left the cave; and the nymphs went with her weeping, and around them the surge of the sea was sundered. And when they came to deep-soiled Troy-land they went up upon the shore in order, where the ships of the Myrmidons were drawn up thickly around fleet Achilles. And as he groaned heavily his lady mother stood beside him, and with a shrill cry clasped the head of her child, and spake unto him winged words of lamentation: "My child, why weepest thou? what sorrow hath come to thy heart? Tell it forth, hide it not. One thing at least hath been accomplished of Zeus according to the prayer thou madest, holding up to him thy hands, that the sons of the Achaians should all be pent in at the ships, through lack of thee, and should suffer hateful things."

Then groaning heavily spake unto her Achilles fleet of foot: "My mother, that prayer truly hath the Olympian accomplished for me. But what delight have I therein, since my dear comrade is dead, Patroklos, whom I honoured above all my comrades as it were my very self? Him have I lost, and Hector that slew him hath stripped from him the armour great and fair, a wonder to behold, that the gods gave to Peleus a splendid gift, on the day when they laid thee in the bed of a mortal man. Would thou hadst abode among the deathless daughters of the sea, and Peleus had wedded a mortal bride! But now, that thou mayest have sorrow a thousandfold in thy heart for a dead son, never shalt thou welcome him back home, since my soul biddeth me also live no longer nor abide among men, if Hector be not first smitten by my spear and yield his life, and pay for his slaughter of Patroklos, Menoitios' son."

Then answered unto him Thetis shedding tears: "Short-lived, I ween, must thou be then, my child, by what thou sayest, for straightway after Hector is death appointed unto thee."

Then mightily moved spake unto her Achilles fleet of foot: "Straightway may I die, since I might not succour my comrade at his slaying. He hath fallen afar from his country and lacked my help in his sore need. Now therefore, since I go not back to my dear native land, neither have at all been succour to Patroklos nor to all my other comrades that have been slain by noble Hector, but I sit beside my ships a profitless burden of the earth, I that in war am such an one as is none else of the mail-clad Achaians, though in council are others better—may strife perish utterly among gods and men, and wrath that stirreth even a wise man to be vexed, wrath that far sweeter than trickling honey waxeth like smoke in the breasts of men, even as I was wroth even now against Agamemnon king of men. But bygones will we let be, for all our pain, curbing the heart in our breasts under necessity. Now go I forth, that I may light on the destroyer of him I loved, on Hector; then will I accept my death whensoever Zeus willeth to accomplish it and the other immortal gods. For not even the mighty Herakles escaped death, albeit most dear to Kronian Zeus the king, but Fate overcame him and Hera's cruel wrath. So also shall I, if my fate hath been fashioned likewise, lie low when I am dead. But now let me win high renown, let me set some Trojan woman, some deep-bosomed daughter of Dardanos, staunching with both hands the tears upon her tender cheeks and wailing bitterly; yea, let them know that I am come back, though I tarried long from the war. Hold not me then from the battle in thy love, for thou shalt not prevail with me."

Then Thetis the silver-footed goddess answered him saying: "Yea verily, my child, no blame is in this, that thou ward sheer destruction from thy comrades in their distress. But thy fair glittering armour of bronze is held among the Trojans. Hector of the glancing helm beareth it on his shoulders in triumph, yet not for long, I ween, shall he glory therein, for death is hard anigh him. But thou go not yet down into the mellay of war until thou see me with thine eyes come hither. In the morning will I return, at the coming up of the sun, bearing fair armour from the king Hephaistos."

Thus spake she and turned to go from her son, and as she turned she spake among her sisters of the sea: "Ye now go down within the wide bosom of the deep, to visit the Ancient One of the Sea and our father's house, and tell him all. I am going to high Olympus to Hephaistos of noble skill, if haply he will give unto my son noble armour shining gloriously."

Thus spake she, and they forthwith went down beneath the surge of the sea. And the silver-footed goddess Thetis went on to Olympus that she might bring noble armour to her son.

So her unto Olympus her feet bore. But the Achaians with terrible cries were fleeing before man-slaying Hector till they came to the ships and to the Hellespont. Nor might the well-greaved Achaians drag the corpse of Patroklos Achilles' squire out of the darts, for now again overtook him the host and the horses of Troy, and Hector son of Priam, in might as it were a flame of fire. Thrice did glorious Hector seize him from behind by the feet, resolved to drag him away, and mightily called upon the men of Troy. Thrice did the two Aiantes, clothed on with impetuous might, beat him off from the dead man, but he nathless, trusting in his might, anon would charge into the press, anon would stand and cry aloud, but he gave ground never a whit. As when shepherds in the field avail nowise to chase a fiery lion in fierce hunger away from a carcase, so availed not the two warrior Aiantes to scare Hector son of Priam from the dead. And now would he have won the body and gained renown unspeakable, had not fleet wind-footed Iris come speeding from Olympus with a message to the son of Peleus to array him, unknown of Zeus and the other gods, for Hera sent her. And she stood anigh and spake to him winged words: "Rouse thee, son of Peleus, of all men most redoubtable! Succour Patroklos, for whose body is terrible battle afoot before the ships. There slay they one another, these guarding the dead corpse, while the men of Troy are fierce to hale him unto windy Ilios, and chiefliest noble Hector is fain to drag him, and his heart biddeth him fix the head on the stakes of the wall when he hath sundered it from the tender neck. But arise, lie thus no longer! let awe enter thy heart to forbid that Patroklos become the sport of dogs of Troy. Thine were the shame if he go down mangled amid the dead."

Then answered her fleet-footed noble Achilles: "Goddess Iris, what god sent thee a messenger unto me?"

And to him again spake wind-footed fleet Iris: "It was Hera that sent me, the wise wife of Zeus, nor knoweth the high-throned son of Kronos nor any other of the Immortals that on snowy Olympus have their dwelling-place."

And Achilles fleet of foot made answer to her and said: "And how may I go into the fray? The Trojans hold my arms; and my dear mother bade me forbear to array me until I behold her with my eyes returned, for she promised to bring fair armour from Hephaistos. Other man know I none whose noble armour I might put on, save it were the shield of Aias Telamon's son. But himself, I ween, is in the fore-front of the press, dealing death with his spear around Patroklos dead."

Then again spake unto him wind-footed fleet Iris: "Well are we also aware that thy noble armour is held from thee. But go forth unto the trench as thou art and show thyself to the men of Troy, if haply they will shrink back and refrain them from battle, and the warlike sons of the Achaians take breath [amid their toil, for small breathing-time is in the thick of fight]."

Thus spake fleet-footed Iris and went her way. But Achilles dear to Zeus arose, and around his strong shoulders Athene cast her tasselled aegis, and around his head the bright goddess set a crown of a golden cloud, and kindled therefrom a blazing flame. And as when a smoke issueth from a city and riseth up into the upper air, from an island afar off that foes beleaguer, while the others from their city fight all day in hateful war,—but with the going down of the sun blaze out the beacon-fires in line, and high aloft rusheth up the glare for dwellers round about to behold, if haply they may come with ships to help in need—thus from the head of Achilles soared that blaze toward the heavens. And he went and stood beyond the wall beside the trench, yet mingled not among the Achaians, for he minded the wise bidding of his mother. There stood he and shouted aloud, and afar off Pallas Athene uttered her voice, and spread terror unspeakable among the men of Troy. Clear as the voice of a clarion when it soundeth by reason of slaughterous foemen that beleaguer a city, so clear rang forth the voice of Aiakides. And when they heard the brazen voice of Aiakides, the souls of all of them were dismayed, and the horses of goodly manes were fain to turn the chariots backward, for they boded anguish in their hearts. And the charioteers were amazed when they saw the unwearying fire blaze fierce on the head of the great-hearted son of Peleus, for the bright-eyed goddess Athene made it blaze. Thrice from over the trench shouted mightily noble Achilles, and thrice were the men of Troy confounded and their proud allies. Yea there and then perished twelve men of their best by their own chariot wheels and spears. But the Achaians with joy drew Patroklos forth of the darts and laid him on a litter, and his dear comrades stood around lamenting him; and among them followed fleet-footed Achilles, shedding hot tears, for his true comrade he saw lying on the bier, mangled by the keen bronze. Him sent he forth with chariot and horses unto the battle, but home again welcomed never more.

Then Hera the ox-eyed queen sent down the unwearying Sun to be gone unwillingly unto the streams of Ocean. So the Sun set, and the noble Achaians made pause from the stress of battle and the hazardous war.

Now the men of Troy on their side when they were come back out of the violent fray loosed their swift horses from the chariots and gathered themselves in assembly or ever they would sup. Upon their feet they stood in the assembly, neither had any man heart to sit, for fear was fallen upon all because Achilles was come forth, after long ceasing from fell battle. Then began to speak among them wise Polydamas, son of Panthoos, for he alone saw before and after. Comrade of Hector was he, and in the same night were both born, but the one in speech was far the best, the other with the spear. So with good intent toward them he made harangue and spake: "Take good heed on both sides, O my friends; for my part I would have ye go up now to the city, nor wait for bright morning on the plain beside the ships, for we are far off from the wall. So long as this man was wroth with noble Agamemnon, so long were the Achaians easier to fight against, ay and I too rejoiced when I couched nigh their swift ships, trusting that we should seize the curved ships for a prey. But now am I sore afraid of the fleet son of Peleus; so exceeding fierce is his heart, he will not choose to abide in the plain where Trojans and Achaians both in the midst share the spirit of war, but the prize he doeth battle for will be our city and our wives. Now go we up to our fastness; hearken unto me, for thus will it be. Now hath divine night stayed the fleet son of Peleus, but if to-morrow full-armed for the onset he shall light upon us abiding here, well shall each know that it is he, for gladly will whosoever fleeth win to sacred Ilios, and many of the men of Troy shall dogs and vultures devour—far be that from my ear. But if, though loth, we hearken unto my words, this night in counsel we shall possess our strength, and the city shall be guarded of her towers and high gates and tall well-polished doors that fit thereon close-shut. But at dawn of day in armour harnessed will we take our stand along the towers. Ill will he fare if he come forth from the ships to fight with us for our wall. Back to his ships shall he betake him when in vain chase he hath given his strong-necked horses their fill of hasting everywhither beneath the town. But within it never will he have heart to force his way, nor ever lay it waste; ere then shall he be devoured of swift dogs."

Then with stern gaze spake unto him Hector of the glancing helm: "Polydamas, no longer to my liking dost thou speak now, in that thou biddest us go back and be pent within the town. Have ye not had your fill already of being pent behind the towers? Of old time all mortal men would tell of this city of Priam for the much gold and bronze thereof, but now are its goodly treasures perished out of its dwellings, and much goods are sold away to Phrygia and pleasant Maionia, since mighty Zeus dealt evilly with us. But now when the son of crooked-counselling Kronos hath given me to win glory at the ships and to pen the Achaians beside the sea, no longer, fond man, put forth such counsels among the folk. No man of Troy will hearken unto thee, I will not suffer it. But come let us all be persuaded as I shall say. Sup now in your ranks throughout the host, and keep good ward, and each watch in his place. And whoso of the Trojans is grieved beyond measure for his goods, let him gather them together and give them to the people to consume in common, for it is better they have joy thereof than the Achaians. Then at dawn of day in armour harnessed at the hollow ships we will arouse keen war. What though in very truth noble Achilles be arisen beside the ships, ill shall he fare, if he will have it so. I at least will not flee from him out of the dread-sounding war, but full facing him will I stand, to try whether he win great victory, or haply I. The war-god is alike to all and a slayer of him that would slay."

Thus Hector spake, and the men of Troy applauded with fond hearts, for Pallas Athene bereft them of their wit. And they gave assent to the ill advising of Hector, but none hearkened to Polydamas who devised good counsel. Then they supped throughout the host; but the Achaians all night made moan in lamentation for Patroklos. And first of them in the loud lamentation was the son of Peleus, laying upon the breast of his comrade his man-slaying hands and moaning very sore, even as a deep-bearded lion whose whelps some stag-hunter hath snatched away out of a deep wood; and the lion coming afterward grieveth, and through many glens he rangeth on the track of the footsteps of the man, if anywhere he might find him, for most bitter anger seizeth him;—thus Achilles moaning heavily spake among the Myrmidons: "Ay me, vain verily was the word I uttered on that day when I cheered the hero Menoitios in his halls and said that I would bring back to Opoeis his son in glory from the sack of Ilios with the share of spoil that should fall unto him. Not all the purposes of men doth Zeus accomplish for them. It is appointed that both of us redden the same earth with our blood here in Troy-land, for neither shall the old knight Peleus welcome me back home within his halls, nor my mother Thetis, but even here shall earth keep hold on me. Yet now, O Patroklos, since I follow thee under earth, I will not hold thy funeral till I have brought hither the armour and the head of Hector, thy high-hearted slayer, and before thy pyre I will cut the throats of twelve noble sons of the men of Troy, for mine anger thou art slain. Till then beside the beaked ships shalt thou lie as thou art, and around thee deep-bosomed women, Trojan and Dardanian, shall mourn thee weeping night and day, even they whom we toiled to win by our strength and our long spears when we sacked rich cities of mortal men."

Thus spake noble Achilles, and bade his comrades set a great tripod on the fire, that with all speed they might wash from Patroklos the bloody gore. So they set a tripod of ablution on the burning fire, and poured therein water and took wood and kindled it beneath; and the fire wrapped the belly of the tripod, and the water grew hot. And when the water boiled in the bright bronze, then washed they him and anointed with olive oil, and filled his wounds with fresh ointment, and laid him on a bier and covered him with soft cloth from head to foot, and thereover a white robe. Then all night around Achilles fleet of foot the Myrmidons made lament and moan for Patroklos.

Meanwhile Zeus spake unto Hera his sister and wife: "Thou hast accomplished this, O Hera, ox-eyed queen, thou hast aroused Achilles fleet of foot. Verily of thine own children must the flowing-haired Achaians be."

Then answered unto him Hera the ox-eyed queen: "Most dread son of Kronos, what is this word thou hast said? Truly even a man, I ween, is to accomplish what he may for another man, albeit he is mortal and hath not wisdom as we. How then was I who avow me the first of goddesses both by birth and for that I am called thy wife, and thou art king among all Immortals—how was I not in mine anger to devise evil against the men of Troy?"

So debated they on this wise with one another. But Thetis of the silver feet came unto the house of Hephaistos, imperishable, starlike, far seen among the dwellings of Immortals, a house of bronze, wrought by the crook-footed god himself. Him found she sweating in toil and busy about his bellows, for he was forging tripods twenty in all to stand around the wall of his stablished hall, and beneath the base of each he had set golden wheels, that of their own motion they might enter the assembly of the gods and again return unto his house, a marvel to look upon. Thus much were they finished that not yet were the ears of cunning work set thereon; these was he making ready, and welding chains. While hereat he was labouring with wise intent, then drew nigh unto him Thetis, goddess of the silver feet. And Charis went forward and beheld her, fair Charis of the shining chaplet whom the renowned lame god had wedded. And she clasped her hand in hers and spake and called her by her name: "Wherefore, long-robed Thetis, comest thou to our house, honoured that thou art and dear? No frequent comer art thou hitherto. But come onward with me that I may set guest-cheer before thee."

Thus spake the bright goddess and led her on. Then set she her on a silver-studded throne, goodly, of cunning work, and a footstool was beneath her feet; and she called to Hephaistos, the famed artificer, and said unto him: "Hephaistos, come forth hither, Thetis hath need of thee."

And the renowned lame god made answer to her: "Verily a dread and honoured goddess in my sight is she that is within, seeing that she delivered me when pain came upon me from my great fall though the ill-will of my shameless mother who would have fain hid me away, for that I was lame. Then had I suffered anguish of heart had not Eurynome and Thetis taken me into their bosom—Eurynome daughter of Ocean that floweth back ever upon himself. Nine years with them I wrought much cunning work of bronze, brooches and spiral arm-bands and cups and necklaces, in the hollow cave, while around me the stream of Ocean with murmuring foam flowed infinite. Neither knew thereof any other of gods or of mortal men, save only Thetis and Eurynome who delivered me. And now cometh Thetis to our house; wherefore behoveth it me verily in all wise to repay fair-tressed Thetis for the saving of my life. But do thou now set beside her fair entertainment, while I put away my bellows and all my gear."

He said, and from the anvil rose limping, a huge bulk, but under him his slender legs moved nimbly. The bellows he set away from the fire, and gathered all his gear wherewith he worked into a silver chest; and with a sponge he wiped his face and hands and sturdy neck and shaggy breast, and did on his doublet, and took a stout staff and went forth limping; but there were handmaidens of gold that moved to help their lord, the semblances of living maids. In them is understanding at their hearts, in them are voice and strength, and they have skill of the immortal gods. These moved beneath their lord, and he gat him haltingly near to where Thetis was, and set him on a bright seat, and clasped her hand in his and spake and called her by her name: "Wherefore, long-robed Thetis, comest thou to our house, honoured that thou art and dear? No frequent comer art thou hitherto. Speak what thou hast at heart; my soul is fain to accomplish it, if accomplish it I can, and if it be appointed for accomplishment."

Then answered unto him Thetis shedding tears: "Hephaistos, hath there verily been any of all goddesses in Olympus that hath endured so many grievous sorrows at heart as are the woes that Kronian Zeus hath laid upon me above all others? He chose me from among the sisters of the sea to enthrall me to a man, even Peleus Aiakos' son, and with a man I endured wedlock sore against my will. Now lieth he in his halls forspent with grievous age, but other griefs are mine. A son he gave me to bear and nourish, the chief of heroes, and he shot up like a young branch. Like a plant in a very fruitful field I reared him and sent him forth on beaked ships to Ilios to fight against the men of Troy, but never again shall I welcome him back to his home within the house of Peleus. And while he yet liveth in my sight and beholdeth the light of the sun, he sorroweth, neither can I help him any whit though I go unto him. The maiden whom the sons of the Achaians chose out to be his prize, her hath the lord Agamemnon taken back out of his hands. In grief for her wasted he his heart; while the men of Troy were driving the Achaians on their ships, nor suffered them to come forth. And the elders of the Argives entreated him, and told over many noble gifts. Then albeit himself he refused to ward destruction from them, he put his armour on Patroklos and sent him to the war, and much people with him. All day they fought around the Skaian gates and that same day had sacked the town, but that when now Menoitios' valiant son had wrought much harm, Apollo slew him in the forefront of the battle, and gave glory unto Hector. Therefore now come I a suppliant unto thy knees, if haply thou be willing to give my short-lived son shield and helmet, and goodly greaves fitted with ankle-pieces, and cuirass. For the armour that he had erst, his trusty comrade lost when he fell beneath the men of Troy; and my son lieth on the earth with anguish in his soul."

Then made answer unto her the lame god of great renown: "Be of good courage, let not these things trouble thy heart. Would that so might I avail to hide him far from dolorous death, when dread fate cometh upon him, as surely shall goodly armour be at his need, such as all men afterward shall marvel at, whosoever may behold."

Thus saying he left her there and went unto his bellows and turned them upon the fire and bade them work. And the bellows, twenty in all, blew on the crucibles, sending deft blasts on every side, now to aid his labour and now anon howsoever Hephaistos willed and the work went on. And he threw bronze that weareth not into the fire, and tin and precious gold and silver, and next he set on an anvil-stand a great anvil, and took in his hand a sturdy hammer, and in the other he took the tongs.

First fashioned he a shield great and strong, adorning it all over, and set thereto a shining rim, triple, bright-glancing, and therefrom a silver baldric. Five were the folds of the shield itself; and therein fashioned he much cunning work from his wise heart.

There wrought he the earth, and the heavens, and the sea, and the unwearying sun, and the moon waxing to the full, and the signs every one wherewith the heavens are crowned, Pleiads and Hyads and Orion's might, and the Bear that men call also the Wain, her that turneth in her place and watcheth Orion; and alone hath no part in the baths of Ocean.

Also he fashioned therein two fair cities of mortal men. In the one were espousals and marriage feasts, and beneath the blaze of torches they were leading the brides from their chambers through the city, and loud arose the bridal song. And young men were whirling in the dance, and among them flutes and viols sounded high; and the women standing each at her door were marvelling. But the folk were gathered in the assembly place; for there a strife was arisen, two men striving about the blood-price of a man slain; the one claimed to pay full atonement, expounding to the people, but the other denied him and would take naught; and both were fain to receive arbitrament at the hand of a daysman. And the folk were cheering both, as they took part on either side. And heralds kept order among the folk, while the elders on polished stones were sitting in the sacred circle, and holding in their hands staves from the loud-voiced heralds. Then before the people they rose up and gave judgment each in turn. And in the midst lay two talents of gold, to be given unto him who should plead among them most righteously.

But around the other city were two armies in siege with glittering arms. And two counsels found favour among them, either to sack the town or to share all with the towns-folk even whatsoever substance the fair city held within. But the besieged were not yet yielding, but arming for an ambushment. On the wall there stood to guard it their dear wives and infant children, and with these the old men; but the rest went forth, and their leaders were Ares and Pallas Athene, both wrought in gold, and golden was the vesture they had on. Goodly and great were they in their armour, even as gods, far seen around, and the folk at their feet were smaller. And when they came where it seemed good to them to lay ambush, in a river bed where there was a common watering-place of herds, there they set them, clad in glittering bronze. And two scouts were posted by them afar off to spy the coming of flocks and of oxen with crooked horns. And presently came the cattle, and with them two herdsmen playing on pipes, that took no thought of the guile. Then the others when they beheld these ran upon them and quickly cut off the herds of oxen and fair flocks of white sheep, and slew the shepherds withal. But the besiegers, as they sat before the speech-places and heard much din among the oxen, mounted forthwith behind their high-stepping horses, and came up with speed. Then they arrayed their battle and fought beside the river banks, and smote one another with bronze-shod spears. And among them mingled Strife and Tumult, and fell Death, grasping one man alive fresh-wounded, another without wound, and dragging another dead through the mellay by the feet; and the raiment on her shoulders was red with the blood of men. Like living mortals they hurled together and fought, and haled the corpses each of the other's slain.

Furthermore he set in the shield a soft fresh-ploughed field, rich tilth and wide, the third time ploughed; and many ploughers therein drave their yokes to and fro as they wheeled about. Whensoever they came to the boundary of the field and turned, then would a man come to each and give into his hands a goblet of sweet wine, while others would be turning back along the furrows, fain to reach the boundary of the deep tilth. And the field grew black behind and seemed as it were a-ploughing, albeit of gold, for this was the great marvel of the work.

Furthermore he set therein the demesne-land of a king, where hinds were reaping with sharp sickles in their hands. Some armfuls along the swathe were falling in rows to the earth, whilst others the sheaf-binders were binding in twisted bands of straw. Three sheaf-binders stood over them, while behind boys gathering corn and bearing it in their arms gave it constantly to the binders; and among them the king in silence was standing at the swathe with his staff, rejoicing in his heart. And henchmen apart beneath an oak were making ready a feast, and preparing a great ox they had sacrificed; while the women were strewing much white barley to be a supper for the hinds.

Also he set therein a vineyard teeming plenteously with clusters, wrought fair in gold; black were the grapes, but the vines hung throughout on silver poles. And around it he ran a ditch of cyanus, and round that a fence of tin; and one single pathway led to it, whereby the vintagers might go when they should gather the vintage. And maidens and striplings in childish glee bare the sweet fruit in plaited baskets. And in the midst of them a boy made pleasant music on a clear-toned viol, and sang thereto a sweet Linos-song with delicate voice; while the rest with feet falling together kept time with the music and song.

Also he wrought therein a herd of kine with upright horns, and the kine were fashioned of gold and tin, and with lowing they hurried from the byre to pasture beside a murmuring river, beside the waving reed. And herdsmen of gold were following with the kine, four of them, and nine dogs fleet of foot came after them. But two terrible lions among the foremost kine had seized a loud-roaring bull that bellowed mightily as they haled him, and the dogs and the young men sped after him. The lions rending the great bull's hide were devouring his vitals and his black blood; while the herdsmen in vain tarred on their fleet dogs to set on, for they shrank from biting the lions but stood hard by and barked and swerved away.

Also the glorious lame god wrought therein a pasture in a fair glen, a great pasture of white sheep, and a steading, and roofed huts, and folds.

Also did the glorious lame god devise a dancing-place like unto that which once in wide Knosos Daidalos wrought for Ariadne of the lovely tresses. There were youths dancing and maidens of costly wooing, their hands upon one another's wrists. Fine linen the maidens had on, and the youths well-woven doublets faintly glistening with oil. Fair wreaths had the maidens, and the youths daggers of gold hanging from silver baldrics. And now would they run round with deft feet exceeding lightly, as when a potter sitting by his wheel that fitteth between his hands maketh trial of it whether it run: and now anon they would run in lines to meet each other. And a great company stood round the lovely dance in joy; [and among them a divine minstrel was making music on his lyre,] and through the midst of them, leading the measure, two tumblers whirled.

Also he set therein the great might of the River of Ocean around the uttermost rim of the cunningly-fashioned shield.

Now when he had wrought the shield great and strong, then wrought he him a corslet brighter than a flame of fire, and he wrought him a massive helmet to fit his brows, goodly and graven, and set thereon a crest of gold, and he wrought him greaves of pliant tin.

So when the renowned lame god had finished all the armour, he took and laid it before the mother of Achilles. Then she like a falcon sprang down from snowy Olympus, bearing from Hephaistos the glittering arms.

BOOK XIX

How Achilles and Agamemnon were reconciled before the assembly of the Achaians, and Achilles went forth with them to battle.

Now Morning saffron-robed arose from the streams of Ocean to bring light to gods and men, and Thetis came to the ships, bearing his gift from the god. Her dear son she found fallen about Patroklos and uttering loud lament; and round him many of his company made moan. And the bright goddess stood beside him in their midst, and clasped her hand in his and spake and called upon his name: "My child, him who lieth here we must let be, for all our pain, for by the will of gods from the beginning was he brought low. But thou take from Hephaistos arms of pride, arms passing goodly, such as no man on his shoulders yet hath borne."

Thus spake the goddess and in front of Achilles laid the arms, and they rang all again in their glory. And awe fell on all the Myrmidons, nor dared any to gaze thereon, for they were awe-stricken. But when Achilles looked thereon, then came fury upon him the more, and his eyes blazed terribly forth as it were a flame beneath their lids: glad was he as he held in his hands that splendid gift of a god. But when he had satisfied his soul in gazing on the glory of the arms, straightway to his mother spake he winged words: "My mother, the arms the god has given are such as it beseemeth that the work of Immortals should be, and that no mortal man should have wrought. Now therefore will I arm me in them, but I have grievous fear lest meantime on the gashed wounds of Menoitios' valiant son flies light and breed worms therein, and defile his corpse—for the life is slain out of him—and so all his flesh shall rot."

Then answered him Thetis, goddess of the silver feet: "Child, have no care for this within thy mind. I will see to ward from him the cruel tribes of flies which prey on men slain in fight: for even though he lie till a whole year's course be run, yet his flesh shall be sound continually, or better even than now. But call thou the Achaian warriors to the place of assembly, and unsay thy wrath against Agamemnon shepherd of the host, and then arm swiftly for battle, and clothe thee with thy strength."

Thus saying she filled him with adventurous might, while on Patroklos she shed ambrosia and red nectar through his nostrils, that his flesh might abide the same continually.

But noble Achilles went down the beach of the sea, crying his terrible cry, and roused the Achaian warriors. And they who before were wont to abide in the circle of the ships, and they who were helmsmen and kept the steerage of the ships, or were stewards there and dealt out food, even these came then to the place of assembly, because Achilles was come forth, after long ceasing from grievous war. Limping came two of Ares' company, Tydeus' son staunch in fight and noble Odysseus, each leaning on his spear, for their wounds were grievous still; and they went and sate them down in the forefront of the assembly. And last came Agamemnon king of men, with his wound upon him, for him too in the stress of battle Koön Antenor's son had wounded with his bronze-tipped spear. But when all the Achaians were gathered, then uprose fleet-footed Achilles and spake in their midst: "Son of Atreus, was this in any wise the better way for both thee and me, what time with grief at our hearts we waxed fierce in soul-devouring strife for the sake of a girl? Would that Artemis had slain her with her arrow at the ships, on the day whereon I took her to me, when I had spoiled Lyrnessos; so should not then so many Achaians have bitten the wide earth beneath their enemies' hands, by reason of my exceeding wrath. It hath been well for Hector and the Trojans, but the Achaians I think shall long remember the strife that was betwixt thee and me. But bygones will we let be, for all our pain, and curb under necessity the spirit within our breasts. I now will stay my anger: it beseems me not implacably for ever to be wroth; but come rouse speedily to the fight the flowing-haired Achaians, that I may go forth against the men of Troy and put them yet again to the proof, if they be fain to couch hard by the ships. Methinks that some among them shall be glad to rest their knees when they are fled out of the fierceness of the battle, and from before our spear."

He spake, and the well-greaved Achaians rejoiced that the great-hearted son of Peleus had made renouncement of his wrath. Then among them spake Agamemnon king of men, speaking from the place where he sat, not arisen to stand forth in their midst: "O Danaan friends and heroes, men of Ares' company, seemly is it to listen to him who standeth up to speak, nor behoveth it to break in upon his words: even toward a skilled man that were hard. For amid the uproar of many men how should one listen, or yet speak? even the clearest-voiced speech is marred. To the son of Peleus I will declare myself, but ye other Argives give heed, and each mark well my word. Oft have the Achaians spoken thus to me, and upbraided me; but it is not I who am the cause, but Zeus and Destiny and Erinys that walketh in the darkness, who put into my soul fierce madness on the day when in the assembly I, even I, bereft Achilles of his meed. What could I do? it is God who accomplisheth all. Eldest daughter of Zeus is Ate who blindeth all, a power of bane: delicate are her feet, for not upon earth she goeth, but walketh over the heads of men, making men to fall; and entangleth this one or that. Yea even Zeus was blinded upon a time, he who they say is greatest among gods and men; yet even him Hera with female wile deceived, on the day when Alkmene in fair-crowned Thebes was to bring forth the strength of Herakles. For then proclaimed he solemnly among all the gods: 'Hear me ye all, both gods and goddesses, while I utter the counsel of my soul within my heart. This day shall Eileithuia, the help of travailing women, bring to the light a man who shall be lord over all that dwell round about, among the race of men who are sprung of me by blood.' And to him in subtlety queen Hera spake: 'Thou wilt play the cheat and not accomplish thy word. Come now, Olympian, swear me a firm oath that verily and indeed shall that man be lord over all that dwell round about, who this day shall fall between a woman's feet, even he among all men who are of the lineage of thy blood.' So spake she, and Zeus no wise perceived her subtlety, but sware a mighty oath, and therewith was he sore blinded. For Hera darted from Olympus' peak, and came swiftly to Achaian Argos, where she knew was the stately wife of Sthenelos son of Perseus, who also was great with child, and her seventh month was come. Her son Hera brought to the light, though his tale of months was untold, but she stayed Alkmene's bearing and kept the Eileithuiai from her aid. Then she brought the tidings herself and to Kronos' son Zeus she spake: 'Father Zeus of the bright lightning, a word will I speak to thee for thy heed. To-day is born a man of valour who shall rule among the Argives, Eurystheus, son of Sthenelos the son of Perseus, of thy lineage; not unmeet is it that he be lord among Argives.' She said, but sharp pain smote him in the depths of his soul, and straightway he seized Ate by her bright-haired head in the anger of his soul, and sware a mighty oath that never again to Olympus and the starry heaven should

Ate come, who blindeth all alike. He said, and whirling her in his hand flung her from the starry heaven, and quickly came she down among the works of men. Yet ever he groaned against her when he beheld his beloved son in cruel travail at Eurystheus' hest. Thus also I, what time great Hector of the glancing helm was slaying Argives at the sterns of our ships, could not be unmindful of Ate, who blinded me at the first. But since thus blinded was I, and Zeus bereft me of my wit, fain am I to make amends, and recompense manifold for the wrong. Only arise thou to the battle and rouse the rest of the host. Gifts am I ready to offer, even all that noble Odysseus went yesterday to promise in thy hut. So, if thou wilt, stay a while, though eager, from battle, and squires shall take the gifts from my ship and carry them to thee, that thou mayest see that what I give sufficeth thee."

Then answered him Achilles swift of foot: "Most noble son of Atreus, Agamemnon king of men, for the gifts, to give them as it beseemeth, if so thou wilt, or to withhold, is in thy choice. But now let us bethink us of battle with all speed; this is no time to dally here with subtleties, for a great work is yet undone. Once more must Achilles be seen in the forefront of the battle, laying waste with his brazen spear the battalions of the men of Troy. Thereof let each of you think as he fighteth with his man."

Then Odysseus of many counsels answered him and said: "Nay yet, for all thy valour, godlike Achilles, not against Ilios lead thou the sons of Achaians fasting to fight the men of Troy, since not of short spell shall the battle be, when once the ranks of men are met, and God shall breathe valour into both. But bid the Achaians taste at the swift ships food and wine; for thence is vigour and might. For no man fasting from food shall be able to fight with the foe all day till the going down of the sun; for though his spirit be eager for battle yet his limbs unaware grow weary, and thirst besetteth him, and hunger, and his knees in his going fail. But the man who having his fill of food and wine fighteth thus all day against the enemy, his heart is of good cheer within him, nor anywise tire his limbs, ere all give back from the battle. So come, disperse the host and bid them make ready their meal. And the gifts let Agamemnon king of men bring forth into the midst of the assembly, that all Achaians may behold them with their eyes, and thou be glad at heart. And let him swear to thee an oath, standing in the midst of the Argives, that he hath never gone up into the damsel's bed or lain with her, [O prince, as is the wont of man with woman]; and let thine own spirit be placable within thy breast. Then let him make thee a rich feast of reconcilement in his hut, that thou have nothing lacking of thy right. And thou, son of Atreus, toward others also shalt be more righteous hereafter; for no shame it is that a man that is a king should make amends if he have been the first to deal violently."

Then to him spake Agamemnon king of men: "Son of Laertes, I rejoice to listen to thy speech; for rightfully hast thou told over all. And the oath I am willing to swear, yea my heart biddeth it, nor will I forswear myself before God. Let Achilles abide for a space, eager for battle though he be, and all ye others abide together, until the gifts come forth from my hut, and we make faithful oath with sacrifice. But thee thyself I thus charge and bid. Choose thee young men, princes of the Achaian folk, and bear my gifts from my ship, even all that we promised yesterday to Achilles, and take with thee the women. And let Talthybios speedily make me ready a boar-swine in the midst of the wide Achaian host, to sacrifice to Zeus and to the Sun."

And to him in answer swift-footed Achilles spake: "Most noble son of Atreus, Agamemnon king of men, at some other time were it even better ye should be busied thus, when haply there shall be some pause of war, and the spirit within my breast shall be less fierce. But now they lie mangled on the field—even they whom Hector son of Priam slew, when Zeus gave him glory—and ye call men to their food. Verily for my part I would bid the sons of the Achaians to fight now unfed and fasting, and with the setting sun make ready a mighty meal, when we shall have avenged the shame. Till then down my throat at least nor food nor drink shall go, since my comrade is dead, who in my hut is lying mangled by the sharp spear, with his feet toward the door, and round him our comrades mourn; wherefore in my heart is no thought of those matters, but of slaying, and blood, and grievous moans of men."

Then answered him Odysseus of many counsels: "O Achilles, Peleus' son, mightiest of Achaians far, better and mightier not a little art thou than I with the spear, but in counsel I may surpass thee greatly, since I was born first and know more things: wherefore let thy heart endure to listen to my speech. Quickly have men surfeit of battle, of that wherein the sword streweth most straw yet is the harvest scantiest, when Zeus inclineth his balance, who is disposer of the wars of men. But it cannot be that the Achaians fast to mourn a corpse; for exceeding many and thick fall such on every day; when then should there be rest from toil? Nay, it behoveth to bury him who is dead, steeling our hearts, when once we have wept him for a day; but such as are left alive from hateful war must take thought of meat and drink, that yet more against our foes we may fight relentlessly ever, clad in unyielding bronze. Then let none of the host hold back awaiting other summons; this is the summons, and ill shall it be for whoso is left behind at the Argive ships; but all together as one we will rouse against the horse-taming Trojans the fury of war."

He spoke, and took with him the sons of noble Nestor, and Meges son of Phyleus, and Thoas, and Meriones, and Lykomedes son of Kreiontes, and Melanippos. And they went on their way to the hut of Agamemnon, Atreus' son. Forthwith as the word was spoken so was the deed done. Seven tripods they bare from the hut, as he promised him, and twenty bright caldrons, and twelve horses, and anon they led forth women skilled in goodly arts, seven, and the eighth was fair-faced Briseis. Then Odysseus, having weighed ten talents of gold in all, led the way, and with him young men of the Achaians bare the gifts. These they set in the midst of the place of assembly, and Agamemnon rose up, and beside that shepherd of the host stood Talthybios, whose voice was like a god's, and held a boar between his hands. And the son of Atreus drawing with his hands his knife, which ever hung beside the mighty scabbard of his sword, cut off the first hairs from the boar, and lifting up his hands he prayed to Zeus, and all the Argives sat silent in their places, duly hearkening to the king. And he prayed aloud, looking up to the wide heaven: "Be Zeus before all witness, highest and best of gods, and Earth, and Sun, and Erinyes, who under earth take vengeance upon men, whosoever forsweareth himself, that never have I laid hand on the damsel Briseis, neither to lie with her nor anywise else, but she has abode untouched within my huts. And if aught that I swear be false, may the gods give me all sorrows manifold, that they send on him who sinneth against them in his oath."

He said, and cut the boar's throat with the pitiless knife. And the body Talthybios whirled and threw into the great wash of the hoary sea, to be the food of fishes; but Achilles arose up and spake in the midst of the warrior Argives: "Father Zeus, sore madness dealest thou verily to men. Never could the son of Atreus have stirred the soul within my breast, nor led off the damsel implacably against my will, had not Zeus willed that on many of the Achaians death should come. But now go forth to your meal, that we may join battle thereupon."

Thus he spake and dispersed the assembly with all speed.

The rest were scattered each to his own ship, but the great-hearted Myrmidons took up the gifts, and bare them to the ship of godlike Achilles. And they laid them in the huts and set the women there, and gallant squires drave the horses among their troop.

But Briseis that was like unto golden Aphrodite, when she beheld Patroklos mangled by the keen spear, fell about him and made shrill lament, and tore with her hands her breast and tender neck, and beautiful face. And she spake amid her weeping, that woman like unto goddesses: "Patroklos, dearest to my hapless heart, alive I left thee when I left this hut, but now, O prince of the people, I am come back to find thee dead; thus evil ever followeth evil in my lot. My husband, unto whom my father and lady mother gave me, I beheld before our city mangled with the keen spear, and my three brothers whom my own mother bore, my near and dear, who all met their day of doom. But thou, when swift Achilles slew my husband and wasted godlike Mynes' city, wouldst ever that I should not even weep, and saidest that thou wouldst make me godlike Achilles' wedded wife, and that ye would take me in your ships to Phthia and make me a marriage feast among the Myrmidons. Therefore with all my soul I mourn thy death, for thou wert ever kind."

Thus spake she weeping, and thereon the women wailed, in semblance for Patroklos, but each for her own woe. But round Achilles gathered the elders of the Achaians, praying him that he would eat; but he denied them with a groan: "I pray you, if any kind comrade will hearken to me, bid me not sate my heart with meat and drink, since terrible grief is come upon me. Till the sun go down I will abide, and endure continually until then."

He spoke, and his speech made the other chiefs depart, but the two sons of Atreus stayed, and noble Odysseus, and Nestor and Idomeneus and Phoinix, ancient knight, soothing him in his exceeding sorrow, but he could no whit be soothed until he had entered the mouth of bloody war. And bethinking him he sighed very heavily and spake aloud: "Thou too, O hapless, dearest of my friends, thyself wouldst verily of yore set forth in our hut with ready speed a savoury meal, what time the Achaians hasted to wage against the horse-taming Trojans dolorous war. But now thou liest mangled, and my heart will none of meat and drink, that stand within, for desire of thee. Nought worse than this could I endure, not though I should hear of my father's death, who now I ween in Phthia is shedding big tears for lack of a son so dear, even me that in an alien land for sake of baleful Helen do battle with the men of Troy; nor though it were my beloved son who is reared for me in Skyros (if still at least is godlike Neoptolemos alive). For hitherto had my soul within me trusted that I alone should perish far from horse-pasturing Argos, here in the Trojan land, but that thou shouldst return to Phthia, so that thou mightest take me the child in thy swift black ship from Skyros and show him everything—my substance and servants, and high-roofed mighty hall. For Peleus I ween already must be dead and gone, or else in feeble life he hath sorrow of hateful age, and of waiting ever for bitter news of me, till he hear that I am dead."

Thus spake he weeping, and the elders mourned with him, bethinkng them what each had left at home. And when the son of Kronos beheld them sorrowing he pitied them, and forthwith to Athene spake he winged words: "My child, thou hast then left utterly the man of thy heart. Hath Achilles then no longer a place within thy thought? He before the steep-prowed ships sits mourning his dear comrade; the rest are gone to their meal, but he is fasting and unfed. But go, distil into his breast nectar and pleasant ambrosia, that no pains of hunger come on him."

Thus saying he sped forward Athene who before was fain. And she, like a falcon wide-winged and shrill-voiced, hurled herself forth from heaven through the upper air. So while the Achaians were arming presently throughout the camp, she in Achilles' breast distilled nectar and pleasant ambrosia, that grievous hunger might not assail his knees, and then herself was gone to the firm house of her mighty father. Then the Achaians poured forth from the swift ships. As when thick snowflakes flutter down from Zeus, chill beneath the blast of Boreas born in the upper air, so thick from the ships streamed forth bright glittering helms and bossy shields, strong-plated cuirasses and ashen spears. And the sheen thereof went up to heaven and all the earth around laughed in the flash of bronze, and there went a sound beneath the feet of the men, and in the midst of them noble Achilles harnessed him. His teeth gnashed together, and his eyes blazed as it were the flame of a fire, for into his heart was intolerable anguish entered in. Thus wroth against the men of Troy he put on the gift of the god, which Hephaistos wrought him by his art. First on his legs he set the fair-greaves fitted with silver ankle-pieces, and next he donned the cuirass about his breast. Then round his shoulders he slung the bronze sword silver-studded; then lastly he took the great and strong shield, and its brightness shone afar off as the moon's. Or as when over the sea there appeareth to sailors the brightness of a burning fire, and it burneth on high among the mountains in some lonely steading—sailors whom storm-blasts bear unwilling over the sea, the home of fishes, afar from them they love:—so from Achilles' goodly well-dight shield the brightness thereof shot up toward heaven. And he lifted the stout helmet and set it on his head, and like a star it shone, the horse-hair crested helmet, and around it waved plumes of gold that Hephaistos had set thick about the crest. Then noble Achilles proved him in his armour to know whether it fitted unto him, and whether his glorious limbs ran free; and it became to him as it were wings, and buoyed up the shepherd of hosts.

And forth from its stand he drew his father's spear,

heavy and great and strong: that spear could none other of the Achaians wield, but Achilles alone awaited to wield it, the Pelian ashen spear that Cheiron gave to his father dear, from a peak of Pelion, to be the death of warriors. And Automedon and Alkimos went about to yoke the horses, and put on them fair breast-straps, and bits within their jaws, and stretched the reins behind to the firm-built chariot. Then Automedon took the bright lash, fitted to his hand, and sprang up behind the horses, and after him mounted Achilles armed, effulgent in his armour like bright Hyperion. And terribly he called upon the horses of his sire: "Xanthos and Balios, famed children of Podarge, in other sort take heed to bring your charioteer safe back to the Danaan host, when we have done with battle, and leave him not as ye left Patroklos to lie there dead."

Then the horse Xanthos of glancing feet made answer unto him from beneath the yoke;—and he bowed with his head, and all his mane fell from the yoke-cushion beside the yoke and touched the ground;—for the white-armed goddess Hera gave him speech: "Yea verily for this hour, dread Achilles, we will still bear thee safe, yet is thy death-day nigh at hand, neither shall we be cause thereof, but a mighty god, and forceful Fate. For not through sloth or heedlessness of ours did the men of Troy from Patroklos' shoulders strip his arms, but the best of the gods, whom bright-haired Leto bore, slew him in the forefront of the battle, and to Hector gave renown. We even with the wind of Zephyr, swiftest, they say, of all winds, well might run; nathless to thee thyself it is appointed to be slain in fight by a god and by a man."

Now when he had thus spoken the Erinyes stayed his voice. And sore troubled did fleet-footed Achilles answer him: "Xanthos, why prophesiest thou my death? nowise behoveth it thee. Well know I of myself that it is appointed me to perish here, far from my father dear and mother;

howbeit anywise I will not refrain till I give the Trojans surfeit of war."

He said, and with a cry among the foremost held on his whole-hooved steeds.

BOOK XX

How Achilles made havoc among the men of Troy.

So by the beaked ships around thee, son of Peleus, hungry for war, the Achaians armed; and over against them the men of Troy, upon the high ground of the plain.

But Zeus bade Themis call the gods to council from many-folded Olympus' brow; and she ranged all about and bade them to the house of Zeus. There was no River came not up, save only Ocean, nor any nymph, of all that haunt fair thickets and springs of rivers and grassy water-meadows. And they came to the house of Zeus who gathereth the clouds, and sat them down in the polished colonnades which Hephaistos in the cunning of his heart had wrought for father Zeus.

Thus gathered they within the doors of Zeus; nor was the Earthshaker heedless of the goddess' call, but from the salt sea came up after the rest, and set him in the midst, and inquired concerning the purpose of Zeus: "Wherefore, O Lord of the bright lightning, hast thou called the gods again to council? Say, ponderest thou somewhat concerning the Trojans and Achaians? for lo, the war and the fighting of them are kindled very high."

And Zeus who gathereth the clouds answered him, saying: "Thou knowest, O Earthshaker, the purpose within my breast, wherefor I gathered you hither; even in their perishing have I regard unto them. But for me I will abide here, sitting within a fold of Olympus, where I will gladden my heart with gazing; but go all ye forth that ye come among the Trojans and Achaians and succour these or those, howsoever each of you hath a mind. For if Achilles alone shall fight against the Trojans, not even a little while shall they hold back the son of Peleus, the fleet of foot. Nay, but even aforetime they trembled when they looked upon him; now therefore that his wrath for his friend is waxen terrible I fear me lest he overleap the bound of fate, and storm the wall."

Thus spake the son of Kronos, and roused unabating war. For on this side and on that the gods went forth to war: to the company of the ships went Hera, and Pallas Athene, and Poseidon, Earth-enfolder, and the Helper Hermes, pre-eminent in subtle thoughts; and with these went Hephaistos in the greatness of his strength, halting, but his shrunk legs moved nimbly under him: but to the Trojans went Ares of the glancing helm, and with him Phoebus of the unshorn hair, and archer Artemis, and Leto and Xanthos and laughter-loving Aphrodite.

Now for so long as gods were afar from mortal men, so long waxed the Achaians glorious, for that Achilles was come forth among them, and his long ceasing from grim battle was at an end. And the Trojans were smitten with sore trembling in the limbs of every one of them, in terror when they beheld the son of Peleus, fleet of foot, blazing in his arms, peer of man-slaying Ares. But when among the mellay of men the Olympians were come down, then leapt up in her might Strife, rouser of hosts, then sent forth Athene a cry, now standing by the hollowed trench without the wall, and now on the echoing shores she shouted aloud. And a shout uttered Ares against her, terrible as the blackness of the storm, now from the height of the city to the Trojans calling clear, or again along Simois shore over Kallikolonë he sped.

So urged the blessed gods both hosts to battle, then themselves burst into fierce war. And terribly thundered the father of gods and men from heaven above; and from beneath Poseidon made the vast earth shake and the steep mountain tops. Then trembled all the spurs of many-fountained Ida, and all her crests, and the city of the Trojans, and the ships of the Achaians. And the Lord of the Underworld, Aïdoneus, had terror in hell, and leapt from his throne in that terror and cried aloud, lest the world be cloven above him by Poseidon, Shaker of earth, and his dwelling-place be laid bare to mortals and immortals—grim halls, and vast, and lothly to the gods. So loud the roar rose of that battle of gods. For against King Poseidon stood Phoebus Apollo with his winged arrows, and against Enyalios stood Athene, bright-eyed goddess, and against Hera she of the golden shafts and echoing chase, even archer Artemis, sister of the Far-darter; and against Leto the strong Helper Hermes, and against Hephaistos the great deep-eddying River, whom gods call Xanthos and men Skamandros.

Thus gods with gods were matched. Meanwhile Achilles yearned above all to meet Hector, son of Priam, in the fray; for with that blood chiefliest his spirit bade him sate Ares, stubborn lord of war. But straightway Apollo, rouser of hosts, moved Aineias to go to meet the son of Peleus, and filled him with brave spirit: and he made his own voice like the voice of Lykaon the son of Priam; in his semblance spake Apollo, son of Zeus: "Aineias, counsellor of Trojans, where now are thy threats wherewith thou didst boast to the Trojan lords over thy wine, saying thou wouldest stand up in battle against Achilles, Peleus' son?"

And to him Aineias answered and said: "Son of Priam, why biddest thou me thus face the fierce son of Peleus in battle, though I be not fain thereto? Not for the first time now shall I match me with Achilles, fleet of foot; once before drave he me with his spear from Ida, when he harried our kine and wasted Lyrnessos and Pedasos; but Zeus delivered me out of his hand and put strength into my knees that they were swift. Else had I fallen beneath the hands of Achilles, and of Athene who went before and gave him light, and urged him to slay Leleges and Trojans with his spear of bronze. Therefore it is impossible for man to face Achilles in fight, for that ever some god is at his side to ward off death. Ay, and at any time his spear flieth straight, neither ceaseth till it have pierced through flesh of man. But if God once give us fair field of battle, not lightly shall he overcome me, not though he boast him made of bronze throughout."

And to him in answer spake Apollo son of Zeus: "Yea, hero, pray thou too to the everliving gods; for thou too, men say, wast born of Aphrodite daughter of Zeus, and Achilles' mother is of less degree among the gods. For thy mother is child of Zeus, his but of the Ancient One of the Sea. Come, bear up thy unwearying spear against him, let him nowise turn thee back with revilings and bitter words."

He said, and breathed high spirit into the shepherd of the host, and he went onward through the forefront of the fighting, harnessed in flashing bronze. But white-armed Hera failed not to discern Anchises' son as he went through the press of men to meet the son of Peleus, and gathering the gods about her she spake among them thus: "Consider ye twain, Poseidon and Athene, within your hearts, what shall come of these things that are done. Here is Aineias gone forth harnessed in flashing bronze, to meet the son of Peleus, and it is Phoebus Apollo that hath sent him. Come then, be it ours to turn him back straightway; or else let some one of us stand likewise beside Achilles and give him mighty power, so that he fail not in his spirit, but know that they who love him are the best of the Immortals, and that they who from of old ward war and fighting from the Trojans are vain as wind. All we from Olympus are come down to mingle in this fight that he take no hurt among the Trojans on this day—afterward he shall suffer whatsoever things Fate span for him with her thread, at his beginning, when his mother bare him. If Achilles learn not this from voice divine, then shall he be afraid when some god shall come against him in the battle; for gods revealed are hard to look upon."

Then to her made answer Poseidon, Shaker of the earth: "Hera, be not fierce beyond wisdom; it behoveth thee not. Not fain am I at least to match gods with gods in strife. Let us go now into some high place apart and seat us there to watch, and battle shall be left to men. Only if Ares or Phoebus Apollo fall to fighting, or put constraint upon Achilles and hinder him from fight, then straightway among us too shall go up the battle-cry of strife; right soon, methinks, shall they hie them from the issue of the fray back to Olympus to the company of the gods, overcome by the force of our hands."

Thus spake the blue-haired god, and led the way to the mounded wall of heaven-sprung Herakles, that lofty wall built him by the Trojans and Pallas Athene, that he might escape the monster and be safe from him, what time he should make his onset from the beach to the plain. There sate them down Poseidon and the other gods, and clothed their shoulders with impenetrable cloud. And they of the other part sat down on the brows of Kallikolonë around thee, Archer Phoebus, and Ares waster of cities. Thus they on either side sat devising counsels, but shrank all from falling to grievous war, and Zeus from his high seat commanded them.

Meanwhile the whole plain was filled with men and horses, and ablaze with bronze; and the earth rang with the feet of them as they rushed together in the fray. Two men far better than the rest were meeting in the midst between the hosts, eager for battle, Aineias, Anchises' son, and noble Achilles. First came on Aineias threateningly, tossing his strong helm; his rapid shield he held before his breast, and brandished his bronze spear. And on the other side the son of Peleus rushed to meet him, like a lion, a ravaging lion whom men desire to slay, a whole tribe assembled: and first he goeth his way unheeding, but when some warrior youth hath smitten him with a spear, then he gathereth himself open-mouthed, and foam cometh forth about his teeth, and his stout spirit groaneth in his heart, and with his tail he scourgeth either side his ribs and flanks and goadeth himself on to fight, and glaring is borne straight on them by his passion, to try whether he shall slay some man of them, or whether himself shall perish in the forefront of the throngs: thus was Achilles driven of his passion and valiant spirit to go forth to meet Aineias great of heart. And when they were come near against each other, then first to Aineias spake fleet-footed noble Achilles: "Aineias, wherefore hast thou so far come forward from the crowd to stand against me: doth thy heart bid thee fight with me in hope of holding Priam's honour and lordship among the horse-taming Trojans? Nay, though thou slay me, not for that will Priam lay his kingdom in thy hands, for he hath sons, and is sound and of unshaken mind. Or have the Trojans allotted thee some lot of ground more choice than all the rest, fair land of tilth and orchard, that thou mayest dwell therein, if thou slay me? But methinks thou wilt find the slaying hard; for once before, I ween, have I made thee flee before my spear. Hast thou forgotten the day when thou wert alone with the kine, and I made thee run swift-footed down Ida's steeps in haste? —then didst thou not look behind thee in thy flight. Thence fleddest thou to Lernessos, but I wasted it, having fought against it with the help of Athene and of father Zeus, and carried away women captive, bereaving them of their day of freedom: only thee Zeus shielded, and other gods. But not this time, methinks, shall they shield thee, as thou imaginest in thy heart: therefore I bid thee go back into the throng and come not forth against me, while as yet thou art unhurt—after the event even a fool is wise."

Then to him in answer again Aineias spake; "Son of Peleus, think not with words to affright me as a child, since

I too well know myself how to speak taunts and unjust speech. We know each other's race and lineage in that we have heard the fame proclaimed by mortal men, but never hast thou set eyes on my parents, or I on thine. Thou, they say, art son of noble Peleus, and of Thetis of the fair tresses, the daughter of the sea: the sire I boast is Anchises great of heart, and my mother is Aphrodite. Of these shall one pair or the other mourn their dear son to-day; for verily not with idle words shall we two satisfy our strife and depart out of the battle. But, if thou wilt, learn also this, that thou mayest well know our lineage, known to full many men: First Zeus the cloud-gatherer begat Dardanos, and he stablished Dardania, for not yet was holy Ilios built upon the plain to be a city of mortal men, but still they dwelt on slopes of many-fountained Ida. Then Dardanos begat a son, king Erichthonios, who became richest of mortal men. Three thousand mares had he that pastured along the marsh meadow, rejoicing in their tender foals. Of them was Boreas enamoured as they grazed, and in semblance of a dark-maned horse he covered them: then they having conceived bare twelve fillies. These when they bounded over Earth the grain-giver would run upon the topmost ripened ears of corn and break them not; and when they bounded over the broad backs of the sea they would run upon the crests of the breakers of the hoary brine. Then Erichthonios begat Tros to be lord over the Trojans, and to Tros three noble sons were born, Ilos and Assarakos and godlike Ganymedes, who became the most beautiful of mortal men. Him the gods caught up to be cupbearer to Zeus, for sake of his beauty, that he might dwell among immortals. Then Ilos again begat a son, noble Laomedon, and Laomedon begat Tithonos and Priam and Lampos and Klytios and Hiketaon, of the stock of Ares. And Assarakos begat Kapys, and Kapys Anchises, and Anchises me; but Priam begat the goodly Hector.

"Lo then of this blood and lineage declare I myself unto

thee. But for valour, Zeus increaseth it in men or minisheth it according as he will, for he is lord of all. But come, let us talk thus together no longer like children, standing in mid onset of war. For there are revilings in plenty for both of us to utter—a hundred-thwarted ship would not suffice for the load of them. Glib is the tongue of man, and many words are therein of every kind, and wide is the range of his speech hither and thither. Whatsoever word thou speak, such wilt thou hear in answer. But what need that we should bandy strife and wrangling each against each, like women, who when they wax wroth for some heart-wasting quarrel go forth into the mid street and wrangle each against each with words true and false; for these too anger bids them speak. But not by speech shalt thou turn me from the battle that I desire, until we have fought together, point to point: come then, and straightway we will each try the other with bronze-headed spears."

He said, and against that other's dread and mighty shield hurled his great spear, and the shield rang loud beneath the spear-point. And the son of Peleus held away the shield from him with his stout hand, in fear, for he thought that the far-shadowing spear of Aineias great of heart would lightly pierce it through—fond man, and knew not in his mind and heart that not lightly do the glorious gifts of gods yield to force of mortal men. So did not the great spear of wise Aineias pierce that shield, for the gold resisted it, even the gift of the god. Yet through two folds he drave it, but three remained, for five folds had the lame god welded, two bronze, and two inside of tin, and one of gold; therein was stayed the ashen spear.

Then Achilles in his turn hurled his far-shadowing spear, and smote upon the circle of the shield of Aineias, beneath the edge of the rim, where the bronze ran thinnest round, and the bull-hide was thinnest thereon; and right through sped the Pelian ashen spear, and the shield cracked under it. And Aineias crouched and held up the shield away from him in dread; and the spear flew over his back and fixed itself in the earth, having divided asunder the two circles of the sheltering shield. And having escaped the long spear he stood still, and a vast anguish drowned his eyes, affrighted that the spear was planted by him so nigh. But Achilles drew his sharp sword and furiously made at him, crying his terrible cry: then Aineias grasped in his hand a stone (a mighty deed) such as two men, as men now are, would not avail to lift, but he with ease wielded it all alone. Then would Aineias have smitten him with the stone as he charged, either on helm or shield, which had warded from him bitter death, and then would the son of Peleus have closed and slain him with his sword, had not Poseidon, Shaker of earth, marked it with speed, and straightway spoken among the immortal gods: "Alas, woe is me for Aineias great of heart, who quickly will go down to Hades slain by the son of Peleus, for that he will obey the words of Apollo the far-darter, fond man, but nowise shall the god help him from grievous death. But wherefore now is he to suffer ill in his innocence, causelessly for others' wickedness, yet welcome ever are his offerings to the gods who inhabit the spacious heaven? Come, let us guide him out of death's way, lest the son of Kronos be wroth, if Achilles slay him; for it is appointed to him to escape, that the race of Dardanos perish not without seed or sign, even Dardanos whom the son of Kronos loved above all the children born to him from the daughters of men. For the race of Priam hath Zeus already hated. But thus shall the might of Aineias reign among the Trojans, and his children's children, who shall be born in the aftertime."

And him then answered Hera the ox-eyed queen: "Shaker of earth, thyself with thine own mind take counsel, whether thou wilt save Aineias, or leave him [to be slain, brave though he be, by Achilles, Peleus' son]. For by many oaths among all the Immortals have we two sworn, even

Pallas Athene and I, never to help the Trojans from their evil day, not even when all Troy shall burn in the burning of fierce fire, and they that burn her shall be the warlike sons of the Achaians."

Now when Poseidon Shaker of earth heard that, he went up amid the battle and the clash of spears, and came where Aineias and renowned Achilles were. Then presently he shed mist over the eyes of Achilles, Peleus' son, and drew the bronze-headed ashen spear from the shield of Aineias great of heart, and set it before Achilles' feet, and lifted Aineias and swung him high from off the earth. Over many ranks of warriors, of horses many, sprang Aineias soaring in the hand of the god, and lighted at the farthest verge of the battle of many onsets, where the Kaukones were arraying them for the fight. Then hard beside him came Poseidon, Shaker of earth, and spake aloud to him winged words: "Aineias, what god is it that biddeth thee fight infatuate against Peleus' vehement son, who is both a better man than thou and dearer to Immortals? Rather withdraw thee whensoever thou fallest in with him, lest even contrary to thy fate thou enter the house of Hades. But when Achilles shall have met his death and doom, then be thou of good courage to fight among the foremost, for there shall none other of the Achaians slay thee."

He spoke, and left him there, when he had shown him all these things. Then quickly from Achilles' eyes he purged the magic mist; and he stared with wide eyes, and in trouble spake unto his proud soul: "Ha! verily a great marvel behold I here with mine eyes. My spear lieth here upon the ground, nor can I anywise see the man at whom I hurled it with intent to slay him. Truly then is Aineias likewise dear to the immortal gods, howbeit I deemed that his boasting thereof was altogether vanity. Away with him! not again will he find heart to make trial of me, now that once more he has escaped death to his joy. But come, I will call on the warlike Danaans and go forth to make trial of some other Trojan face to face."

He said, and leapt along the lines, and called upon each man: "No longer stand afar from the men of Troy, noble Achaians, but come let man match man and throw his soul into the fight. Hard is it for me, though I be strong, to assail so vast a folk and fight them all: not even Ares, though an immortal god, nor Athene, could plunge into the jaws of such a fray and toil therein. But to my utmost power with hands and feet and strength no whit, I say, will I be slack, nay, never so little, but right through their line will I go forward, nor deem I that any Trojan shall be glad who shall come nigh my spear."

Thus spake he urging them. But to the Trojans glorious Hector called aloud, and proclaimed that he would go forth against Achilles: "High-hearted Trojans, fear not Peleus' son. I too in words could fight even Immortals, but with the spear it were hard, for they are stronger far. Neither shall Achilles accomplish all his talk, but part thereof he is to accomplish, and part to break asunder in the midst. And against him will I go forth, though the hands of him be even as fire, yea though his hands be as fire and his fierceness as the flashing steel."

Thus spake he urging them, and the Trojans raised their spears for battle; and their fierceness was mingled confusedly, and the battle-cry arose. Then Phoebus Apollo stood by Hector and spake to him: "Hector, no longer challenge Achilles at all before the lines, but in the throng await him and from amid the roar of the battle, lest haply he spear thee or come near and smite thee with his sword."

Thus spake he, and Hector again fell back into the crowd of men, for he was amazed when he heard the sound of a god's voice.

But Achilles sprang in among the Trojans, his heart clothed with strength, crying his terrible cry, and first he took Iphition, Otrynteus' valiant son, a leader of much people, born of a Naiad nymph to Otrynteus waster of cities, beneath snowy Tmolos, in Hyde's rich domain. Him as he came right on did goodly Achilles smite with his hurled spear, down through the midst of his head, and it was rent asunder utterly. And he fell with a crash, and goodly Achilles exulted over him. "Low liest thou, son of Otrynteus, most redoubtable of men; here is thy death, thy birth was on the Gygaian lake, where is thy sire's demesne, by Hyllos rich in fish and eddying Hermos."

Thus spake he exultant, but darkness fell upon the eyes of Iphition: him the chariots of the Achaians clave with their tires asunder in the forefront of the battle, and over him Achilles pierced in the temples, through his bronze-cheeked helmet, Demoleon, brave stemmer of battle, Antenor's son. No stop made the bronze helmet, but there-through sped the spear-head and clave the bone, and the brain within was all scattered: that stroke made ending of his zeal. Then Hippodamas, as he leapt from his chariot and fled before him, Achilles wounded in the back with his spear: and he breathed forth his spirit with a roar, as when a dragged bull roareth that the young men drag to the altar of the Lord of Helike; for in such hath the Earthshaker his delight: thus roared Hippodamas as from his bones fled forth his haughty spirit. But Achilles with his spear went on after godlike Polydoros, Priam's son. Him would his sire continually forbid to fight, for that among his children he was youngest born and best beloved, and overcame all in fleetness of foot. Just then in boyish folly, displaying the swiftness of his feet, he was rushing through the fore-fighters, until he lost his life. Him in the midst did fleet-footed noble Achilles smite with a javelin, in his back as he darted by, where his belt's golden buckles clasped, and the breast and back plates overlapped: and right through beside the navel went the spear-head, and he fell on his knee with a cry, and dark cloud covered him round about, and he clasped his bowels to him with his hands as he sank.

Then when Hector saw his brother Polydoros clasping his bowels with his hands, and sinking to the earth, a mist fell over his eyes, nor longer might he endure to range so far apart, but he came up against Achilles brandishing his sharp spear, and like a flame of fire. And Achilles when he saw him, sprang up, and spake exultingly: "Behold the man who hath deepest stricken into my soul, who slew my dear-prized friend; not long shall we now shrink from each other along the highways of the war."

He said, and looking grimly spake unto goodly Hector: "Come thou near, that the sooner thou mayest arrive at the goal of death."

Then to him, unterrified, said Hector of the glancing helm: "Son of Peleus, think not with words to affright me as a child, since I too know myself how to speak taunts and unjust speech. And I know that thou art a man of might, and a far better man than I. Yet doth this issue lie in the lap of the gods, whether I though weaker shall take thy life with my hurled spear, for mine too hath been found keen ere now."

He said, and poised his spear and hurled it, and Athene with a breath turned it back from glorious Achilles, breathing very lightly; and it came back to goodly Hector, and fell there before his feet. Then Achilles set fiercely upon him, eager to slay him, crying his terrible cry. But Apollo caught Hector up, very easily, as a god may, and hid him in thick mist. Thrice then did fleet-footed noble Achilles make onset with his spear of bronze, and thrice smote the thick mist. [But when the fourth time he had come godlike on,] then with dread shout he spake to him winged words: "Dog, thou art now again escaped from death; yet came ill very nigh thee; but now hath Phoebus Apollo saved thee, to whom thou must surely pray when thou goest forth amid the clash of spears. Verily I will slay thee yet when I meet thee hereafter, if any god is helper of me too. Now will I make after the rest, whomsoever I may seize."

Thus speaking he pierced Dryops in the midst of his neck with his spear, and he fell down before his feet. But he left him where he lay, and hurled at Demuchos Philetor's son, a good man and a tall, and stayed him with a stroke upon his knees; then smote him with his mighty sword and reft him of life. Then springing on Laogonos and Dardanos, sons of Bias, he thrust both from their chariot to the ground, one with a spear-cast smiting and the other in close battle with his sword. Then Tros, Alastor's son—he came and clasped his knees to pray him to spare him, and let him go alive, and slay him not, having compassion on his like age, fond fool, and knew not that he might not gain his prayers; for nowise soft of heart or tender was that man, but of fierce mood—with his hands he touched Achilles' knees, eager to entreat him, but he smote him in the liver with his sword, and his liver fell from him, and black blood therefrom filled his bosom, and he swooned, and darkness covered his eyes. Then Achilles came near and struck Mulios in the ear, and right through the other ear went the bronze spear-head. Then he smote Agenor's son Echeklos on the midst of the head with his hilted sword, and all the sword grew hot thereat with blood; and dark death seized his eyes, and forceful fate. Then next Deukalion, just where the sinews of the elbow join, there pierced he him through the forearm with his bronze spear-head; so abode he with his arm weighed down, beholding death before him; and Achilles smiting the neck with his sword swept far both head and helm, and the marrow rose out of the backbone, and the corpse lay stretched upon the earth. Then went he onward after Peires' noble son, Rhigmos, who had come from deep-soiled Thrace: him in the midst he smote with his hurled javelin, and the point fixed in his lung, and he fell forth of his chariot. And Areïthoös his squire, as he turned the horses round, he pierced in the back with his sharp spear, and thrust him from the car, and the horses ran wild with fear.

As through deep glens rageth fierce fire on some parched mountain-side, and the deep forest burneth, and the wind driving it whirleth every way the flame, so raged he every way with his spear, as it had been a god, pressing hard on the men he slew; and the black earth ran with blood. For even as when one yoketh wide-browed bulls to tread white barley in a stablished threshing-floor, and quickly is it trodden out beneath the feet of the loud-lowing bulls, thus beneath great-hearted Achilles his whole-hooved horses trampled corpses and shields together; and with blood all the axle-tree below was sprinkled and the rims that ran around the car, for blood-drops from the horses' hooves splashed them, and blood-drops from the tires of the wheels. But the son of Peleus pressed on to win him glory, flecking with gore his irresistible hands.

BOOK XXI

How Achilles fought with the River, and chased the men of Troy within their gates.

But when now they came unto the ford of the fair-flowing river, even eddying Xanthos, whom immortal Zeus begat, there sundering them he chased the one part to the plain toward the city, even where the Achaians were flying in affright the day before, when glorious Hector was in his fury—thither poured some in flight, and Hera spread before them thick mist to hinder them:—but half were pent into the deep-flowing silver-eddied river, and fell therein with a mighty noise, and the steep channel sounded, and the banks around rang loudly; for with shouting they swam therein hither and thither, whirled round the eddies. And as when at the rush of fire locusts take wing to fly unto a river, and the unwearying fire flameth forth on them with sudden onset, and they huddle in the water; so before Achilles was the stream of deep-eddying Xanthos filled with the roar and the throng of horses and men.

Then the seed of Zeus left behind him his spear upon the bank, leant against tamarisk bushes, and leapt in, as it were a god, keeping his sword alone, and devised grim work at heart, and smote as he turned him every way about: and their groaning went up ghastly as they were stricken by the sword, and the water reddened with blood. As before a dolphin of huge maw fly other fish and fill the nooks of some fair-havened bay, in terror, for he devoureth amain whichsoever of them he may catch; so along the channels of that dread stream the Trojans crouched beneath the precipitous sides. And when his hands were weary of slaughter he chose twelve young men alive out of the river, an atonement for Patroklos Menoitios' son that was dead. These brought he forth amazed like fawns, and bound behind them their hands with well-cut thongs, which they themselves wore on their pliant doublets, and gave them to his comrades to lead down to the hollow ships. Then again he made his onset, athirst for slaying.

There met he a son of Dardanid Priam, in flight out of the river, Lykaon, whom once himself he took and brought unwilling out of his father's orchard, in a night assault; he was cutting with keen bronze young shoots of a wild fig-tree, to be hand-rails of a chariot; but to him an unlooked-for bane came goodly Achilles. And at that time he sold him into well-peopled Lemnos, sending him on ship-board, and the son of Jason gave a price for him; and thence a guest friend freed him with a great ransom, Eëtion of Imbros, and sent him to goodly Arisbe; whence flying secretly he came to his father's house. Eleven days he rejoiced among his friends after he was come from Lemnos, but on the twelfth once more God brought him into the hands of Achilles, who was to send him to the house of Hades though nowise fain to go. Him when fleet-footed noble Achilles saw bare of helm and shield, neither had he a spear, but had thrown all to the ground; for he sweated grievously as he tried to flee out of the river, and his knees were failing him for weariness: then in wrath spake Achilles to his great heart: "Ha! verily great marvel is this that I behold with my eyes. Surely then will the proud Trojans whom I have slain rise up again from beneath the murky gloom, since thus hath this man come back escaped from his pitiless fate, though sold into goodly Lemnos, neither hath the deep of the hoary sea stayed him, that holdeth many against their will. But come then, of our spear's point shall he taste, that I may see and learn in my mind whether likewise he shall come back even from beneath, or whether the life-giving Earth shall hold him down, she that holdeth so even the strong."

Thus pondered he in his place; but the other came near amazed, fain to touch his knees, for his soul longed exceedingly to flee from evil death and black destruction. Then goodly Achilles lifted his long spear with intent to smite him, but he stooped and ran under it and caught his knees; and the spear went over his back and stood in the ground, hungering for flesh of men. Then Lykaon besought him, with one hand holding his knees, while with the other he held the sharp spear and loosed it not, and spake to him winged words: "I cry thee mercy, Achilles; have thou regard and pity for me: to thee, O fosterling of Zeus, am I in the bonds of suppliantship. For at thy table first I tasted meal of Demeter on the day when thou didst take me captive in the well-ordered orchard, and didst sell me away from my father and my friends unto goodly Lemnos, and I fetched thee the price of a hundred oxen. And now have I been ransomed for thrice that, and this is my twelfth morn since I came to Ilios after much pain. Now once again hath ruinous fate delivered me into thy hands; surely I must be hated of father Zeus, that he hath given me a second time unto thee; and to short life my mother bare me, Laothoë, old Altes' daughter—Altes who ruleth among the war-loving Leleges, holding steep Pedasos on the Satnioeis. His daughter Priam had to wife, with many others, and of her were we two born, and thou wilt butcher both. Him among the foremost of the foot-soldiers didst thou lay low, even godlike Polydoros, when thou smotest him with thy sharp spear: and now will it go hard with me here, for no hope have I to escape thy hands, since God hath delivered me thereunto. Yet one thing will I tell thee, and do thou lay it to heart: slay me not, since I am not of the same mother as Hector, who slew thy comrade the gentle and brave."

Thus spake to him the noble son of Priam, beseeching

him with words, but he heard a voice implacable: "Fond fool, proffer me no ransom, nor these words. Until Patroklos met his fated day, then was it welcomer to my soul to spare the men of Troy, and many I took alive and sold beyond the sea: but now there is none shall escape death, whomsoever before Ilios God shall deliver into my hands —yea, even among all Trojans, but chiefest among Priam's sons. Ay, friend, thou too must die: why thus lamentest thou? Patroklos too is dead, who was better far than thou. Seest thou not also what manner of man am I for might and goodliness? and a good man was my father, and a goddess mother bare me. Yet over me too hang death and forceful fate. There cometh morn or eve or some noonday when my life too some man shall take in battle, whether with spear he smite or arrow from the string."

Thus spake he, and the other's knees and heart were unstrung. He let go Achilles' spear, and sat with both hands outspread. But Achilles drew his sharp sword and smote on the collar-bone beside the neck, and all the two-edged sword sank into him, and he lay stretched prone upon the earth, and blood flowed dark from him and soaked the earth. Him seized Achilles by the foot and sent him down the stream, and over him exulting spake winged words: "There lie thou among the fishes, which shall lick off thy wound's blood heedlessly, nor shall thy mother lay thee on a bed and mourn for thee, but Skamandros shall bear thee on his eddies into the broad bosom of the sea. Leaping along the wave shall many a fish dart up to the dark ripple to eat of the white flesh of Lykaon. So perish all, until we reach the citadel of sacred Ilios, ye flying and I behind destroying. Nor even the River, fair-flowing, silver-eddied, shall avail you, to whom long time forsooth ye sacrifice many bulls, and among his eddies throw whole-hooved horses down alive. For all this yet shall ye die the death, until ye pay all for Patroklos' slaying and the slaughter of

Achaians whom at the swift ships ye slew while I tarried afar."

Thus spake he, but the River waxed ever more wroth in his heart, and sought in his soul how he should stay goodly Achilles from his work, and ward destruction from the Trojans. Meanwhile the son of Peleus with his far-shadowing spear leapt, fain to slay him, upon Asteropaios son of Pelegon, whom wide-flowing Axios begat of Periboia eldest of the daughters of Akessamenos, for with her lay that deep-eddying River. Upon him set Achilles, and Asteropaios stood against him from the river, holding two spears; for Xanthos put courage into his heart, being angered for the slaughtered youths whom Achilles was slaughtering along the stream and had no pity on them. Then when the twain were come nigh in onset on each other, unto him first spake fleet-footed noble Achilles: "Who and whence art thou of men, that darest to come against me? Ill-fated are they whose children match them with my might."

And to him made answer Pelegon's noble son: "High-hearted son of Peleus, why askest thou my lineage? I come from deep-soiled Paionia, a land far off, leading Paionian men with their long spears, and this now is the eleventh morn since I am come to Ilios. My lineage is of wide-flowing Axios, who begat Pelegon famous with the spear, and he, men say, was my father. Now fight we, noble Achilles!"

Thus spake he in defiance, and goodly Achilles lifted the Pelian ash: but the warrior Asteropaios hurled with both spears together, for he could use both hands alike, and with the one spear smote the shield, but pierced it not right through, for the gold stayed it, the gift of a god; and with the other he grazed the elbow of Achilles' right arm, and there leapt forth dark blood, but the point beyond him fixed itself in the earth, eager to batten on flesh. Then in his turn Achilles hurled on Asteropaios his straight-flying ash, fain to have slain him, but missed the man and struck the high bank, and quivering half its length in the bank he left the ashen spear. Then the son of Peleus drew his sharp sword from his thigh and leapt fiercely at him, and he availed not to draw with his stout hand Achilles' ashen shaft from the steep bank. Thrice shook he it striving to draw it forth, and thrice gave up the strain, but the fourth time he was fain to bend and break the ashen spear of the seed of Aiakos, but ere that Achilles closing on him reft him of life with his sword. For in the belly he smote him beside the navel, and all his bowels gushed out to the earth, and darkness covered his eyes as he lay gasping. Then Achilles trampling on his breast stripped off his armour and spake exultingly: "Lie there! It is hard to strive against children of Kronos' mighty son, even though one be sprung from a River-god. Thou truly declarest thyself the seed of a wide-flowing River, but I avow me of the lineage of great Zeus. My sire is a man ruling many Myrmidons, Peleus the son of Aiakos, and Aiakos was begotten of Zeus. As Zeus is mightier than seaward-murmuring rivers, so is the seed of Zeus made mightier than the seed of a river. Nay, there is hard beside thee a great river, if he may anywise avail; but against Zeus the son of Kronos it is not possible to fight. For him not even king Acheloïos is match, nor yet the great strength of deep-flowing Ocean, from whom all rivers flow and every sea, and all springs and deep wells: yea, even he hath fear of the lightning of great Zeus and his dread thunder, when it pealeth out of heaven."

He said, and from the steep bank drew his bronze spear, and left there Asteropaios whom he had slain, lying in the sands, and the dark water flooded him. Around him eels and fishes swarmed, tearing and gnawing the fat about his kidneys. But Achilles went on after the charioted Paiones who still along the eddying river huddled in fear, when they saw their best man in the stress of battle slain violently by the hands and the sword of the son of Peleus. There slew he Thersilochos and Mydon and Astypylos and Mnesos and Thrasios and Ainios and Ophelestes; and more yet of the Paiones would swift Achilles have slain, had not the deep-eddying River called unto him in wrath, in semblance of a man, and from an eddy's depth sent forth a voice: "O Achilles, thy might and thy evil work are beyond the measure of men; for gods themselves are ever helping thee. If indeed the son of Kronos hath delivered thee all the Trojans to destroy, at least drive them forth from me and do thy grim deeds on the plain, for filled with dead men is my pleasant bed, nor can I pour my stream to the great sea, being choked with dead, and thou slayest ruthlessly. Come then, let be; I am astonied, O captain of hosts."

And to him answered Achilles fleet of foot: "So be it, heaven-sprung Skamandros, even as thou biddest. But the proud Trojans I will not cease from slaying until I have driven them into their city, and have made trial with Hector face to face whether he is to vanquish me or I him."

Thus saying, he set upon the Trojans, like a god. Then unto Apollo spake the deep-eddying River: "Out on it, lord of the silver bow, child of Zeus, thou hast not kept the ordinance of Kronos' son, who charged thee straitly to stand by the Trojans and to help them, until eve come with light late-setting, and darken the deep-soiled earth."

He said, and spear-famed Achilles sprang from the bank and leapt into his midst; but he rushed on him in a furious wave, and stirred up all his streams in tumult, and swept down the many dead who lay thick in him, slain by Achilles; these out to land he cast with bellowing like a bull, and saved the living under his fair streams, hiding them within eddies deep and wide. But terribly around Achilles arose his tumultuous wave, and the stream smote violently against his shield, nor availed he to stand firm upon his feet. Then he grasped a tall fair-grown elm, and it fell uprooted and tore away all the bank, and reached over the fair river bed with its thick shoots, and stemmed the River himself, falling all within him: and Achilles, struggling out of the eddy, made haste to fly over the plain with his swift feet, for he was afraid. But the great god ceased not, but arose upon him with darkness on his crest, that he might stay noble Achilles from slaughter, and ward destruction from the men of Troy. And the son of Peleus rushed away a spear's throw, with the swoop of a black eagle, the mighty hunter, strongest at once and swiftest of winged birds. Like him he sped, and on his breast the bronze rang terribly as he fled from beneath the onset, and behind him the River rushed on with a mighty roar. As when a field-waterer from a dark spring leadeth water along a bed through crops and garden grounds, a mattock in his hands, casting forth hindrances from the ditch, and as it floweth all pebbles are swept down, and swiftly gliding it murmureth down a sloping place, and outrunneth him that is its guide:—thus ever the river wave caught up Achilles for all his speed; for gods are mightier than men. For whensoever fleet-footed noble Achilles struggled to stand against it, and know whether all immortals be upon him who inhabit spacious heaven, then would a great wave of the heaven-sprung River beat upon his shoulders from above, and he sprang upward with his feet, sore vexed at heart; and the River was wearying his knees with violent rush beneath, and devouring the earth from under his feet. Then the son of Peleus cried aloud, looking up to the broad heaven: "Zeus, Father, how doth none of the gods take it on him in pity to save me from the River! after that let come to me what may. None other of the inhabitants of Heaven is chargeable so much, but only my dear mother, who beguiled me with false words, saying that under the wall of the mail-clad men of Troy I must die by the swift arrows of Apollo. Would that Hector had slain me, the best of men bred here: then brave had been the slayer, and a brave man had he slain. But now by a sorry death am I doomed to die, pent in this mighty river, like a swineherd boy whom a torrent sweepeth down as he essayeth to cross it in a storm."

Thus spake he, and quickly Poseidon and Athene came near and stood beside him, in the likeness of men, and taking his hands in theirs pledged him in words. And the first that spake was Poseidon, Shaker of the earth: "Son of Peleus, tremble not, neither be afraid; such helpers of thee are we from the gods, approved of Zeus, even Pallas Athene and I, for to be vanquished of a river is not appointed thee, but he will soon give back, and thou wilt thyself perceive it: but we will give thee wise counsel, if thou wilt obey it; hold not thy hand from hazardous battle until within Ilios' famous walls thou have pent the Trojan host, even all that flee before thee. But do thou, when thou hast taken the life of Hector, go back unto the ships; this glory we give unto thee to win."

They having thus spoken departed to the immortals, but he toward the plain—for the bidding of gods was strong upon him—went onward; and all the plain was filled with water-flood, and many beautiful arms and corpses of slain youths were drifting there. So upward sprang his knees as he rushed against the stream right on, nor stayed him the wide-flowing River, for Athene put great strength in him. Neither did Skamandros slacken his fierceness, but yet more raged against the son of Peleus, and he curled crestwise the billow of his stream, lifting himself on high, and on Simoeis he called with a shout: "Dear brother, the strength of this man let us both join to stay, since quickly he will lay waste the great city of king Priam, and the Trojans abide not in the battle. Help me with speed, and fill thy streams with water from thy springs, and urge on all thy torrents, and raise up a great wave, and stir huge roaring of tree-stumps and stones, that we may stay the fierce man who now is lording it, and deeming himself match for gods. For neither, I ween, will strength avail him, nor comeliness anywise, nor that armour beautiful, which deep beneath the flood shall be o'erlaid with slime, and himself I will wrap him in my sands and pour round him countless shingle without stint, nor shall the Achaians know where to gather his bones, so vast a shroud of silt will I heap over them. Where he dieth there shall be his tomb, neither shall he have need of any barrow to be raised, when the Achaians make his funeral."

He said, and rushed in tumult on Achilles, raging from on high, thundering with foam and blood and bodies of dead men. Then did a dark wave of the heaven-sprung River stand towering up and would overwhelm the son of Peleus. But Hera cried aloud in terror for Achilles, lest the great deep-eddying River sweep him away, and straightway she called to Hephaistos, her dear son: "Rise, lame god, O my son; it was against thee we thought that eddying Xanthos was matched in fight. Help with all speed, put forth large blast of flame. Then will I go to raise a strong storm out of the sea of the west wind and the white south which shall utterly consume the dead Trojans and their armour, blowing the angry flame. Thou along Xanthos' banks burn up his trees and wrap himself in fire, nor let him anywise turn thee back by soft words or by threat, nor stay thy rage—only when I cry to thee with my voice, then hold the unwearying fire."

Thus spake she, and Hephaistos made ready fierce-blazing fire. First on the plain fire blazed, and burnt the many dead who lay there thick, slain by Achilles; and all the plain was parched and the bright water stayed. And as when in late summer the north wind swiftly parcheth a new watered orchard, and he that tilleth it is glad, thus was the whole plain parched, and Hephaistos consumed the dead; then against the river he turned his gleaming flame. Elms burnt and willow-trees and tamarisks, and lotos burnt and rush and galingale, which round the fair streams of the river grew in multitude. And the eels and fishes beneath the eddies were afflicted, which through the fair streams tumbled this way and that, in anguish at the blast of crafty Hephaistos. And the strong River burned, and spake and called to him by name: "Hephaistos, there is no god can match with thee, nor will I fight thee thus ablaze with fire. Cease strife, yea, let noble Achilles drive the Trojans forthwith out of their city; what have I to do with strife and succour?"

Thus spake he, burnt with fire, for his fair streams were bubbling. And as a caldron boileth within, beset with much fire, melting the lard of some fatted hog spurting up on all sides, and logs of firewood lie thereunder,—so burned his fair streams in the fire, and the water boiled. He had no mind to flow, but refrained him, for the breath of cunning Hephaistos violently afflicted him. Then unto Hera, earnestly beseeching her, he spake winged words: "Hera, wherefore hath thy son assailed my stream to vex it above others? I am less chargeable than all the rest that are helpers of the Trojans. But lo, I will give over, if thou wilt, and let thy son give over too. And I further will swear even this, that never will I ward the day of evil from the Trojans, not even when all Troy is burning in the blaze of hungry fire, and the warlike sons of Achaians are the burners thereof."

Then when the white-armed goddess Hera heard his speech, straightway she spake unto Hephaistos her dear son: "Hephaistos, hold, famed son; it befitteth not thus for mortals' sake to do violence to an immortal god."

Thus said she and Hephaistos quenched the fierce-blazing fire, and the wave once more rolled down the fair river-bed.

So when the rage of Xanthos was overcome, both ceased, for Hera stayed them, though in wrath. But among the other gods fell grievous bitter strife, and their hearts were carried diverse in their breasts. And they clashed together with a great noise, and the wide earth groaned, and the clarion of great Heaven rang around. Zeus heard as he sate upon Olympus, and his heart within him laughed pleasantly when he beheld that strife of gods. Then no longer stood they asunder, for Ares piercer of shields began the battle and first made for Athene with his bronze spear, and spake a taunting word: "Wherefore, O dogfly, dost thou match gods with gods in strife, with stormy daring, as thy great spirit moveth thee? Rememberest thou not how thou movedst Diomedes Tydeus' son to wound me, and thyself didst take a visible spear and thrust it straight at me and pierce through my fair skin? Therefore deem I now that thou shalt pay me for all that thou hast done."

Thus saying he smote on the dread tasselled aegis that not even the lightning of Zeus can overcome—thereon smote bloodstained Ares with his long spear. But she, giving back, grasped with stout hand a stone that lay upon the plain, black, rugged, huge, which men of old time set to be the landmark of a field; this hurled she, and smote impetuous Ares on the neck, and unstrung his limbs. Seven roods he covered in his fall, and soiled his hair with dust, and his armour rang upon him. And Pallas Athene laughed, and spake to him winged words exultingly: "Fool, not even yet hast thou learnt how far better than thou I claim to be, that thus thou matchest thy might with mine. Thus shalt thou satisfy thy mother's curses, who deviseth mischief against thee in her wrath, for that thou hast left the Achaians and givest the proud Trojans aid."

Thus having said she turned from him her shining eyes. Him did Aphrodite daughter of Zeus take by the hand and lead away, groaning continually, for scarce gathered he his spirit back to him. But when the white-armed goddess Hera was aware of them, straightway she spake unto Athene winged words: "Out on it, child of aegis-bearing Zeus, maiden invincible, lo there the dogfly is leading Ares destroyer of men out of the fray of battle down the throng —nay then, pursue her."

She said, and Athene sped after her with heart exultant, and made at her and smote her with stout hand upon the breast, and straightway her knees and heart were unstrung. So they twain lay on the bounteous earth, and she spake winged words exultingly: "Such let all be who give the Trojans aid when they fight against the mailed Argives. Be they even so bold and brave as Aphrodite when she came to succour Ares and defied my might. Then should we long ago have ceased from war, having laid waste the stablished citadel of Ilios."

[She said, and the white-armed goddess Hera smiled.] Then to Apollo spake the earth-shaking lord: "Phoebus, why stand we apart? It befitteth not after the rest have begun: that were the more shameful if without fighting we should go to Olympus to the bronze-thresholded house of Zeus. Begin, for thou art younger; it were not meet for me, since I was born first and know more. Fond god, how foolish is thy heart! Thou rememberest not all the ills we twain alone of gods endured at Ilios, when by ordinance of Zeus we came to proud Laomedon and served him through a year for promised recompense, and he laid on us his commands. I round their city built the Trojans a wall, wide and most fair, that the city might be unstormed, and thou, Phoebus, didst herd shambling crookhorned kine among the spurs of woody many-folded Ida. But when the joyous seasons were accomplishing the term of hire, then redoubtable Laomedon robbed us of all hire, and sent us off with threats. He threatened that he would bind together our feet and hands and sell us into far-off isles, and the ears of both of us he vowed to shear off with the sword. So we went home with angry hearts, wroth for the hire he promised and gave us not. To his folk now thou showest favour, nor essayest with us how the proud Trojans may be brought low and perish miserably with their children and noble wives."

Then to him answered King Apollo the Far-darter: "Shaker of the earth, of no sound mind wouldst thou repute me if I should fight against thee for the sake of pitiful mortals, who like unto leaves now live in glowing life, consuming the fruit of the earth, and now again pine into death. Let us with all speed cease from combat, and let them do battle by themselves."

Thus saying he turned away, for he felt shame to deal in blows with his father's brother. But his sister upbraided him sore, the queen of wild beasts, huntress Artemis, and spake a taunting word: "So then thou fleëst, Far-darter, and hast quite yielded to Poseidon the victory, and given him glory for naught! Fond god, why bearest thou an ineffectual bow in vain? Let me not hear thee again in the halls of our sire boast as before among the immortal gods that thou wouldst stand up to fight against Poseidon."

Thus spake she, but far-darting Apollo answered her not. But angrily the noble spouse of Zeus [upbraided the Archer Queen with taunting words:] "How now art thou fain, bold vixen, to set thyself against me? Hard were it for thee to match my might, bow-bearer though thou art, since against women Zeus made thee a lion, and giveth thee to slay whomso of them thou wilt. Truly it is better on the mountains to slay wild beasts and deer than to fight amain with mightier than thou. But if thou wilt, try war, that thou mayest know well how far stronger am I, since thou matchest thy might with mine."

She said, and with her left hand caught both the other's hands by the wrist, and with her right took the bow from off her shoulders, and therewith, smiling, beat her on the ears as she turned this way and that; and the swift arrows fell out of her quiver. And weeping from before her the goddess fled like a dove that from before a falcon flieth to a hollow rock, a cleft—for she was not fated to be caught; —thus Artemis fled weeping, and left her bow and arrows where they lay. Then to Leto spake the Guide, the slayer of Argus: "Leto, with thee will I nowise fight; a grievous thing it is to come to blows with wives of cloud-gathering

Zeus; but boast to thy heart's content among the immortal gods that thou didst vanquish me by might and main."

Thus said he, and Leto gathered up the curved bow and arrows fallen hither and thither amid the whirl of dust: so taking her daughter's bow she went back. And the maiden came to Olympus, to the bronze-thresholded house of Zeus, and weeping set herself on her father's knee, while round her her divine vesture quivered: and her father, Kronos' son, took her to him and asked of her, laughing gently: "Who of the inhabitants of heaven, dear child, hath dealt with thee thus [hastily, as though thou hadst been doing some wrong thing openly]?"

And to him in answer spake the fair-crowned queen of the echoing chase: "It was thy wife that buffeted me, father, the white-armed Hera, from whom are strife and contention come upon the immortals."

Thus talked they unto one another. Then Phoebus Apollo entered into sacred Ilios, for he was troubled for the wall of the well-builded city, lest the Danaans waste it before its hour upon that day. But the other ever-living gods went to Olympus, some angry and some greatly triumphing, and sat down beside Zeus who hideth himself in dark clouds.

Now Achilles was still slaying the Trojans, both themselves and their whole-hooved horses. And as when a smoke goeth up to the broad heaven, when a city burneth, kindled by the wrath of gods, and causeth toil to all, and griefs to many, thus caused Achilles toil and griefs to the Trojans. And the old man Priam stood on the sacred tower, and was aware of dread Achilles, how before him the Trojans thronged in rout, nor was any succour found of them. Then with a cry he went down from the tower, to rouse the gallant warders along the walls: "Hold open the gates in your hands until the folk come to the city in their rout, for closely is Achilles chasing them—now trow I there will be deadly deeds. But when they are gathered within the wall and are taking breath, then again shut back the gate-wings firmly builded; for I fear lest that murderous man spring in within the wall."

Thus spake he, and they opened the gates and thrust back the bolts; and the gates flung back gave safety. Then Apollo leapt forth to the front that he might ward destruction from the Trojans. They straight for the city and the high wall were fleeing, parched with thirst and dust-grimed from the plain, and Achilles chased them vehemently with his spear, for strong frenzy possessed his heart continually, and he thirsted to win him renown. Then would the sons of the Achaians have taken high-gated Troy, had not Phoebus Apollo aroused goodly Agenor, Antenor's son, a princely man and a strong. In his heart he put good courage, and himself stood by his side that he might ward off the grievous visitations of death, leaning against the oak, and he was shrouded in thick mist. So when Agenor was aware of Achilles waster of cities, he halted, and his heart much wavered as he stood; and in trouble he spake to his great heart: "Ay me, if I flee before mighty Achilles, there where the rest are driven terror-struck, nathless will he overtake me and slaughter me as a coward. Or what if I leave these to be driven before Achilles the son of Peleus, and flee upon my feet from the wall by another way to the Ileian plain, until I come to the spurs of Ida, and hide me in the underwood? So then at evening, having bathed in the river and refreshed me of sweat, I might return to Ilios. Nay, why doth my heart debate thus within me? Lest he might be aware of me as I get me from the city for the plain, and speeding after overtake me with swift feet; then will it no more be possible to avoid the visitation of death, for he is exceeding mighty above all mankind. What then if in front of the city I go forth to meet him? Surely his flesh too is penetrable by sharp bronze, and there is but one life within, and men say he is mortal, howbeit Zeus the son of Kronos giveth him renown."

Thus saying, he gathered himself to await Achilles, and within him his stout heart was set to strive and fight. As a leopardess goeth forth from a deep thicket to affront a huntsman, nor is afraid at heart, nor fleeth when she heareth the bay of hounds; for albeit the man first smite her with thrust or throw, yet even pierced through with the spear she ceaseth not from her courage until she either grapple or be slain, so noble Antenor's son, goodly Agenor, refused to flee till he should put Achilles to the proof, but held before him the circle of his shield, and aimed at him with his spear, and cried aloud: "Doubtless thou hopest in thy heart, noble Achilles, on this day to sack the city of the proud men of Troy. Fond man, there shall many woful things yet be wrought before it, for within it we are many men and staunch, who in front of our parents dear and wives and sons keep Ilios safe; but thou shalt here meet death, albeit so redoubtable and bold a man of war."

He said, and hurled his sharp spear with weighty hand, and smote him on the leg beneath the knee, nor missed his mark, and the greave of new-wrought tin rang terribly on him; but the bronze bounded back from him it smote, nor pierced him, for the god's gift drave it back. Then the son of Peleus in his turn made at godlike Agenor, but Apollo suffered him not to win renown, but caught away Agenor, and shrouded him in thick mist, and sent him in peace to be gone out of the war. Then by wile he kept the son of Peleus away from the folk, for in complete semblance of Agenor himself he stood before the feet of Achilles, who hasted to run upon him and chase him. And while he chased him over the wheat-bearing plain, edging him toward the deep-eddying river Skamandros, as he ran but a little in front of him (for by wile Apollo beguiled him that he kept ever hoping to overtake him in the race), meantime the other Trojans in common rout came gladly unto their fastness, and the city was filled with the throng of them. Neither had they heart to await one another outside the city and wall, and to know who might have escaped and who had perished in the fight, but impetuously they poured into the city, whomsoever of them his feet and knees might save.

BOOK XXII

How Achilles fought with Hector, and slew him, and brought his body to the ships.

THUS they throughout the city, scared like fawns, were cooling their sweat and drinking and slaking their thirst, leaning on the fair battlements, while the Achaians drew near the wall, setting shields to shoulders. But Hector deadly fate bound to abide in his place, in front of Ilios and the Skaian gates. Then to the son of Peleus spake Phoebus Apollo: "Wherefore, son of Peleus, pursuest thou me with swift feet, thyself being mortal and I a deathless god? Thou hast not even yet known me, that I am a god, but strivest vehemently. Truly thou regardest not thy task among the affliction of the Trojans whom thou affrightedst, who now are gathered into the city, while thou hast wandered hither. Me thou wilt never slay, for I am not subject unto death."

Then mightily moved spake unto him Achilles fleet of foot: "Thou hast baulked me, Far-darter, most mischievous of all the gods, in that thou hast turned me hither from the wall: else should full many yet have bitten the dust or ever within Ilios had they come. Now hast thou robbed me of great renown, and lightly hast saved them, because thou hadst no vengeance to fear thereafter. Verily I would avenge me on thee, had I but the power."

Thus saying toward the city he was gone in pride of heart, rushing like some victorious horse in a chariot, that runneth lightly at full speed over the plain; so swiftly plied Achilles in his feet and knees. Him the old man Priam first beheld as he sped across the plain, blazing as the star that cometh forth at harvest-time, and plain seen his rays shine forth amid the host of stars in the darkness of night, the star whose name men call Orion's Dog. Brightest of all is he, yet for an evil sign is he set, and bringeth much fever upon hapless men. Even so on Achilles' breast the bronze gleamed as he ran. And the old man cried aloud and beat upon his head with his hands, raising them on high, and with a cry called aloud beseeching his dear son; for he before the gates was standing, all hot for battle with Achilles. And the old man spake piteously unto him, stretching forth his hands: "Hector, beloved son, I pray thee await not this man alone with none beside thee, lest thou quickly meet thy doom, slain by the son of Peleus, since he is mightier far, a merciless man. Would the gods loved him even as do I! then quickly would dogs and vultures devour him on the field—thereby would cruel pain go from my heart—the man who hath bereft me of many valiant sons, slaying them and selling them captive into far-off isles. Ay even now twain of my children, Lykaon and Polydoros, I cannot see among the Trojans that throng into the fastness, sons whom Laothoë bare me, a princess among women. If they be yet alive amid the enemy's host, then will we ransom them with bronze and gold, for there is store within, for much goods gave the old man famous Altes to his child. If they be dead, then even in the house of Hades shall they be a sorrow to my soul and to their mother, even to us who gave them birth, but to the rest of the folk a briefer sorrow, if but thou die not by Achilles' hand. Nay, come within the wall, my child, that thou preserve the men and women of Troy, neither give great triumph to the son of Peleus, and be thyself bereft of sweet life. Have compassion also on me, the helpless one, who still can feel, ill-fated; whom the father, Kronos' son, will bring to nought by a grievous doom in the path of old age, having seen full many ills, his sons perishing and his daughters carried away captive, and his chambers laid waste and infant children hurled to the ground in terrible war, and his sons' wives dragged away by the ruinous hands of the Achaians. Myself then last of all at the street door will ravening dogs tear, when some one by stroke or throw of the sharp bronze hath bereft my limbs of life—even the dogs I reared in my halls about my table and to guard my door, which then having drunk my blood, maddened at heart shall lie in the gateway. A young man all beseemeth, even to be slain in war, to be torn by the sharp bronze and lie on the field; though he be dead yet is all honourable to him, whate'er be seen: but when dogs defile the hoary head and hoary beard and the secret parts of an old man slain, this is the most piteous thing that cometh upon hapless men."

Thus spake the old man, and grasped his hoary hairs, plucking them from his head, but he persuaded not Hector's soul. Then his mother in her turn wailed tearfully, loosening the folds of her robe, while with the other hand she showed her breast; and through her tears spake to him winged words: "Hector, my child, have regard unto this bosom and pity me, if ever I gave thee consolation of my breast. Think of it, dear child, and from this side of the wall drive back the foe, nor stand in front to meet him. He is merciless; if he slay thee it will not be on a bed that I or thy wife wooed with many gifts shall bewail thee, my own dear child, but far away from us by the ships of the Argives will swift dogs devour thee."

Thus they with wailing spake to their dear son, beseeching him sore, yet they persuaded not Hector's soul, but he stood awaiting Achilles as he drew nigh in giant might. As a serpent of the mountains upon his den awaiteth a man, having fed on evil poisons, and fell wrath hath entered into him, and terribly he glareth as he coileth himself about his den, so Hector with courage unquenchable gave not back, leaning his shining shield against a jutting tower. Then sore troubled he spake to his great heart: "Ay me, if I go within the gates and walls, Polydamas will be first to bring reproach against me, since he bade me lead the Trojans to the city during this ruinous night, when noble Achilles arose. But I regarded him not, yet surely it had been better far. And now that I have undone the host by my wantonness, I am ashamed before the men of Troy and women of trailing robes, lest at any time some worse man than I shall say: 'Hector by trusting his own might undid the host.' So will they speak; then to me would it be better far to face Achilles and either slay him and go home, or myself die gloriously before the city. Or what if I lay down my bossy shield and my stout helm, and lean my spear against the wall, and go of myself to meet noble Achilles and promise him that Helen, and with her all possessions that Alexandros brought in hollow ships to Troy, the beginning of strife, we will give to the sons of Atreus to take away, and therewithal to divide in half with the Achaians all else that this city holdeth: and if thereafter I obtain from the Trojans an oath of the Elders that they will hide nothing but divide all in twain [whatever wealth the pleasant city hold within]? But wherefore doth my heart debate thus? I might come unto him and he would not pity or regard me at all, but presently slay me unarmed as, it were but a woman, if I put off my armour. No time is it now to dally with him from oak-tree or from rock, like youth with maiden, as youth and maiden hold dalliance one with another. Better is it to join battle with all speed: let us know upon which of us twain the Olympian shall bestow renown."

Thus pondered he as he stood, but nigh on him came Achilles, peer of Enyalios warrior of the waving helm, brandishing from his right shoulder the Pelian ash, his terrible spear; and all around the bronze on him flashed like the gleam of blazing fire or of the Sun as he ariseth. And trembling seized Hector as he was aware of him, nor endured he to abide in his place, but left the gates behind him and fled in fear. And the son of Peleus darted after him, trusting in his swift feet. As a falcon upon the mountains, swiftest of winged things, swoopeth fleetly after a trembling dove; and she before him fleëth, while he with shrill screams hard at hand still darteth at her, for his heart urgeth him to seize her; so Achilles in hot haste flew straight for him, and Hector fled beneath the Trojans' wall, and plied swift knees. They past the watch-place and wind-waved wild fig-tree sped ever, away from under the wall, along the waggon-track, and came to the two fair-flowing springs, where two fountains rise that feed deep-eddying Skamandros. The one floweth with warm water, and smoke goeth up therefrom around as it were from a blazing fire, while the other even in summer floweth forth like cold hail or snow or ice that water formeth. And there beside the springs are broad washing-troughs hard by, fair troughs of stone, where wives and fair daughters of the men of Troy were wont to wash bright raiment, in the old time of peace, before the sons of the Achaians came. Thereby they ran, he flying, he pursuing. Valiant was the flier but far mightier he who fleetly pursued him. For not for beast of sacrifice or for an ox-hide were they striving, such as are prizes for men's speed of foot, but for the life of horse-taming Hector was their race. And as when victorious whole-hooved horses run rapidly round the turning-points, and some great prize lieth in sight, be it a tripod or a woman, in honour of a man that is dead, so thrice around Priam's city circled those twain with flying feet, and all the gods were gazing on them. Then among them spake first the father of gods and men: "Ay me, a man beloved I see pursued around the wall. My heart is woe for Hector, who hath burnt for me many thighs of oxen amid the crests of many-folded Ida, and other times on the city-height; but now is goodly Achilles pursuing him with swift feet round Priam's town. Come, give your counsel, gods, and devise whether we shall save him from death or now at last slay him, valiant though he be, by the hand of Achilles Peleus' son."

Then to him answered the bright-eyed goddess Athene: "O Father, Lord of the bright lightning and the dark cloud, what is this thou hast said? A man that is a mortal, doomed long ago by fate, wouldst thou redeem back from ill-boding death? Do it, but not all we other gods approve."

And unto her in answer spake cloud-gathering Zeus: "Be of good cheer, Trito-born, dear child: not in full earnest speak I, and I would fain be kind to thee. Do as seemeth good to thy mind, and draw not back."

Thus saying he roused Athene, that already was set thereon, and from the crests of Olympus she darted down.

But after Hector sped fleet Achilles chasing him vehemently. And as when on the mountains a hound hunteth the fawn of a deer, having started it from its covert, through glens and glades, and if it crouch to baffle him under a bush, yet scenting it out the hound runneth constantly until he find it; so Hector baffled not Peleus' fleet-footed son. Oft as he set himself to dart under the well-built walls over against the Dardanian gates, if haply from above they might succour him with darts, so oft would Achilles gain on him and turn him toward the plain, while himself he sped ever on the city-side. And as in a dream one faileth in chase of a flying man—the one faileth in his flight and the other in his chase—so failed Achilles to overtake him in the race, and Hector to escape. And thus would Hector have avoided the visitation of death, had not this time been utterly the last wherein Apollo came nigh to him, who nerved his strength and his swift knees. For to the host did noble Achilles sign with his head, and forbade them to hurl bitter darts against Hector, lest any smiting him should gain renown, and he himself come second. But when the fourth time they had reached the springs, then the Father hung his golden balances, and set therein two lots of dreary death, one of Achilles, one of horse-taming Hector, and held them by the midst and poised. Then Hector's fated day sank down, and fell to the house of Hades, and Phoebus Apollo left him. But to Peleus' son came the bright-eyed goddess Athene, and standing near spake to him winged words: "Now verily, glorious Achilles dear to Zeus, I have hope that we twain shall carry off great glory to the ships for the Achaians, having slain Hector, for all his thirst for fight. No longer is it possible for him to escape us, not even though far-darting Apollo should travail sore, grovelling before the Father, aegis-bearing Zeus. But do thou now stand and take breath, and I will go and persuade this man to confront thee in fight."

Thus spake Athene, and he obeyed, and was glad at heart, and stood leaning on his bronze-pointed ashen-spear. And she left him and came to noble Hector, like unto Deiphobos in shape and in strong voice, and standing near spake to him winged words: "Dear brother, verily fleet Achilles doth thee violence, chasing thee round Priam's town with swift feet: but come let us make a stand and await him on our defence."

Then answered her great Hector of the glancing helm: "Deiphobos, verily aforetime wert thou far dearest of my brothers, whom Hekabe and Priam gendered, but now methinks I shall honour thee even more, in that thou hast dared for my sake, when thou sawest me, to come forth of the wall, while the others tarry within."

Then to him again spake the bright-eyed goddess Athene: "Dear brother, of a truth my father and lady mother and my comrades around besought me much, entreating me in turn, to tarry there, so greatly do they all tremble before him; but my heart within was sore with dismal grief. And now fight we with straight-set resolve and let there be no sparing of spears, that we may know whether Achilles is to slay us and carry our bloody spoils to the hollow ships, or whether he might be vanquished by thy spear."

Thus saying Athene in her subtlety led him on. And when they were come nigh in onset on one another, to Achilles first spake great Hector of the glancing helm: "No longer, son of Peleus, will I fly thee, as before I thrice ran round the great town of Priam, and endured not to await thy onset. Now my heart biddeth me stand up against thee; I will either slay or be slain. But come hither and let us pledge us by our gods, for they shall be best witnesses and beholders of covenants: I will entreat thee in no outrageous sort, if Zeus grant me to outstay thee, and if I take thy life, but when I have despoiled thee of thy glorious armour, O Achilles, I will give back thy dead body to the Achaians, and do thou the same."

But unto him with grim gaze spake Achilles fleet of foot: "Hector, talk not to me, thou madman, of covenants. As between men and lions there is no pledge of faith, nor wolves and sheep can be of one mind, but imagine evil continually against each other, so is it impossible for thee and me to be friends, neither shall be any pledge between us until one or other shall have fallen and glutted with blood Ares, the stubborn god of war. Bethink thee of all thy soldiership: now behoveth it thee to quit thee as a good spearman and valiant man of war. No longer is there way of escape for thee, but Pallas Athene will straightway subdue thee to my spear; and now in one hour shalt thou pay back for all my sorrows for my friends whom thou hast slain in the fury of thy spear."

He said, and poised his far-shadowing spear and hurled. And noble Hector watched the coming thereof and avoided it; for with his eye on it he crouched, and the bronze spear flew over him, and fixed itself in the earth; but Pallas Athene caught it up and gave it back to Achilles, unknown of Hector shepherd of hosts. Then Hector spake unto the noble son of Peleus: "Thou hast missed, so nowise yet, godlike Achilles, hast thou known from Zeus the hour of my doom, though thou thoughtest it. Cunning of tongue art thou and a deceiver in speech, that fearing thee I might forget my valour and strength. Not as I flee shalt thou plant thy spear in my reins, but drive it straight through my breast as I set on thee, if God hath given thee to do it. Now in thy turn avoid my spear of bronze. O that thou mightst take it all into thy flesh! Then would the war be lighter to the Trojans, if but thou wert dead, for thou art their greatest bane."

He said, and poised his long-shadowed spear and hurled it, and smote the midst of the shield of Peleus' son, and missed him not: but far from the shield the spear leapt back. And Hector was wroth that his swift weapon had left his hand in vain, and he stood downcast, for he had no second ashen spear. And he called with a loud shout to Deiphobos of the white shield, and asked of him a long spear, but he was nowise nigh. Then Hector knew the truth in his heart, and spake and said: "Ay me, now verily the gods have summoned me to death. I deemed the warrior Deiphobos was by my side, but he is within the wall, and it was Athene who played me false. Now therefore is evil death come very nigh me, not far off, nor is there way of escape. This then was from of old the pleasure of Zeus and of the far-darting son of Zeus, who yet before were fain to succour me: but now my fate hath found me. At least let me not die without a struggle or ingloriously, but in some great deed of arms whereof men yet to be born shall hear."

Thus saying he drew his sharp sword that by his flank hung great and strong, and gathered himself and swooped like a soaring eagle that darteth to the plain through the dark clouds to seize a tender lamb or crouching hare. So Hector swooped, brandishing his sharp sword. And Achilles made at him, for his heart was filled with wild fierceness, and before his breast he made a covering with his fair graven shield, and tossed his bright four-plated helm; and round it waved fair golden plumes [that Hephaistos had set thick about the crest]. As a star goeth among stars in the darkness of night, Hesperos, fairest of all stars set in heaven, so flashed there forth a light from the keen spear Achilles poised in his right hand, devising mischief against noble Hector, eyeing his fair flesh to find the fittest place. Now for the rest of him his flesh was covered by the fair bronze armour he stripped from strong Patroklos when he slew him, but there was an opening where the collar bones coming from the shoulders clasp the neck, even at the gullet, where destruction of life cometh quickliest; there, as he came on, noble Achilles drave at him with his spear, and right through the tender neck went the point. Yet the bronze-weighted ashen spear clave not the windpipe, so that he might yet speak words of answer to his foe. And he fell down in the dust, and noble Achilles spake exultingly: "Hector, thou thoughtest, whilst thou wert spoiling Patroklos, that thou wouldst be safe, and didst reck nothing of me who was afar, thou fool. But away among the hollow ships his comrade, a mightier far, even I, was left behind, who now have unstrung thy knees. Thee shall dogs and birds tear foully, but his funeral shall the Achaians make."

Then with faint breath spake unto him Hector of the glancing helm: "I pray thee by thy life and knees and parents leave me not for dogs of the Achaians to devour by the ships, but take good store of bronze and gold, gifts that my father and lady mother shall give to thee, and give them home my body back again, that the Trojans and Trojans' wives give me my due of fire after my death."

But unto him with grim gaze spake Achilles fleet of foot: "Entreat me not, dog, by knees or parents. Would that my heart's desire could so bid me myself to carve and eat raw thy flesh, for the evil thou hast wrought me, as surely is there none that shall keep the dogs from thee, not even should they bring ten or twenty fold ransom and here weigh it out, and promise even more, not even were Priam Dardanos' son to bid pay thy weight in gold, not even so shall thy lady mother lay thee on a bed to mourn her son, but dogs and birds shall devour thee utterly."

Then dying spake unto him Hector of the glancing helm: "Verily I know thee and behold thee as thou art, nor was I destined to persuade thee; truly thy heart is iron in thy breast. Take heed now lest I draw upon thee wrath of gods, in the day when Paris and Phoebus Apollo slay thee, for all thy valour, at the Skaian gate."

He ended, and the shadow of death came down upon him, and his soul flew forth of his limbs and was gone to the house of Hades, wailing her fate, leaving her vigour and youth. Then to the dead man spake noble Achilles: "Die: for my death, I will accept it whensoever Zeus and the other immortal gods are minded to accomplish it."

He said, and from the corpse drew forth his bronze spear, and set it aside, and stripped the bloody armour from the shoulders. And other sons of Achaians ran up around, who gazed upon the stature and marvellous goodliness of Hector. Nor did any stand by but wounded him, and thus would many a man say looking toward his neighbour: "Go to, of a truth far easier to handle is Hector now than when he burnt the ships with blazing fire." Thus would many a man say, and wound him as he stood hard by. And when fleet noble Achilles had despoiled him, he stood up among the Achaians and spake winged words: "Friends, chiefs and counsellors of the Argives, since the gods have vouchsafed us to vanquish this man who hath done us more evil than all the rest together, come let us make trial in arms round about the city, that we may know somewhat of the Trojans' purpose, whether since he hath fallen they will forsake the citadel, or whether they are minded to abide, albeit Hector is no more. But wherefore doth my heart debate thus? There lieth by the ships a dead man unbewailed, unburied, Patroklos; him will I not forget, while I abide among the living and my knees can stir. Nay if even in the house of Hades the dead forget their dead, yet will I even there be mindful of my dear comrade. But come, ye sons of the Achaians, let us now, singing our song of victory, go back to the hollow ships and take with us our foe. Great glory have we won; we have slain the noble Hector, unto whom the Trojans prayed throughout their city, as he had been a god."

He said, and devised foul entreatment of noble Hector. The tendons of both feet behind he slit from heel to ankle-joint, and thrust therethrough thongs of ox-hide, and bound him to his chariot, leaving his head to trail. And when he had mounted the chariot and lifted therein the famous armour, he lashed his horses to speed, and they nothing loth flew on. And dust rose around him that was dragged, and his dark hair flowed loose on either side, and in the dust lay all his once fair head, for now had Zeus given him over to his foes to entreat foully in his own native land.

Thus was his head all grimed with dust. But his mother when she beheld her son, tore her hair and cast far from her her shining veil, and cried aloud with an exceeding bitter cry. And piteously moaned his father, and around them the folk fell to crying and moaning throughout the town. Most like it seemed as though all beetling Ilios were burning utterly in fire. Scarcely could the folk keep back the old man in his hot desire to get him forth of the Dardanian gates. For he besought them all, casting himself down in the mire, calling on each man by his name: "Hold, friends, and though you love me leave me to get me forth of the city alone and go unto the ships of the Achaians. Let me pray this accursed horror-working man, if haply he may feel shame before his age-fellows and pity an old man. He also hath a father such as I am, Peleus, who begat and reared him to be a bane of Trojans—and most of all to me hath he brought woe. So many sons of mine hath he slain in their flower—yet for all my sorrow for the rest I mourn them all less than this one alone, for whom my sharp grief will bring me down to the house of Hades—even Hector. Would that he had died in my arms; then would we have wept and wailed our fill, his mother who bore him to her ill hap, and I myself."

Thus spake he wailing, and all the men of the city made moan with him. And among the women of Troy, Hekabe led the wild lament: "My child, ah, woe is me! wherefore should I live in my pain, now thou art dead, who night and day wert my boast through the city, and blessing to all, both men and women of Troy throughout the town, who hailed thee as a god, for verily an exceeding glory to them wert thou in thy life:—now death and fate have overtaken thee."

Thus spake she wailing. But Hector's wife knew not as yet, for no true messenger had come to tell her how her husband abode without the gates, but in an inner chamber of the lofty house she was weaving a double purple web, and broidering therein manifold flowers. Then she called to her goodly-haired handmaids through the house to set a great tripod on the fire, that Hector might have warm washing when he came home out of the battle—fond heart, and was unaware how, far from all washings, bright-eyed Athene had slain him by the hand of Achilles. But she heard shrieks and groans from the battlements, and her limbs reeled, and the shuttle fell from her hands to earth. Then again among her goodly-haired maids she spake: "Come two of ye this way with me that I may see what deeds are done. It was the voice of my husband's noble mother that I heard, and in my own breast my heart leapeth to my mouth and my knees are numbed beneath me: surely some evil thing is at hand against the children of Priam. Would that such word might never reach my ear! yet terribly I dread lest noble Achilles have cut off bold Hector from the city by himself and chased him to the plain and ere this ended his perilous pride that possessed him, for never would he tarry among the throng of men but ran out before them far, yielding place to no man in his hardihood."

Thus saying she sped through the chamber like one mad, with beating heart, and with her went her handmaidens. But when she came to the battlements and the throng of men, she stood still upon the wall and gazed, and beheld him dragged before the city:—swift horses dragged him recklessly toward the hollow ships of the Achaians. Then dark night came on her eyes and shrouded her, and she fell backward and gasped forth her spirit. From off her head she shook the bright attiring thereof, frontlet and net and woven band, and veil, the veil that golden Aphrodite gave her on the day when Hector of the glancing helm led her forth of the house of Eëtion, having given bride-gifts untold. And around her thronged her husband's sisters and his brothers' wives, who held her up among them, distraught even to death. But when at last she came to herself and her soul returned into her breast, then wailing with deep sobs she spake among the women of Troy: "O Hector, woe is me! to one fate then were we both born, thou in Troy in the house of Priam, and I in Thebe under woody Plakos, in the house of Eëtion, who reared me from a little one—ill-fated sire of cruel-fated child. Ah, would he had begotten me not. Now thou to the house of Hades beneath the secret places of the earth departest, and me in bitter mourning thou leavest a widow in thy halls: and thy son is but an infant child—son of unhappy parents, thee and me—nor shalt thou profit him, Hector, since thou art dead, neither he thee. For even if he escape the Achaians' woful war, yet shall labour and sorrow cleave unto him hereafter, for other men shall seize his lands. The day of orphanage sundereth a child from his fellows, and his head is bowed down ever, and his cheeks are wet with tears. And in his need the child seeketh his father's friends, plucking this one by cloak and that by coat, and one of them that pity him holdeth his cup a little to his mouth, and moisteneth his lips, but his palate he moisteneth not. And some child unorphaned thrusteth him from the feast with blows and taunting words, 'Out with thee! no father of thine is at our board.' Then weeping to his widowed mother shall he return, even Astyanax, who erst upon his father's knee ate only marrow and fat flesh of sheep; and when sleep fell on him and he ceased from childish play, then in bed in his nurse's arms he would slumber softly nested, having satisfied his heart with good things; but now that he hath lost his father he will suffer many ills, Astyanax—that name the Trojans gave him, because thou only wert the defence of their gates and their long walls. But now by the beaked ships, far from thy parents, shall coiling worms devour thee when the dogs have had their fill, as thou liest naked; yet in these halls lieth raiment of thine, delicate and fair, wrought by the hands of women. But verily all these will I consume with burning fire—to thee no profit, since thou wilt never lie therein, yet that this be honour to thee from the men and the women of Troy."

Thus spake she wailing, and the women joined their moan.

BOOK XXIII

Of the funeral of Patroklos, and the funeral games.

THUS they throughout the city made moan: but the Achaians when they were come to the ships and to the Hellespont were scattered each to his own ship: only the Myrmidons Achilles suffered not to be scattered, but spake among his comrades whose delight was in war: "Fleet-horsed Myrmidons, my trusty comrades, let us not yet unyoke our whole-hooved steeds from their cars, but with horses and chariots let us go near and mourn Patroklos, for such is the honour of the dead. Then when we have our fill of grievous wailing, we will unyoke the horses and all sup here."

He said, and they with one accord made lamentation, and Achilles led their mourning. So thrice around the dead they drave their well-maned steeds, moaning; and Thetis stirred among them desire of wailing. Bedewed were the sands with tears, bedewed the warriors' arms; so great a lord of fear they sorrowed for. And Peleus' son led their loud wail, laying his man-slaying hands on his comrade's breast: "All hail, Patroklos, even in the house of Hades; for all that I promised thee before am I accomplishing, seeing I have dragged hither Hector to give raw unto dogs to devour, and twelve noble children of the Trojans to slaughter before thy pyre, because of mine anger at thy slaying."

He said, and devised foul entreatment of noble Hector, stretching him prone in the dust beside the bier of Menoitios' son. And the rest put off each his glittering bronze arms, and unyoked their high-neighing horses, and sate them down numberless beside the ship of fleet-footed Aiakides, and he gave them ample funeral feast. Many sleek oxen were stretched out, their throats cut with steel, and many sheep and bleating goats, and many white-tusked boars well grown in fat were spitted to singe in the flame of Hephaistos; so on all sides round the corpse in cupfuls blood was flowing.

But the fleet-footed prince, the son of Peleus, was brought to noble Agamemnon by the Achaian chiefs, hardly persuading him thereto, for his heart was wroth for his comrade. And when they were come to Agamemnon's hut, forthwith they bade clear-voiced heralds set a great tripod on the fire, if haply they might persuade the son of Peleus to wash from him the bloody gore. But he denied them steadfastly, and sware moreover an oath: "Nay, verily by Zeus, who is highest and best of gods, not lawful is it that water should come nigh my head or ever I shall have laid Patroklos on the fire, and heaped a barrow, and shaved my hair, since never again shall second grief thus reach my heart, while I remain among the living. Yet now for the present let us yield us to our mournful meal: but with the morning, O king of men Agamemnon, rouse the folk to bring wood and furnish all that it beseemeth a dead man to have when he goeth beneath the misty gloom, to the end that untiring fire may burn him quickly from sight, and the host betake them to their work."

Thus spake he, and they listened readily to him and obeyed, and eagerly making ready each his meal they supped, and no lack had their soul of equal feast. But when they had put off from them the desire of meat and drink, the rest went down each man to his tent to take his rest, but the son of Peleus upon the beach of the sounding sea lay groaning heavily, amid the host of Myrmidons, in an open place, where waves were breaking on the shore. Now when sleep took hold on him, easing the cares of his heart, deep sleep that fell about him, (for sore tired were his glorious knees with onset upon Hector toward windy

Ilios), then came there unto him the spirit of hapless Patroklos, in all things like his living self, in stature, and fair eyes, and voice, and the raiment of his body was the same; and he stood above Achilles' head and spake to him: "Thou sleepest, and hast forgotten me, O Achilles. Not in my life wast thou ever unmindful of me, but in my death. Bury me with all speed, that I pass the gates of Hades. Far off the spirits banish me, the phantoms of men outworn, nor suffer me to mingle with them beyond the River, but vainly I wander along the wide-gated dwelling of Hades. Now give me, I pray pitifully of thee, thy hand, for never more again shall I come back from Hades, when ye have given me my due of fire. Never among the living shall we sit apart from our dear comrades and take counsel together, but me hath the harsh fate swallowed up which was appointed me even from my birth. Yea and thou too thyself, Achilles peer of gods, beneath the wall of the noble Trojans art doomed to die. Yet one thing will I say, and charge thee, if haply thou will have regard thereto. Lay not my bones apart from thine, Achilles, but together, even as we were nurtured in your house, when Menoitios brought me yet a little one from Opöeis to your country by reason of a grievous man-slaying, on the day when I slew Amphidamas' son, not willing it, in childish wrath over the dice. Then took me the knight Peleus into his house and reared me kindly and named me thy squire: so therefore let one coffer hide our bones, [a golden coffer, two handled, thy lady mother's gift]."

Then made answer unto him Achilles fleet of foot: "Wherefore, O my brother, hast thou come hither, and chargest me everything that I should do? Verily I will accomplish all, and have regard unto thy bidding. But stand more nigh me; for one moment let us throw our arms around each other, and take our fill of dolorous lament."

He spake, and reached forth with his hands, but clasped him not; for like a vapour the spirit was gone beneath the earth with a faint shriek. And Achilles sprang up marvelling, and smote his hands together, and spake a word of woe: "Ay me, there remaineth then even in the house of Hades a spirit and phantom of the dead, albeit the life be not anywise therein: for all night long hath the spirit of hapless Patroklos stood over me, wailing and making moan, and charged me everything that I should do, and wondrous like his living self it seemed."

Thus said he, and stirred in all of them yearning to make lament; and rosy-fingered Morn shone forth on them while they still made moan around the piteous corpse. Then lord Agamemnon sped mules and men from all the huts to fetch wood; and a man of valour watched thereover, even Meriones, squire of kindly Idomeneus. And they went forth with wood-cutting axes in their hands and well-woven ropes, and before them went the mules, and uphill and downhill and sideways and across they went. But when they came to the spurs of many-fountained Ida, straightway they set them lustily to hew high-foliaged oaks with the long-edged bronze, and with loud noise fell the trees. Then splitting them asunder the Achaians bound them behind the mules, and they tore up the earth with their feet as they made for the plain through the thick underwood. And all the woodcutters bare logs; for thus bade Meriones, squire of kindly Idomeneus. And on the shore they threw them down in line, where Achilles purposed a mighty tomb for Patroklos and for himself.

Then when they had laid down all about great piles of wood, they sate them down all together and abode. Then straightway Achilles bade the warlike Myrmidons gird on their arms, and each yoke the horses to his chariots; and they arose and put their armour on, and mounted their chariots, both fighting men and charioteers. In front were the men in chariots, and a cloud of footmen followed after, numberless; and in the midst his comrades bare Patroklos. And they heaped all the corpse with their hair that they cut off and threw thereon; and behind did goodly Achilles bear the head, sorrowing; for a noble comrade was he speeding forth unto the realm of Hades.

And when they came to the place where Achilles had bidden them, they set down the dead, and piled for him abundant wood. Then fleet-footed noble Achilles bethought him of one thing more: standing apart from the pyre he shore off a golden lock, the lock whose growth he nursed to offer unto the River Spercheios, and sore troubled spake he, looking forth over the wine-dark sea: "Spercheios, in other wise vowed my father Peleus unto thee that I returning thither to my native land should shear my hair for thee and offer a holy hecatomb, and fifty rams should sacrifice there above thy springs, where is thy sacred close and altar burning spice. So vowed the old man, but thou hast not accomplished him his desire. And now since I return not to my dear native land, unto the hero Patroklos I may give this hair to take away."

Thus saying he set the hair in the hands of his dear comrade, and stirred in all of them yearning to make lament. And so would the light of the sun have gone down on their lamentation, had not Achilles said quickly to Agamemnon as he stood beside him: "Son of Atreus—for to thy words most will the host of the Achaians have regard—of lamentation they may sate them to the full. But now disperse them from the burning and bid them make ready their meal, and we to whom the dead is dearest will take pains for these things; yet let the chiefs tarry nigh unto us."

Then when Agamemnon king of men heard that, he forthwith dispersed the host among the trim ships, but the nearest to the dead tarried there and piled the wood, and made a pyre a hundred feet this way and that, and on the pyre's top set the corpse, with anguish at their hearts. And many lusty sheep and shambling crook-horned oxen they flayed and made ready before the pyre; and taking from all of them the fat, great-hearted Achilles wrapped the corpse therein from head to foot, and heaped the flayed bodies round. And he set therein two-handled jars of honey and oil, leaning them against the bier; and four strong-necked horses he threw swiftly on the pyre, and groaned aloud. Nine house-dogs had the dead chief: of them did Achilles slay twain and throw them on the pyre. And twelve valiant sons of great-hearted Trojans he slew with the sword—for he devised mischief in his heart—and he set to the merciless might of the fire, to feed thereon. Then moaned he aloud, and called on his dear comrade by his name: "All hail to thee, O Patroklos, even in the house of Hades, for all that I promised thee before am I now accomplishing. Twelve valiant sons of great-hearted Trojans, behold these all in company with thee the fire devoureth: but Hector son of Priam will I nowise give to the fire to feed upon, but to dogs."

Thus spake he threatening, but no dogs might deal with Hector, for day and night Aphrodite daughter of Zeus kept off the dogs, and anointed him with rose-sweet oil ambrosial that Achilles might not tear him when he dragged him. And over him Phoebus Apollo brought a dark cloud from heaven to earth and covered all that place whereon the dead man lay, lest meanwhile the sun's strength shrivel his flesh round about upon his sinews and limbs.

But the pyre of dead Patroklos kindled not. Then fleet-footed noble Achilles had a further thought: standing aside from the pyre he prayed to the two Winds of North and West, and promised them fair offerings, and pouring large libations from a golden cup besought them to come, that the corpses might blaze up speedily in the fire, and the wood make haste to be enkindled. Then Iris, when she heard his prayer, went swiftly with the message to the Winds. They within the house of the gusty West Wind were feasting all together at meat, when Iris sped thither, and halted on the threshold of stone. And when they saw her with their eyes, they sprang up and called to her every one to sit by him.

But she refused to sit, and spake her word: "No seat for me; I must go back to the streams of Ocean, to the Ethiopians' land where they sacrifice hecatombs to the immortal gods, that I too may feast at their rites. But Achilles is praying the North Wind and the loud West to come, and promising them fair offerings, that ye may make the pyre be kindled whereon lieth Patroklos, for whom all the Achaians are making moan."

She having thus said departed, and they arose with a mighty sound, rolling the clouds before them. And swiftly they came blowing over the sea, and the wave rose beneath their shrill blast; and they came to deep-soiled Troy, and fell upon the pile, and loudly roared the mighty fire. So all night drave they the flame of the pyre together, blowing shrill; and all night fleet Achilles, holding a two-handled cup, drew wine from a golden bowl, and poured it forth and drenched the earth, calling upon the spirit of hapless Patroklos. As a father waileth when he burneth the bones of his son, new-married, whose death is woe to his hapless parents, so wailed Achilles as he burnt the bones of his comrade, going heavily round the burning pile, with many moans.

But at the hour when the Morning Star goeth forth to herald light upon the earth, the star that saffron-mantled Dawn cometh after, and spreadeth over the salt sea, then grew the burning faint, and the flame died down. And the Winds went back again to betake them home over the Thracian main, and it roared with a violent swell. Then the son of Peleus turned away from the burning and lay down wearied, and sweet sleep leapt on him. But they who were with Atreus' son gathered all together, and the noise and clash of their approach aroused him; and he sate upright and spake a word to them: "Son of Atreus and ye other chiefs of the Achaians, first quench with gleaming wine all the burning so far as the fire's strength hath reached, and then let us gather up the bones of Patroklos,

Menoitios' son, singling them well, and easy are they to discern, for he lay in the middle of the pyre, while the rest apart at the edge burnt confusedly, horses and men. And his bones let us put within a golden urn, and double-folded fat, until that I myself be hidden in Hades. But no huge barrow I bid you toil to raise—a seemly one, no more: then afterward do ye Achaians build it broad and high, whosoever of you after I am gone may be left in the benched ships."

Thus spake he, and they hearkened to the fleet-footed son of Peleus. First quenched they with gleaming wine the burning so far as the flame went, and the ash had settled deep: then with lamentation they gathered up the white bones of their gentle comrade into a golden urn and double-folded fat, and placed the urn in the hut and covered it with a linen veil. And they marked the circle of the barrow, and set the foundations thereof around the pyre, and straightway heaped thereon a heap of earth. Then when they had heaped up the barrow they were for going back. But Achilles stayed the folk in that place, and made them sit in wide assembly, and from his ships he brought forth prizes, caldrons and tripods, and horses and mules and strong oxen, and fair-girdled women, and grey iron.

First for fleet chariot-racers he ordained a noble prize, a woman skilled in fair handiwork for the winner to lead home, and an eared tripod that held two-and-twenty measures; these for the first man; and for the second he ordained a six-year-old mare unbroke, with a mule foal in her womb; and for the third he gave a goodly caldron yet untouched by fire, holding four measures, bright as when first made; and for the fouth he ordained two talents of gold; and for the fifth a two-handled urn untouched of fire. Then he stood up and spake a word among the Argies: "Son of Atreus and ye other well-greaved Achaians, for the chariot-racers these prizes lie awaiting them in the lists. If in some other's honour we Achaians were now holding our games, it would be I who should win the first prize and bear it to my hut; for ye know how far my pair of horses are first in excellence, for they are immortal, and Poseidon gave them to my father Peleus, and he again to me. But verily I will abide, I and my whole-hooved horses, so glorious a charioteer have they lost, and one so kind, who on their manes full often poured smooth oil, when he had washed them in clear water. For him they stand and mourn, and their manes are trailing on the ground, and there stand they with sorrow at their hearts. But ye others throughout the host get ye to your places, whosoever of the Achaians hath trust in his horses and firm-jointed car."

Thus spake the son of Peleus, and the fleet chariot-racers were gathered. First of all arose up Eumelos king of men, Admetos' son, a skilful charioteer; and next to him arose Tydeus' son, valiant Diomedes, and yoked his horses of the breed of Tros, which on a time he seized from Aineias, when Apollo saved their lord. And after him arose Atreus' son, fair-haired heaven-sprung Menelaos, and yoked him a swift pair, Aithe, Agamemnon's mare, and his own horse Podargos. Her unto Agamemnon did Anchises' son Echepolos give in fee, that he might escape from following him to windy Ilios and take his pleasure at home; for great wealth had Zeus given him, and he dwelt in Sikyon of spacious lawns:—so Menelaos yoked her, and she longed exceedingly for the race. And fourth, Antilochos made ready his fair-maned horses, even the noble son of Nestor, high-hearted king, who was the son of Neleus; and fleet horses bred at Pylos drew his car. And his father standing by his side spake counselling him to his profit, though himself was well advised: "Antilochos, verily albeit thou art young, Zeus and Poseidon have loved thee and taught thee all skill with horses; wherefore to teach thee is no great need, for thou well knowest how to wheel round the post; yet are thy horses very slow in the race: therefore methinks there will be sad work for thee. For the horses of the others are fleeter, yet the men know not more cunning than thou hast. So come, dear son, store thy mind with all manner of cunning, that the prize escape thee not. By cunning is a woodman far better than by force; by cunning doth a helmsman on the wine-dark deep steer his swift ship buffeted by winds; by cunning hath charioteer the better of charioteer. For whoso trusting in his horses and car alone wheeleth heedlessly and wide at either end, his horses swerve on the course, and he keepeth them not in hand. But whoso is of crafty mind, though he drive worse horses, he ever keeping his eye upon the post turneth closely by it, neither is unaware how far at first to force his horses by the ox-hide reins, but holdeth them safe in hand and watcheth the leader in the race. Now will I tell thee a certain sign, and it shall not escape thee. A fathom's height above the ground standeth a withered stump, whether of oak or pine: it decayeth not in the rain, and two white stones on either side thereof are fixed at the joining of the track, and all round it is smooth driving ground. Whether it be a monument of some man dead long ago, or have been made their goal in the race by ancient men, this now is the mark fixed by fleet-footed goodly Achilles. Wherefore do thou drive close and bear thy horses and chariot hard thereon, and lean thy body on the well-knit car slightly to their left, and call upon the off-horse with voice and lash, and give him rein from thy hand. But let the near horse hug the post so that the nave of the well-wrought wheel seem to graze it—yet beware of touching the stone, lest thou wound the horses and break the chariot; so would that be triumph to the rest and reproach unto thyself. But, dear son, be wise and on thy guard; for if at the turning-post thou drive past the rest, there is none shall overtake thee from behind or pass thee by, not though he drave the goodly Arion in pursuit, the fleet horse of Adrastos, of divine descent, or the horses of Laomedon, best of all bred in this land."

Thus spake Neleïan Nestor and sate him down again in

his place, when he had told his son the sum of every matter.

And Meriones was the fifth to make ready his sleek-coated steeds. Then went they up into their chariots, and cast in the lots: and Achilles shook them, and forth leapt the lot of Antilochos Nestor's son, and the next lot had lord Eumelos, and next to him the son of Atreus, spear-famed Menelaos, and next to him drew Meriones his place; then lastly Tydeides, far the best of all, drew his lot for his chariot's place. Then they stood side by side, and Achilles showed to them the turning-post, far off in the smooth plain; and beside it he placed an umpire, godlike Phoinix, his father's follower, that he might note the running and tell the truth thereof.

Then all together lifted the lash above their steeds, and smote them with the reins, and called on them eagerly with words: and they forthwith sped swiftly over the plain, leaving the ships behind; and beneath their breasts stood the rising dust like a cloud or whirlwind, and their manes waved on the blowing wind. And the chariots ran sometimes on the bounteous earth, and other whiles would bound into the air. And the drivers stood in the cars, and the heart of every man beat in desire of victory, and they called every man to his horses, that flew amid their dust across the plain.

But when the fleet horses were now running the last part of the course, back toward the grey sea, then was manifest the prowess of each, and the horses strained in the race; and presently to the front rushed the fleet mares of Pheres' grandson, and next to them Diomedes' stallions of the breed of Tros, not far apart, but hard anigh, for they seemed ever as they would mount Eumelos' car, and with their breath his back was warm and his broad shoulders, for they bent their heads upon him as they flew along. Thus would Tydeus' son have either outstripped the other or made it a dead heat, had not Phoebus Apollo been wroth with him and smitten from his hand the shining lash. Then from his eyes ran tears of anger, for that he saw the mares still at speed, even swiftlier than before, while his own horses were thrown out, as running without spur. But Athene was not unaware of Apollo's guile against Tydeides, and presently sped after the shepherd of hosts, and gave him back the lash, and put spirit into his steeds. Then in wrath after the son of Admetos was the goddess gone, and brake his steeds' yoke, and the mares ran sideways off the course, and the pole was twisted to the ground. And Eumelos was hurled out of the car beside the wheel, and his elbows and mouth and nose were flayed, and his forehead bruised above his eyebrows; and his eyes filled with tears and his lusty voice was choked. Then Tydeides held his whole-hooved horses on one side, darting far out before the rest, for Athene put spirit into his steeds and shed glory on himself. Now next after him came golden-haired Menelaos Atreus' son. But Antilochos called to his father's horses: "Go ye too in, strain to your fleetest pace. Truly I nowise bid you strive with those, the horses of wise Tydeides, unto which Athene hath now given speed, and shed glory on their charioteer. But overtake Atreides' horses with all haste, and be not outstripped by them, lest Aithe that is but a mare pour scorn on you. Why are ye outstripped, brave steeds? Thus will I tell you, and verily it shall be brought to pass—ye will find no tendance with Nestor shepherd of hosts, but straightway he will slay you with the edge of the sword if through heedlessness we win but the worse prize. Have after them at your utmost speed, and I for my part will devise a plan to pass them in the strait part of the course, and this shall fail me not."

Thus spake he, and they fearing the voice of the prince ran swiftlier some little while; and presently did the good warrior Antilochos espy a strait place in a sunk part of the way. There was a rift in the earth, where torrent water gathered and brake part of the track away, and hollowed all the place; there drave Menelaos, shunning the encounter of the wheels. But Antilochos turned his whole-hooved horses out of the track, and followed him a little at one side. And the son of Atreus took alarm and shouted to Antilochos: "Antilochos, thou art driving recklessly—hold in thy horses! The road is straitened, soon thou mayest pass me in a wider place, lest thou foul my chariot and undo us both."

Thus spake he, but Antilochos drave even fiercelier than before, plying his lash, as though he heard him not. As far as is the range of a disk swung from the shoulder when a young man hurleth it, making trial of his force, even so far ran they on; then the mares of Atreus' son gave back, for he ceased of himself to urge them on, lest the whole-hooved steeds should encounter on the track, and overset the well-knit cars, and the drivers fall in the dust in their zeal for victory. So upbraiding Antilochos spake golden-haired Menelaos: "Antilochos, no mortal man is more malicious than thou. Go thy mad way, since falsely have we Achaians called thee wise. Yet even so thou shalt not bear off the prize unchallenged to an oath."

Thus saying he called aloud to his horses: "Hold ye not back nor stand still with sorrow at heart. Their feet and knees will grow weary before yours, for they both lack youth."

Thus spake he, and they fearing the voice of the prince sped faster on, and were quickly close upon the others.

Now the Argives sitting in concourse were gazing at the horses, and they came flying amid their dust over the plain. And the first aware of them was Idomeneus, chief of the Cretans, for he was sitting outside the concourse in the highest place of view, and when he heard the voice of one that shouted, though afar off, he knew it; and he was aware of a horse showing plainly in the front, a chestnut all the rest of him, but in the forehead marked with a white star round like the moon. And he stood upright and spoke among the Argives: "Friends, chiefs, and counsellors of the Argives, is it I alone who see the horses, or do ye also? A new pair seem to me now to be in front, and a new charioteer appeareth; the mares which led in the outward course must have been thrown out there in the plain. For I saw them turning first the hither post, but now can see them nowhere, though my eyes are gazing everywhere along the Trojan plain. Did the reins escape the charioteer so that he could not drive aright round the post and failed in the turn? There, methinks, must he have been cast forth, and have broken his chariot, and the mares must have left the course, in the wildness of their heart. But stand up ye too and look, for myself I discern not certainly, but the first man seemeth to me one of Aitolian race, and he ruleth among Argives, the son of horse-taming Tydeus, stalwart Diomedes."

Then fleet Aias Oileus' son rebuked him in unseemly sort: "Idomeneus, why art thou a braggart of old? As yet far off the high-stepping mares are coursing over the wide plain. Neither art thou so far the youngest among the Argives, nor do thy eyes look so far the keenliest from thy head, yet continually braggest thou. It beseemeth thee not to be a braggart, for there are here better men. And the mares leading are they that led before, Eumelos' mares, and he standeth and holdeth the reins within the car."

Then wrathfully in answer spake the chief of Cretans: "Aias, master of railing, ill-counselled, in all else art thou behind other Argives, for thy mind is unfriendly. Come then let us wager a tripod or caldron, and make Agamemnon Atreus' son our umpire, which mares are leading, that thou mayest pay and learn."

Thus said he, and straightay fleet Aias Oileus' son arose angrily to answer with harsh words: and strife between the twain would have gone further, had not Achilles himself stood up and spake a word: "No longer answer each other with harsh words, Aias and Idomeneus, ill words, for it beseemeth not. Surely ye are displeased with any other who should do thus. Sit ye in the concourse and keep your eyes upon the horses; soon they in zeal for victory will come hither, and then shall ye know each of you the Argives' horses, which follow, and which lead."

He said, and the son of Tydeus came driving up, and with his lash smote now and again from the shoulder, and his horses were stepping high as they sped swiftly on their way. And sprinklings of dust smote ever the charioteer, and his chariot overlaid with gold and tin ran behind his fleet-footed steeds, and small trace was there of the wheel-tires behind in the fine dust, as they flew speeding on. Then he drew up in the mid concourse, and much sweat poured from the horses' heads and chests to the ground. And Diomedes leapt to earth from the shining car, and leant his lash against the yoke. Then stalwart Sthenelos tarried not, but promptly took the prize, and gave to his proud comrades the woman to lead and the eared tripod to bear away, and he loosed the horses from the yoke.

And next after him drave Neleian Antilochos his horses, by craft, not swiftness, having passed by Menelaos; yet even now Menelaos held his swift steeds hard anigh. As far as a horse is from the wheel, which draweth his master, straining with the car over the plain—his hindmost tail-hairs touch the tire, for the wheel runneth hard anigh nor is much space between, as he speedeth far over the plain—by so much was Menelaos behind high-born Antilochos, howbeit at first he was a whole disk-cast behind, but quickly he was catching Antilochos up, for the high mettle of Agamemnon's mare, sleek-coated Aithe, was rising in her. And if yet further both had had to run he would have passed his rival nor left it even a dead heat. But Meriones, stout squire of Idomeneus, came in a spear-throw behind famous Menelaos, for tardiest of all were his sleek-coated horses, and slowest he himself to drive a chariot in the race. Last of them all came Admetos' son, dragging his goodly car, driving his steeds in front. Him when fleet-footed noble Achilles beheld he pitied him, and he stood up and spake winged words among the Argives: "Last driveth his whole-hooved horses the best man of them all. But come let us give him a prize, as is seemly, prize for the second place, but the first let the son of Tydeus take."

Thus spake he, and all applauded that he bade. And he would have given him the mare, for the Achaians applauded, had not Antilochos, son of great-hearted Nestor, risen up and answered Peleian Achilles on behalf of his right: "O Achilles, I shall be sore angered with thee if thou accomplish this word, for thou art minded to take away my prize, because thou thinkest of how his chariot and fleet steeds miscarried, and himself withal, good man though he be. Nay, it behoved him to pray to the Immortals, then would he not have come in last of all in the race. But if thou pitiest him and he be dear to thy heart, there is much gold in thy hut, bronze is there and sheep, handmaids are there and whole-hooved horses. Thereof take thou and give unto him afterward even a richer prize, or even now at once, that the Achaians may applaud thee. But the mare I will not yield; for her let what man will essay the battle at my hands."

Thus spake he, and fleet-footed noble Achilles smiled, pleased with Antilochos, for he was his dear comrade; and spake in answer to him winged words: "Antilochos, if thou wouldst have me give Eumelos some other thing beside from out my house, that also will I do. I will give unto him a breast-plate that I took from Asteropaios, of bronze, whereon a casting of bright tin is overlaid, and of great worth will it be to him." He said, and bade his dear comrade Automedon bring it from the hut, and he went and brought it. [Then he placed it in Eumelos' hands, and he received it gladly.]

But Menelaos also arose among them, sore at heart, angered exceedingly against Antilochos; and the herald set the staff in his hand, and called for silence among the Argives; then spake among them that godlike man: "Antilochos, who once wert wise, what thing is this thou hast done? Thou hast shamed my skill and made my horses fail, thrusting thine own in front that are far worse. Come now, ye chiefs and counsellors of the Argives, give judgment between us both, and favour neither: lest some one of the mail-clad Achaians say at any time: 'By constraining Antilochos through false words hath Menelaos gone off with the mare, for his horses were far worse, howbeit he hath advantage in rank and power.' Nay, I myself will bring the issue about, and I deem that none other of the Danaans shall reproach me, for the trial shall be just. Antilochos, fosterling of Zeus, come thou hither and as it is ordained stand up before thy horses and chariot and take in thy hand the pliant lash wherewith thou dravest erst, and touching thy horses swear by the Enfolder and Shaker of the earth that not wilfully didst thou hinder my chariot by guile."

Then answered him wise Antilochos: "Bear with me now, for far younger am I than thou, king Menelaos, and thou art before me and my better. Thou knowest how a young man's transgressions come about, for his mind is hastier and his counsel shallow. So let thy heart suffer me, and I will of myself give to thee the mare I have taken. Yea, if thou shouldst ask some other greater thing from my house, I were fain to give it thee straightway, rather than fall for ever from my place in thy heart, O fosterling of Zeus, and become a sinner against the gods."

Thus spake great-hearted Nestor's son, and brought the mare and put her in the hand of Menelaos. And his heart was gladdened as when the dew cometh upon the ears of ripening harvest-corn, what time the fields are bristling. So gladdened was thy soul, Menelaos, within thy heart. And he spake unto Antilochos and uttered winged words: "Antilochos, now will I of myself put away mine anger against thee, since nowise formerly wert thou flighty or light-minded, howbeit now thy reason was overcome of youthfulness. Another time be loth to outwit better men. Not easily should another of the Achaians have persuaded me, but thou hast suffered and toiled greatly, and thy brave father and brother, for my sake: therefore will I hearken to thy prayer, and will even give unto thee the mare, though she is mine, that these also may know that my heart was never overweening or implacable."

He said, and gave the mare to Noëmon Antilochos' comrade to lead away, and then took the shining caldron. And Meriones took up the two talents of gold in the fourth place, as he had come in. So the fifth prize was left unclaimed, a two-handled cup; to Nestor gave Achilles this, bearing it to him through the concourse of Argives, and stood by him and said: "Lo now for thee too, old man, be this a treasure, a memorial of Patroklos' burying; for no more shalt thou behold him among the Argives. Now give I thee this prize unwon, for not in boxing shalt thou strive, neither wrestle, nor enter on the javelin match, nor race with thy feet; for grim old age already weigheth on thee."

Thus saying he placed it in his hand, and Nestor received it gladly, and spake unto him winged words: "Ay, truly all this, my son, thou hast meetly said; for no longer are my limbs, friend, firm, nor my feet, nor do my arms at all swing lightly from my shoulders either side. Would that my youth were such and my force so firm as when the Epeians were burying lord Amarynkes at Buprasion, and his sons held the king's funeral games. Then was no man found like me, neither of the Epeians nor of the Pylians themselves or the great-hearted Aitolians. In boxing I overcame Klytomedes, son of Enops, and in wrestling Ankaios of Pleuron, who stood up against me, and in the foot-race I outran Iphiklos, a right good man, and with the spear outthrew Phyleus and Polydoros; only in the chariot-race the two sons of Aktor beat me [by crowding their horses in front of me, jealous for victory, because the chief prizes were left at home.] Now they were twins—one ever held the reins, the reins he ever held, the other called on the horses with the lash. Thus was I once, but now let younger men join in such feats; I must bend to grievous age, but then was I of mark among heroes. But come hold funeral for thy comrade too with games. This gift do I accept with gladness, and my heart rejoiceth that thou rememberest ever my friendship to thee —(nor forget I thee)—and the honour wherewith it is meet that I be honoured among the Achaians. And may the gods for this grant thee due grace."

Thus spake he, and Peleides was gone down the full concourse of Achaians, when he had hearkened to all the thanks of Neleus' son. Then he ordained prizes of the violent boxing match; a sturdy mule he led forth and tethered amid the assembly, a six-year mule unbroken, hardest of all to break; and for the loser set a two-handled cup. Then he stood up and spake a word among the Argives: "Son of Atreus and ye other well-greaved Achaians, for these rewards we summon two men of the best to lift up their hands to box amain. He to whom Apollo shall grant endurance to the end, and all the Achaians acknowledge it, let him take the sturdy mule and return with her to his hut; and the loser shall take with him the two-handled cup."

Thus spake he, and forthwith arose a man great and valiant and skilled in boxing, Epeios son of Panopeus, and laid his hand on the sturdy mule and said aloud: "Let one come nigh to bear off the two-handled cup; the mule I say none other of the Achaians shall take for victory with his fists, for I claim to be the best man here. Sufficeth it not that I fall short of you in battle? Not possible is it that in all arts a man be skilled. Thus proclaim I, and it shall be accomplished: I will utterly bruise mine adversary's flesh and break his bones, so let his friends abide together here to bear him forth when vanquished by my hands."

Thus spake he, and they all kept deep silence. And alone arose against him Euryalos, a godlike man, son of king Mekisteus the son of Talaos, Mekisteus, who came on a time to Thebes when Oedipus had fallen, to his burial, and there he overcame all the sons of Kadmos. Thus Tydeides famous with the spear made ready Euryalos for the fight, cheering him with speech, and greatly desired for him victory. And first he cast about him a girdle, and next gave him well-cut thongs of the hide of an ox of the field. And the two boxers being girt went into the midst of the ring, and both lifting up their stalwart hands fell to, and their hands joined battle grievously. Then was there terrible grinding of teeth, and sweat flowed from all their limbs. And noble Epeios came on, and as the other spied for an opening, smote him on the cheek, nor could he much more stand, for his fair limbs failed straightway under him. And as when beneath the North Wind's ripple a fish leapeth on a tangle-covered beach, and then the black wave hideth it, so leapt up Euryalos at that blow. But great-hearted Epeios took him in his hands and set him upright, and his dear comrades stood around him, and led him through the ring with trailing feet, spitting out clotted blood, drooping his head awry, and they set him down in his swoon among them and themselves went forth and fetched the two-handled cup.

Then Peleus' son ordained straightway the prizes for a third contest, offering them to the Danaans, for the grievous wrestling match: for the winner a great tripod for standing on the fire, prized by the Achaians among them at twelve oxen's worth; and for the loser he brought a woman into the midst, skilled in manifold work, and they prized her at four oxen. And he stood up and spake a word among the Argives: "Rise, ye who will essay this match."

Thus said he, and there arose great Aias son of Telamon, and Odysseus of many wiles stood up, the crafty-minded. And the twain being girt went into the midst of the ring, and clasped each the other in his arms with stalwart hands, like gable rafters of a lofty house which some famed craftsman joineth, that he may baffle the wind's force. And their backs creaked, gripped firmly under the vigorous hands, and sweat ran down in streams, and frequent weals along their ribs and shoulders sprang up, red with blood, while ever they strove amain for victory, to win the wrought tripod. Neither could Odysseus trip Aias and bear him to the ground, nor Aias him, for Odysseus' strength withheld him. But when they began to irk the well-greaved Achaians, then said to Odysseus great Aias, Telamon's son: "Heaven-sprung son of Laertes, Odysseus of many wiles, or lift thou me, or I will thee, and the issue shall be with Zeus."

Having thus said he lifted him, but Odysseus was not unmindful of his craft. He smote deftly from behind the hollow of Aias' knee, and loosed his limbs, and threw him down backward, and Odysseus fell upon his chest, and the folk gazed and marvelled. Then in his turn much-enduring noble Odysseus tried to lift, and moved him a little from the ground, but lifted him not, so he crooked his knee within the other's, and both fell on the ground nigh to each other, and were soiled with dust. And now starting up again a third time would they have wrestled, had not Achilles himself arisen and held them back: "No longer press each the other, nor wear you out with pain. Victory is with both; take equal prizes and depart, that other Achaians may contend."

Thus spake he, and they were fain to hear and to obey, and wiped the dust from them and put their doublets on.

Then straightway the son of Peleus set forth other prizes for fleetness of foot; a mixing-bowl of silver, chased; six measures it held, and in beauty it was far the best in all the earth, for artificers of Sidon wrought it cunningly, and men of the Phoenicians brought it over the misty sea, and landed it in harbour, and gave it a gift to Thoas; and Euneos son of Jason gave it to the hero Patroklos a ransom for Lykaon Priam's son. Now this cup did Achilles set forth as a prize in honour of his friend, for whoso should be fleetest in speed of foot. For the second he set an ox great and very fat, and for the last prize half a talent of gold. And he stood up and spake a word among the Argives: "Rise, ye who will essay this match."

Thus spake he, and straightway arose fleet Aias Oileus' son, and Odysseus of many wiles, and after them Nestor's son Antilochos, for he was best of all the youth in the foot-race. Then they stood side by side, and Achilles showed to them the goal. Right eager was the running from the start, but Oileus' son forthwith shot to the front, and close behind him came noble Odysseus, as close as is a weaving-rod to a fair-girdled woman's breast when she pulleth it deftly with her hands, drawing the spool along the warp, and holdeth the rod nigh her breast—so close ran Odysseus behind Aias and trod in his footsteps or ever the dust had settled there, and on his head fell the breath of noble Odysseus as he ran ever lightly on, and all the Achaians applauded his struggle for the victory and called on him as he laboured hard. But when they were running the last part of the course, forthwith Odysseus prayed in his soul to bright-eyed Athene: "Hearken, goddess, come thou a good helper of my feet."

Thus prayed he, and Pallas Athene hearkened to him, and made his limbs feel light, both feet and hands. But when they were now nigh darting on the prize, then Aias slipped as he ran, for Athene marred his race, where filth was strewn from the slaughter of loud-bellowing oxen that fleet Achilles slew in honour of Patroklos: and Aias' mouth and nostrils were filled with that filth of oxen. So much-enduring noble Odysseus, as he came in first, took up the mixing-bowl, and famous Aias took the ox. And he stood holding in his hand the horn of the ox of the field, sputtering away the filth, and spake among the Argives: "Out on it, it was the goddess who marred my running, she who from of old like a mother standeth by Odysseus' side and helpeth him."

So spake he, but they all laughed pleasantly to behold him. Then Antilochos smiling bore off the last prize, and spake his word among the Argives: "Friends, ye will all bear me witness when I say that even herein also the immortals favour elder men. For Aias is a little older than I, but Odysseus of an earlier generation and earlier race of men. A green old age is his, they say, and hard were it for any Achaian to rival him in speed, save only Achilles."

Thus spake he, and gave honour to the fleet son of Peleus. And Achilles answered him and said: "Antilochos, not unheeded shall thy praise be given; a half-talent of gold I will give thee over and above." He said, and set it in his hands, and Antilochos received it gladly.

[Then Peleus' son brought a long-shadowed spear into the ring and laid it there, and a shield and helmet, the arms of Sarpedon whereof Patroklos spoiled him. And he stood up and spake a word among the Argives: "To win these arms we bid two warriors of the best put on their armour and take flesh-cleaving bronze to make trial of each other before the host whether of the two shall first reach the other's fair flesh and touch the inward parts through armour and dark blood. To him will I give this silver-studded sword, a goodly Thracian sword that I took from Asteropaios; and these arms let both bear away to hold in common, and a fair feast will we set before them in the huts."

Thus spake he, and then arose Telamon's son great Aias, and up rose Tydeus' son, stalwart Diomedes. So when on either side the assembly they had armed them, they met together in the midst eager for battle, with terrible gaze; and wonder fell on all the Achaians. But when they were now nigh in onset on each other, thrice they came on and thrice drew nigh to smite. Then Aias smote on the round shield, but pierced not to the flesh, for the breastplate within kept off the spear. But the son of Tydeus over his great shield kept ever aiming at the neck with the point of his bright spear. Then fearing for Aias the Achaians bade them cease and each take equal prize. But to Tydeus' son the hero gave the great sword, bringing it with its scabbard and well-cut belt.

Then the son of Peleus set an unwrought metal mass which anciently the mighty Eëtion was wont to whirl; but him fleet noble Achilles slew, and brought the mass in his ships with his other possessions. And he stood up and spake a word among the Argives: "Rise, ye who will essay this match. The winner of this, even though his rich fields be very far remote, will have it for use five rolling years, for his shepherd or ploughman will not for want of iron have to go into the town, but this will give it them."

Thus said he, and then arose warlike Polypoites, and the valiant strength of godlike Leonteus, and Aias son of Telamon and noble Epeios. And they stood in order, and noble Epeios took the weight, and whirled and flung it; and all the Achaians laughed to see it. Then next Leonteus, of the stock of Ares, threw; and thirdly great Aias Telamon's son hurled it from his stalwart hand, and overpassed the marks of all. But when warlike Polypoites took the mass he flung it as far as a herdsman flingeth his staff, when it flieth whirling through herds of kine;—so far cast he beyond all the space, and the people shouted aloud. And the comrades of strong Polypoites arose and bare the king's prize to the hollow ships.

Then for the archers he set a prize of dark iron—ten double-headed axes he set, and ten single; and set up the mast of a dark-prowed ship far off in the sands, and bound a pigeon thereto by the foot with a fine cord, and bade shoot thereat:—"Whosoever shall hit the pigeon let him take all the double axes home with him, and whoso shall miss the bird but hit the cord, he shall take the single, since his shot is worse."

Thus spake he, and then arose the strength of the chief Teukros, and Meriones arose, Idomeneus' brave brother in arms. And they took lots and shook them in a brazen helm, and Teukros drew the first place by lot. Forthwith he shot an arrow with power, but made no vow to offer a famous hecatomb of firstling lambs to the Lord of archery. The bird he missed—Apollo grudged him that—but struck the cord beside its foot, where the bird was tied, and the keen dart cut the cord clean away. Then the bird shot up toward heaven, and the cord hung loose toward earth; and the Achaians shouted. Then Meriones made haste and took from Teukros' hand the bow;—an arrow he had ready, while the other aimed—and vowed withal to far-darting Apollo a famous hecatomb of firstling lambs. High up under the clouds he saw the pigeon; there, as she circled round, he struck her in the midst beneath her wing, and right through her went the dart, and fell back and fixed itself in the ground before Meriones' foot; but the bird lighting on the mast of the dark-prowed ship hung down her neck, and her feathered pinions drooped. And quickly life fled from her limbs, and she fell far down from the mast; and the folk looked on and marvelled. And Meriones took up all the ten double axes, and Teukros bare the single to the hollow ships.]

Then Peleus' son brought and set in the ring a far-shadowing spear and a caldron that knew not the fire, an ox's worth, embossed with flowers; and men that were casters of the javelin arose up. There rose Atreus' son wide-ruling Agamemnon, and Meriones, Idomeneus' brave squire. And swift-footed noble Achilles spake among them: "Son of Atreus, for that we know how far thou excellest all, and how far the first thou art in the might of thy throw, take thou this prize with thee to the hollow ships, and to the hero Meriones let us give the spear, if thou art willing in thy heart: thus I at least advise."

Thus spake he, nor disregarded him Agamemnon king of men. So to Meriones he gave the spear of bronze, but to the herald Talthybios the hero gave the goodliest prize.

BOOK XXIV

How the body of Hector was ransomed, and of his funeral.

THEN the assembly was broken up, and the tribes were scattered to betake them each to their own swift ships. The rest bethought them of supper and sweet sleep to have joy thereof; but Achilles wept, remembering his dear comrade, nor did sleep that conquereth all take hold on him; but he kept turning him to this side and to that, yearning for Patroklos' manhood and excellent valour, and all the toils he achieved with him and the woes he bare, cleaving the battles of men and the grievous waves. As he thought thereon he shed big tears, now lying on his side, now on his back, now on his face; and then anon he would arise upon his feet and roam wildly beside the beach of the salt sea. Nor would he be unaware of the Dawn when she arose over the sea and shores. But when he had yoked the swift steeds to his car he would bind Hector behind his chariot to drag him withal; and having thrice drawn him round the barrow of the dead son of Menoitios he rested again in his hut, and left Hector lying stretched on his face in the dust. But Apollo kept away all defacement from his flesh, for he had pity on him even in death, and covered him all with his golden aegis, that Achilles might not tear him when he dragged him.

Thus Achilles in his anger entreated noble Hector shamefully; but the blessed gods when they beheld him pitied him, and urged the clear-sighted slayer of Argus to steal the corpse away. So to all the others seemed it good, yet not to Hera or Poseidon or the bright-eyed Maiden, but they continued as when at the beginning sacred Ilios became hateful to them, and Priam and his people, by reason of the sin of Alexandros in that he contemned those goddesses when they came to his steading, and preferred her who brought him deadly lustfulness. But when the twelfth morn from that day arose, then spake among the Immortals Phoebus Apollo: "Hard of heart are ye, O gods, and cruel. Hath Hector never burnt for you thigh-bones of unblemished bulls and goats? Now have ye not taken heart to rescue even his corpse for his wife to look upon and his mother and his child and his father Priam and his people, who speedily would burn him in the fire and make his funeral. But fell Achilles, O gods, ye are fain to abet, whose mind is nowise just nor the purpose in his breast to be turned away, but he is cruelly minded as a lion that in great strength and at the bidding of his proud heart goeth forth against men's flocks to make his meal; even thus Achilles hath cast out pity, neither hath he shame, that doth both harm and profit men greatly. It must be that many a man lose even some dearer one than was this, a brother of the same womb born or perchance a son; yet bringeth he his wailing and lamentation to an end, for an enduring soul have the Fates given unto men. But Achilles after bereaving noble Hector of his life bindeth him behind his horses and draggeth him around the tomb of his dear comrade: not, verily, is that more honourable or better for him. Let him take heed lest we wax wroth with him, good man though he be, for in his fury he is entreating shamefully the senseless clay."

Then in anger spake unto him white-armed Hera: "Even thus mightest thou speak, O Lord of the silver bow, if ye are to give equal honour to Achilles and to Hector. Hector is but a mortal and was suckled at a woman's breast, but Achilles is child of a goddess whom I myself bred up and reared and gave to a man to be his wife, even to Peleus who was dearest of all men to the Immortals' heart. And all ye gods came to her bridal, and thou among them wert feasting with thy lyre, O lover of ill company, faithless ever."

Then to her in answer spake Zeus who gathereth the clouds: "Hera, be not wroth utterly with the gods: for these men's honour is not to be the same, yet Hector also was dearest to the gods of all mortals that are in Ilios. So was he to me at least, for nowise failed he in the gifts I loved. Never did my altar lack seemly feast, drink-offering and the steam of sacrifice, even the honour that falleth to our due. But verily we will say no more of stealing away brave Hector, for it cannot be hidden from Achilles, for his mother abideth ever nigh to him night and day. But I were fain that some one of the gods would call Thetis to come near to me, that I may speak unto her a wise word, so that Achilles may take gifts from Priam and give Hector back."

Thus spake he, and airy-footed Iris sped forth upon the errand and between Samothrace and rocky Imbros leapt into the black sea, and the waters closed above her with a noise. And she sped to the bottom like a weight of lead that mounted on horn of a field-ox goeth down bearing death to ravenous fishes. And she found Thetis in a hollow cave; about her sat gathered other goddesses of the sea, and she in their midst was wailing for the fate of her noble son who must perish in deep-soiled Troy, far from his native land. And standing near, fleet-footed Iris spake to her: "Rise, Thetis; Zeus of immortal counsels calleth thee."

And to her made answer Thetis the silver-footed goddess: "Wherefore biddeth me that mighty god? I shrink from mingling among the Immortals, for I have countless woes at heart. Yet go I, nor shall his word be in vain, whatsoever he saith."

Thus having said the noble goddess took to her a dark-hued robe, no blacker raiment was there found than that. Then she went forth, and wind-footed swift Iris led the way before her, and around them the surge of the sea was sundered. And when they had come forth upon the shore they sped up to heaven, and found the far-seeing son of Kronos, and round him sat gathered all the other blessed gods that are for ever. Then she sat down beside father Zeus, and Athene gave her place. And Hera set a fair golden cup in her hand and cheered her with words, and Thetis drank, and gave back the cup. Then began speech to them the father of gods and men: "Thou art come to Olympus, divine Thetis, in thy sorrow, with violent grief at thy heart; I know it of myself. Nevertheless will I tell thee wherefore I called thee hither. Nine days hath dispute arisen among the Immortals concerning the corpse of Hector and Achilles waster of cities. Fain are they to send clear-sighted Argeïphontes to steal the body away, but now hear what glory I accord herein to Achilles, that I may keep through times to come thy honour and good will. Go with all speed to the host and bear to thy son my bidding. Say to him that the gods are displeased at him, and that I above all Immortals am wroth, because with furious heart he holdeth Hector at the beaked ships and hath not given him back, if haply he may fear me and give Hector back. But I will send Iris to great-hearted Priam to bid him go to the ships of the Achaians to ransom his dear son, and carry gifts to Achilles that may gladden his heart."

Thus spake he, and Thetis the silver-footed goddess was not disobedient to his word, and sped darting upon her way down from the peaks of Olympus. And she came to her son's hut; there found she him making grievous moan, and his dear comrades round were swiftly making ready and furnishing their early meal, and a sheep great and fleecy was being sacrificed in the hut. Then his lady-mother sate her down close beside him, and stroked him with her hand and spake to him by his name: "My child, how long with lamentation and woe wilt thou devour thine heart, taking thought of neither food nor rest? good were even a woman's embrace, for not long shalt thou be left alive to me; already death and forceful fate are standing nigh thee. But hearken forthwith unto me, for I am the messenger of Zeus to thee. He saith that the gods are displeased at thee, and that himself above all Immortals is wroth, because with furious heart thou holdest Hector at the beaked ships and hast not given him back. But come restore him, and take ransom for the dead."

Then to her in answer spake fleet-footed Achilles: "So be it: whoso bringeth ransom let him take back the dead, if verily with heart's intent the Olympian biddeth it himself."

So they in the assembly of the ships, mother and son, spake to each other many winged words. But the son of Kronos thus bade Iris go to holy Ilios: "Go forth, fleet Iris, leave the abode of Olympus and bear my message within Ilios to great-hearted Priam that he go to the ships of the Achaians and ransom his dear son and carry gifts to Achilles that may gladden his heart; let him go alone, and no other man of the Trojans go with him. Only let some elder herald attend on him to guide the mules and smooth-wheeled waggon and carry back to the city the dead man whom noble Achilles slew. Let not death be in his thought nor any fear; such guide will we give unto him, even the slayer of Argus, who shall lead him until his leading bring him to Achilles. And when he shall have led him within the hut, neither shall Achilles himself slay him nor suffer any other herein, for not senseless is he or unforeseeing or wicked, but with all courtesy he will spare a suppliant man."

Thus spake he, and airy-footed Iris sped forth upon the errand. And she came to the house of Priam, and found therein crying and moan. His children sitting around their father within the court were bedewing their raiment with their tears, and the old man in their midst was close wrapped all over in his cloak; and on his head and neck was much mire that he had gathered in his hands as he grovelled upon the earth. And his daughters and his sons' wives were wailing throughout the house, bethinking them of all those valiant men who had lost their lives at the hands of the Argives and were lying low. And the messenger of Zeus stood beside Priam and spake softly unto him, and trembling came upon his limbs: "Be of good cheer in thy heart, O Priam son of Dardanos, and be not dismayed for anything, for no evil come I hither to forebode to thee, but with good will. I am the messenger of Zeus to thee, who, though he be afar off, hath great care and pity for thee. The Olympian biddeth thee ransom noble Hector and carry gifts to Achilles that may gladden his heart: go thou alone, let none other of the Trojans go with thee. Only let some elder herald attend on thee to guide the mules and the smooth-wheeled waggon to carry back to the city the dead man whom noble Achilles slew. Let not death be in thy thought, nor any fear; such guide shall go with thee, even the slayer of Argus, who shall lead thee until his leading bring thee to Achilles. And when he shall have led thee into the hut, neither shall Achilles himself slay thee nor suffer any other herein, for not senseless is he or unforeseeing or wicked, but with all courtesy he will spare a suppliant man."

Thus having spoken fleet Iris departed from him; and he bade his sons make ready the smooth-wheeled mule waggon, and bind the wicker carriage thereon. And himself he went down to his fragrant chamber, of cedar wood, high-roofed, that held full many jewels: and to Hekabe his wife he called and spake: "Lady, from Zeus hath an Olympian messenger come to me, that I go to the ships of the Achaians and ransom my dear son, and carry gifts to Achilles that may gladden his heart. Come tell me how seemeth it to thy mind, for of myself at least my desire and heart bid me mightily to go thither to the ships and enter the wide camp of the Achaians."

Thus spake he, but his wife lamented aloud and made

answer unto him: "Woe is me, whither is gone thy mind whereby aforetime thou wert famous among stranger men and among them thou rulest? How art thou fain to go alone to the ships of the Achaians, to meet the eyes of the man who hath slain full many of thy brave sons? of iron verily is thy heart. For if he light on thee and behold thee with his eyes, a savage and ill-trusted man is this, and he will not pity thee, neither reverence thee at all. Nay, now let us sit in the hall and make lament afar off. Even thus did forceful Fate erst spin for Hector with her thread at his beginning, when I bare him, even I that he should glut fleet-footed dogs, far from his parents, in the dwelling of a violent man whose inmost vitals I were fain to fasten and feed upon; then would his deeds against my son be paid again to him, for not playing the coward was he slain of him, but championing the men and deep-bosomed women of Troy, neither bethought he him of shelter or of flight."

Then to her in answer spake the old man godlike Priam: "Stay me not, for I am fain to go, neither be thyself a bird of ill boding in my halls, for thou wilt not change my mind. Were it some other and a child of earth that bade me this, whether some seer or of the priests that divine from sacrifice, then would we declare it false and have no part therein; but now, since I have heard the voice of the goddess myself and looked upon her face, I will go forth, and her word shall not be void. And if it be my fate to die by the ships of the mail-clad Achaians, so would I have it; let Achilles slay me with all speed, when once I have taken in my arms my son, and have satisfied my desire with moan."

He spake, and opened fair lids of chests wherefrom he chose twelve very goodly women's robes and twelve cloaks of single fold and of coverlets a like number and of fair sheets, and of doublets thereupon. And he weighed and brought forth talents of gold ten in all, and two shining tripods and four caldrons, and a goblet exceeding fair that men of Thrace had given him when he went thither on an embassy, a chattel of great price, yet not that even did the old man grudge from his halls, for he was exceeding fain at heart to ransom his dear son. Then he drave out all the Trojans from the colonnade, chiding them with words of rebuke: "Begone, ye that dishonour and do me shame! Have ye no mourning of your own at home that ye come to vex me here? Think ye it a small thing that Zeus Kronos' son hath given me this sorrow, to lose him that was the best man of my sons? Nay, but ye too shall feel it, for easier far shall ye be to the Achaians to slay now he is dead. But for me, ere I behold with mine eyes the city sacked and wasted, let me go down into the house of Hades."

He said, and with his staff chased forth the men, and they went forth before the old man in his haste. Then he called unto his sons, chiding Helenos and Paris and noble Agathon and Pammon and Antiphonos, and Polites of the loud war-cry, and Deiphobos and Hippothoos and proud Dios; nine were they whom the old man called and bade unto him: "Haste ye, ill sons, my shame; would that ye all in Hector's stead had been slain at the swift ships! Woe is me all unblest, since I begat sons the best men in wide Troy-land, but none of them is left for me to claim, neither godlike Mestor, nor Troilos with his chariot of war, nor Hector who was a god among men, neither seemed he as the son of a mortal man but of a god:—all these hath Ares slain, and here are my shames all left to me, false-tongued, light-heeled, the heroes of the dance, plunderers of your own people's sheep and kids. Will ye not make me ready a wain with all speed, and lay all these thereon, that we get us forward on our way?"

Thus spake he, and they fearing their father's voice brought forth the smooth-running mule chariot, fair and new, and bound the body thereof on the frame; and from its peg they took down the mule yoke, a boxwood yoke with knob well fitted with guiding-rings; and they brought forth the yoke-band of nine cubits with the yoke. The yoke they set firmly on the polished pole on the rest at the end thereof, and slipped the ring over the upright pin, which with three turns of the band they lashed to the knob, and then belayed it close round the pole and turned the tongue thereunder. Then they brought from the chamber and heaped on the polished wain the countless ransom of Hector's head, and yoked strong-hooved harness mules, which on a time the Mysians gave to Priam, a splendid gift. But to Priam's car they yoked the horses that the old man kept for his use and reared at the polished crib.

Thus in the high palace were Priam and the herald letting yoke their cars, with wise thoughts at their hearts, when nigh them came Hekabe sore at heart, with honey-sweet wine in her right hand in a golden cup that they might make libation ere they went. And she stood before the horses and spake a word to Priam by name: "Lo now make libation to father Zeus and pray that thou mayest come back home from among the enemy, since thy heart speedeth thee forth to the ships, though fain were I thou wentest not. And next pray to Kronion of the Storm-cloud, the god of Ida, that beholdeth all Troy-land beneath, and ask of him a bird of omen, even the swift messenger that is dearest of all birds to him and of mightiest strength, to appear upon thy right, that seeing the sign with thine own eyes thou mayest go in trust thereto unto the ships of the fleet-horsed Danaans. But if far-seeing Zeus shall not grant unto thee his messenger, I at least shall not bid thee on to go among the ships of the Achaians how fain soever thou mayest be."

Then answered and spake unto her godlike Priam: "Lady, I will not disregard this hest of thine, for good it is to lift up hands to Zeus, if haply he will have pity."

Thus spake the old man, and bade a house-dame that served him pour pure water on his hands; and she came near to serve him with water in a ewer to wash withal. And when he had washed his hands he took a goblet from his wife: then he stood in the midst of the court and prayed and poured forth wine as he looked up to heaven, and spake a word aloud: "Father Zeus that bearest sway from Ida, most glorious and most great, grant that I find welcome and pity under Achilles' roof, and send a bird of omen, even the swift messenger that is dearest of all birds to thee and of mightiest strength, to appear upon the right, that seeing this sign with mine own eyes I may go trusting therein unto the ships of the fleet-horsed Danaans."

Thus spake he praying, and Zeus of wise counsels hearkened unto him, and straightway sent forth an eagle, surest omen of winged birds, the dusky hunter called of men the Black Eagle. Wide as the door, well locking, fitted close, of some rich man's high-roofed hall, so wide were his wings either way; and he appeared to them speeding on the right hand above the city. And when they saw the eagle they rejoiced and all their hearts were glad within their breasts.

Then the old man made haste to go up into his car, and drave forth from the doorway and the echoing portico. In front the mules drew the four-wheeled wain, and wise Idaios drave them; behind came the horses which the old man urged with the lash at speed along the city: and his friends all followed lamenting loud as though he were faring to his death. And when they were come down from the city and were now on the plain, then went back again to Ilios his sons and marriage kin. But the two coming forth upon the plain were not unbeheld of far-seeing Zeus. But he looked upon the old man and had compassion on him, and straightway spake unto Hermes his dear son: "Hermes, since unto thee especially is it dear to companion men, and thou hearest whomsoever thou wilt, go forth and so guide Priam to the hollow ships of the Achaians that no man behold or be aware of him, among all the Danaans' host, until he come to the son of Peleus."

Thus spake he, and the Messenger, the slayer of Argus, was not disobedient unto his word. Straightway beneath his feet he bound on his fair sandals, golden, divine, that bare him over the wet sea and over the boundless land with the breathings of the wind. And he took up his wand wherewith he entranceth the eyes of such men as he will, and others he likewise waketh out of sleep: this did the strong slayer of Argus take in his hand, and flew. And quickly came he to Troy-land and the Hellespont, and went on his way in semblance as a young man that is a prince, with the new down on his chin, as when the youth of men is the comeliest.

Now the others, when they had driven beyond the great barrow of Ilios, halted the mules and horses at the river to drink; for darkness was come down over the earth. Then the herald beheld Hermes from hard by, and marked him, and spake and said to Priam: "Consider, son of Dardanos; this is matter of prudent thought. I see a man, methinks we shall full soon be rent in pieces. Come, let us flee in our chariot, or else at least touch his knees and entreat him that he have mercy on us."

Thus spake he, and the old man was confounded, and he was dismayed exceedingly, and the hair on his pliant limbs stood up, and he stood still amazed. But the Helper came nigh of himself and took the old man's hand, and spake and questioned him: "Whither, father, dost thou thus guide these horses and mules through the divine night, when other mortals are asleep? Hadst thou no fear of the fierce-breathing Achaians, thy bitter foes that are hard anigh thee? If one of them should espy thee carrying such treasures through the swift black night, what then would be thy thought? Neither art thou young thyself, and thy companion here is old, that ye should make defence against a man that should assail thee first. But I will nowise harm thee, yea I will keep any other from thy hurt: for the similitude of my dear father I see in thee."

And to him in answer spake the old man, godlike Priam: "Even so, kind son, are all these things as thou sayest. Nevertheless hath some god stretched forth his hand even over me in that he hath sent a wayfarer such as thou to meet me, a bearer of good luck, by the nobleness of thy form and semblance; and thou art wise of heart and of blessed parents art thou sprung."

And to him again spake the Messenger, the slayer of Argus: "All this, old sire, hast thou verily spoken aright. But come say this and tell me truly whether thou art taking forth a great and goodly treasure unto alien men, where it may abide for thee in safety, or whether by this ye are all forsaking holy Ilios in fear; so far the best man among you hath perished, even thy son; for of battle with the Achaians abated he never a jot."

And to him in answer spake the old man, godlike Priam: "Who art thou, noble sir, and of whom art born? For meetly hast thou spoken of the fate of my hapless son."

And to him again spake the Messenger, the slayer of Argus: "Thou art proving me, old sire, in asking me of noble Hector. Him have I full oft seen with mine eyes in glorious battle, and when at the ships he was slaying the Argives he drave thither, piercing them with the keen bronze, and we stood still and marvelled thereat, for Achilles suffered us not to fight, being wroth against Atreus' son. His squire am I, and came in the same well-wrought ship. From the Myrmidons I come, and my father is Polyktor. Wealthy is he, and an old man even as thou, and six other sons hath he, and I am his seventh. With the others I cast lots, and it fell to me to fare hither with the host. And now am I come from the ships to the plain, for at day-break the glancing-eyed Achaians will set the battle in array around the town. For it chafeth them to be sitting here, nor can the Achaian lords hold in their fury for the fray."

And the old man, godlike Priam, answered him, saying: "If verily thou art a squire of Achilles Peleus' son, come tell me all the truth, whether still my son is by the ships, or whether ere now Achilles hath riven him limb from limb and cast him to the dogs."

Then to him again spake the Messenger the slayer of Argus: "Old sire, not yet have dogs or birds devoured him, but there lieth he still by Achilles' ship, even as he fell, among the huts, and the twelfth morn now hath risen upon him, nor doth his flesh corrupt at all, neither worms consume it, such as devour men slain in war. Truly Achilles draggeth him recklessly around the barrow of his dear comrade so oft as divine day dawneth, yet marreth he him not; thou wouldst marvel if thou couldst go see thyself how dewy fresh he lieth, and is washed clean of blood, nor anywhere defiled; and all his wounds wherewith he was stricken are closed; howbeit many plunged their points in him. So careful are the blessed gods of thy son, though he be but a dead corpse, for they held him dear at heart."

Thus spake he, and the old man rejoiced, and answered him, saying: "My son, it is verily a good thing to give due offerings withal to the Immortals, for never did my child —if that child indeed I had—forget in our halls the gods who inhabit Olympus. Therefore have they remembered this for him, albeit his portion is death. But come now take from me this goodly goblet, and guard me myself and guide me, under Heaven, that I may come unto the hut of Peleus' son."

Then spake unto him again the Messenger the slayer of Argus: "Thou art proving me, old sire, who am younger than thou, but thou wilt not prevail upon me, in that thou biddest me take gifts from thee without Achilles' privity. I were afraid and shamed at heart to defraud him, lest some evil come to pass on me hereafter. But as thy guide I would go even unto famous Argos, accompanying thee courteously in swift ship or on foot. Not from scorn of thy guide would any assail thee then."

Thus spake the Helper, and leaping on the chariot behind the horses he swiftly took lash and reins into his hands, and breathed brave spirit into horses and mules. But when they were come to the towers and trench of the ships, there were the sentinels just busying them about their supper. Then the Messenger, the slayer of Argus, shed sleep upon them all, and straightway opened the gates and thrust back the bars, and brought within Priam and the splendid gifts upon his wain. And they came to the lofty hut of the son of Peleus, which the Myrmidons made for their king and hewed therefor timber of the pine, and thatched it with downy thatching-rush that they mowed in the meadows, and around it made for him their lord a great court with close-set palisades; and the door was barred by a single bolt of pine that three Achaians wont to drive home, and three drew back that mighty bar—three of the rest, but Achilles by himself would drive it home. Then opened the Helper Hermes the door for the old man, and brought in the splendid gifts for Peleus' fleet-footed son, and descended from the chariot to the earth and spake aloud: "Old sire, I that have come to thee am an immortal god, even Hermes, for my father sent me to companion thee on thy way. But now will I depart from thee nor come within Achilles' sight; it were cause of wrath that an immortal god should thus show favour openly unto mortals. But thou go in and clasp the knees of Peleus' son and entreat him for his father's sake and his mother's of the lovely hair and for his child's sake that thou mayest move his soul."

Thus Hermes spake, and departed unto high Olympus. But Priam leapt from the car to the earth, and left Idaios in his place; he stayed to mind the horses and mules; but the old man made straight for the house where Achilles dear to Zeus was wont to sit. And therein he found the man himself, and his comrades sate apart: two only, the hero Automedon and Alkimos, of the stock of Ares, were busy in attendance; and he was lately ceased from meat, even from eating and drinking: and still the table stood beside him. But they were unaware of great Priam as he came in, and so stood he anigh and clasped in his hands the knees of Achilles, and kissed his hands, terrible, man-slaying, that slew many of Priam's sons. And as when a grievous curse cometh upon a man who in his own country hath slain another and escapeth to a land of strangers, to the house of some rich man, and wonder possesseth them that look on him—so Achilles wondered when he saw godlike Priam, and the rest wondered likewise, and looked upon one another. Then Priam spake and entreated him, saying: "Bethink thee, O Achilles like to gods, of thy father that is of like years with me, on the grievous pathway of old age. Him haply are the dwellers round about entreating evilly, nor is there any to ward from him ruin and bane. Nevertheless while he heareth of thee as yet alive he rejoiceth in his heart, and hopeth withal day after day that he shall see his dear son returning from Troy-land. But I, I am utterly unblest, since I begat sons the best men in wide Troy-land, but declare unto thee that none of them is left. Fifty I had, when the sons of the Achaians came; nineteen were born to me of one mother, and concubines bare the rest within my halls. Now of the more part had impetuous Ares unstrung the knees, and he who was yet left and guarded city and men, him slewest thou but now as he fought for his country, even Hector. For his sake come I unto the ships of the Achaians that I may win him back from thee, and I bring with me untold ransom. Yea, fear thou the gods, Achilles, and have compassion on me, even me, bethinking thee of thy father. Lo, I am yet more piteous than he, and have braved what none other man on earth hath braved before, to stretch forth my hand toward the face of the slayer of my sons."

Thus spake he, and stirred within Achilles desire to make lament for his father. And he touched the old man's hand and gently moved him back. And as they both bethought them of their dead, so Priam for man-slaying Hector wept sore as he was fallen before Achilles' feet, and Achilles wept for his own father, and now again for Patroklos, and their moan went up throughout the house. But when noble Achilles had satisfied him with lament, and the desire thereof departed from his heart and limbs, straightway he sprang from his seat and raised the old man by his hand, pitying his hoary head and hoary beard, and spake unto him winged words and said: "Ah hapless! many ill things verily thou hast endured in thy heart. How durst thou come alone to the ships of the Achaians and to meet the eyes of the man who hath slain full many of thy brave sons? of iron verily is thy heart. But come then set thee on a seat, and we will let our sorrows lie quiet in our hearts, for all our pain, for no avail cometh of chill lament. This is the lot the gods have spun for miserable men, that they should live in pain; yet themselves are sorrowless. For two urns stand upon the floor of Zeus filled with his evil gifts, and one with blessings. To whomsoever Zeus whose joy is in the lightning dealeth a mingled lot, that man chanceth now upon ill and now again on good, but to whom he giveth but of the bad kind him he bringeth to scorn, and evil famine chaseth him over the goodly earth, and he is a wanderer honoured of neither gods nor men. Even thus to Peleus gave the gods splendid gifts from his birth, for he excelled all men in good fortune and wealth, and was king of the Myrmidons, and mortal though he was the gods gave him a goddess to be his bride. Yet even on him God brought evil, seeing that there arose to him no offspring of princely sons in his halls, save that he begat one son to an untimely death. Neither may I tend him as he groweth old, since very far from my country I am dwelling in Troy-land, to vex thee and thy children. And of thee, old sire, we have heard how of old time thou wert happy, even how of all that Lesbos, seat of Makar, boundeth to the north thereof and Phrygia farther up and the vast Hellespont—of all these folk, men say, thou wert the richest in wealth and in sons, but after that the Powers of Heaven brought this bane on thee, ever are battles and man-slayings around thy city. Keep courage, and lament not unabatingly in thy heart. For nothing wilt thou avail by grieving for thy son, neither shalt thou bring him back to life or ever some new evil come upon thee."

Then made answer unto him the old man, godlike Priam: "Bid me not to a seat, O fosterling of Zeus, so long as Hector lieth uncared for at the huts, but straightway give him back that I may behold him with mine eyes; and accept thou the great ransom that we bring. So mayest thou have pleasure thereof, and come unto thy native land, since thou hast spared me from the first."

Then fleet-footed Achilles looked sternly upon him and said: "No longer chafe me, old sire; of myself am I minded to give Hector back to thee, for there came to me a messenger from Zeus, even my mother who bare me, daughter of the Ancient One of the Sea. And I know, O Priam, in my mind, nor am unaware that some god it is that hath guided thee to the swift ships of the Achaians. For no mortal man, even though in prime of youth, would dare to come among the host, for neither could he escape the watch, nor easily thrust back the bolt of our doors. Therefore now stir my heart no more amid my troubles, lest I leave not even thee in peace, old sire, within my hut, albeit thou art my suppliant, and lest I transgress the commandment of Zeus."

Thus spake he, and the old man feared, and obeyed his word. And the son of Peleus leapt like a lion through the door of the house, not alone, for with him went two squires, the hero Automedon and Alkimos, they whom above all his comrades Achilles honoured, save only Patroklos that was dead. They then loosed from under the yoke the horses and mules, and led in the old man's crier-herald and set him on a chair, and from the wain of goodly felloes they took the countless ransom set on Hector's head. But they left two robes and a well-spun doublet, that Achilles might wrap the dead therein when he gave him to be carried home. And he called forth handmaids and bade them wash and anoint him when they had borne him apart, so that Priam should not look upon his son, lest he should not refrain the wrath at his sorrowing heart when he should look upon his son, and lest Achilles' heart be vexed thereat and he slay him and transgress the commandment of Zeus. So when the handmaids had washed the body and anointed it with oil, and had thrown over it a fair robe and a doublet, then Achilles himself lifted it and laid it on a bier, and his comrades with him lifted it onto the polished waggon. Then he groaned aloud and called on his dear comrade by his name: "Patroklos, be not vexed with me if thou hear even in the house of Hades that I have given back noble Hector unto his dear father, for not unworthy is the ransom he hath given me, whereof I will deal to thee again thy rightful share."

Thus spake noble Achilles, and went back into the hut, and sate him down on the cunningly-wrought couch whence he had arisen by the opposite wall, and spake a word to Priam: "Thy son, old sire, is given back as thou wouldest and lieth on a bier, and with the break of day thou shalt see him thyself as thou carriest him. But now bethink we us of supper. For even faired-haired Niobe bethought her of meat, she whose twelve children perished in her halls, six daughters and six lusty sons. The sons Apollo, in his anger against Niobe, slew with arrows from his silver bow, and the daughters archer Artemis, for that Niobe matched herself against fair-cheeked Leto, saying that the goddess bare but twain but herself many children: so they though they were but twain destroyed the others all. Nine days they lay in their blood, nor was there any to bury them, for Kronion turned the folk to stones. Yet on the tenth day the gods of heaven buried them, and she then bethought her of meat, when she was wearied out with weeping tears. And somewhere now among the cliffs, on the lonely mountains, even on Sipylos, where they say are the couching-places of nymphs that dance around Acheloös, there she, albeit a stone, broodeth still over her troubles from the gods. But come let us too, noble father, take thought of meat, and afterward thou shalt mourn over thy dear son as thou carriest him to Ilios; and many tears shall be his due."

Thus spake fleet Achilles, and sprang up, and slew a pure white sheep, and his comrades skinned and made it ready in seemly fashion, and divided it cunningly and pierced it with spits, and roasted it carefully and drew all off. And Automedon took bread and served it on a table in fair baskets, while Achilles dealt out the flesh. And they stretched forth their hands to the good cheer lying ready before them. But when they had put off the desire of meat and drink, then Priam son of Dardanos marvelled at Achilles to see how great he was and how goodly, for he was like a god to look upon. And Achilles marvelled at Priam son of Dardanos, beholding his noble aspect and hearkening to his words. But when they had gazed their fill upon one another, then first spake the old man, godlike Priam, to Achilles: "Now presently give me whereon to lie, fosterling of Zeus, that of sweet sleep also we may now take our fill at rest: for never yet have mine eyes closed beneath their lids since at thy hands my son lost his life, but I continually mourn and brood over countless griefs, grovelling in the courtyard-close amid the mire. Now at last have I tasted bread and poured bright wine down my throat, but till now I had tasted nought."

He said, and Achilles bade his comrades and handmaids to set a bedstead beneath the portico, and to cast thereon fair shining rugs and spread coverlets above and thereon to lay thick mantles to be a clothing over all. And the maids went forth from the inner hall with torches in their hands, and quickly spread two beds in haste. Then with bitter meaning said fleet-footed Achilles unto Priam: "Lie thou without, dear sire, lest there come hither one of the counsellors of the Achaians, such as ever take counsel with me by my side, as custom is. If any of such should behold thee through the swift black night, forthwith he might haply tell it to Agamemnon shepherd of the host, and thus would there be delay in giving back the dead. But come say this to me and tell it true, how many days' space thou art fain to make funeral for noble Hector, so that for so long I may myself abide and may keep back the host."

And the old man, godlike Priam, answered him saying: "If thou art verily willing that I accomplish noble Hector's funeral, by doing as thou sayest, O Achilles, thou wilt do me grace. For thou knowest how we are pent within the city, and wood from the mountain is far to fetch, and the Trojans are much in fear. Nine days will we make moan for him in our halls, and on the tenth we will hold funeral and the folk shall feast, and on the eleventh we will make a barrow over him, and on the twelfth we will do battle if need be."

Then again spake the fleet noble Achilles unto him saying: "All this, O ancient Priam, shall be as thou biddest; for I will hold back the battle even so long a time as thou tellest me."

Thus speaking he clasped the old man's right hand at the wrist, lest he should be anywise afraid at heart. So they in the forepart of the house laid them down, Priam and the herald, with wise thoughts at their hearts, but Achilles slept in a recess of the firm-wrought hut, and beside him lay fair-cheeked Briseis.

Now all other gods and warriors lords of chariots slumbered all night, by soft sleep overcome. But not on the Helper Hermes did sleep take hold as he sought within his heart how he should guide forth king Priam from the ships unespied of the trusty sentinels. And he stood above his head and spake a word to him: "Old sire, no thought then hast thou of any evil, seeing thou yet sleepest among men that are thine enemies, for that Achilles spared thee. Truly now hast thou won back thy dear son, and at great price. But for thy life will thy sons thou hast left behind be offering threefold ransom, if but Agamemnon Atreus' son be aware of thee, and aware be all the Achaians."

Thus spake he, and the old man feared, and roused the herald. And Hermes yoked the horses and mules for them, and himself drave them lightly through the camp, and none was aware of them.

But when they came to the ford of the fair-flowing river, [even eddying Xanthos, begotten of immortal Zeus,] then Hermes departed up to high Olympus, and Morning of the saffron robe spread over all the earth. And they with wail and moan drave the horses to the city, and the mules drew the dead. Nor marked them any man or fair-girdled woman until Kassandra, peer of golden Aphrodite, having gone up upon Pergamos, was aware of her dear father as he stood in the car, and the herald that was crier to the town. Then beheld she him that lay upon the bier behind the mules, and thereat she wailed and cried aloud throughout all the town: "O men and women of Troy, come ye hither and look upon Hector, if ever while he was alive ye rejoiced when he came back from battle, since great joy was he to the city and all the folk."

Thus spake she, nor was man or woman left within the city, for upon all came unendurable grief. And near the gates they met Priam bringing home the dead. First bewailed him his dear wife and lady mother, as they cast them on the fair-wheeled wain and touched his head; and around them stood the throng and wept. So all day long unto the setting of the sun they had lamented Hector in tears without the gate, had not the old man spoken from the car among the folk: "Give me place for the mules to pass through; hereafter ye shall have your fill of wailing, when I have brought him unto his home."

Thus spake he, and they parted asunder and gave place to the wain. And the others when they had brought him to the famous house, laid him on a fretted bed, and set beside him minstrels leaders of the dirge, who wailed a mournful lay, while the women made moan with them. And among the women white-armed Andromache led the lamentation, while in her hands she held the head of Hector slayer of men: "Husband, thou art gone young from life, and leavest me a widow in thy halls. And the child is yet but a little one, child of ill-fated parents, thee and me; nor methinks shall he grow up to manhood, for ere then shall this city be utterly destroyed. For thou art verily perished who didst watch over it, who guardedst it and keptest safe its noble wives and infant little ones. These soon shall be voyaging in the hollow ships, yea and I too with them, and thou, my child, shalt either go with me unto a place where thou shalt toil at unseemly tasks, labouring before the face of some harsh lord, or else some Achaian will take thee by the arm and hurl thee from the battlement, a grievous death, for that he is wroth because Hector slew his brother or father or son, since full many of the Achaians at Hector's hands have bitten the firm earth. For no light hand had thy father in the grievous fray. Therefore the folk lament him throughout the city, and woe unspeakable and mourning hast thou left to thy parents, Hector, but with me chiefliest shall grievous pain abide. For neither didst thou stretch thy hands to me from a bed in thy death, neither didst speak to me some memorable word that I might have thought on evermore as my tears fall night and day."

Thus spake she wailing, and the women joined their moan. And among them Hekabe again led the loud lament: "Hector, of all my children far dearest to my heart, verily while thou wert alive dear wert thou to the gods, and even in thy doom of death have they had care for thee. For other sons of mine whom he took captive would fleet Achilles sell beyond the unvintaged sea unto Samos and Imbros and smoking Lemnos, but when with keen-edged bronze he had bereft thee of thy life he was fain to drag thee oft around the tomb of his comrade, even Patroklos whom thou slewest, yet might he not raise him up thereby. But now all dewy and fresh thou liest in our halls, like one on whom Apollo, lord of the silver bow, hath descended and slain him with his gentle darts."

Thus spake she wailing, and stirred unending moan. Then thirdly Helen led their sore lament: "Hector, of all my brethren of Troy far dearest to my heart! Truly my lord is godlike Alexandros who brought me to Troy-land—would I had died ere then. For this is now the twentieth year since I went thence and am gone from my own native land, but never yet heard I evil or despiteful word from thee; nay, if any other haply upbraided me in the palace-halls, whether brother or sister of thine or brother's fair-robed wife, or thy mother—but thy father is ever kind to me as he were my own—then wouldst thou soothe such with words and refrain them, by the gentleness of thy spirit and by thy gentle words. Therefore bewail I thee with pain at heart, and my hapless self with thee, for no more is any left in wide Troy-land to be my friend and kind to me, but all men shudder at me."

Thus spake she wailing, and therewith the great multitude of the people groaned. But the old man Priam spake a word among the folk: "Bring wood, men of Troy, unto the city, and be not anywise afraid at heart of a crafty ambush of the Achaians; for this message Achilles gave me when he sent me from the black ships, that they should do us no hurt until the twelft morn arise."

Thus spake he, and they yoked oxen and mules to wains, and quickly then they flocked before the city. So nine days they gathered great store of wood. But when the tenth morn rose with light for men, then bare they forth brave Hector, weeping tears, and on a lofty pyre they laid the dead man, and thereon cast fire.

But when the daughter of Dawn, rosy-fingered Morning, shone forth, then gathered the folk around glorious Hector's pyre. First quenched they with bright wine all the burning, so far as the fire's strength went, and then his brethren and comrades gathered his white bones lamenting, and big tears flowed down their cheeks. And the bones they took and laid in a golden urn, shrouding them in soft purple robes, and straightway laid the urn in a hollow grave and piled thereon great close-set stones, and heaped with speed a barrow, while watchers were set everywhere around, lest the well-greaved Achaians should make onset before the time. And when they had heaped the barrow they went back, and gathered them together and feasted right well in noble feast at the palace of Priam, Zeus-fostered king.

Thus held they funeral for Hector tamer of horses.

Above the din of slayers and of slain
  And diapason of the war-god's cry;
  Behind the dazzle and stress of chivalry
And glow meridian of the Ilian plain,
The finer ear discerned a secret strain,
  A vision pierced to the diviner eye;
  The far-off echo of a woman's sigh,
Weakness made perfect unto strength in pain.
  Before the throne of great Achilles see
    The broken king kissing the deadly hands
      Whereby his house is left him desolate;
      And in the shadow of the Skaian gate,
    Her babe foredoomed upon her bosom, stands
  Smiling amid her tears, Andromache.

W. L.

THE ODYSSEY

PREFACE

THERE would have been less controversy about the proper method of Homeric translation, if critics had recognised that the question is a purely relative one, that of Homer there can be no final translation. The taste and the literary habits of each age demand different qualities in poetry, and therefore a different sort of rendering of Homer. To the men of the time of Elizabeth, Homer would have appeared bald, it seems, and lacking in ingenuity, if he had been presented in his antique simplicity. For the Elizabethan age, Chapman supplied what was then necessary, and the mannerisms that were then deemed of the essence of poetry, namely, daring and luxurious conceits. Thus in Chapman's verse Troy must 'shed her towers for tears of overthrow,' and when the winds toss Odysseus about, their sport must be called 'the horrid tennis.'

In the age of Anne, 'dignity' and 'correctness' had to be given to Homer, and Pope gave them by aid of his dazzling rhetoric, his antitheses, his *netteté*, his command of every conventional and favourite artifice. Without Chapman's conceits, Homer's poems would hardly have been what the Elizabethans took for poetry; without Pope's smoothness, and Pope's points, the *Iliad* and *Odyssey* would have seemed tame, rude, and harsh in the age of Anne. These great translations must always live as English poems. As transcripts of Homer they are like pictures drawn from a lost point of view. *Chaque siècle depuis le xvi*[e] *a eu de ce côté son belvéder différent.* Again, when Europe woke to a sense, an almost exaggerated and certainly uncritical sense, of the value of her songs of the people, of all the ballads that Herder, Scott, Lönnrot, and the rest collected, it was commonly said that Homer was a ballad-minstrel, that the translator must imitate the simplicity, and even adopt the formulæ of the ballad. Hence came the renderings of Maginn, the experiments of Mr. Gladstone, and others. There was some excuse for the error of critics who asked for a Homer in ballad rhyme. The Epic poet, the poet of gods and heroes, did indeed inherit some of the formulæ of the earlier *Volks-lied*. Homer, like the author of *The Song of Roland*, like the singers of the *Kalevala*, uses constantly recurring epithets, and repeats, word for word, certain emphatic passages, messages, and so on. That custom is essential in the ballad, it is an accident not the essence of the epic. The epic is a poem of complete and elaborate art, but it still bears some birth-marks, some signs of the early popular chant, out of which it sprung, as the garden-rose springs from the wild stock. When this is recognised the demand for ballad-like simplicity and 'ballad-slang' ceases to exist, and then all Homeric translations in the ballad manner cease to represent our conception of Homer. After the belief in the ballad manner follows the recognition of the romantic vein in Homer, and, as a result, came Mr. Worsley's admirable Odyssey. This masterly translation does all that can be done for the Odyssey in the romantic style. The smoothness of the verse, the wonderful closeness to the original, reproduce all of Homer, in music and in meaning, that can be rendered in English verse. There still, however, seems an aspect of the Homeric poems, and a demand in connection with Homer to be recognised, and to be satisfied.

Sainte-Beuve says, with reference probably to M. Leconte de Lisle's prose version of the epics, that some people treat the epics too much as if they were sagas. Now the Homeric epics are sagas, but then they are the sagas of the divine heroic age of Greece, and thus are told with an art which is not the art of the Northern poets. The epics are stories about the adventures of men living in most respects like the men of our own race who dwelt in Iceland, Norway, Denmark, and Sweden. The epics are, in a way, and as as far as manners and institutions are concerned, historical documents. Whoever regards them in this way, must wish to read them exactly as they have reached us, without modern ornament, with nothing added or omitted. He must recognise, with Mr. Matthew Arnold, that what he now wants, namely, the simple truth about the matter of the poem, can only be given in prose, 'for in a verse translation no original work is any longer recognisable.' It is for this reason that we have attempted to tell once more, in simple prose, the story of Odysseus. We have tried to transfer, not all the truth about the poem, but the historical truth, into English. In this process Homer must lose at least half his charm, his bright and equable speed, the musical current of that narrative, which, like the river of Egypt, flows from an indiscoverable source, and mirrors the temples and the palaces of unforgotten gods and kings. Without this music of verse, only a half truth about Homer can be told, but then it is that half of the truth which, at this moment, it seems most necessary to tell. This is the half of the truth that the translators who use verse cannot easily tell. They *must* be adding to Homer, talking with Pope about 'tracing the mazy lev'ret o'er the lawn,' or with Mr. Worsley about the islands that are 'stars of the blue Ægæan,' or with Dr. Hawtrey about 'the earth's soft arms,' when Homer says nothing at all about the 'mazy lev'ret,' or the 'stars of the blue Aegaean,' or the 'soft arms' of earth. It would be impertinent indeed to blame any of these translations in their place. They give that which the romantic reader of poetry, or the student of the age of Anne, looks for in verse; and without tags of this sort, a translation of Homer in verse cannot well be made to hold together.

There can be then, it appears, no final English translation of Homer. In each there must be, in addition to what is Greek and eternal, the element of what is modern, personal, and fleeting. Thus we trust that there may be room for 'the pale and far-off shadow of a prose translation,' of which the aim is limited and humble. A prose translation cannot give the movement and the fire of a successful translation in verse; it only gathers, as it were, the crumbs which fall from the richer table, only tells the story, without the song. Yet to a prose translation is permitted, perhaps, that close adherence to the archaisms of the epic, which in verse become mere oddities. The double epithets, the recurring epithets of Homer, if rendered into verse, delay and puzzle the reader, as the Greek does not delay nor puzzle him. In prose he may endure them, or even care to study them as the survivals of a stage of taste, which is found in its prime in the sagas. These double and recurring epithets of Homer are a softer form of the quaint Northern periphrases, which make the sea the 'swan's bath,' gold, the 'dragon's hoard,' men, the 'ring-givers,' and so on. We do not know whether it is necessary to defend our choice of a somewhat antiquated prose. Homer has no ideas which cannot be expressed in words that are 'old and plain,' and to words that are old and plain, and, as a rule, to such terms as, being used by the Translators of the Bible, are still not unfamiliar, we have tried to restrict ourselves. It may be objected, that the employment of language which does not come spontaneously to the lips, is an affectation out of place in a version of the Odyssey. To this we may answer that the Greek Epic dialect, like the English of our Bible, was a thing of slow growth and composite nature, that it was never a spoken language, nor, except for certain poetical purposes, a written language. Thus the Biblical English seems as nearly analogous to the Epic Greek, as anything that our tongue has to offer.

We have received much help from many friends, and especially from Mr. R. W. Raper, Fellow of Trinity College, Oxford, and Mr. Gerald Balfour, Fellow of Trinity College, Cambridge, who have aided us with many suggestions while the book was passing through the press.

In the interpretation of B. i. 411, ii. 191, v. 90, and 471, we have departed from the received view, and followed Mr. Raper, who, however, has not been able to read through the proof-sheets further than Book xii.

We have adopted La Roche's text (Homeri Odyssea, J. La Roche, Leipzig, 1867).

The Arguments prefixed to the Books are taken, with very slight alterations, from Hobbes' Translation of the Odyssey.

It is hoped that the Introduction added to the second edition may illustrate the growth of those national legends on which Homer worked, and may elucidate the plot of the Odyssey.

PREFACE TO THE THIRD EDITION

We owe our thanks to the Rev. E. Warre, of Eton College, for certain corrections on nautical points. In particular, he has convinced us that the raft of Odysseus in B. v. is a raft strictly so called, and that it is not, under the poet's description, elaborated into a ship, as has been commonly supposed. The translation of the passage is accordingly altered.

As one that for a weary space has lain
  Lulled by the song of Circe and her wine
  In gardens near the pale of Proserpine,
Where that Ægæan isle forgets the main,
And only the low lutes of love complain,
  And only shadows of wan lovers pine,
  As such an one were glad to know the brine
Salt on his lips, and the large air again,
So gladly, from the songs of modern speech
  Men turn, and see the stars, and feel the free
    Shrill wind beyond the close of heavy flowers
    And through the music of the languid hours
They hear like ocean on a western beach
  The surge and thunder of the Odyssey.

A. L.

INTRODUCTION

Composition and Plot of the Odyssey

The *Odyssey* is generally supposed to be somewhat the later in date of the two most ancient Greek poems which are concerned with the events and consequences of the Trojan war. As to the actual history of that war, it may be said that nothing is known. We may conjecture that some contest between peoples of more or less kindred stocks, who occupied the isles and the eastern and western shores of the Aegean, left a strong impression on the popular fancy. Round the memories of this contest would gather many older legends, myths, and stories, not peculiarly Greek or even 'Aryan,' which previously floated unattached, or were connected with heroes whose fame was swallowed up by that of a newer generation. It would be the work of minstrels, priests, and poets, as the national spirit grew conscious of itself, to shape all these materials into a definite body of tradition. This is the rule of development—first scattered stories, then the union of these into a *national* legend. The growth of later national legends, which we are able to trace, historically, has generally come about in this fashion. To take the best known example, we are able to compare the real history of Charlemagne with the old epic poems on his life and exploits. In these poems we find that facts are strangely exaggerated, and distorted; that purely fanciful additions are made to the true records, that the more striking events of earlier history are crowded into the legend of Charles, that mere fairy tales, current among African as well as European peoples, are transmuted into false history, and that the anonymous characters of fairy tales are converted into historical personages. We can also watch the process by which feigned genealogies were constructed, which connected the princely houses of France with the imaginary heroes of the epics. The conclusion is that the poetical history of Charlemagne has only the faintest relations to the true history. And we are justified in supposing that quite as little of the real history of events can be extracted from the tale of Troy, as from the *Chansons de Geste*.

By the time the *Odyssey* was composed, it is certain that a poet had before him a well-arranged mass of legends and traditions from which he might select his materials. The author of the *Iliad* has an extremely full and curiously consistent knowledge of the local traditions of Greece, the memories which were cherished by Thebans, Pylians, people of Mycenae, of Argos, and so on. Both the *Iliad* and the *Odyssey* assume this knowledge in the hearers of the poems, and take for granted some acquaintance with other legends, as with the story of the Argonautic Expedition. Now that story itself is a tissue of popular tales,—still current in many distant lands,—but all woven by the Greek genius into the history of Iason.

The history of the return of Odysseus as told in the *Odyssey*, is, in the same way, a tissue of old *märchen*. These must have existed for an unknown length of time before they gravitated into the cycle of the tale of Troy.

The extraordinary artistic skill with which legends and myths, originally unconnected with each other, are woven into the plot of the *Odyssey*, so that the marvels of savage and barbaric fancy become indispensable parts of an artistic whole, is one of the chief proofs of the unity of authorship of that poem. We now go on to sketch the plot, which is a marvel of construction.

Odysseus was the King of Ithaca, a small and rugged island on the western coast of Greece. When he was but lately married to Penelope, and while his only son Telemachus was still an infant, the Trojan war began. It is scarcely necessary to say that the object of this war, as conceived by the poets, was to win back Helen, the wife of Menelaus, from Paris, the son of Priam, King of Troy. As Menelaus was the brother of Agamemnon, the Emperor, so to speak, or recognised chief of the petty kingdoms of Greece, the whole force of these kingdoms was at his disposal. No prince came to the leaguer of Troy from a home more remote than that of Odysseus. When Troy was taken, in the tenth year of the war, his homeward voyage was the longest and most perilous.

The action of the *Odyssey* occupies but the last six weeks of the ten years during which Odysseus was wandering. Two nights in these six weeks are taken up, however, by his own narrative of his adventures (to the Phaeacians, p. xx) in the previous ten years. With this explanatory narrative we must begin, before coming to the regular action of the poem.

After the fall of Troy, Odysseus touched at Ismarus, the city of a Thracian people, whom he attacked and plundered, but by whom he was at last repulsed. The north wind then carried his ships to Malea, the extreme southern point of Greece. Had he doubled Malea safely, he would probably have reached Ithaca in a few days, would have found Penelope unvexed by wooers, and Telemachus a boy of ten years old. But this was not to be.

The 'ruinous winds' drove Odysseus and his ships for ten days, and on the tenth they touched the land of the Lotus-Eaters, whose flowery food causes sweet forgetfulness. Lotus-land was possibly in Western Libya, but it is more probable that ten days' voyage from the southern point of Greece brought Odysseus into an unexplored region of fairy-land. Egypt, of which Homer had some knowledge, was but five days' sail from Crete. Lotus-land, therefore, being ten days' sail from Malea, was well over the limit of the discovered world. From this country Odysseus went on till he reached the land of the lawless Cyclôpes, a pastoral people of giants. Later Greece feigned that the Cyclôpes dwelt near Mount Etna, in Sicily. Homer leaves their place of abode in the vague. Among the Cyclôpes, Odysseus had the adventure on which his whole fortunes hinged. He destroyed the eye of the cannibal giant, Polyphemus, a son of Poseidon, the God of the Sea. To avenge this act, Poseidon drove Odysseus wandering for ten long years, and only suffered him to land in Ithaca, 'alone, in evil case, to find troubles in his house.' This is a very remarkable point in the plot. The story of the crafty adventurer and the blinding of the giant, with the cunning device by which the hero escaped, exists in the shape of a detached *märchen* or fairy-tale among races who never heard of Homer. And when we find the story among Oghuzians, Esthonians, Basques, and Celts, it seems natural to suppose that these people did not break a fragment out of the *Odyssey*, but that the author of the *Odyssey* took possession of a legend out of the great traditional store of fiction. From the wide distribution of the tale, there is reason to suppose that it is older than Homer, and that it was not originally told of Odysseus, but was attached to his legend, as floating jests of unknown authorship are attributed to eminent wits. It has been remarked with truth that in this episode Odysseus acts out of character, that he is foolhardy as well as cunning. Yet the author of the *Odyssey*, so far from merely dovetailing this story at random into his narrative, has made his whole plot turn on the injury to the Cyclops. Had he not foolishly exposed himself and his companions, by his visit to the Cyclops, Odysseus would never have been driven wandering for ten weary years. The prayers of the blinded Cyclops were heard and fulfilled by Poseidon.

From the land of the Cyclops, Odysseus and his company sailed to the Isle of Aeolus, the king of the winds. This place too is well undefined; we only learn that, even with the most favourable gale, it was ten days' sail from Ithaca. In the Isle of Aeolus Odysseus abode for a month, and then received from the king a bag in which all the winds were bound, except that which was to waft the hero to his home. This sort of bag was probably not unfamiliar to superstitious Greek sailors who had dealings with witches, like the modern wise women of the Lapps. The companions of the hero opened the bag when Ithaca was in sight, the winds rushed out, the ships were borne back to the Aeolian Isle, and thence the hero was roughly dismissed by Aeolus. Seven days' sail brought him to Lamos, a city of the cannibal Laestrygonians. Their country, too, is in No-man's-land, and nothing can be inferred from the fact that their fountain was called Artacia, and that there was an Artacia in Cyzicus. In Lamos a very important adventure befell Odysseus. The cannibals destroyed all his fleet, save one ship, with which he made his escape to the Isle of Circé. Here the enchantress turned part of the crew into swine, but Odysseus, by aid of the god Hermes, redeemed them, and became the lover of Circé. This adventure, like the story of the Cyclops, is a fairy tale of great antiquity. Dr. Gerland, in his *Alt Griechische Märchen in der Odyssee*, has shown that the story makes part of the collection of Somadeva, a store of Indian tales, of which 1200 A.D. is the approximate date. Circé appears as a Yackshini, and is conquered when an adventurer seizes her flute, whose magic music turns men into beasts. The Indian Circé had the habit of eating the animals into which she transformed men.

We must suppose that the affairs with the Cicones, the Lotus-eaters, the Cyclops, Aeolus, and the Laestrygonians occupied most of the first year after the fall of Troy. A year was then spent in the Isle of Circé, after which the sailors were eager to make for home. Circé commanded them to go down to Hades, to learn the homeward way from the ghost of the Theban prophet Teiresias. The descent into hell, for some similar purpose, is common in the epics of other races, such as the Finns, and the South Sea Islanders. The narrative of Odysseus's visit to the dead (Book xi) is one of the most moving passages in the whole poem.

From Teiresias Odysseus learned that, if he would bring his companions home, he must avoid injuring the sacred cattle of the Sun, which pastured in the Isle of Thrinacia. If these were harmed, he would arrive in Ithaca alone, or in the words of the Cyclops's prayer, 'in evil plight, with loss of all his company, on board the ship of strangers, to find sorrow in his house.' On returning to the Isle Aeaean, Odysseus was warned by Circé of the dangers he would encounter. He and his friends set forth, escaped the Sirens (a sort of mermaidens), evaded the Clashing Rocks, which close on ships (a fable known to the Aztecs), passed Scylla (the *pieuvre* of antiquity) with loss of some of the company, and reached Thrinacia, the Isle of the Sun. Here the company of Odysseus, constrained by hunger, devoured the sacred kine of the Sun, for which offence they were punished by a shipwreck, when all were lost save Odysseus. He floated ten days on a raft, and then reached the isle of the goddess Calypso, who kept him as her lover for eight years.

The first two years after the fall of Troy are now accounted for. They were occupied, as we have seen, by adventures with the Cicones, the Lotus-eaters, the Cyclops, Aeolus, the Laestrygonians, by a year's residence with Circé, by the descent into Hades, the encounters with the Sirens, and Scylla, and the fatal sojourn in the Isle of Thrinacia. We leave Odysseus alone, for eight years, consuming his own heart, in the island paradise of Calypso.

In Ithaca, the hero's home, things seem to have passed smoothly till about the sixth year after the fall of Troy. Then the men of the younger generation, the island chiefs, began to woo Penelope, and to vex her son Telemachus. Laertes, the father of Odysseus, was too old to help, and

Penelope only gained time by her famous device of weaving and unweaving the web. The wooers began to put compulsion on the Queen, quartering themselves upon her, devouring her substance, and insulting her by their relations with her handmaids. Thus Penelope pined at home, amidst her wasting possessions. Telemachus fretted in vain, and Odysseus was devoured by grief and home-sickness in the Isle of Calypso. When he had lain there for nigh eight years, the action of the *Odyssey* begins, and occupies about six weeks.

Day 1 (Book i).

The *ordained* time has now arrived, when by the counsels of the Gods, Odysseus is to be brought home to free his house, to avenge himself on the wooers, and recover his kingdom. The chief agent in his restoration is Pallas Athene; the first book opens with her prayer to Zeus that Odysseus may be delivered. For this purpose Hermes is to be sent to Calypso to bid her release Odysseus, while Pallas Athene in the shape of Mentor, a friend of Odysseus, visits Telemachus in Ithaca. She bids him call an assembly of the people, dismiss the wooers to their homes, and his mother to her father's house, and go in quest of his own father, in Pylos, the city of Nestor, and Sparta, the home of Menelaus. Telemachus recognises the Goddess, and the first day closes.

Day 2 (Book ii).

Telemachus assembles the people, but he has not the heart to carry out Athene's advice. He cannot send the wooers away, or turn his mother out of her house. He rather weakly appeals to the wooers' consciences, and announces his intention of going to seek his father. They answer with scorn, but are warned of their fate, which is even at the doors, by Halitherses. His prophecy (first made when Odysseus set out for Troy) tallies with the prophecy of Teiresias, and the prayer of the Cyclops. The reader will observe a series of portents, prophecies, and omens, which grow more numerous and admonishing as their doom draws nearer to the wooers. Their hearts, however, are hardened, and they mock at Telemachus, who, after an interview with Athene, borrows a ship and secretly sets out for Pylos. Athene accompanies him, and his friends man his galley.

Day 3 (Book iii).

They reach Pylos, and are kindly received by the aged Nestor, who has no news about Odysseus. After sacrifice, Athene disappears.

Day 4 (Book iii).

The fourth day is occupied with sacrifice, and the talk of Nestor. In the evening Telemachus (leaving his ship and friends at Pylos) drives his chariot into Pherae, half-way to Sparta; Peisistratus, the son of Nestor, accompanies him.

Day 5 (Book iv).

Telemachus and Peisistratus arrive at Sparta, where Menelaus and Helen receive them kindly.

Day 6 (Book iv).

Menelaus tells how he himself came home in the eighth year after the fall of Troy. He had heard from Proteus, the Old Man of the Sea, that Odysseus was alive, and a captive on an island of the deep. Menelaus invites Telemachus to stay with him for eleven days or twelve, which Telemachus declines to do. It will later appear that he made an even longer stay at Sparta, though whether he changed his mind, or whether we have here an inadvertence of the poet's, it is hard to determine. This blemish has been used as an argument against the unity of authorship, but writers of all ages have made graver mistakes.

On this same day (the sixth) the wooers in Ithaca learned that Telemachus had really set out to 'cruise after his father.' They sent some of their number to lie in ambush for him, in a certain strait which he was likely to pass on his return to Ithaca. Penelope also heard of her son's departure, but was consoled by a dream.

Day 7 (Book v).

The seventh day finds us again in Olympus. Athene again urges the release of Odysseus, and Hermes is sent to bid Calypso let the hero go. Zeus prophesies that after twenty days' sailing, Odysseus will reach Scheria, and the hospitable Phaeacians, a people akin to the Gods, who will convey him to Ithaca. Hermes accomplishes the message to Calypso.

Days 8-12-32 (Book v).

These days are occupied by Odysseus in making and launching a raft; on the twelfth day from the beginning of the action he leaves Calypso's isle. He sails for eighteen days, and on the eighteenth day of his voyage (the twenty-ninth from the beginning of the action) he sees Scheria. Poseidon raises a storm against him, and it is not till the thirty-second day from that in which Athene visited Telemachus that he lands in Scheria, the country of the Phaeacians. Here he is again in fairy-land. A rough, but perfectly recognisable form of the Phaeacian myth, is found in an Indian collection of *märchen* (already referred to) of the twelfth century A.D. Here the Phaeacians are the Vidyâdhâris, and their old enemies the Cyclôpes are the Rakshashas, a sort of giants. The Indian Odysseus, who seeks the city of gold, passes by the home of an Indian Aeolus, Satyavrata. His later adventures are confused, and the Greek version retains only the more graceful fancies of the *märchen.*

DAY 33 (Book vi).

Odysseus meets Nausicaa, daughter of Alcinous, the Phaeacian King, and by her aid, and that of Athene, is favourably received at the palace, and tells how he came from Calypso's island. His name is still unknown to his hosts.

DAY 34 (Books vii, viii, ix, x, xi, xii).

The Phaeacians and Odysseus display their skill in sports. Nausicaa bids Odysseus farewell. Odysseus recounts to Alcinous, and Arete, the Queen, those adventures in the two years between the fall of Troy and his captivity in the island of Calypso, which we have already described (pp. xiii-xvii).

DAY 35 (Book xiii).

Odysseus is conveyed to Ithaca, in the evening, on one of the magical barques of the Phaeacians.

DAY 36 (Books xiii, xiv, xv).

He wakens in Ithaca, which he does not at first recognise. He learns from Athene, for the first time, that the wooers beset his house. She disguises him as an old man, and bids him go to the hut of the swineherd Eumaeus, who is loyal to his absent lord. Athene then goes to Lacedaemon, to bring back Telemachus, who has now resided there for a month. Odysseus won the heart of Eumaeus, who of course did not recognise him, and slept in the swineherd's hut, while Athene was waking Telemachus, in Lacedaemon, and bidding him 'be mindful of his return.'

DAY 37 (Book xv).

Is spent by Odysseus in the swineherd's hut. Telemachus reaches Pherae, half-way to Pylos.

DAY 38 (Book xv).

Telemachus reaches Pylos, but does not visit Nestor. To save time he goes at once on board ship, taking with him an unfortunate outlaw, Theoclymenus, a second-sighted man, of the family of Melampus, in which the gift of prophecy was hereditary. The ship passed the Elian coast at night, and evaded the ambush of the wooers. Meanwhile Odysseus was sitting up almost till dawn, listening to the history of Eumaeus, the swineherd.

DAY 39 (Books xv, xvi).

Telemachus reaches the Isle of Ithaca, sends his ship to the city, but himself, by advice of Athene, makes for the hut of Eumaeus, where he meets, but naturally does not recognise, his disguised father. He sends Eumaeus to Penelope with news of his arrival, and then Athene reveals Odysseus to Telemachus. The two plot the death of the wooers. Odysseus bids Telemachus remove, on a favourable opportunity, the arms which were disposed as trophies on the walls of the hall at home. (There is a slight discrepancy between the words of this advice and the manner in which it is afterwards executed.) During this interview, the ship of Telemachus, the wooers who had been in ambush, and Eumaeus, all reached the town of Ithaca. In the evening Eumaeus returned to his hut, where Athene had again disguised Odysseus.

DAY 40 (Books xvii, xviii, xix, xx).

The story is now hastening to its close, and many events are crowded into the fortieth day. Telemachus goes from the swineherd's hut to the city, and calls his guest, Theoclymenus, to the palace. The second-sighted man prophesies of the near revenge of Odysseus. In the afternoon, Odysseus (still disguised) and Eumaeus reach the city, the dog Argos recognises the hero, and dies. Odysseus goes begging through his own hall, and is struck by Antinous, the proudest of the wooers. Late in the day Eumaeus goes home, and Odysseus fights with the braggart beggar Irus. Still later, Penelope appears among the wooers, and receives presents from them. When the wooers have withdrawn, Odysseus and Telemachus remove the weapons from the hall to the armoury. Afterwards Odysseus has an interview with Penelope (who does not recognise him), but he is recognised by his old nurse Eurycleia. Penelope mentions her purpose to wed the man who on the following day, the feast of the Archer-god Apollo, shall draw the bow of Odysseus, and send an arrow through the holes in twelve axe-blades, set up in a row. Thus the poet shows that Odysseus has arrived in Ithaca not a day too soon. Odysseus is comforted by a vision of Athene, and

DAY 41 (Books xx, xxi, xxii, xxiii).

by the ominous prayer uttered by a weary woman grinding at the mill. The swineherd and the disloyal Melanthius arrive at the palace. The wooers defer the plot to kill Telemachus, as the day is holy to Apollo. Odysseus is led up from his seat near the door to a place beside Telemachus at the chief's table. The wooers mock Telemachus, and the second-sighted Theoclymenus sees the ominous shroud of death covering their bodies, and the walls dripping with blood. He leaves the doomed company. In the trial of the bow, none of the wooers can draw it; meanwhile Odysseus has declared himself to the neatherd and the swineherd. The former bars and fastens the outer gates of the court, the latter bids Eurycleia bar the doors of the women's chambers which lead out of the hall. Odysseus now gets the bow into his hands, strings it, sends the arrow through the axe-blades, and then leaping on the threshold of stone, deals his shafts among the wooers. Telemachus, the neatherd, and Eumaeus, aiding him, he slaughters all the crew, despite the treachery of Melanthius. The paramours of the wooers are hanged, and Odysseus, after some delay, is recognised by Penelope.

DAY 42 (Books xxiii, xxiv).

This day is occupied with the recognition of Odysseus by his aged father Laertes, and with the futile attempt of the kinsfolk of the wooers to avenge them on Odysseus. Athene reconciles the feud, and the toils of Odysseus are accomplished.

The reader has now before him a chronologically arranged sketch of the action of the *Odyssey*. It is, perhaps, apparent, even from this bare outline, that the composition is elaborate and artistic, that the threads of the plot are skilfully separated and combined. The germ of the whole epic is probably the popular tale, known all over the world, of the warrior who, on his return from a long expedition, has great difficulty in making his prudent wife recognise him. The incident occurs as a detached story in China, and in most European countries it is told of a crusader. We may suppose it to be older than the legend of Troy, and to have gravitated into the cycle of that legend. The years of the hero's absence are then filled up with adventures (the Cyclops, Circé, the Phaeacians, the Sirens, the descent into hell) which exist as scattered tales, or are woven into the more elaborate epics of Gaels, Aztecs, Hindoos, Tartars,

South Sea Islanders, Finns, Russians, Scandinavians, and Eskimo. The whole is surrounded with the atmosphere of the kingly age of Greece, and the result is the *Odyssey*, with that unity of plot and variety of character which must have been given by one masterly constructive genius. The date at which the poet of the *Odyssey* lived may be approximately determined by his consistent descriptions of a peculiar and definite condition of society, which had ceased to exist in the ninth century B.C., and of a stage of art in which Phoenician and Assyrian influences predominated. (*Die Kunst bei Homer*. Brunn.) As to the mode of composition, it would not be difficult to show that at least the *a priori* Wolfian arguments against the early use of writing for literary purposes have no longer the cogency which they were once thought to possess. But this is matter for a separate investigation.

BOOK I

In a Council of the Gods, Poseidon absent, Pallas procureth an order for the restitution of Odysseus; and appearing to his son Telemachus, in human shape, adviseth him to complain of the Wooers before the Council of the people, and then go to Pylos and Sparta to inquire about his father.

TELL me, Muse, of that man, so ready at need, who wandered far and wide, after he had sacked the sacred citadel of Troy, and many were the men whose towns he saw and whose mind he learnt, yea, and many the woes he suffered in his heart upon the deep, striving to win his own life and the return of his company. Nay, but even so he saved not his company, though he desired it sore. For through the blindness of their own hearts they perished, fools, who devoured the oxen of Helios Hyperion: but the god took from them their day of returning. Of these things, goddess, daughter of Zeus, whencesoever thou hast heard thereof, declare thou even unto us.

Now all the rest, as many as fled from sheer destruction, were at home, and had escaped both war and sea, but Odysseus only, craving for his wife and for his homeward path, the lady nymph Calypso held, that fair goddess, in her hollow caves, longing to have him for her lord. But when now the year had come in the courses of the seasons, wherein the gods had ordained that he should return home to Ithaca, not even there was he quit of labours, not even among his own; but all the gods had pity on him save Poseidon, who raged continually against godlike Odysseus, till he came to his own country. Howbeit Poseidon had now departed for the distant Ethiopians, the Ethiopians that are sundered in twain, the uttermost of men, abiding some where Hyperion sinks and some where he rises. There he looked to receive his hecatomb of bulls and dams, there he made merry sitting at the feast, but the other gods were gathered in the halls of Olympian Zeus. Then among them the father of gods and men began to speak, for he bethought him in his heart of noble Aegisthus, whom the son of Agamemnon, far-famed Orestes, slew. Thinking upon him he spake out among the Immortals:

'Lo you now, how vainly mortal men do blame the gods! For of us they say comes evil, whereas they even of themselves, through the blindness of their own hearts, have sorrows beyond that which is ordained. Even as of late Aegisthus, beyond that which was ordained, took to him the wedded wife of the son of Atreus and killed her lord on his return, and that with sheer doom before his eyes, since we had warned him by the embassy of Hermes the keen-sighted, the slayer of Argos, that he should neither kill the man, nor woo his wife. For the son of Atreus shall be avenged at the hand of Orestes, so soon as he shall come to man's estate and long for his own country. So spake Hermes, yet he prevailed not on the heart of Aegisthus, for all his good will; but now hath he paid one price for all.'

And the goddess, grey-eyed Athene, answered him, saying: 'O father, our father Cronides, throned in the highest, that man assuredly lies in a death that is his due; so perish likewise all who work such deeds! But my heart is rent for wise Odysseus, the hapless one, who far from his friends this long while suffereth affliction in a seagirt isle, where is the navel of the sea, a woodland isle, and therein a goddess hath her habitation, the daughter of the wizard Atlas, who knows the depths of every sea, and himself upholds the tall pillars which keep earth and sky asunder. His daughter it is that holds the hapless man in sorrow: and ever with soft and guileful tales she is wooing him to forgetfulness of Ithaca. But Odysseus yearning to see if it were but the smoke leap upwards from his own land, hath a desire to die. As for thee, thine heart regardeth it not at all, Olympian! What! did not Odysseus by the ships of the Argives make thee free offering of sacrifice in the wide Trojan land? Wherefore wast thou then so wroth with him, O Zeus?'

And Zeus the cloud-gatherer answered her, and said: 'My child, what word hath escaped the door of thy lips? Yea, how should I forget divine Odysseus, who in understanding is beyond mortals and beyond all men hath done sacrifice to the deathless gods, who keep the wide heaven? Nay, but it is Poseidon, the girdler of the earth, that hath been wroth continually with quenchless anger for the Cyclops' sake whom he blinded of his eye, even godlike Polyphemus whose power is mightiest amongst all the Cyclôpes. His mother was the nymph Thoösa, daughter of Phorcys, lord of the unharvested sea, and in the hollow caves she lay with Poseidon. From that day forth Poseidon the earth-shaker doth not indeed slay Odysseus, but driveth him wandering from his own country. But come, let us here one and all take good counsel as touching his returning, that he may be got home; so shall Poseidon let go his displeasure, for he will in no wise be able to strive alone against all, in despite of all the deathless gods.'

Then the goddess, grey-eyed Athene, answered him, and said: 'O father, our father Cronides, throned in the highest, if indeed this thing is now well pleasing to the blessed gods, that wise Odysseus should return to his own home, let us then speed Hermes the Messenger, the slayer of Argos, to the island of Ogygia. There with all speed let him declare to the lady of the braided tresses our unerring counsel, even the return of the patient Odysseus, that so he may come to his home. But as for me I will go to Ithaca that I may rouse his son yet the more, planting might in his heart, to call an assembly of the long-haired

Achaeans and speak out to all the wooers who slaughter continually the sheep of his thronging flocks, and his kine with trailing feet and shambling gait. And I will guide him to Sparta and to sandy Pylos to seek tidings of his dear father's return, if peradventure he may hear thereof and that so he may be had in good report among men.'

She spake and bound beneath her feet her lovely golden sandals, that wax not old, and bare her alike over the wet sea and over the limitless land, swift as the breath of the wind. And she seized her doughty spear, shod with sharp bronze, weighty and huge and strong, wherewith she quells the ranks of heroes with whomsoever she is wroth, the daughter of the mighty sire. Then from the heights of Olympus she came glancing down, and she stood in the land of Ithaca, at the entry of the gate of Odysseus, on the threshold of the courtyard, holding in her hand the spear of bronze, in the semblance of a stranger, Mentes the captain of the Taphians. And there she found the lordly wooers: now they were taking their pleasure at draughts in front of the doors, sitting on hides of oxen, which themselves had slain. And of the henchmen and the ready squires, some were mixing for them wine and water in bowls, and some again were washing the tables with porous sponges and were setting them forth, and others were carving flesh in plenty.

And godlike Telemachus was far the first to descry her, for he was sitting with a heavy heart among the wooers dreaming on his good father, if haply he might come somewhence, and make a scattering of the wooers there throughout the palace, and himself get honour and bear rule among his own possessions. Thinking thereupon, as he sat among wooers, he saw Athene—and he went straight to the outer porch, for he thought it blame in his heart that a stranger should stand long at the gates: and halting nigh her he clasped her right hand and took from her the spear of bronze, and uttered his voice and spake unto her winged words:

'Hail, stranger, with us thou shalt be kindly entreated, and thereafter, when thou hast tasted meat, thou shalt tell us that whereof thou hast need.'

Therewith he led the way, and Pallas Athene followed. And when they were now within the lofty house, he set her spear that he bore against a tall pillar, within the polished spear-stand, where stood many spears besides, even those of Odysseus of the hardy heart; and he led the goddess and seated her on a goodly carven chair, and spread a linen cloth thereunder, and beneath was a footstool for the feet. For himself he placed an inlaid seat hard by, apart from the company of the wooers, lest the stranger should be disquieted by the noise and should have a loathing for the meal, being come among overweening men, and also that he might ask him about his father that was gone from his home.

Then a handmaid bare water for the washing of hands in a goodly golden ewer, and poured it forth over a silver basin to wash withal, and drew to their side a polished table. And a grave dame bare wheaten bread and set it by them, and laid on the board many dainties, giving freely of such things as she had by her. And a carver lifted and placed by them platters of divers kinds of flesh, and nigh them he set golden bowls, and a henchman walked to and fro pouring out to them the wine.

Then in came the lordly wooers; and they sat them down in rows on chairs and on high seats, and henchmen poured water on their hands, and maidservants piled wheaten bread by them in baskets, and pages crowned the bowls with drink; and they stretched forth their hands upon the good cheer spread before them. Now when the wooers had put from them the desire of meat and drink, they minded them of other things, even of the song and dance: for these are crown of the feast. And a henchman placed a beauteous lyre in the hands of Phemius, who was minstrel to the wooers despite his will. Yea, and as he touched the lyre he lifted up his voice in sweet song.

But Telemachus spake unto grey-eyed Athene, holding his head close to her that those others might not hear: 'Dear stranger, wilt thou of a truth be wroth at the word that I shall say? Yonder men verily care for such things as these, the lyre and song, lightly, as they that devour the livelihood of another without atonement, of that man whose white bones, it may be, lie wasting in the rain upon the mainland, or the billow rolls them in the brine. Were but these men to see him returned to Ithaca, they all would pray rather for greater speed of foot than for gain of gold and raiment. But now he hath perished, even so, an evil doom, and for us is no comfort, no, not though any of earthly men should say that he will come again. Gone is the day of his returning! But come, declare me this, and tell me all plainly: Who art thou of the sons of men, and whence? Where is thy city, where are they that begat thee? Say, on what manner of ship didst thou come, and how did sailors bring thee to Ithaca, and who did they avow themselves to be, for in no wise do I deem that thou camest hither by land. And herein tell me true, that I may know for a surety whether thou art a newcomer, or whether thou art a guest of the house, seeing that many were the strangers that came to our home, for that *he* too had voyaged much among men.'

Then the goddess, grey-eyed Athene, answered him: 'Yea now, I will plainly tell thee all. I avow me to be Mentes, son of wise Anchialus, and I bear rule among the Taphians, lovers of the oar. And now am I come to shore, as thou seest, with ship and crew, sailing over the wine-dark sea, unto men of strange speech, even to Temesa, in quest of copper, and my cargo is shining iron. And there my ship is lying toward the upland, away from the city, in the harbour of Rheithron beneath wooded Neïon: and we declare ourselves to be friends one of the other, and of houses friendly, from of old. Nay, if thou wouldest be assured, go ask the old man, the hero Laertes, who they say no more comes to the city, but far away toward the upland suffers affliction, with an ancient woman for his handmaid, who sets by him meat and drink, whensoever weariness takes hold of his limbs, as he creeps along the knoll of his vineyard plot. And now am I come; for verily they said that *he*, thy father, was among his people; but lo, the gods withhold him from his way. For goodly Odysseus hath not yet perished on the earth; but still, methinks, he lives and is kept on the wide deep in a sea-girt isle, and hard men constrain him, wild folk that hold him, it may be, sore against his will. But now of a truth will I utter my word of prophecy, as the Immortals bring it into my heart and as I deem it will be accomplished, though no soothsayer am I, nor skilled in the signs of birds. Henceforth indeed for no long while shall he be far from his own dear country, not though bonds of iron bind him; he will advise him of a way to return, for he is a man of many devices. But come, declare me this, and tell me all plainly, whether indeed, so tall as thou art, thou art sprung from the loins of Odysseus. Thy head surely and thy beauteous eyes are wondrous like to his, since full many a time have we held converse together ere he embarked for Troy, whither the others, aye the bravest of the Argives, went in hollow ships. From that day forth neither have I seen Odysseus, nor he me.'

Then wise Telemachus answered her, and said: 'Yea, sir, now will I plainly tell thee all. My mother verily saith that I am his; for myself I know not, for never man yet knew of himself his own descent. O that I had been the son of some blessed man, whom old age overtook among his own possessions! But now of him that is the most hapless of mortal men, his son they say that I am, since thou dost question me hereof.'

Then the goddess, grey-eyed Athene, spake unto him,

and said: 'Surely no nameless lineage have the gods ordained for thee in days to come, since Penelope bore thee so goodly a man. But come, declare me this, and tell it all plainly. What feast, nay, what rout is this? What hast thou to do therewith? Is it a clan drinking, or a wedding feast, for here we have no banquet where each man brings his share? In such wise, flown with insolence, do they seem to me to revel wantonly through the house: and well might any man be wroth to see so many deeds of shame, whatso wise man came among them.'

Then wise Telemachus answered her, and said: 'Sir, forasmuch as thou questionest me of these things and inquirest thereof, our house was once like to have been rich and honourable, while yet that man was among his people. But now the gods willed it otherwise, in evil purpose, who have made him pass utterly out of sight as no man ever before. Truly I would not even for his death make so great sorrow, had he fallen among his fellows in the land of the Trojans, or in the arms of his friends when he had wound up the clew of war. Then would the whole Achaean host have builded him a barrow, and even for his son would he have won great glory in the after days. But now the spirits of the storm have swept him away inglorious. He is gone, lost to sight and hearsay, but for me hath he left anguish and lamentation; nor henceforth is it for him alone that I mourn and weep, since the gods have wrought for me other sore distress. For all the noblest that are princes in the isles, in Dulichium and Same and wooded Zacynthus, and as many as lord it in rocky Ithaca, all these woo my mother and waste my house. But as for her she neither refuseth the hated bridal, nor hath the heart to make an end: so they devour and minish my house, and ere long will they make havoc likewise of myself.'

Then in heavy displeasure spake unto him Pallas Athene: 'God help thee! thou art surely sore in need of Odysseus that is afar, to stretch forth his hands upon the shameless wooers. If he could but come now and stand at the entering in of the gate, with helmet and shield and lances twain, as mighty a man as when first I marked him in our house drinking and making merry what time he came up out of Ephyra from Ilus son of Mermerus! For even thither had Odysseus gone on his swift ship to seek a deadly drug, that he might have wherewithal to smear his bronze-shod arrows: but Ilus would in no wise give it him, for he had in awe the everliving gods. But my father gave it him, for he bare him wondrous love. O that Odysseus might in such strength consort with the wooers: so should they all have swift fate and bitter wedlock! Howbeit these things surely lie on the knees of the gods, whether he shall return or not, and take vengeance in his halls. But I charge thee to take counsel how thou mayest thrust forth the wooers from the hall. Come now, mark and take heed unto my words. On the morrow call the Achaean lords to the assembly, and declare thy saying to all, and take the gods to witness. As for the wooers bid them scatter them each one to his own, and for thy mother, if her heart is moved to marriage, let her go back to the hall of that mighty man her father, and her kinsfolk will furnish a wedding feast, and array the gifts of wooing exceeding many, all that should go back with a daughter dearly beloved. And to thyself I will give a word of wise counsel, if perchance thou wilt hearken. Fit out a ship, the best thou hast, with twenty oarsmen, and go to inquire concerning thy father that is long afar, if perchance any man shall tell thee aught, or if thou mayest hear the voice from Zeus, which chiefly brings tidings to men. Get thee first to Pylos and inquire of goodly Nestor, and from thence to Sparta to Menelaus of the fair hair, for he came home the last of the mail-coated Achaeans. If thou shalt hear news of the life and the returning of thy father, then verily thou mayest endure the wasting for yet a year. But if thou shalt hear that he is dead and gone, return then to thine own dear country and pile his mound, and over it pay burial rites, full many as is due, and give thy mother to a husband. But when thou hast done this and made an end, thereafter take counsel in thy mind and heart, how thou mayest slay the wooers in thy halls, whether by guile or openly; for thou shouldest not carry childish thoughts, being no longer of years thereto. Or hast thou not heard what renown the goodly Orestes gat him among all men in that he slew the slayer of his father, guileful Aegisthus, who killed his famous sire? And thou, too, my friend, for I see that thou art very comely and tall, be valiant, that even men unborn may praise thee. But I will now go down to the swift ship and to my men, who methinks chafe much at tarrying for me; and do thou thyself take heed and give ear unto my words.'

Then wise Telemachus answered her, saying: 'Sir, verily thou speakest these things out of a friendly heart, as a father to his son, and never will I forget them. But now I pray thee abide here, though eager to be gone, to the end that after thou hast bathed and had all thy heart's desire, thou mayst wend to the ship joyful in spirit, with a costly gift and very goodly, to be an heirloom of my giving, such as dear friends give to friends.'

Then the goddess, grey-eyed Athene, answered him: 'Hold me now no longer, that am eager for the way. But whatsoever gift thine heart shall bid thee give me, when I am on my way back let it be mine to carry home: bear from thy stores a gift right goodly, and it shall bring thee the worth thereof in return.'

So spake she and departed, the grey-eyed Athene, and like an eagle of the sea she flew away, but in his spirit she planted might and courage, and put him in mind of his father yet more than heretofore. And he marked the thing and was amazed, for he deemed that it was a god: and anon he went among the wooers, a godlike man.

Now the renowned minstrel was singing to the wooers,

and they sat listening in silence; and his song was of the pitiful return of the Achaeans, that Pallas Athene laid on them as they came forth from Troy. And from her upper chamber the daughter of Icarius, wise Penelope, caught the glorious strain, and she went down the high stairs from her chamber, not alone, for two of her handmaids bare her company. Now when the fair lady had come unto the wooers, she stood by the pillar of the well-builded roof holding glistening tire before her face; and a faithful maiden stood on either side her. Then she fell a-weeping, and spake unto the divine minstrel:

'Phemius, since thou knowest many other charms for mortals, deeds of men and gods, which bards rehearse, some one of these do thou sing as thou sittest by them, and let them drink their wine in silence; but cease from this pitiful strain, that ever wastes my heart within my breast, since to me above all women hath come a sorrow comfortless. So dear a head do I long for in constant memory, namely, that man whose fame is noised abroad from Hellas to mid Argos.'

Then wise Telemachus answered her, and said: 'O my mother, why then dost thou grudge the sweet minstrel to gladden us as his spirit moves him? It is not minstrels who are in fault, but Zeus, methinks, is in fault, who gives to men, that live by bread, to each one as he will. As for him it is no blame if he sings the ill-faring of the Danaans; for men always prize that song the most, which rings newest in their ears. But let thy heart and mind endure to listen, for not Odysseus only lost in Troy the day of his returning, but many another likewise perished. Howbeit go to thy chamber and mind thine own housewiferies, the loom and distaff, and bid thy handmaids ply their tasks. But speech shall be for men, for all, but for me in chief; for mine is the lordship in the house.'

Then in amaze she went back to her chamber, for she laid up the wise saying of her son in her heart. She ascended to her upper chamber with the women her handmaids, and then was bewailing Odysseus, her dear lord, till grey-eyed Athene cast sweet sleep upon her eyelids.

Now the wooers clamoured throughout the shadowy halls, and each one uttered a prayer to be her bedfellow. And wise Telemachus first spake among them:

'Wooers of my mother, men despiteful out of measure, let us feast now and make merry and let there be no brawling; for, lo, it is a good thing to list to a minstrel such as him, like to the gods in voice. But in the morning let us all go to the assembly and sit us down, that I may declare my saying outright, to wit that ye leave these halls: and busy yourselves with other feasts, eating your own substance, going in turn from house to house. But if ye deem this a likelier and a better thing, that one man's goods should perish without atonement, then waste ye as ye will; and I will call upon the everlasting gods, if haply Zeus may grant that acts of recompense be made: so should ye hereafter perish within the halls without atonement.'

So spake he, and all that heard him bit their lips and marvelled at Telemachus, in that he spake boldly.

Then Antinous, son of Eupeithes, answered him: 'Telemachus, in very truth the gods themselves instruct thee to be proud of speech and boldly to harangue. Never may Cronion make thee king in seagirt Ithaca, which thing is of inheritance thy right!'

Then wise Telemachus answered him, and said: 'Antinous, wilt thou indeed be wroth at the word that I shall say? Yea, at the hand of Zeus would I be fain to take even this thing upon me. Sayest thou that this is the worst hap that can befall a man? Nay, verily, it is no ill thing to be a king: the house of such an one quickly waxeth rich and himself is held in greater honour. Howsoever there are many other kings of the Achaeans in seagirt Ithaca, kings young and old; some one of them shall surely have this kingship since goodly Odysseus is dead. But as for me, I will be lord of our own house and thralls, that goodly Odysseus gat me with his spear.'

Then Eurymachus, son of Polybus, answered him, saying: 'Telemachus, on the knees of the gods it surely lies, what man is to be king over the Achaeans in seagirt Ithaca. But mayest thou keep thine own possessions and be lord in thine own house! Never may that man come, who shall wrest from thee thy substance violently in thine own despite, while Ithaca yet stands. But I would ask thee, friend, concerning the stranger—whence he is, and of what land he avows him to be? Where are his kin and his native fields? Doth he bear some tidings of thy father on his road, or cometh he thus to speed some matter of his own? In such wise did he start up, and lo, he was gone, nor tarried he that we should know him;—and yet he seemed no mean man to look upon.'

Then wise Telemachus answered him, and said: 'Eurymachus, surely the day of my father's returning hath gone by. Therefore no more do I put faith in tidings, whencesoever they may come, neither have I regard unto any divination, whereof my mother may inquire at the lips of a diviner, when she hath bidden him to the hall. But as for that man, he is a friend of my house from Taphos, and he avows him to be Mentes, son of wise Anchialus, and he hath lordship among the Taphians, lovers of the oar.'

So spake Telemachus, but in his heart he knew the deathless goddess. Now the wooers turned them to the dance and the delightsome song, and made merry, and waited till evening should come on. And as they made merry, dusk evening came upon them. Then they went each one to his own house to lie down to rest.

But Telemachus, where his chamber was builded high up in the fair court, in a place with wide prospect, thither betook him to his bed, pondering many thoughts in his mind; and with him went trusty Eurycleia, and bare for him torches burning. She was the daughter of Ops, son of Peisenor, and Laertes bought her on a time with his wealth, while as yet she was in her first youth, and gave for her the worth of twenty oxen. And he honoured her even as he honoured his dear wife in the halls, but he never lay with her, for he shunned the wrath of his lady. She went with Telemachus and bare for him the burning torches: and of all the women of the household she loved him most, and she had nursed him when a little one. Then he opened the doors of the well-builded chamber and sat down on the bed and took off his soft doublet, and put it in the wise old woman's hands. So she folded the doublet and smoothed it, and hung it on a pin by the jointed bedstead, and went forth on her way from the room, and pulled to the door with the silver handle, and drew home the bar with the thong. There, all night through, wrapt in a fleece of wool, he meditated in his heart upon the journey that Athene had showed him.

BOOK II

Telemachus complains in vain, and borrowing a ship, goes secretly to Pylos by night. And how he was there received.

Now so soon as early Dawn shone forth, the rosy-fingered, the dear son of Odysseus gat him up from his bed, and put on his raiment and cast his sharp sword about his shoulder, and beneath his smooth feet he bound his goodly sandals, and stept forth from his chamber in presence like a god. And straightway he bade the clear-voiced heralds to call the long-haired Achaeans to the assembly. And the heralds called the gathering, and the Achaeans were assembled quickly. Now when they were gathered and come together, he went on his way to the assembly holding in his hand a spear of bronze,—not alone he went, for two swift hounds bare him company. Then Athene shed on him a wondrous grace, and all the people marvelled at him as he came. And he sat him in his father's seat and the elders gave place to him.

Then the lord Aegyptus spake among them first; bowed was he with age, and skilled in things past number. Now for this reason he spake that his dear son, the warrior Antiphus, had gone in the hollow ships to Ilios of the goodly steeds; but the savage Cyclops slew him in his hollow cave, and made of him then his latest meal. Three other sons Aegyptus had, and one consorted with the wooers, namely Eurynomus, but two continued in their father's fields; yet even so forgat he not that son, still mourning and sorrowing. So weeping for his sake he made harangue and spake among them:

'Hearken now to me, ye men of Ithaca, to the word that I shall say. Never hath our assembly or session been since the day that goodly Odysseus departed in the hollow ships. And now who was minded thus to assemble us? On what man hath such sore need come, of the young men or of the elder born? Hath he heard some tidings of the host now returning, which he might plainly declare to us, for that he first learned thereof, or doth he show forth and tell some other matter of the common weal? Methinks he is a true man—good luck be with him! Zeus vouchsafe him some good thing in his turn, even all his heart's desire!'

So spake he, and the dear son of Odysseus was glad at the omen of the word; nor sat he now much longer, but he burned to speak, and he stood in mid assembly; and the herald Peisenor, skilled in sage counsels, placed the staff in his hands. Then he spake, accosting the old man first:

'Old man, he is not far off, and soon shalt thou know it for thyself, he who called the folk together, even I: for sorrow hath come to me in chief. Neither have I heard any tidings of the host now returning, which I may plainly declare to you, for that I first learned thereof; neither do I show forth or tell any other matter of the common weal, but mine own need, for that evil hath befallen my house, a double woe. First, I have lost my noble sire, who sometime was king among you here, and was gentle as a father; and now is there an evil yet greater far, which surely shall soon make grievous havoc of my whole house and ruin all my livelihood. My mother did certain wooers beset sore against her will, even the sons of those men that here are the noblest. They are too craven to go to the house of her father Icarius, that he may himself set the bride-price for his daughter, and bestow her on whom he will, even on him who finds favour in his sight. But they resorting to our house day by day sacrifice oxen and sheep and fat goats, and keep revel, and drink the dark wine recklessly, and lo, our great wealth is wasted, for there is no man now alive such as Odysseus was, to keep ruin from the house. As for me I am no wise strong like him to ward mine own; verily to the end of my days shall I be a weakling and all unskilled in prowess. Truly I would defend me if but strength were mine; for deeds past sufferance have now been wrought, and now my house is wasted utterly beyond pretence of right. Resent it in your own hearts, and have regard to your neighbours who dwell around, and tremble ye at the anger of the gods, lest haply they turn upon you in wrath at your evil deeds. I pray you by Olympian Zeus and by Themis, who looseth and gathereth the meetings of men, let be, my friends, and leave me alone to waste in bitter grief;—unless it so be that my father, the good Odysseus, out of evil heart wrought harm to the goodly-greaved Achaeans, in quittance whereof ye now work me harm out of evil hearts, and spur on these men. Better for me that ye yourselves should eat up my treasures and my flocks. Were *ye* so to devour them, ere long would some recompense be made, for we would urge our plea throughout the town, begging back our substance, until all should be restored. But now without remedy are the pains that ye lay up in my heart.'

So spake he in wrath, and dashed the staff to the ground, and brake forth in tears; and pity fell on all the people. Then all the others held their peace, and none had the heart to answer Telemachus with hard words, but Antinous alone made answer, saying:

'Telemachus, proud of speech and unrestrained in fury, what is this thou hast said to put us to shame, and wouldest fasten on us reproach? Behold the fault is not in the Achaean wooers, but in thine own mother, for she is the craftiest of women. For it is now the third year, and the fourth is fast going by, since she began to deceive the minds of the Achaeans in their breasts. She gives hope to all, and makes promises to every man, and sends them messages, but her mind is set on other things. And she hath devised in her heart this wile besides; she set up in her halls a mighty web, fine of woof and very wide, whereat she would weave, and anon she spake among us:

' "Ye princely youths, my wooers, now that the goodly Odysseus is dead, do ye abide patiently, how eager soever to speed on this marriage of mine, till I finish the robe. I would not that the threads perish to no avail, even this shroud for the hero Laertes, against the day when the ruinous doom shall bring him low, of death that lays men at their length. So shall none of the Achaean women in the land count it blame in me, as well might be, were he to lie without a winding-sheet, a man that had gotten great possessions."

'So spake she, and our high hearts consented thereto. So then in the day time she would weave the mighty web, and in the night unravel the same, when she had let place the torches by her. Thus for the space of three years she hid the thing by craft and beguiled the minds of the Achaeans; but when the fourth year arrived and the seasons came round, then at the last one of her women who knew all declared it, and we found her unravelling the splendid web. Thus she finished it perforce and sore against her will. But as for thee, the wooers make thee answer thus, that thou mayest know it in thine own heart, thou and all the Achaeans! Send away thy mother, and bid her be married to whosoever her father commands, and whoso is well pleasing unto her. But if she will continue for long to vex the sons of the Achaeans, pondering in her heart those things that Athene hath given her beyond women, knowledge of all fair handiwork, yea, and cunning wit, and wiles—so be it! Such wiles as hers we have never yet heard that any even of the women of old did know, of those that aforetime were fair-tressed Achaean ladies, Tyro, and Alcmene, and Mycene with the bright crown. Not one of these in the imaginations of their hearts was like unto Penelope, yet herein at least her imagining was not good. For in despite of her the wooers will devour thy living and thy substance, so long as she is steadfast in such purpose as the gods now put within her breast: great renown for herself she winneth, but for thee regret for thy much livelihood. But we will neither go to our own lands, nor otherwhere, till she marry that man whom she will of the Achaeans.'

Then wise Telemachus answered him, saying: 'Antinous, I may in no wise thrust forth from the house, against her will, the woman that bare me, that reared me: while as for my father he is abroad on the earth, whether he be alive or dead. Moreover it is hard for me to make heavy restitution to Icarius, as needs I must, if of mine own will I send my mother away. For I shall have evil at his hand, at the hand of her father, and some god will give me more besides, for my mother will call down the dire Avengers as she departs from the house, and I shall have blame of men; surely then I will never speak this word. Nay, if your own heart, even yours, is indignant, quit ye my halls, and busy yourselves with other feasts, eating your own substance, and going in turn from house to house. But if ye deem this a likelier and a better thing, that one man's goods should perish without atonement, then waste ye as ye will: and I will call upon the everlasting gods, if haply Zeus may grant that acts of recompense be made: so should ye hereafter perish in the halls without atonement.'

So spake Telemachus, and in answer to his prayer did Zeus, of the far-borne voice, send forth two eagles in flight, from on high, from the mountain-crest. Awhile they flew as fleet as the blasts of the wind, side by side, with straining of their pinions. But when they had now reached the mid assembly, the place of many voices, there they wheeled about and flapped their strong wings, and looked down upon the heads of all, and destruction was in their gaze. Then tore they with their talons each the other's cheeks and neck on every side, and so sped to the right across the dwellings and the city of the people. And the men marvelled at the birds when they had sight of them, and pondered in their hearts the things that should come to pass. Yea and the old man, the lord Halitherses son of Mastor, spake among them, for he excelled his peers in knowledge of birds, and in uttering words of fate. With good will he made harangue and spake among them:

'Hearken to me now, ye men of Ithaca, to the word that I shall say: and mainly to the wooers do I show forth and tell these things, seeing that a mighty woe is rolling upon them. For Odysseus shall not long be away from his friends, nay, even now, it may be, he is near, and sowing the seeds of death and fate for these men, every one; and he will be a bane to many another likewise of us who dwell in clear-seen Ithaca. But long ere that falls out let us advise us how we may make an end of their mischief; yea, let them of their own selves make an end, for this is the better way for them, as will soon be seen. For I prophesy not as one unproved, but with sure knowledge; verily, I say, that for him all things now are come to pass, even as I told him, what time the Argives embarked for Ilios, and with them went the wise Odysseus. I said that after sore affliction, with the loss of all his company, unknown to all, in the twentieth year he should come home. And behold, all these things now have an end.'

And Eurymachus, son of Polybus, answered him, saying: 'Go now, old man, get thee home and prophesy to thine own children, lest haply they suffer harm hereafter: but herein am I a far better prophet than thou. Howbeit there be many birds that fly to and fro under the sun's rays, but all are not birds of fate. Now as for Odysseus, he hath perished far away, as would that thou too with him hadst been cut off: so wouldst thou not have babbled thus much prophecy, nor wouldst thou hound on Telemachus that is already angered, expecting a gift for thy house, if perchance he may vouchsafe thee aught. But now will I speak out, and my word shall surely be accomplished. If thou, that knowest much lore from of old, shalt beguile with words a younger man, and rouse him to indignation, first it shall be a great grief to him:—and yet he can count on no aid from these who hear him;—while upon thee, old man, we will lay a fine, that thou mayest pay it and chafe at heart, and sore pain shall be thine. And I myself will give a word of counsel to Telemachus in presence of you all. Let him command his mother to return to her father's house; and her kinsfolk will furnish a wedding feast, and array the gifts of wooing, exceeding many, all that should go back with a daughter dearly beloved. For ere that, I trow, we sons of the Achaeans will not cease from our rough wooing, since, come what may, we fear not any man, no, not Telemachus, full of words though he be, nor soothsaying do we heed, whereof thou, old man, pratest idly, and art hated yet the more. His substance too shall be woefully devoured, nor shall recompense ever be made, so long as she shall put off the Achaeans in the matter of her marriage; while we in expectation, from day to day, vie one with another for the prize of her perfection, nor go we after other women whom it were meet that we should each one wed.'

Then wise Telemachus answered him, saying: 'Eurymachus, and ye others, that are lordly wooers, I entreat you no more concerning this nor speak thereof, for the gods have knowledge of it now and all the Achaeans. But come, give me a swift ship and twenty men, who shall accomplish for me my voyage to and fro. For I will go to Sparta and to sandy Pylos to inquire concerning the return of my father that is long afar, if perchance any man shall tell me aught, or if I may hear the voice from Zeus, that chiefly brings tidings to men. If I shall hear news of the life and the returning of my father, then verily I may endure the wasting for yet a year; but if I shall hear that he is dead and gone, let me then return to my own dear country, and pile his mound, and over it pay burial rites full many as is due, and I will give my mother to a husband.'

So with that word he sat him down; then in the midst uprose Mentor, the companion of noble Odysseus. He it was to whom Odysseus, as he departed in the fleet, had given the charge over all his house, that it should obey the old man, and that he should keep all things safe. With good will he now made harangue and spake among them:

'Hearken to me now, ye men of Ithaca, to the word that I shall say. Henceforth let not any sceptred king be kind and gentle with all his heart, nor minded to do righteousness: for behold, there is none that remembereth divine Odysseus of the people whose lord he was, and was gentle as a father. Howsoever, it is not that I grudge the lordly wooers their deeds of violence in the evil devices of their heart. For at the hazard of their own heads they violently devour the household of Odysseus, and say of him that he will come no more again. But I am indeed wroth with the rest of the people, to see how ye all sit thus speechless, and do not cry shame upon the wooers, and put them down, ye that are so many and they so few.'

And Leocritus, son of Euenor, answered him, saying: 'Mentor infatuate, with thy wandering wits, what word hast thou spoken, that callest upon them to put us down? Nay, it is a hard thing to fight about a feast, and that with men who are even more in number than you. Though Odysseus of Ithaca himself should come and were eager of heart to drive forth from the hall the lordly wooers that feast throughout his house, yet should his wife have no joy of his coming, though she yearns for him;—but even there should he meet foul doom, if he fought with those that outnumbered him; so thou hast not spoken aright. But as for the people, come now, scatter yourselves each one to his own lands, but Mentor and Halitherses will speed this man's voyage, for they are friends of his house from of old. Yet after all, methinks, that long time he will abide and seek tidings in Ithaca, and never accomplish this voyage.'

Thus he spake, and in haste they broke up the assembly. So they were scattered each one to his own dwelling, while the wooers departed to the house of divine Odysseus.

Then Telemachus, going far apart to the shore of the sea, laved his hands in the grey sea water, and prayed unto Athene, saying: 'Hear me, thou who yesterday didst come in thy godhead to our house, and badest me go in a ship across the misty seas, to seek tidings of the return of my father that is long gone: but all this my purpose do the Achaeans delay, and mainly the wooers in the naughtiness of their pride.'

So spake he in prayer, and Athene drew nigh him in the likeness of Mentor, in fashion and in voice, and she spake and hailed him in winged words:

'Telemachus, even hereafter thou shalt not be craven or witless, if indeed thou hast a drop of thy father's blood and a portion of his spirit; such an one was he to fulfil both word and work. Nor, if this be so, shall thy voyage be vain or unfulfilled. But if thou art not the very seed of him and of Penelope, then have I no hope that thou wilt accomplish thy desire. For few children, truly, are like their father; lo, the more part are worse, yet a few are better than the sire. But since thou shalt not even hereafter be craven or witless, nor hath the wisdom of Odysseus failed thee quite, so is there good hope of thine accomplishing this work. Wherefore now take no heed of the counsel or the purpose of the senseless wooers, for they are in no way wise or just: neither know they aught of death and of black fate, which already is close upon them, that they are all to perish in one day. But the voyage on which thy heart is set shall not long be lacking to thee—so faithful a friend of thy father am I, who will furnish thee a swift ship and myself be thy companion. But go thou to the house, and consort with the wooers, and make ready corn, and bestow all in vessels, the wine in jars and barley-flour, the marrow of men, in well-sewn skins; and I will lightly gather in the township a crew that offer themselves willingly. There are many ships, new and old, in seagirt Ithaca; of these I will choose out the best for thee, and we will quickly rig her and launch her on the broad deep.'

So spake Athene, daughter of Zeus, and Telemachus made no long tarrying, when he had heard the voice of the goddess. He went on his way towards the house, heavy at heart, and there he found the noble wooers in the halls, flaying goats and singeing swine in the court. And Antinous laughed out and went straight to Telemachus, clasped his hand and spake and hailed him:

'Telemachus, proud of speech and unrestrained in fury, let no evil word any more be in thy heart, nor evil work, but let me see thee eat and drink as of old. And the Achaeans will make thee ready all things without fail, a ship and chosen oarsmen, that thou mayest come the quicker to fair Pylos, to seek tidings of thy noble father.'

Then wise Telemachus answered him, saying: 'Antinous, in no wise in your proud company can I sup in peace, and make merry with a quiet mind. Is it a little thing, ye wooers, that in time past ye wasted many good things of my getting, while as yet I was a child? But now that I am a man grown, and learn the story from the lips of others, and my spirit waxeth within me, I will seek to let loose upon you evil fates, as I may, going either to Pylos for help, or abiding here in this township. Yea, I will go, nor vain shall the voyage be whereof I speak; a passenger on another's ship go I, for I am not to have a ship nor oarsmen of mine own; so in your wisdom ye have thought it for the better.'

He spake and snatched his hand from out the hand of Antinous, lightly, and all the while the wooers were busy feasting through the house; and they mocked him and sharply taunted him, and thus would some proud youth speak:

'In very truth Telemachus planneth our destruction. He will bring a rescue either from sandy Pylos, or even it may be from Sparta, so terribly is he set on slaying us. Or else he will go to Ephyra, a fruitful land, to fetch a poisonous drug that he may cast it into the bowl and make an end of all of us.'

And again another proud youth would say: 'Who knows but that he himself, if he goes hence on the hollow ship, may perish wandering far from his friends, even as Odysseus? So should we have yet more ado, for then must we divide among us all his substance, and moreover give the house to his mother to possess it, and to him whosoever should wed her.'

So spake they; but he stepped down into the vaulted treasure-chamber of his father, a spacious room, where gold and bronze lay piled, and raiment in coffers, and fragrant olive oil in plenty. And there stood casks of sweet wine and old, full of the unmixed drink divine, all orderly ranged by the wall, ready if ever Odysseus should come home, albeit after travail and much pain. And the close-fitted doors, the folding doors, were shut, and night and day there abode within a dame in charge, who guarded all the fulness of her wisdom, Eurycleia, daughter of Ops son of Peisenor. Telemachus now called her into the chamber and spake unto her, saying:

'Mother, come draw off for me sweet wine in jars, the choicest next to that thou keepest mindful ever of that ill-fated one, Odysseus, of the seed of Zeus, if perchance he may come I know not whence, having avoided death and the fates. So fill twelve jars, and close each with his lid, and pour me barley-meal into well-sewn skins, and let there be twenty measures of the grain of bruised barley-meal. Let none know this but thyself! As for these things let them all be got together; for in the evening I will take them with me, at the time that my mother hath gone to her upper chamber and turned her thoughts to sleep. Lo, to Sparta I go and to sandy Pylos to seek tidings of my dear father's return, if haply I may hear thereof.'

So spake he, and the good nurse Eurycleia wailed aloud, and making lament spake to him winged words: 'Ah, wherefore, dear child, hath such a thought arisen in thine heart? How shouldst thou fare over wide lands, thou that art an only child and well-beloved? As for him he hath perished, Odysseus of the seed of Zeus, far from his own country in the land of strangers. And yonder men, so soon as thou art gone, will devise mischief against thee thereafter, that thou mayest perish by guile, and they will share among them all this wealth of thine. Nay, abide here, settled on thine own lands: thou hast no need upon the deep unharvested to suffer evil and go wandering.'

Then wise Telemachus answered her, saying: 'Take heart, nurse, for lo, this my purpose came not but of a god. But swear to tell no word thereof to my dear mother, till at least it shall be the eleventh or twelfth day from hence, or till she miss me of herself, and hear of my departure, that so she may not mar her fair face with her tears.'

Thus he spake, and the old woman sware a great oath by the gods not to reveal it. But when she had sworn and done that oath, straightway she drew off the wine for him in jars, and poured barley-meal into well-sewn skins, and Telemachus departed to the house and consorted with the wooers.

Then the goddess, grey-eyed Athene, turned to other thoughts. In the likeness of Telemachus she went all through the city, and stood by each one of the men and spake her saying, and bade them gather at even by the swift ship. Furthermore, she craved a swift ship of

Noemon, famous son of Phromius, ana right gladly he promised it.

Now the sun sank and all the ways were darkened. Then at length she let drag the swift ship to the sea and stored within it all such tackling as decked ships carry. And she moored it at the far end of the harbour and the good company were gathered together, and the goddess cheered on all.

Then the goddess, grey-eyed Athene, turned to other thoughts. She went on her way to the house of divine Odysseus; and there she shed sweet sleep upon the wooers and made them distraught in their drinking, and cast the cups from their hands. And they arose up to go to rest throughout the city, nor sat they yet a long while, for slumber was falling on their eyelids. Now grey-eyed Athene spake unto Telemachus, and called him from out the fair-lying halls, taking the likeness of Mentor, both in fashion and in voice:

'Telemachus, thy goodly-greaved companions are sitting already at their oars, it is thy despatch they are awaiting. Nay then, let us go, that we delay them not long from the way.'

Therewith Pallas Athene led the way quickly, and he followed hard in the steps of the goddess. Now when they had come down to the ship and to the sea, they found the long-haired youths of the company on the shore; and the mighty prince Telemachus spake among them:

'Come hither, friends, let us carry the corn on board, for all is now together in the room, and my mother knows nought thereof, nor any of the maidens of the house: one woman only heard my saying.'

Thus he spake and led the way, and they went with him. So they brought all and stowed it in the decked ship, according to the word of the dear son of Odysseus. Then Telemachus climbed the ship, and Athene went before him, and behold, she sat her down in the stern, and near her sat Telemachus. And the men loosed the hawsers and climbed on board themselves, and sat down upon the benches. And grey-eyed Athene sent them a favourable gale, a fresh West Wind, singing over the wine-dark sea.

And Telemachus called unto his company and bade them lay hands on the tackling, and they hearkened to his call. So they raised the mast of pine tree and set it in the hole of the cross plank, and made it fast with forestays, and hauled up the white sails with twisted ropes of oxide. And the wind filled the belly of the sail, and the dark wave seethed loudly round the stem of the running ship, and she fleeted over the wave, accomplishing her path. Then they made all fast in the swift black ship, and set mixing bowls brimmed with wine, and poured drink offering to the deathless gods that are from everlasting, and in chief to the grey-eyed daughter of Zeus. So all night long and through the dawn the ship cleft her way.

BOOK III

Nestor entertains Telemachus at Pylos and tells him how the Greeks departed from Troy; and sends him for further information to Sparta.

Now the sun arose and left the lovely mere, speeding to the brazen heaven, to give light to the immortals and to mortal men on the earth, the graingiver, and they reached Pylos, the stablished castle of Neleus. There the people were doing sacrifice on the sea shore, slaying black bulls without spot to the dark-haired god, the shaker of the earth. Nine companies there were, and five hundred men sat in each, and in every company they held nine bulls ready to hand. Just as they had tasted the inner parts, and were burning the slices of the thighs on the altar to the god, the others were bearing straight to land, and brailed up the sails of the gallant ship, and moored her, and themselves came forth. And Telemachus too stept forth from the ship, and Athene led the way. And the goddess, grey-eyed Athene, spake first to him, saying:

'Telemachus, thou needest not now be abashed, no, not one whit. For to this very end didst thou sail over the deep, that thou mightest hear tidings of thy father, even where the earth closed over him, and what manner of death he met. But come now, go straight to Nestor, tamer of horses: let us learn what counsel he hath in the secret of his heart. And beseech him thyself that he may give unerring answer; and he will not lie to thee, for he is very wise.'

The wise Telemachus answered, saying: 'Mentor, and

how shall I go, how shall I greet him, I, who am untried in words of wisdom? Moreover a young man may well be abashed to question an elder.'

Then the goddess, grey-eyed Athene, spake to him again: 'Telemachus, thou shalt bethink thee of somewhat in thine own breast, and somewhat the god will give thee to say. For thou, methinks, of all men wert not born and bred without the will of the gods.'

So spake Pallas Athene and led the way quickly; and he followed hard in the steps of the goddess. And they came to the gathering and the session of the men of Pylos. There was Nestor seated with his sons, and round him his company making ready the feast, and roasting some of the flesh and spitting other. Now when they saw the strangers, they went all together, and clasped their hands in welcome, and would have them sit down. First Peisistratus, son of Nestor, drew nigh, and took the hands of each, and made them to sit down at the feast on soft fleeces upon the sea sand, beside his brother Thrasymedes and his father. And he gave them messes of the inner meat, and poured wine into a golden cup, and, pledging her, he spake unto Pallas Athene, daughter of Zeus, lord of the aegis:

'Pray now, my guest, to the lord Poseidon, even as it is his feast whereon ye have chanced in coming hither. And when thou hast made drink-offering and prayed, as is due, give thy friend also the cup of honeyed wine to make offering thereof, inasmuch as he too, methinks, prayeth to the deathless gods, for all men stand in need of the gods. Howbeit he is younger and mine own equal in years, therefore to thee first will I give the golden chalice.'

Therewith he placed in her hand the cup of sweet wine. And Athene rejoiced in the wisdom and judgment of the man, in that he had given to her first the chalice of gold. And straightway she prayed, and that instantly, to the lord Poseidon:

'Hear me, Poseidon, girdler of the earth, and grudge not

the fulfilment of this labour in answer to our prayer. To Nestor first and to his sons vouchsafe renown, and thereafter grant to all the people of Pylos a gracious recompense for this splendid hecatomb. Grant moreover that Telemachus and I may return, when we have accomplished that for which we came hither with our swift black ship.'

Now as she prayed on this wise, herself the while was fulfilling the prayer. And she gave Telemachus the fair two-handled cup; and in like manner prayed the dear son of Odysseus. Then, when the others had roasted the outer parts and drawn them off the spits, they divided the messes and shared the glorious feast. But when they had put from them the desire of meat and drink, Nestor of Gerenia, lord of chariots, first spake among them:

'Now is the better time to inquire and ask of the strangers who they are, now that they have had their delight of food. Strangers, who are ye? Whence sail ye over the wet ways? On some trading enterprise, or at adventure do ye rove, even as sea-robbers, over the brine, for they wander at hazard of their own lives bringing bale to alien men?'

Then wise Telemachus answered him and spake with courage, for Athene herself had put boldness in his heart, that he might ask about his father who was afar, and that he might be had in good report among men:

'Nestor, son of Neleus, great glory of the Achaeans, thou askest whence we are, and I will surely tell thee all. We have come forth out of Ithaca that is below Neïon; and this our quest whereof I speak is a matter of mine own, and not of the common weal. I follow after the far-spread rumour of my father, if haply I may hear thereof, even of the goodly steadfast Odysseus, who upon a time, men say, fought by thy side and sacked the city of the Trojans. For of all the others, as many as warred with the Trojans, we hear tidings, and where each one fell by a pitiful death; but even the death of this man

Cronion hath left untold. For none can surely declare the place where he hath perished, whether he was smitten by foemen on the mainland, or lost upon the deep among the waves of Amphitrite. So now am I come hither to thy knees, if perchance thou art willing to tell me of his pitiful death, as one that saw it with thine own eyes, or heard the story from some other wanderer,—for his mother bare him to exceeding sorrow. And speak me no soft words in ruth or pity, but tell me plainly what sight thou didst get of him. Ah! I pray thee, if ever at all my father, noble Odysseus, made promise to thee of word or work, and fulfilled the same in the land of the Trojans, where ye Achaeans suffered affliction; these things, I pray thee, now remember and tell me truth.'

Then Nestor of Gerenia, lord of chariots, answered him: 'My friend, since thou hast brought sorrow back to mind, behold, this is the story of the woe which we endured in that land, we sons of the Achaeans, unrestrained in fury, and of all that we bore in wanderings after spoil, sailing with our ships over the misty deep, wheresoever Achilles led; and of all our war round the mighty burg of king Priam. Yea and there the best of us were slain. There lies valiant Aias, and there Achilles, and there Patroclus, the peer of the gods in counsel, and there my own dear son, strong and noble, Antilochus, that excelled in speed of foot and in the fight. And many other ills we suffered beside these; who of mortal men could tell the tale? Nay none, though thou wert to abide here for five years, ay and for six, and ask of all the ills which the goodly Achaeans then endured. Ere all was told thou wouldst be weary and turn to thine own country. For nine whole years we were busy about them, devising their ruin with all manner of craft; and scarce did Cronion bring it to pass. There never a man durst match with him in wisdom, for goodly Odysseus very far outdid the rest in all manner of craft, Odysseus thy father, if indeed thou art his son,—amazement comes upon me as I look at thee; for verily thy speech is like unto his; none would say that a younger man would speak so like an elder. Now look you, all the while that myself and goodly Odysseus were there, we never spake diversely either in the assembly or in the council, but always were of one mind, and advised the Argives with understanding and sound counsel, how all might be for the very best. But after we had sacked the steep city of Priam, and had departed in our ships, and a god had scattered the Achaeans, even then did Zeus devise in his heart a pitiful returning for the Argives, for in no wise were they all discreet or just. Wherefore many of them met with an ill faring by reason of the deadly wrath of the grey-eyed goddess, the daughter of the mighty sire, who set debate between the two sons of Atreus. And they twain called to the gathering of the host all the Achaeans, recklessly and out of order, against the going down of the sun; and lo, the sons of the Achaeans came heavy with wine. And the Atreidae spake out and told the reason wherefore they had assembled the host. Then verily Menelaus charged all the Achaeans to bethink them of returning over the broad back of the sea, but in no sort did he please Agamemnon, whose desire was to keep back the host and to offer holy hecatombs, that so he might appease that dread wrath of Athene. Fool! for he knew not this, that she was never to be won; for the mind of the everlasting gods is not lightly turned to repentance. So these twain stood bandying hard words; but the goodly-greaved Achaeans sprang up with a wondrous din, and twofold counsels found favour among them. So that one night we rested, thinking hard things against each other, for Zeus was fashioning for us a ruinous doom. But in the morning, we of the one part drew our ships to the fair salt sea, and put aboard our wealth, and the low-girdled Trojan women. Now one half the people abode steadfastly there with Agamemnon, son of Atreus, shepherd of the host; and half of us embarked and drave to sea and swiftly the ships sailed, for a god made smooth the sea with the depths thereof. And when we came to Tenedos, we did sacrifice to the gods, being eager for the homeward way; but Zeus did not yet purpose our returning, nay, hard was he, that roused once more an evil strife among us. Then some turned back their curved ships, and went their way, even the company of Odysseus, the wise and manifold in counsel, once again showing a favour to Agamemnon, son of Atreus. But I fled on with the squadron that followed me, for I knew how now the god imagined mischief. And the warlike son of Tydeus fled and roused his men thereto. And late in our track came Menelaus of the fair hair, who found us in Lesbos, considering about the long voyage, whether we should go seaward of craggy Chios, by the isle of Psyria, keeping the isle upon our left, or inside Chios past windy Mimas. So we asked the god to show us a sign, and a sign he declared to us, and bade us cleave a path across the middle sea to Euboea, that we might flee the swiftest way from sorrow. And a shrill wind arose and blew, and the ships ran most fleetly over the teeming ways, and in the night they touched at Geraestus. So there we sacrificed many thighs of bulls to Poseidon, for joy that we had measured out so great a stretch of sea. It was the fourth day when the company of Diomede son of Tydeus, tamer of horses, moored their gallant ships at Argos; but I held on for Pylos, and the breeze was never quenched from the hour that the god sent it forth to blow. Even so I came, dear child, without tidings, nor know I aught of those others, which of the Achaeans were saved and which were lost. But all that I hear tell of as I sit in our halls, thou shalt learn as it is meet, and I will hide nothing from thee. Safely, they say, came the Myrmidons the wild spearsmen, whom the famous son of high-souled Achilles led; and safely Philoctetes, the glorious son of Poias. And Idomeneus brought all his company to Crete, all that escaped the war, and from him the sea gat none. And of the son of Atreus even yourselves have heard, far apart though ye dwell, how he came, and how Aegisthus devised his evil end, but verily he himself paid a terrible reckoning. So good a thing it is that a son of the dead should still be left, even as that son also took vengeance on the slayer of his father, guileful Aegisthus, who slew his famous sire. And thou too, my friend, for I see thee very comely and tall, be valiant, that even men unborn may praise thee.'

And wise Telemachus answered him, and said: 'Nestor, son of Neleus, great glory of the Achaeans, verily and indeed he avenged himself, and the Achaeans shall noise his fame abroad, that even those may hear who are yet for to be. Oh that the gods would clothe me with such strength as his, that I might take vengeance on the wooers for their cruel transgression, who wantonly devise against me infatuate deeds! But the gods have woven for me the web of no such weal, for me or for my sire. But now I must in any wise endure it.'

Then Nestor of Gerenia, lord of chariots, made answer: 'Dear friend, seeing thou dost call these things to my remembrance and speak thereof, they tell me that many wooers for thy mother's hand plan mischief within the halls in thy despite. Say, dost thou willingly submit thee to oppression, or do the people through the land hate thee, obedient to the voice of a god? Who knows but that Odysseus may some day come and requite their violence, either himself alone or all the host of the Achaeans with him? Ah, if but grey-eyed Athene were inclined to love thee, as once she cared exceedingly for the renowned Odysseus in the land of the Trojans, where we Achaeans were sore afflicted,—for never yet have I seen the gods show forth such manifest love, as then did Pallas Athene standing manifest by him,—if she would be pleased so to love thee and to care for thee, then might certain of them clean forget their marriage.'

And wise Telemachus answered him, saying: 'Old man, in no wise methinks shall this word be accomplished. This is a hard saying of thine, awe comes over me. Not for my hopes shall this thing come to pass, not even if the gods so willed it.'

Then the goddess, grey-eyed Athene, spake to him again: 'Telemachus, what word hath escaped the door of thy lips? Lightly might a god, if so he would, bring a man safe home even from afar. Rather myself would I have travail and much pain ere I came home and saw the day of my returning, than come back and straightway perish on my own hearth-stone, even as Agamemnon perished by guile at the hands of his own wife and of Aegisthus. But lo you, death, which is common to all, the very gods cannot avert even from the man they love, when the ruinous doom shall bring him low of death that lays men at their length.'

And wise Telemachus answered her, saying: 'Mentor, no longer let us tell of these things, sorrowful though we be. There is none assurance any more of his returning, but already have the deathless gods devised for him death and black fate. But now I would question Nestor, and ask him of another matter, as one who above all men knows judgments and wisdom: for thrice, men say, he hath been king through the generations of men; yea, like an immortal he seems to me to look upon. Nestor, son of Neleus, now tell me true: how died the son of Atreus, Agamemnon of the wide domain? Where was Menelaus? What death did crafty Aegisthus plan for him, in that he killed a man more valiant far than he? Or was Menelaus not in Argos of Achaia but wandering elsewhere among men, and that other took heart and slew Agamemnon?'

Then Nestor of Gerenia, lord of chariots, answered him: 'Yea now, my child, I will tell thee the whole truth. Verily thou guessest aright even of thyself how things would have fallen out, if Menelaus of the fair hair, the son of Atreus, when he came back from Troy, had found Aegisthus yet alive in the halls. Then even in his death would they not have heaped the piled earth over him, but dogs and fowls of the air would have devoured him as he lay on the plain far from the town. Nor would any of the Achaean women have bewailed him; so dread was the deed he contrived. Now we sat in leaguer there, achieving many adventures; but he the while in peace in the heart of Argos, the pastureland of horses, spake ofttimes, tempting her, to the wife of Agamemnon. Verily at the first she would none of the foul deed, the fair Clytemnestra, for she had a good understanding. Moreover, there was with her a minstrel, whom the son of Atreus straitly charged as he went to Troy to have a care of his wife. But when at last the doom of the gods bound her to her ruin, then did Aegisthus carry the minstrel to a lonely isle, and left him there to be the prey and spoil of birds; while as for her, he led her to his house, a willing lover with a willing lady. And he burnt many thigh slices upon the holy altars of the gods, and hung up many offerings, woven-work and gold, seeing that he had accomplished a great deed, beyond all hope. Now we, I say, were sailing together on our way from Troy, the son of Atreus and I, as loving friends. But when we had reached holy Sunium, the headland of Athens, there Phoebus Apollo slew the pilot of Menelaus with the visitation of his gentle shafts, as he held between his hands the rudder of the running ship, even Phrontis, son of Onetor, who excelled the tribes of men in piloting a ship, whenso the storm-winds were hurrying by. Thus was Menelaus holden there, though eager for the way, till he might bury his friend and pay the last rites over him. But when he in his turn, faring over the wine-dark sea in hollow ships, reached in swift course the steep mount of Malea, then it was that Zeus of the far-borne voice devised a hateful path, and shed upon them the breath of the shrill winds, and great swelling waves arose like unto mountains. There sundered he the fleet in twain, and part thereof he brought nigh to Crete, where the Cydonians dwelt about the streams of Iardanus. Now there is a certain cliff, smooth and sheer towards the sea, on the border of Gortyn, in the misty deep, where the South-West Wind drives a great wave against the left headland, towards Phaestus, and a little rock keeps back the mighty water. Thither came one part of the fleet, and the men scarce escaped destruction, but the ships were broken by the waves against the rock; while those other five dark-prowed ships the wind and the water bare and brought nigh to Egypt. Thus Menelaus, gathering much livelihood and gold, was wandering there with his ships among men of strange speech, and even then Aegisthus planned that pitiful work at home. And for seven years he ruled over Mycenae, rich in gold, after he slew the son of Atreus, and the people were subdued unto him. But in the eighth year came upon him goodly Orestes back from Athens to be his bane, and slew the slayer of his father, guileful Aegisthus, who killed his famous sire. Now when he had slain him, he made a funeral feast to the Argives over his hateful mother, and over the craven Aegisthus. And on the selfsame day there came to him Menelaus of the loud war-cry, bringing much treasure, even all the freight of his ships. So thou, my friend, wander not long far away from home, leaving thy substance behind thee and men in thy house so wanton, lest they divide and utterly devour all thy wealth, and thou shalt have gone on a vain journey. Rather I bid and command thee to go to Menelaus, for he hath lately come from a strange country, from the land of men whence none would hope in his heart to return, whom once the storms have driven wandering into so wide a sea. Thence not even the birds can make their way in the space of one year, so great a sea it is and terrible.

But go now with thy ship and with thy company, or if thou hast a mind to fare by land, I have a chariot and horses at thy service, yea and my sons to do thy will, who will be thy guides to goodly Lacedaemon, where is Menelaus of the fair hair. Do thou thyself entreat him, that he may give thee unerring answer. He will not lie to thee, for he is very wise.'

Thus he spake, and the sun went down and darkness came on. Then the goddess, grey-eyed Athene, spake among them, saying: 'Yea, old man, thou hast told all this thy tale aright. But come, cut up the tongues of the victims and mix the wine, that we may pour forth before Poseidon and the other deathless gods, and so may bethink us of sleep, for it is the hour for sleep. For already has the light gone beneath the west, and it is not seemly to sit long at a banquet of the gods, but to be going home.'

So spake the daughter of Zeus, and they hearkened to her voice. And the henchmen poured water over their hands, and pages crowned the mixing bowls with drink, and served out the wine to all, after they had first poured for libation into each cup in turn; and they cast the tongues upon the fire, and stood up and poured the drink-offering thereon. But when they had poured forth and had drunken to their heart's content, Athene and godlike Telemachus were both set on returning to the hollow ship; but Nestor would have stayed them, and accosted them, saying: 'Zeus forfend it, and all the other deathless gods, that we should depart from my house to the swift ship, as from the dwelling of one that is utterly without raiment or a needy man, who hath not rugs or blankets many in his house whereon to sleep softly, he or his guests. Nay not so, I have rugs and fair blankets by me. Never, methinks, shall the dear son of this man, even of Odysseus, lay him down upon the ship's deck, while as yet I am alive, and my children after me are left in my hall to entertain strangers, whoso may chance to come to my house.'

Then the goddess, grey-eyed Athene, spake to him again: 'Yea, herein hast thou spoken aright, dear father: and Telemachus may well obey thee, for before all things this is meet. Behold, he shall now depart with thee, that he may sleep in thy halls; as for me I will go to the black ship, that I may cheer my company and tell them all. For I avow me to be the one elder among them; those others are but younger men, who follow for love of him, all of them of like age with the high-souled Telemachus. There will I lay me down by the black hollow ship this night; but in the morning I will go to the Cauconians high of heart, where somewhat of mine is owing to me, no small debt nor of yesterday. But do thou send this man upon his way with thy chariot and thy son, since he hath come to thy house, and give him horses the lightest of foot and chief in strength.'

Therewith grey-eyed Athene departed in the semblance of a sea-eagle; and amazement fell on all that saw it, and the old man he marvelled when his eyes beheld it. And he took the hand of Telemachus and spake and hailed him;

'My friend, methinks that thou wilt in no sort be a coward and a weakling, if indeed in thy youth the gods thus follow with thee to be thy guides. For truly this is none other of those who keep the mansions of Olympus, save only the daughter of Zeus, the driver of the spoil, the maiden Tritoborn, she that honoured thy good father too among the Argives. Nay be gracious, queen, and vouchsafe a goodly fame to me, even to me and to my sons and to my wife revered. And I in turn will sacrifice to thee a yearling heifer, broad of brow, unbroken, which man never yet hath led beneath the yoke. Such an one will I offer to thee, and gild her horns with gold.'

Even so he spake in prayer, and Pallas Athene heard him. Then Nestor of Gerenia, lord of chariots, led them, even his sons and the husbands of his daughters, to his own fair house. But when they had reached this prince's famous halls, they sat down all orderly on seats and high chairs; and when they were come, the old man mixed well for them a bowl of sweet wine, which now in the eleventh year from the vintaging the housewife opened, and unloosed the string that fastened the lid. The old man let mix a bowl thereof, and prayed instantly to Athene as he poured forth before her, even to the daughter of Zeus, lord of the aegis.

But after they had poured forth and had drunken to their hearts' content, these went each one to his own house to lie down to rest. But Nestor of Gerenia, lord of chariots, would needs have Telemachus, son of divine Odysseus, to sleep there on a jointed bedstead beneath the echoing gallery, and by him Peisistratus of the good ashen spear, leader of men, who alone of his sons was yet unwed in his halls. As for him he slept within the inmost chamber of the lofty house, and the lady his wife arrayed for him bedstead and bedding.

So soon as early Dawn shone forth, the rosy-fingered, Nestor of Gerenia, lord of chariots, gat him up from his bed, and he went forth and sat him down upon the smooth stones, which were before his lofty doors, all polished, white and glistening, whereon Neleus sat of old, in counsel the peer of the gods. Howbeit, stricken by fate, he had ere now gone down to the house of Hades, and to-day Nestor of Gerenia in his turn sat thereon, warder of the Achaeans, with his staff in his hands. And about him his sons were gathered and come together, issuing from their chambers, Echephron and Stratius, and Perseus and Aretus and the godlike Thrasymedes. And sixth and last came the hero Peisistratus. And they led godlike Telemachus and set him by their side, and Nestor of Gerenia, lord of chariots, spake first among them:

'Quickly, my dear children, accomplish my desire, that

first of all the gods I may propitiate Athene, who came to me in visible presence to the rich feast of the god. Nay then, let one go to the plain for a heifer, that she may come as soon as may be, and that the neatherd may drive her: and let another go to the black ship of high-souled Telemachus to bring all his company, and let him leave two men only. And let one again bid Laerces the goldsmith to come hither that he may gild the horns of the heifer. And ye others, abide ye here together and speak to the handmaids within that they make ready a banquet through our famous halls, and fetch seats and logs to set about the altar, and bring clear water.'

Thus he spake and lo, they all hastened to the work. The heifer she came from the field, and from the swift gallant ship came the company of great-hearted Telemachus; the smith came holding in his hands his tools, the instruments of his craft, anvil and hammer and well-made pincers, wherewith he wrought the gold; Athene too came to receive her sacrifice. And the old knight Nestor gave gold, and the other fashioned it skilfully, and gilded therewith the horns of the heifer, that the goddess might be glad at the sight of her fair offering. And Stratius and goodly Echephron led the heifer by the horns. And Aretus came forth from the chamber bearing water for the washing of hands in a basin of flowered work, and in the other hand he held the barley-meal in a basket; and Thrasymedes, steadfast in the battle, stood by holding in his hand a sharp axe, ready to smite the heifer. And Perseus held the dish for the blood, and the old man Nestor, driver of chariots, performed the first rite of the washing of hands and the sprinkling of the meal, and he prayed instantly to Athene as he began the rite, casting into the fire the lock from the head of the victim.

Now when they had prayed and tossed the sprinkled grain, straightway the son of Nestor, gallant Thrasymedes, stood by and struck the blow; and the axe severed the tendons of the neck and loosened the might of the heifer; and the women raised their cry, the daughters and the sons' wives and the wife revered of Nestor, Eurydice, eldest of the daughters of Clymenus. And now they lifted the victim's head from the wide-wayed earth, and held it so, while Peisistratus, leader of men, cut the throat. And after the black blood had gushed forth and the life had left the bones, quickly they broke up the body, and anon cut slices from the thighs all duly, and wrapt the same in the fat, folding them double, and laid raw flesh thereon. So that old man burnt them on the cleft wood, and poured over them the red wine, and by his side the young men held in their hands the five-pronged forks. Now after that the thighs were quite consumed and they had tasted the inner parts, they cut the rest up small and spitted and roasted it, holding the sharp spits in their hands.

Meanwhile she bathed Telemachus, even fair Polycaste, the youngest daughter of Nestor, son of Neleus. And after she had bathed him and anointed him with olive oil, and cast about him a goodly mantle and a doublet, he came forth from the bath in fashion like the deathless gods. So he went and sat him down by Nestor, shepherd of the people.

Now when they had roasted the outer flesh, and drawn it off the spits, they sat down and fell to feasting, and honourable men waited on them, pouring wine into the golden cups. But when they had put from them the desire of meat and drink, Nestor of Gerenia, lord of chariots, first spake among them:

'Lo now, my sons, yoke for Telemachus horses with flowing manes and lead them beneath the car, that he may get forward on his way.'

Even so he spake, and they gave good heed and hearkened; and quickly they yoked the swift horses beneath the chariot. And the dame that kept the stores placed therein corn and wine and dainties, such as princes eat, the fosterlings of Zeus. So Telemachus stept up into the goodly car, and with him Peisistratus son of Nestor, leader of men, likewise climbed the car and grasped the reins in his hands, and he touched the horses with the whip to start them, and nothing loth the pair flew toward the plain, and left the steep citadel of Pylos. So all day long they swayed the yoke they bore upon their necks.

Now the sun sank and all the ways were darkened. And they came to Pherae, to the house of Diocles, son of Orsilochus, the child begotten of Alpheus. There they rested for the night, and by them he set the entertainment of strangers.

Now so soon as early Dawn shone forth, the rosy-fingered, they yoked the horses and mounted the inlaid car. And forth they drave from the gateway and the echoing gallery, and Peisistratus touched the horses with the whip to start them, and the pair flew onward nothing loth. So they came to the wheat-bearing plain, and thenceforth they pressed toward the end: in such wise did the swift horses speed forward. Now the sun sank and all the ways were darkened.

BOOK IV

Telemachus's entertainment at Sparta, where Menelaus tells him what befell many of the Greeks on their return; that Odysseus was with Calypso in the isle Ogygia, as he was told by Proteus.

AND they came to Lacedaemon lying low among the caverned hills, and drave to the dwelling of renowned Menelaus. Him they found giving a feast in his house to many friends of his kin, a feast for the wedding of his noble son and daughter. His daughter he was sending to the son of Achilles, cleaver of the ranks of men, for in Troy he first had promised and covenanted to give her, and now the gods were bringing about their marriage. So now he was speeding her on her way with chariot and horses, to the famous city of the Myrmidons, among whom her lord bare rule. And for his son he was bringing to his home the daughter of Alector out of Sparta, for his well-beloved son, strong Megapenthes, born of a slave woman, for the gods no more showed promise of seed to Helen, from the day that she bare a lovely child, Hermione, as fair as golden Aphrodite. So they were feasting through the great vaulted hall, the neighbours and the kinsmen of renowned Menelaus, making merry; and among them a divine minstrel was singing to the lyre, and as he began the song two tumblers in the company whirled through the midst of them.

Meanwhile those twain, the hero Telemachus and the splendid son of Nestor, made halt at the entry of the gate, they and their horses. And the lord Eteoneus came forth and saw them, the ready squire of renowned Menelaus; and he went through the palace to bear the tidings to the shepherd of the people, and standing near spake to him winged words:

'Menelaus, fosterling of Zeus, here are two strangers, whosoever they be, two men like to the lineage of great Zeus. Say, shall we loose their swift horses from under the yoke, or send them onward to some other host who shall receive them kindly?'

Then in sore displeasure spake to him Menelaus of the fair hair: 'Eteoneus son of Boethous, truly thou wert not a fool aforetime, but now for this once, like a child thou talkest folly. Surely ourselves ate much hospitable cheer of other men, ere we twain came hither, even if in time to come Zeus haply give us rest from affliction. Nay go, unyoke the horses of the strangers, and as for the men, lead them forward to the house to feast with us.'

So spake he, and Eteoneus hasted from the hall, and called the other ready squires to follow with him. So they loosed the sweating horses from beneath the yoke, and fastened them at the stalls of the horses, and threw beside them spelt, and therewith mixed white barley, and tilted the chariot against the shining faces of the gateway, and led the men into the hall divine. And they beheld and marvelled as they gazed throughout the palace of the king, the fosterling of Zeus; for there was a gleam as it were of sun or moon through the lofty palace of renowned Menelaus. But after they had gazed their fill, they went to the polished baths and bathed them. Now when the maidens had bathed them and anointed them with olive oil, and cast about them thick cloaks and doublets, they sat on chairs by Menelaus, son of Atreus. And a handmaid bare water for the hands in a goodly golden ewer and poured it forth over a silver basin to wash withal; and to their side she drew a polished table, and a grave dame bare food and set it by them, and laid upon the board many dainties, giving freely of such things as she had by her, and a carver lifted and placed by them platters of divers kinds of flesh, and nigh them he set golden bowls. So Menelaus of the fair hair greeted the twain and spake:

'Taste ye food and be glad, and thereafter when ye have supped, we will ask what men ye are; for the blood of your parents is not lost in you, but ye are of the line of men that are sceptred kings, the fosterlings of Zeus; for no churls could beget sons like you.'

So spake he, and took and set before them the fat oxchine roasted, which they had given him as his own mess by way of honour. And they stretched forth their hands upon the good cheer set before them. Now when they had put from them the desire of meat and drink Telemachus spake to the son of Nestor, holding his head close to him, that those others might not hear:

'Son of Nestor, delight of my heart, mark the flashing of bronze through the echoing halls, and the flashing of gold and of amber and of silver and of ivory. Such like, methinks, is the court of Olympian Zeus within, for the world of things that are here; wonder comes over me as I look thereon.'

And as he spake Menelaus of the fair hair was ware of him, and uttering his voice spake to them winged words:

'Children dear, of a truth no one of mortal men may contend with Zeus, for his mansions and his treasures are everlasting: but of men there may be who will vie with me in treasure, or there may be none. Yea, for after many a woe and wanderings manifold, I brought my wealth home in ships, and in the eighth year came hither. I roamed over Cyprus and Phoenicia and Egypt, and reached the Ethiopians and Sidonians and Erembi and Libya, where lambs are horned from the birth. For there the ewes yean thrice within the full circle of a year; there neither lord nor shepherd lacketh aught of cheese or flesh or of sweet milk, but ever the flocks yield store of milk continual.

While I was yet roaming in those lands, gathering much livelihood, meantime another slew my brother privily, at unawares, by the guile of his accursed wife. Thus, look you, I have no joy of my lordship among these my possessions; and ye are like to have heard hereof from your fathers, whosoever they be, for I have suffered much and let a house go to ruin that was stablished fair, and had in it much choice substance. I would that I had but a third part of those my riches, and dwelt in my halls, and that those men were yet safe, who perished of old in the wide land of Troy, far from Argos, the pastureland of horses. Howbeit, though I bewail them all and sorrow oftentimes as I sit in our halls,—awhile indeed I satisfy my soul with lamentation, and then again I cease; for soon hath man enough of chill lamentation—yet for them all I make no such dole, despite my grief, as for one only, who causes me to loathe both sleep and meat, when I think upon him. For no one of the Achaeans toiled so greatly as Odysseus toiled and adventured himself: but to him it was to be but labour and trouble, and to me grief ever comfortless for his sake, so long he is afar, nor know we aught, whether he be alive or dead. Yea methinks they lament him, even that old Laertes and the constant Penelope and Telemachus, whom he left a child new-born in his house.'

So spake he, and in the heart of Telemachus he stirred a yearning to lament his father; and at his father's name he let a tear fall from his eyelids to the ground, and held up his purple mantle with both his hands before his eyes. And Menelaus marked him and mused in his mind and his heart whether he should leave him to speak of his father, or first question him and prove him in every word.

While yet he pondered these things in his mind and in his heart, Helen came forth from her fragrant vaulted chamber, like Artemis of the golden arrows; and with her came Adrastê and set for her the well-wrought chair, and

Alcippê bare a rug of soft wool, and Phylo bare a silver basket which Alcandrê gave her, the wife of Polybus, who dwelt in Thebes of Egypt, where is the chiefest store of wealth in the houses. He gave two silver baths to Menelaus, and tripods twain, and ten talents of gold. And besides all this, his wife bestowed on Helen lovely gifts; a golden distaff did she give, and a silver basket with wheels beneath, and the rims thereof were finished with gold. This it was that the handmaid Phylo bare and set beside her, filled with dressed yarn, and across it was laid a distaff charged with wool of violet blue. So Helen sat her down in the chair, and beneath was a footstool for the feet. And anon she spake to her lord and questioned him of each thing:

'Menelaus, fosterling of Zeus, know we now who these men avow themselves to be that have come under our roof? Shall I dissemble or shall I speak the truth? Nay, I am minded to tell it. None, I say, have I ever yet seen so like another, man nor woman—wonder comes over me as I look on him—as this man is like the son of great-hearted Odysseus, Telemachus, whom he left a new-born child in his house, when for the sake of me, shameless woman that I was, ye Achaeans came up under Troy with bold war in your hearts.'

And Menelaus of the fair hair answered her, saying: 'Now I too, lady, mark the likeness even as thou tracest it. For such as these were his feet, such his hands, and the glances of his eyes, and his head, and his hair withal. Yea, and even now I was speaking of Odysseus, as I remembered him, of all his woeful travail for my sake; when, lo, he let fall a bitter tear beneath his brows, and held his purple cloak up before his eyes.'

And Peisistratus, son of Nestor, answered him, saying: 'Menelaus, son of Atreus, fosterling of Zeus, leader of the host, assuredly this is the son of that very man, even as thou sayest. But he is of a sober wit, and thinketh it shame in his heart as on this his first coming to make show of presumptuous words in the presence of thee, in whose voice we twain delight as in the voice of a god. Now Nestor of Gerenia, lord of chariots, sent me forth to be his guide on the way: for he desired to see thee that thou mightest put into his heart some word or work. For a son hath many griefs in his halls when his father is away, if perchance he hath none to stand by him. Even so it is now with Telemachus; his father is away, nor hath he others in the township to defend him from distress.'

And Menelaus of the fair hair answered him, and said: 'Lo now, in good truth there has come unto my house the son of a friend indeed, who for my sake endured many adventures. And I thought to welcome him on his coming more nobly than all the other Argives, if but Olympian Zeus, of the far-borne voice, had vouchsafed us a return over the sea in our swift ships,—that such a thing should be. And in Argos I would have given him a city to dwell in, and stablished for him a house, and brought him forth from Ithaca with his substance and his son and all his people, making one city desolate of those that lie around, and are in mine own domain. Then ofttimes would we have held converse here, and naught would have parted us, the welcoming and the welcomed, ere the black cloud of death overshadowed us. Howsoever, the god himself, methinks, must have been jealous hereof, who from that hapless man alone cut off his returning.'

So spake he, and in the hearts of all he stirred the desire of lamentation. She wept, even Argive Helen the daughter of Zeus, and Telemachus wept, and Menelaus the son of Atreus; nay, nor did the son of Nestor keep tearless eyes. For he bethought him in his heart of noble Antilochus, whom the glorious son of the bright Dawn had slain. Thinking upon him he spake winged words:

'Son of Atreus, the ancient Nestor in his own halls was ever wont to say that thou wert wise beyond man's wisdom, whensoever we made mention of thee and asked one another concerning thee. And now, if it be possible, be persuaded by me, who for one have no pleasure in weeping at supper time—the new-born day will right soon be upon us. Not indeed that I deem it blame at all to weep for any mortal who hath died and met his fate. Lo, this is now the only due we pay to miserable men, to cut the hair and let the tear fall from the cheek. For I too have a brother dead, nowise the meanest of the Argives, and thou art like to have known him, for as for me I never encountered him, never beheld him. But men say that Antilochus outdid all, being excellent in speed of foot and in the fight.'

And Menelaus of the fair hair answered him, and said: 'My friend, lo, thou hast said all that a wise man might say or do, yea, and an elder than thou;—for from such a sire too thou art sprung, wherefore thou dost even speak wisely. Right easily known is that man's seed, for whom Cronion weaves the skein of luck at bridal and at birth: even as now hath he granted prosperity to Nestor for ever for all his days, that he himself should grow into a smooth old age in his halls, and his sons moreover should be wise and the best of spearmen. But we will cease now the weeping which was erewhile made, and let us once more bethink us of our supper, and let them pour water over our hands. And again in the morning there will be tales for Telemachus and me to tell one to the other, even to the end.'

So spake he, and Asphalion poured water over their hands, the ready squire of renowned Menelaus. And they put forth their hands upon the good cheer spread before them.

Then Helen, daughter of Zeus, turned to new thoughts. Presently she cast a drug into the wine whereof they drank, a drug to lull all pain and anger, and bring forgetfulness of every sorrow. Whoso should drink a draught thereof, when it is mingled in the bowl, on that day he would let no tear fall down his cheeks, not though his mother and his father died, not though men slew his brother or dear son with the sword before his face, and his own eyes beheld it. Medicines of such virtue and so helpful had the daughter of Zeus, which Polydamna, the wife of Thon, had given her, a woman of Egypt, where earth the grain-giver yields herbs in greatest plenty, many that are healing in the cup, and many baneful. There each man is a leech skilled beyond all human kind; yea, for they are of the race of Paeëon. Now after she had cast in the drug and bidden pour forth of the wine, she made answer once again, and spake unto her lord:

'Son of Atreus, Menelaus, fosterling of Zeus, and lo, ye sons of noble men, forasmuch as now to one and now to another Zeus gives good and evil, for to him all things are possible,—now, verily, sit ye down and feast in the halls, and take ye joy in the telling of tales, and I will tell you one that fits the time. Now all of them I could not tell or number, so many as were the adventures of Odysseus of the hardy heart; but, ah, what a deed was this he wrought and dared in his hardiness in the land of the Trojans, where ye Achaeans suffered affliction. He subdued his body with unseemly stripes, and a sorry covering he cast about his shoulders, and in the fashion of a servant he went down into the wide-wayed city of the foemen, and he did himself in the guise of another, a beggar, though in no wise such an one was he at the ships of the Achaeans. In this semblance he passed into the city of the Trojans, and they wist not who he was, and I alone knew him in that guise, and I kept questioning him, but in his subtlety he avoided me. But when at last I was about washing him and anointing him with olive oil, and had put on him raiment, and sworn a great oath not to reveal Odysseus amid the Trojans, ere he reached the swift ships and the huts, even then he told me all the purpose of the Achaeans. And after slaying many of the Trojans with the long sword, he returned to the Argives and brought back word again of all. Then the other Trojan women wept aloud, but my soul was glad, for already my heart was turned to go back again even to my home: and now at the last I groaned for the blindness that Aphrodite gave me, when she led me thither away from mine own country, forsaking my child and my bridal chamber and my lord, that lacked not aught whether for wisdom or yet for beauty.'

And Menelaus of the fair hair answered her, saying: 'Verily all this tale, lady, thou hast duly told. Ere now have I learned the counsel and the thought of many heroes, and travelled over many a land, but never yet have mine eyes beheld any such man of heart as was Odysseus; such another deed as he wrought and dared in his hardiness even in the shapen horse, wherein sat all we chiefs of the Argives, bearing to the Trojans death and doom. Anon thou camest thither, and sure some god must have bidden thee, who wished to bring glory to the Trojans. Yea and godlike Deiphobus went with thee on thy way. Thrice thou didst go round about the hollow ambush and handle it, calling aloud on the chiefs of the Argives by name, and making thy voice like the voices of the wives of all the Argives. Now I and the son of Tydeus and goodly Odysseus sat in the midst and heard thy call; and verily we twain had a desire to start up and come forth or presently to answer from within; but Odysseus stayed and held us there, despite our eagerness. Then all the other sons of the Achaeans held their peace, but Anticlus alone was still minded to answer thee. Howbeit Odysseus firmly closed his mouth with strong hands, and so saved all the Achaeans, and held him until such time as Pallas Athene led thee back.'

Then wise Telemachus answered him, and said: 'Menelaus, son of Atreus, fosterling of Zeus, leader of the host, all the more grievous it is! for in no way did this courage ward from him pitiful destruction, not though his heart within him had been very iron. But come, bid us to bed, that forthwith we may take our joy of rest beneath the spell of sleep.'

So spake he, and Argive Helen bade her handmaids set out bedsteads beneath the gallery, and fling on them fair purple blankets and spread coverlets above, and thereon lay thick mantles to be a clothing over all. So they went from the hall with torch in hand, and spread the beds, and the henchman led forth the guests. Thus they slept there in the vestibule of the house, the hero Telemachus and the splendid son of Nestor. But the son of Atreus slept, as his custom was, in the inmost chamber of the lofty house, and by him lay long-robed Helen, that fair lady.

Soon as early Dawn shone forth, the rosy-fingered, Menelaus of the loud war-shout gat him up from his bed and put on his raiment, and cast his sharp sword about his shoulder, and beneath his smooth feet bound his goodly sandals, and stept forth from his chamber, in presence like a god, and sat by Telemachus, and spake and hailed him:

'To what end hath thy need brought thee hither, hero Telemachus, unto fair Lacedaemon, over the broad back of the sea? Is it a matter of the common weal or of thine own? Herein tell me the plain truth.'

Then wise Telemachus answered him, and said: 'Menelaus, son of Atreus, fosterling of Zeus, leader of the host, I have come if perchance thou mayest tell me some tidings of my father. My dwelling is being devoured and my fat lands are ruined, and of unfriendly men my house is full,—who slaughter continually my thronging flocks, and my kine with trailing feet and shambling gait,—none other than the wooers of my mother, despiteful out of measure. So now am I come hither to thy knees, if haply thou art willing to tell me of his pitiful death, as one that saw it perchance with thine own eyes, or heard the story from some other wanderer; for his mother bare him to exceeding sorrow. And speak me no soft words in ruth or pity, but tell me plainly how thou didst get sight of him. Ah,

I pray thee, if ever at all my father, good Odysseus, made promise to thee of word or work and fulfilled the same in the land of the Trojans, where ye Achaeans suffered affliction, these things, I pray thee, now remember and tell me truth.'

Then in heavy displeasure spake to him Menelaus of the fair hair: 'Out upon them, for truly in the bed of a brave-hearted man were they minded to lie, very cravens as they are! Even as when a hind hath couched her newborn fawns unweaned in a strong lion's lair, and searcheth out the mountain-knees and grassy hollows, seeking pasture, and afterward the lion cometh back to his bed, and sendeth forth unsightly death upon that pair, even so shall Odysseus send forth unsightly death upon the wooers. Would to our father Zeus and Athene and Apollo, would that in such might as when of old in stablished Lesbos he rose up and wrestled a match with Philomeleides and threw him mightily, and all the Achaeans rejoiced; would that in such strength Odysseus might consort with the wooers: then should they all have swift fate, and bitter wedlock! But for that whereof thou askest and entreatest me, be sure I will not swerve from the truth in aught that I say, nor deceive thee; but of all that the ancient one of the sea, whose speech is sooth, declared to me, not a word will I hide or keep from thee.

'In the river Aegyptus, though eager I was to press onward home, the gods they stayed me, for that I had not offered them the acceptable sacrifice of hecatombs, and the gods ever desired that men should be mindful of their commandments. Now there is an island in the wash of the waves over against Aegyptus, and men call it Pharos, within one day's voyage of a hollow ship, when shrill winds blow fair in her wake. And therein is a good haven, whence men launch the gallant ships into the deep when they have drawn a store of deep black water. There the gods held me twenty days, nor did the sea-winds ever show their breath, they that serve to waft ships over the broad back of the sea. And now would all our corn have been spent, and likewise the strength of the men, except some goddess had taken pity on me and saved me, Eidotheë, daughter of mighty Proteus, the ancient one of the sea. For most of all I moved her heart, when she met me wandering alone apart from my company, who were ever roaming round the isle, fishing with bent hooks, for hunger was gnawing at their belly. So she stood by, and spake and uttered her voice, saying:

'"Art thou so very foolish, stranger, and feeble-witted, or art thou wilfully remiss, and hast pleasure in suffering? So long time art thou holden in the isle and canst find no issue therefrom, while the heart of thy company faileth within them?"

'Even so she spake, and I answered her saying: "I will speak forth, what goddess soever thou art, and tell thee that in no wise am I holden here by mine own will, but it needs must be that I have sinned against the deathless gods, who keep the wide heaven. Howbeit, do thou tell me—for the gods know all things—which of the immortals it is that binds me here and hath hindered me from my way, and declare as touching my returning how I may go over the teeming deep."

'So I spake, and straightway the fair goddess made answer: "Yea now, sir, I will plainly tell thee all. Hither resorteth that ancient one of the sea, whose speech is sooth, the deathless Egyptian Proteus, who knows the depths of every sea, and is the thrall of Poseidon, and who, they say, is my father that begat me. If thou couldst but lay an ambush and catch him, he will surely declare to thee the way and the measure of thy path, and will tell thee of thy returning, how thou mayest go over the teeming deep. Yea, and he will show thee, O fosterling of Zeus, if thou wilt, what good thing and what evil hath been wrought in thy halls, whilst thou hast been faring this long and grievous way."

'So she spake, but I answered and said unto her: "Devise now thyself the ambush to take this ancient one divine, lest by any chance he see me first, or know of my coming, and avoid me. For a god is hard for mortal man to quell."

'So spake I, and straightway the fair goddess made answer: "Yea now, sir, I will plainly tell thee all. So often as the sun in his course stands high in mid heaven, then forth from the brine comes the ancient one of the sea, whose speech is sooth, before the breath of the West Wind he comes, and the sea's dark ripple covers him. And when he is got forth, he lies down to sleep in the hollow of the caves. And around him the seals, the brood of the fair daughter of the brine, sleep all in a flock, stolen forth from the grey sea water, and bitter is the scent they breathe of the deeps of the salt sea. There will I lead thee at the breaking of the day, and couch you all orderly; so do thou choose diligently three of thy company, the best thou hast in thy decked ships. And I will tell thee all the magic arts of that old man. First, he will number the seals and go over them; but when he has told their tale and beheld them, he will lay him down in the midst, as a shepherd 'mid the sheep of his flock. So soon as ever ye shall see him couched, even then mind you of your might and strength, and hold him there, despite his eagerness and striving to be free. And he will make assay, and take all manner of shapes of things that creep upon the earth, of water likewise, and of fierce fire burning. But do ye grasp him steadfastly and press him yet the more, and at length when he questions thee in his proper shape, as he was when first ye saw him laid to rest, then, hero, hold thy strong hands, and let the ancient one go free, and ask him which of the gods is hard upon thee, and as touching thy returning, how thou mayest go over the teeming deep."

'Therewith she dived beneath the heaving sea, but I

betook me to the ships where they stood in the sand, and my heart was darkly troubled as I went. But after I had come down to the ship and to the sea, and we had made ready our supper and immortal night had come on, then did we lay us to rest upon the sea-beach. So soon as early Dawn shone forth, the rosy-fingered, in that hour I walked by the shore of the wide-wayed sea, praying instantly to the gods; and I took with me three of my company, in whom I trusted most for every enterprise.

'Meanwhile, so it was that she had plunged into the broad bosom of the sea, and had brought from the deep the skins of four sea-calves, and all were newly flayed, for she was minded to lay a snare for her father. She scooped lairs on the sea-sand, and sat awaiting us, and we drew very nigh her, and she made us all lie down in order, and cast a skin over each. There would our ambush have been most terrible, for the deadly stench of the sea-bred seals distressed us sore: nay, who would lay him down by a beast of the sea? But herself she wrought deliverance, and devised a great comfort. She took ambrosia of a very sweet savour, and set it beneath each man's nostril, and did away with the stench of the beast. So all the morning we waited with steadfast heart, and the seals came forth in troops from the brine, and then they couched them all orderly by the sea-beach. And at high day the ancient one came forth from out of the brine, and found his fatted seals, yea and he went along their line and told their tale; and first among the sea-beasts he reckoned us, and guessed not that there was guile, and afterward he too laid him down. Then we rushed upon him with a cry, and cast our hands about him, nor did that ancient one forget his cunning. Now behold, at the first he turned into a bearded lion, and thereafter into a snake, and a pard, and a huge boar; then he took the shape of running water, and of a tall and flowering tree. We the while held him close with steadfast heart. But when now that ancient one of the magic arts was aweary, then at last he questioned me and spake unto me, saying:

'"Which of the gods was it, son of Atreus, that aided thee with his counsel, that thou mightest waylay and take me perforce? What wouldest thou thereby?"

'Even so he spake, but I answered him saying: "Old man, thou knowest all, wherefore dost thou question me thereof with crooked words? For lo, I am holden long time in this isle, neither can I find any issue therefrom, and my heart faileth within me. Howbeit do thou tell me—for the gods know all things—which of the immortals it is that bindeth me here, and hath hindered me from my way; and declare as touching my returning, how I may go over the teeming deep."

'Even so I spake, and he straightway answered me saying: "Nay, surely thou shouldest have done goodly sacrifice to Zeus and the other gods ere thine embarking, that with most speed thou mightest reach thy country, sailing over the wine-dark deep. For it is not thy fate to see thy friends, and come to thy stablished house and thine own country, till thou hast passed yet again within the waters of Aegyptus, the heaven-fed stream, and offered holy hecatombs to the deathless gods who keep the wide heaven. So shall the gods grant thee the path which thou desirest."

'So spake he, but my spirit within me was broken, for that he bade me again to go to Aegyptus over the misty deep, a long and grievous way.

'Yet even so I answered him saying: "Old man, all this will I do, according to thy word. But come, declare me this, and tell it all plainly. Did all those Achaeans return safe with their ships, all whom Nestor and I left as we went from Troy, or perished any by a shameful death aboard his own ship, or in the arms of his friends, after he had wound up the clew of war?"

'So spake I, and anon he answered me saying: "Son of Atreus, why dost thou straitly question me hereof? Nay, it is not for thy good to know or learn my thought; for I tell thee thou shalt not long be tearless, when thou hast heard it all aright. For many of these were taken, and many were left; but two only of the leaders of the mail-coated Achaeans perished in returning; as for the battle, thou thyself wast there. And one methinks is yet alive, and is holden on the wide deep. Aias in truth was smitten in the midst of his ships of the long oars. Poseidon at first brought him nigh to Gyrae, to the mighty rocks, and delivered him from the sea. And so would he have fled his doom, albeit hated by Athene, had he not let a proud word fall in the fatal darkening of his heart. He said that in the gods' despite he had escaped the great gulf of the sea; and Poseidon heard his loud boasting, and presently caught up his trident into his strong hands, and smote the rock Gyraean and cleft it in twain. And the one part abode in his place, but the other fell into the sea, the broken piece whereon Aias sat at the first, when his heart was darkened. And the rock bore him down into the vast and heaving deep; so there he perished when he had drunk of the salt sea water. But thy brother verily escaped the fates and avoided them in his hollow ships, for queen Hera saved him. But now when he was like soon to reach the steep mount of Malea, lo, the storm wind snatched him away and bore him over the teeming deep, making great moan, to the border of the country where of old Thyestes dwelt, but now Aegisthus abode there, the son of Thyestes. But when thence too there showed a good prospect of safe returning, and the gods changed the wind to a fair gale, and they had reached home, then verily did Agamemnon set foot with joy upon his country's soil, and as he touched his own land he kissed it, and many were the hot tears he let fall, for he saw his land and was glad. And it was so that the watchman spied him from his tower, the watchman whom crafty Aegisthus had led and posted there, promising him for a reward two talents of gold.

Now he kept watch for the space of a year, lest Agamemnon should pass by him when he looked not, and mind him of his wild prowess. So he went to the house to bear the tidings to the shepherd of the people. And straightway Aegisthus contrived a cunning treason. He chose out twenty of the best men in the township, and set an ambush, and on the further side of the hall he commanded to prepare a feast. Then with chariot and horse he went to bid to the feast Agamemnon, shepherd of the people; but caitiff thoughts were in his heart. He brought him up to his house, all unwitting of his doom, and when he had feasted him slew him, as one slayeth an ox at the stall. And none of the company of Atreides that were of his following were left, nor any of the men of Aegisthus, but they were all killed in the halls."

'So spake he, and my spirit within me was broken, and I wept as I sat upon the sand, nor was I minded any more to live and to see the light of the sun. But when I had taken my fill of weeping and grovelling on the ground, then spake the ancient one of the sea, whose speech is sooth:

' "No more, son of Atreus, hold this long weeping without cease, for we shall find no help therein. Rather with all haste make essay that so thou mayest come to thine own country. For either thou shalt find Aegisthus yet alive, or it may be Orestes was beforehand with thee and slew him; so mayest thou chance upon his funeral feast."

'So he spake, and my heart and lordly soul again were comforted for all my sorrows, and I uttered my voice and I spake to him winged words:

' "Their fate I now know; but tell me of the third; who is it that is yet living and holden on the wide deep, or perchance is dead? and fain would I hear despite my sorrow."

'So spake I, and straightway he answered, and said: "It is the son of Laertes, whose dwelling is in Ithaca; and I saw him in an island shedding big tears in the halls of the nymph Calypso, who holds him there perforce; so he may not come to his own country, for he has by him no ships with oars, and no companions to send him on his way over the broad back of the sea. But thou, Menelaus, son of Zeus, art not ordained to die and meet thy fate in Argos, the pasture-land of horses, but the deathless gods will convey thee to the Elysian plain and the world's end, where is Rhadamanthus of the fair hair, where life is easiest for men. No snow is there, nor yet great storm, nor any rain; but always ocean sendeth forth the breeze of the shrill West to blow cool on men: yea, for thou hast Helen to wife, and thereby they deem thee to be son of Zeus."

'So spake he, and plunged into the heaving sea; but I betook me to the ships with my godlike company, and my heart was darkly troubled as I went. Now after I had come down to the ship and to the sea, and had made ready our supper, and immortal night had come on, then did we lay us to rest upon the sea-beach. So soon as early Dawn shone forth, the rosy-fingered, first of all we drew down our ships to the fair salt sea and placed the masts and the sails in the gallant ships, and the crew too climbed on board, and sat upon the benches and smote the grey sea water with their oars. Then back I went to the waters of Aegyptus, the heaven-fed stream, and there I moored the ships and offered the acceptable sacrifice of hecatombs. So when I had appeased the anger of the everlasting gods, I piled a barrow to Agamemnon, that his fame might never be quenched. So having fulfilled all, I set out for home, and the deathless gods gave me a fair wind, and brought me swiftly to mine own dear country. But lo, now tarry in my halls till it shall be the eleventh day hence or the twelfth. Then will I send thee with all honour on thy way, and give thee splendid gifts, three horses and a polished car; and moreover I will give thee a goodly chalice, that thou mayest pour forth before the deathless gods, and be mindful of me all the days of thy life.'

Then wise Telemachus answered him, saying: 'Son of Atreus, nay, hold me not long time here. Yea even for a year would I be content to sit by thee, and no desire for home or parents would come upon me; for I take wondrous pleasure in thy tales and talk. But already my company wearieth in fair Pylos, and yet thou art keeping me long time here. And whatsoever gift thou wouldest give me, let it be a thing to treasure; but horses I will take none to Ithaca, but leave them here to grace thine own house, for thou art lord of a wide plain wherein is lotus great plenty, and therein is spear-reed and wheat and rye, and white and spreading barley. In Ithaca there are no wide courses, nor meadow land at all. It is a pasture-land of goats, and more pleasant in my sight than one that pastureth horses; for of the isles that lie and lean upon the sea, none are fit for the driving of horses, or rich in meadow land, and least of all is Ithaca.'

So spake he, and Menelaus of the loud war-cry smiled, and caressed him with his hand, and spake and hailed him: 'Thou art of gentle blood, dear child, so gentle the words thou speakest. Therefore I will make exchange of the presents, as I may. Of the gifts, such as are treasures stored in my house, I will give thee the goodliest and greatest of price. I will give thee a mixing bowl beautifully wrought; it is all of silver, and the lips thereof are finished with gold, the work of Hephaestus; and the hero Phaedimus, the king of the Sidonians, gave it me, when his house sheltered me on my coming thither, and to thee now would I give it.'

Even so they spake one to another, while the guests came to the palace of the divine king. They drave their sheep, and brought wine that maketh glad the heart of man: and their wives with fair tire sent them wheaten bread. Thus were these men preparing the feast in the halls.

But the wooers meantime were before the palace of Odysseus, taking their pleasure in casting of weights and spears, on a levelled place, as heretofore, in their insolence. And Antinous and god-like Eurymachus were seated there, the chief men of the wooers, who were far the most excellent of all. And Noemon, son of Phromius, drew nigh to them and spake unto Antinous and questioned him, saying:

'Antinous, know we at all, or know we not, when Telemachus will return from sandy Pylos? He hath departed with a ship of mine, and I have need thereof, to cross over into spacious Elis, where I have twelve brood mares with hardy mules unbroken at the teat; I would drive off one of these and break him in.'

So spake he, and they were amazed, for they deemed not that Telemachus had gone to Neleian Pylos, but that he was at home somewhere in the fields, whether among the flocks, or with the swineherd.

Then Antinous, son of Eupeithes, spake to him in turn: 'Tell me the plain truth; when did he go, and what noble youths went with him? Were they chosen men of Ithaca or hirelings and thralls of his own? He was in case to bring even that about. And tell me this in good sooth, that I may know for a surety: did he take thy black ship from thee perforce against thy will? or didst thou give it him of free will at his entreaty?'

Then Noemon, son of Phromius, answered him saying: 'I gave it him myself of free will. What can any man do, when such an one, so bestead with care, begs a favour? it were hard to deny the gift. The youths who next to us are noblest in the land, even these have gone with him; and I marked their leader on board ship, Mentor, or a god who in all things resembled Mentor. But one matter I marvel at: I saw the goodly Mentor here yesterday toward dawn, though already he had embarked for Pylos.'

He spake and withal departed to his father's house. And

the proud spirits of these twain were angered, and they made the wooers sit down together and cease from their games. And among them spake Antinous, son of Eupeithes, in displeasure; and his black heart was wholly filled with rage, and his eyes were like flaming fire:

'Out on him, a proud deed hath Telemachus accomplished with a high hand, even this journey, and we thought that he would never bring it to pass! This lad hath clean gone without more ado, in spite of us all; his ship he hath let haul to the sea, and chosen the noblest in the township. He will begin to be our bane even more than heretofore; but may Zeus destroy his might, not ours, ere he reach the measure of manhood! But come, give me a swift ship and twenty men, that I may lie in watch and wait even for him on his way home, in the strait between Ithaca and rugged Samos, that he may have a woeful end of his cruising in quest of his father.'

So spake he, and they all assented thereto, and bade him to the work. And thereupon they arose and went to the house of Odysseus.

Now it was no long time before Penelope heard of the counsel that the wooers had devised in the deep of their heart. For the henchman Medon told her thereof, who stood without the court and heard their purposes, while they were weaving their plot within. So he went on his way through the halls to bring the news to Penelope; and as he stept down over the threshold, Penelope spake unto him:

'Henchman, wherefore have the noble wooers sent thee forth? Was it to tell the handmaids of divine Odysseus to cease from their work, and prepare a banquet for them? Nay, after thus much wooing, never again may they come together, but here this day sup for their last and latest time; all ye who assemble so often, and waste much livelihood, the wealth of wise Telemachus! Long ago when ye were children, ye marked not your fathers' telling, what manner of man was Odysseus among them, one that wrought no iniquity toward any man, nor spake aught unrighteous in the township, as is the wont of divine kings. One man a king is like to hate, another he might chance to love. But never did he do aught at all presumptuously to any man. Nay, it is plain what spirit ye are of, and your unseemly deeds are manifest to all, nor is there any gratitude left for kindness done.'

Then Medon, wise of heart, answered her: 'Would, oh queen, that this were the crowning evil! But the wooers devise another far greater and more grievous, which I pray the son of Cronos may never fulfil! They are set on slaying Telemachus with the edge of the sword on his homeward way; for he is gone to fair Pylos and goodly Lacedaemon, to seek tidings of his father.'

So spake he, but her knees were loosened where she stood, and her heart melted within her, and long time was she speechless, and lo, her eyes were filled with tears and the voice of her utterance was stayed. And at the last she answered him and said:

'Henchman, wherefore I pray thee is my son departed? There is no need that he should go abroad on swift ships, that serve men for horses on the sea, and that cross the great wet waste. Is it that even his own name may no more be left upon earth?'

Then Medon, wise of heart, answered her: 'I know not whether some god set him on, or whether his own spirit stirred him to go to Pylos to seek tidings of his father's return, or to hear what end he met.'

He spake, and departed through the house of Odysseus, and on her fell a cloud of consuming grief; so that she might no more endure to seat her on a chair, whereof there were many in the house, but there she crouched on the threshold of her well-builded chamber, wailing piteously, and her handmaids round her made low moan, as many as were in the house with her, young and old. And Penelope spake among them pouring forth her lamentation:

'Hear me, my friends, for the Olympian sire hath given me pain exceedingly beyond all women who were born and bred in my day. For erewhile I lost my noble lord of the lion heart, adorned with all perfection among the Danaans, my good lord, whose fame is noised abroad from Hellas to mid Argos. And now again the storm-winds have snatched away my well-beloved son without tidings from our halls, nor heard I of his departure. Oh, women, hard of heart, that even ye did not each one let the thought come into your minds, to rouse me from my couch when he went to the black hollow ship, though ye knew full well thereof! For had I heard that he was purposing this journey, verily he should have stayed here still, though eager to be gone, or have left me dead in the halls. Howbeit let someone make haste to call the ancient Dolius, my thrall, whom my father gave me ere yet I had come hither, who keepeth my garden of trees. So shall he go straightway and sit by Laertes, and tell him all, if perchance Laertes may weave some counsel in his heart, and go forth and make his plaint to the people, who are purposed to destroy his seed, and the seed of god-like Odysseus.'

Then the good nurse Eurycleia answered her: 'Dear lady, aye, slay me if thou wilt with the pitiless sword or let me yet live on in the house,—yet will I not hide my saying from thee. I knew all this, and gave him whatsoever he commanded, bread and sweet wine. And he took a great oath of me not to tell thee till at least the twelfth day should come, or thou thyself shouldst miss him and hear of his departure, that thou mightest not mar thy fair flesh with thy tears. But now, wash thee in water, and take to thee clean raiment and ascend to thy upper chamber with the women thy handmaids, and pray to Athene, daughter of Zeus, lord of the aegis. For so may she save him even from death. And heap not troubles on an old man's trouble; for the seed of the son of Arceisius is not, methinks, utterly hated by the blessed gods, but someone will haply yet remain to possess these lofty halls, and the fat fields far away.'

So spake she, and lulled her queen's lamentation, and made her eyes to cease from weeping. So she washed her in water, and took to her clean raiment, and ascended to the upper chamber with the women her handmaids, and placed the meal for sprinkling in a basket, and prayed unto Athene:

'Hear me, child of Zeus, lord of the aegis, unwearied maiden! If ever wise Odysseus in his halls burnt for thee fat slices of the thighs of heifer or of sheep, these things, I pray thee, now remember, and save my dear son, and ward from him the wooers in the naughtiness of their pride.'

Therewith she raised a cry, and the goddess heard her prayer. But the wooers clamoured through the shadowy halls, and thus would some proud youth say:

'Verily this queen of many wooers prepareth our marriage, nor knoweth at all how that for her son death hath been ordained.'

Thus would certain of them speak, but they knew not how these things were ordained. And Antinous made harangue and spake among them:

'Good sirs, my friends, shun all disdainful words alike, lest someone hear and tell it even in the house. But come let us arise, and in silence accomplish that whereof we spake, for the counsel pleased us every one.'

Therewith he chose twenty men that were the best, and they departed to the swift ship and the sea-banks. So first of all they drew the ship down to the deep water, and placed the mast and sails in the black ship, and fixed the oars in leathern loops all orderly, and spread forth the white sails. And squires, haughty of heart, bare for them their arms. And they moored her high out in the shore water, and themselves disembarked. There they supped and waited for evening to come on.

But the wise Penelope lay there in her upper chamber, fasting and tasting neither meat nor drink, musing whether her noble son should escape death, or even fall before the proud wooers. And as a lion broods all in fear among the press of men, when they draw the crafty ring around him, so deeply was she musing when deep sleep came over her. And she sank back in sleep and all her joints were loosened.

Now the goddess, grey-eyed Athene, turned to other thoughts. She made a phantom, and fashioned it after the likeness of a woman, Iphthime, daughter of great-hearted Icarius, whom Eumelus wedded, whose dwelling was in Pherae. And she sent it to the house of divine Odysseus to bid Penelope, amid her sorrow and lamenting, to cease from her weeping and tearful lamentation. So the phantom passed into the chamber by the thong of the bolt, and stood above her head and spake unto her, saying:

'Sleepest thou, Penelope, stricken at heart? Nay, even the gods who live at ease suffer thee not to wail or be afflicted, seeing that thy son is yet to return; for no sinner is he in the eyes of the gods.'

Then wise Penelope made her answer as she slumbered very softly at the gates of dreams:

'Wherefore, sister, hast thou come hither, that before wert not wont to come, for thou hast thine habitation very far away? Biddest thou me indeed to cease from the sorrows and pains, so many that disquiet my heart and soul? Erewhile I lost my noble lord of the lion heart, adorned with all perfection among the Danaans, my true lord, whose fame is noised abroad from Hellas to mid Argos. And now, again my well-beloved son is departed on his hollow ship, poor child, not skilled in toils or in the gatherings of men. For him I sorrow yet more than for my lord, and I tremble and fear for him lest aught befall him, whether, it may be, amid that folk where he is gone, or in the deep. For many foemen devise evil against him, and go about to kill him, or ever he come to his own country.'

And the dim phantom answered her, and said: 'Take courage, and be not so sorely afraid. For lo, such a friend goes to guide him, as all men pray to stand by them, for that she hath the power, even Pallas Athene. And she pitieth thee in thy sorrow, and now hath sent me forth to speak these words to thee.'

And wise Penelope answered her, saying: 'If thou art indeed a god, and hast heard the word of a god, come, I pray thee, and tell me tidings concerning that ill-fated man, whether perchance he is yet alive and sees the light of the sun, or hath already died, and is a dweller in the house of Hades.'

And the dim phantom answered her and said: 'Concerning him I will not tell thee all the tale, whether he be alive or dead; it is ill to speak words light as wind.'

Therewith the phantom slipped away by the bolt of the door and passed into the breath of the wind. And the daughter of Icarius started up from sleep, and her heart was cheered, so clear was the vision that sped toward her in the dead of the night.

Meanwhile the wooers had taken ship and were sailing over the wet ways, pondering in their hearts sheer death for Telemachus. Now there is a rocky isle in the mid sea, midway between Ithaca and rugged Samos, Asteris, a little isle; and there is a harbour therein with a double entrance, where ships may ride. There the Achaeans abode lying in wait for Telemachus.

BOOK V

The Gods in council command Calypso by Hermes to send away Odysseus on a raft of trees; and Poseidon, returning from Ethiopia and seeing him on the coast of Phaeacia, scattered his raft; and how by the help of Ino he was thrown ashore, and slept on a heap of dry leaves till the next day.

Now the Dawn arose from her couch, from the side of the lordly Tithonus, to bear light to the immortals and to mortal men. And lo, the gods were gathering to session, and among them Zeus, that thunders on high, whose might is above all. And Athene told them the tale of the many woes of Odysseus, recalling them to mind; for near her heart was he that then abode in the dwelling of the nymph:

'Father Zeus, and all ye other blessed gods that live for ever, henceforth let not any sceptred king be kind and gentle with all his heart, nor minded to do righteously, but let him always be a hard man and work unrighteousness, for behold, there is none that remembereth divine Odysseus of the people whose lord he was, and was gentle as a father. Howbeit, as for him he lieth in an island suffering strong pains, in the halls of the nymph Calypso, who holdeth him perforce; so he may not reach his own country, for he hath no ships by him with oars, and no companions to send him on his way over the broad back of the sea. And now, again, they are set on slaying his beloved son on his homeward way, for he is gone to fair Pylos and to goodly Lacedaemon, to seek tidings of his father.'

And Zeus, gatherer of the clouds, answered and spake unto her: 'My child, what word hath escaped the door of thy lips? Nay, didst thou not thyself plan this device, that Odysseus may assuredly take vengeance on those men at his coming? As for Telemachus, do thou guide him by thine art, as well thou mayest, that so he may come to his own country all unharmed, and the wooers may return in their ship with their labour all in vain.'

Therewith he spake to Hermes, his dear son: 'Hermes, forasmuch as even in all else thou art our herald, tell unto the nymph of the braided tresses my unerring counsel, even the return of the patient Odysseus, how he is to come to his home, with no furtherance of gods or of mortal men. Nay, he shall sail on a well-bound raft, in sore distress, and on the twentieth day arrive at fertile Scheria, even at the land of the Phaeacians, who are near of kin to the gods. And they shall give him all worship heartily as to a god, and send him on his way in a ship to his own dear country, with gifts of bronze and gold, and raiment in plenty, much store, such as never would Odysseus have won for himself out of Troy, yea, though he had returned unhurt with the share of the spoil that fell to him. On such wise is he fated to see his friends, and come to his high-roofed home and his own country.'

So spake he, nor heedless was the messenger, the slayer of Argos. Straightway he bound beneath his feet his lovely golden sandals, that wax not old, that bare him alike over the wet sea and over the limitless land, swift as the breath of the wind. And he took the wand wherewith he lulls the eyes of whomso he will, while others again he even wakes from out of sleep. With this rod in his hand flew the strong slayer of Argos. Above Pieria he passed and leapt from the upper air into the deep. Then he sped along the wave like the cormorant, that chaseth the fishes through the perilous gulfs of the unharvested sea, and wetteth his thick plumage in the brine. Such like did Hermes ride upon the press of the waves. But when he had now reached that far-off isle, he went forth from the sea of violet blue to get him up into the land, till he came to a great cave, wherein dwelt the nymph of the braided tresses: and he found her within. And on the hearth there was a great fire burning, and from afar through the isle was smelt the fragrance of cleft cedar blazing, and of sandal wood. And the nymph within was singing with a sweet voice as she fared to and fro before the loom, and wove with a shuttle of gold. And round about the cave there was a wood blossoming, alder and poplar and sweet-smelling cypress. And therein roosted birds long of wing, owls and falcons and chattering sea-crows, which have their business in the waters. And lo, there about the hollow cave trailed a gadding garden vine, all rich with clusters. And fountains four set orderly were running with clear water, hard by one another, turned each to his own course. And all around soft meadows bloomed of violets and parsley, yea, even a deathless god who came thither might wonder at the sight and be glad at heart. There the messenger, the slayer of Argos, stood and wondered. Now when he had gazed at all with wonder, anon he went into the wide cave; nor did Calypso, that fair goddess, fail to know him, when she saw him face to face; for the gods use not be strange one to another, the immortals, not though one have his habitation far away. But he found not Odysseus, the great-hearted, within the cave, who sat weeping on the shore even as aforetime, straining his soul with tears and groans and griefs, and as he wept he looked wistfully over the unharvested deep. And Calypso, that fair goddess, questioned Hermes, when she had made him sit on a bright shining seat:

'Wherefore, I pray thee, Hermes, of the golden wand, hast thou come hither, worshipful and welcome, whereas as of old thou wert not wont to visit me? Tell me all thy thought; my heart is set on fulfilling it, if fulfil it I may, and if it hath been fulfilled in the counsel of fate.

But now follow me further, that I may set before thee the entertainment of strangers.'

Therewith the goddess spread a table with ambrosia and set it by him, and mixed the ruddy nectar. So the messenger, the slayer of Argos, did eat and drink. Now after he had supped and comforted his soul with food, at the last he answered, and spake to her on this wise:

'Thou makest question of me on my coming, a goddess of a god, and I will tell thee this my saying truly, at thy command. 'Twas Zeus that bade me come hither, by no will of mine; nay, who of his free will would speed over such a wondrous space of brine, whereby is no city of mortals that do sacrifice to the gods, and offer choice hecatombs? But surely it is in no wise possible for another god to go beyond or to make void the purpose of Zeus, lord of the aegis. He saith that thou hast with thee a man most wretched beyond his fellows, beyond those men that round the burg of Priam for nine years fought, and in the tenth year sacked the city and departed homeward. Yet on the way they sinned against Athene, and she raised upon them an evil blast and long waves of the sea. Then all the rest of his good company was lost, but it came to pass that the wind bare and the wave brought him hither. And now Zeus biddeth thee send him hence with what speed thou mayest, for it is not ordained that he die away from his friends, but rather it is his fate to look on them even yet, and to come to his high-roofed home and his own country.'

So spake he, and Calypso, that fair goddess, shuddered and uttered her voice, and spake unto him winged words: 'Hard are ye gods and jealous exceeding, who ever grudge goddesses openly to mate with men, if any make a mortal her dear bed-fellow. Even so when rosy-fingered Dawn took Orion for her lover, ye gods that live at ease were jealous thereof, till chaste Artemis, of the golden throne, slew him in Ortygia with the visitation of her gentle shafts.

So too when fair-tressed Demeter yielded to her love, and lay with Iasion in the thrice-ploughed fallow field, Zeus was not long without tidings thereof, and cast at him with his white bolt and slew him. So again ye gods now grudge that a mortal man should dwell with me. Him I saved as he went all alone bestriding the keel of a bark, for that Zeus had crushed and cleft his swift ship with a white bolt in the midst of the wine-dark deep. There all the rest of his good company was lost, but it came to pass that the wind bare and the wave brought him hither. And him have I loved and cherished, and I said that I would make him to know not death and age for ever. Yet forasmuch as it is in no wise possible for another god to go beyond, or make void the purpose of Zeus, lord of the aegis, let him away over the unharvested seas, if the summons and the bidding be of Zeus. But I will give him no despatch, not I, for I have no ships by me with oars, nor company to bear him on his way over the broad back of the sea. Yet will I be forward to put this in his mind, and will hide nought, that all unharmed he may come to his own country.'

Then the messenger, the slayer of Argos, answered her: 'Yea, speed him now upon his path and have regard unto the wrath of Zeus, lest haply he be angered and bear hard on thee hereafter.'

Therewith the great slayer of Argos departed, but the lady nymph went on her way to the great-hearted Odysseus, when she had heard the message of Zeus. And there she found him sitting on the shore, and his eyes were never dry of tears, and his sweet life was ebbing away as he mourned for his return; for the nymph no more found favour in his sight. Howsoever by night he would sleep by her, as needs he must, in the hollow caves, unwilling lover by a willing lady. And in the day-time he would sit on the rocks and on the beach, straining his soul with tears, and groans, and griefs, and through his tears he would look wistfully over the unharvested deep. So standing near him that fair goddess spake to him:

'Hapless man, sorrow no more I pray thee in this isle, nor let thy good life waste away, for even now will I send thee hence with all my heart. Nay, arise and cut long beams, and fashion a wide raft with the axe, and lay deckings high thereupon, that it may bear thee over the misty deep. And I will place therein bread and water, and red wine to thy heart's desire, to keep hunger far away. And I will put raiment upon thee, and send a fair gale in thy wake, that so thou mayest come all unharmed to thine own country, if indeed it be the good pleasure of the gods who hold wide heaven, who are stronger than I am both to will and to do.'

So she spake, and the steadfast goodly Odysseus shuddered, and uttering his voice spake to her winged words: 'Herein, goddess, thou hast plainly some other thought, and in no wise my furtherance, for that thou biddest me to cross in a raft the great gulf of the sea so dread and difficult, which not even the swift gallant ships pass over rejoicing in the breeze of Zeus. Nor would I go aboard a raft to displeasure thee, unless thou wilt deign, O goddess, to swear a great oath not to plan any hidden guile to mine own hurt.'

So spake he, and Calypso, the fair goddess, smiled and caressed him with her hand, and spake and hailed him: 'Knavish thou art, and no weakling in wit, thou that hast conceived and spoken such a word. Let earth be now witness hereto, and the wide heaven above, and that falling water of the Styx, the greatest oath and the most terrible to the blessed gods, that I will not plan any hidden guile to thine own hurt. Nay, but my thoughts are such, and such will be my counsel, as I would devise for myself, if ever so sore a need came over me. For I too have a righteous mind, and my heart within me is not of iron, but pitiful even as thine.'

Therewith the fair goddess led the way quickly, and he followed hard in the steps of the goddess. And they reached the hollow cave, the goddess and the man; so he sat him down upon the chair whence Hermes had arisen, and the nymph placed by him all manner of food to eat and drink, such as is meat for men. As for her she sat over against divine Odysseus, and the handmaids placed by her ambrosia and nectar. So they put forth their hands upon the good cheer set before them. But after they had taken their fill of meat and drink, Calypso, the fair goddess, spake first and said:

'Son of Laertes, of the seed of Zeus, Odysseus of many devices, so it is indeed thy wish to get thee home to thine own dear country even in this hour? Good fortune go with thee even so! Yet didst thou know in thine heart what a measure of suffering thou art ordained to fulfil, or ever thou reach thine own country, here, even here, thou wouldst abide with me and keep this house, and wouldst never taste of death, though thou longest to see thy wife, for whom thou hast ever a desire day by day. Not in sooth that I avow me to be less noble than she in form or fashion, for it is in no wise meet that mortal women should match them with immortals, in shape and comeliness.'

And Odysseus of many counsels answered, and spake unto her: 'Be not wroth with me hereat, goddess and queen. Myself I know it well, how wise Penelope is meaner to look upon than thou, in comeliness and stature. But she is mortal and thou knowest not age nor death. Yet even so, I wish and long day by day to fare homeward and see the day of my returning. Yea, and if some god shall wreck me in the wine-dark deep, even so I will endure, with a heart within me patient of affliction. For already have I suffered full much, and much have I toiled in perils of waves and war; let this be added to the tale of those.'

So spake he, and the sun sank and darkness came on.

Then they twain went into the chamber of the hollow rock, and had their delight of love, abiding each by other.

So soon as early Dawn shone forth, the rosy-fingered, anon Odysseus put on him a mantle and doublet, and the nymph clad her in a great shining robe, light of woof and gracious, and about her waist she cast a fair golden girdle, and a veil withal upon her head. Then she considered of the sending of Odysseus, the great-hearted. She gave him a great axe, fitted to his grasp, an axe of bronze double-edged, and with a goodly handle of olive wood fastened well. Next she gave him a polished adze, and she led the way to the border of the isle where tall trees grew, alder and poplar, and pine that reacheth unto heaven, seasoned long since and sere, that might lightly float for him. Now after she had shown him where the tall trees grew, Calypso, the fair goddess, departed homeward. And he set to cutting timber, and his work went busily. Twenty trees in all he felled, and then trimmed them with the axe of bronze, and deftly smoothed them, and over them made straight the line. Meanwhile Calypso, the fair goddess, brought him augers, so he bored each piece and jointed them together, and then made all fast with trenails and dowels. Wide as is the floor of a broad ship of burden, which some man well skilled in carpentry may trace him out, of such beam did Odysseus fashion his broad raft. And thereat he wrought, and set up the deckings, fitting them to the close-set uprights, and finished them off with long gunwales, and therein he set a mast, and a yard-arm fitted thereto, and moreover he made him a rudder to guide the craft. And he fenced it with wattled osier withies from stem to stern, to be a bulwark against the wave, and piled up wood to back them. Meanwhile Calypso, the fair goddess, brought him web of cloth to make his sails; and these too he fashioned very skilfully. And he made fast therein braces and halyards and sheets, and at last he pushed the raft with levers down to the fair salt sea.

It was the fourth day when he had accomplished all. And, lo, on the fifth, the fair Calypso sent him on his way from the island, when she had bathed him and clad him in fragrant attire. Moreover, the goddess placed on board the ship two skins, one of dark wine, and another, a great one, of water, and corn too in a wallet, and she set therein a store of dainties to his heart's desire, and sent forth a warm and gentle wind to blow. And goodly Odysseus rejoiced as he set his sails to the breeze. So he sate and cunningly guided the craft with the helm, nor did sleep fall upon his eyelids, as he viewed the Pleiads and Boötes, that setteth late, and the Bear, which they likewise call the Wain, which turneth ever in one place, and keepeth watch upon Orion, and alone hath no part in the baths of Ocean. This star, Calypso, the fair goddess, bade him to keep ever on the left as he traversed the deep. Ten days and seven he sailed traversing the deep, and on the eighteenth day appeared the shadowy hills of the land of the Phaeacians, at the point where it lay nearest to him; and it showed like a shield in the misty deep.

Now the lord, the shaker of the earth, on his way from the Ethiopians espied him afar off from the mountains of the Solymi: even thence he saw Odysseus as he sailed over the deep; and he was mightily angered in spirit, and shaking his head he communed with his own heart. 'Lo now, it must be that the gods at the last have changed their purposes concerning Odysseus, while I was away among the Ethiopians. And now he is nigh to the Phaeacian land, where it is ordained that he escape the great issues of the woe which hath come upon him. But methinks that even yet I will drive him far enough in the path of suffering.'

With that he gathered the clouds and troubled the waters of the deep, grasping his trident in his hands; and he roused all storms of all manner of winds, and shrouded in clouds the land and sea: and down sped night from heaven. The East Wind and the South Wind clashed, and the stormy West, and the North, that is born in the bright air, rolling onward a great wave. Then were the knees of Odysseus loosened and his heart melted, and heavily he spake to his own great spirit:

'Oh, wretched man that I am! what is to befall me at the last? I fear that indeed the goddess spake all things truly, who said that I should fill up the measure of sorrow on the deep, or ever I came to mine own country; and lo, all these things have an end. In such wise doth Zeus crown the wide heaven with clouds, and hath troubled the deep, and the blasts rush on of all the winds; yea, now is utter doom assured me. Thrice blessed those Danaans, yea, four times blessed, who perished on a time in wide Troy-land, doing a pleasure to the sons of Atreus! Would to God that I too had died, and met my fate on that day when the press of Trojans cast their bronze-shod spears upon me, fighting for the body of the son of Peleus! So should I have gotten my dues of burial, and the Achaeans would have spread my fame; but now it is my fate to be overtaken by a pitiful death.'

Even as he spake, the great wave smote down upon him, driving on in terrible wise, that the raft reeled again. And far therefrom he fell, and lost the helm from his hand; and the fierce blast of the jostling winds came and brake his mast in the midst, and sail and yard-arm fell afar into the deep. Long time the water kept him under, nor could he speedily rise from beneath the rush of the mighty wave: for the garments hung heavy which fair Calypso gave him. But late and at length he came up, and spat forth from his mouth the bitter salt water, which ran down in streams from his head. Yet even so forgat he not his raft, for all his wretched plight, but made a spring after it in the waves, and clutched it to him, and sat in the midst thereof, avoiding the issues of death; and the great wave swept it hither and thither along the stream. And as the North Wind in the harvest tide sweeps the thistledown along the plain, and close the tufts cling each to other, even so the winds bare the raft hither and thither along the main. Now the South would toss it to the North to carry, and now again the East would yield it to the West to chase.

But the daughter of Cadmus marked him, Ino of the fair ankles, Leucothea, who in time past was a maiden of mortal speech, but now in the depths of the salt sea she had gotten her share of worship from the gods. She took pity on Odysseus in his wandering and travail, and she rose, like a sea-gull on the wing, from the depth of the mere, and sat upon the well-bound raft and spake saying:

'Hapless one, wherefore was Poseidon, shaker of the earth, so wondrous wroth with thee, seeing that he soweth for thee the seeds of many evils? Yet shall he not make a full end of thee, for all his desire. But do even as I tell thee, and methinks thou art not witless. Cast off these garments, and leave the raft to drift before the winds, but do thou swim wih thine hands and strive to win a footing on the coast of the Phaeacians, where it is decreed that thou escape. Here, take this veil imperishable and wind it about thy breast; so is there no fear that thou suffer aught or perish. But when thou hast laid hold of the mainland with thy hands, loose it from off thee and cast it into the wine-dark deep far from the land, and thyself turn away.'

With that the goddess gave the veil, and for her part dived back into the heaving deep, like a sea-gull: and the dark wave closed over her. But the steadfast goodly Odysseus pondered, and heavily he spake to his own brave spirit:

'Ah, woe is me! Can it be that some one of the immortals is weaving a new snare for me, that she bids me quit my raft? Nay verily, I will not yet obey, for I had sight of the shore yet a long way off, where she told me that I might escape. I am resolved what I will do;—

and methinks on this wise it is best. So long as the timbers abide in the dowels, so long will I endure steadfast in affliction, but so soon as the wave hath shattered my raft asunder, I will swim, for meanwhile no better counsel may be.'

While yet he pondered these things in his heart and soul, Poseidon, shaker of the earth, stirred against him a great wave, terrible and grievous, and vaulted from the crest, and therewith smote him. And as when a great tempestuous wind tosseth a heap of parched husks, and scatters them this way and that, even so did the wave scatter the long beams of the raft. But Odysseus bestrode a single beam, as one rideth on a courser, and stript him of the garments which fair Calypso gave him. And presently he wound the veil beneath his breast, and fell prone into the sea, outstretching his hands as one eager to swim. And the lord, the shaker of the earth, saw him and shook his head, and communed with his own soul. 'Even so, after all thy sufferings, go wandering over the deep, till thou shalt come among a people, the fosterlings of Zeus. Yet for all that I deem not that thou shalt think thyself too lightly afflicted.' Therewith he lashed his steeds of the flowing manes, and came to Aegae, where is his lordly home.

But Athene, daughter of Zeus, turned to new thoughts. Behold, she bound up the courses of the other winds, and charged them all to cease and be still; but she roused the swift North and brake the waves before him, that so Odysseus, of the seed of Zeus, might mingle with the Phaeacians, lovers of the oar, avoiding death and the fates.

So for two nights and two days he was wandering in the swell of the sea, and much his heart boded of death. But when at last the fair-tressed Dawn brought the full light of the third day, thereafter the breeze fell, and lo, there was a breathless calm, and with a quick glance ahead (he being upborne on a great wave) he saw the land very near. And even as when most welcome to his children is the sight of a father's life, who lies in sickness and strong pains long wasting away, some angry god assailing him; and to their delight the gods have loosed him from his trouble; so welcome to Odysseus showed land and wood; and he swam onward, being eager to set foot on the strand. But when he was within earshot of the shore, and heard now the thunder of the sea against the reefs—for the great wave crashed against the dry land belching in terrible wise, and all was covered with foam of the sea,—for there were no harbours for ships nor shelters, but jutting headlands and reefs and cliffs; then at last the knees of Odysseus were loosened and his heart melted, and in heaviness he spake to his own brave spirit:

'Ah me! now that beyond all hope Zeus hath given me sight of land, and withal I have cloven my way through this gulf of the sea, here there is no place to land on from out of the grey water. For without are sharp crags, and round them the wave roars surging, and sheer the smooth rock rises, and the sea is deep thereby, so that in no wise may I find firm foothold and escape my bane, for as I fain would go ashore, the great wave may haply snatch and dash me on the jagged rock—and a wretched endeavour that would be. But if I swim yet further along the coast to find, if I may, spits that take the waves aslant and havens of the sea, I fear lest the storm-winds catch me again and bear me over the teeming deep, making heavy moan; or else some god may even send forth against me a monster from out of the shore water; and many such pastureth the renowned Amphitrite. For I know how wroth against me hath been the great Shaker of the Earth.'

Whilst yet he pondered these things in his heart and mind, a great wave bore him to the rugged shore. There would he have been stript of his skin and all his bones been broken, but that the goddess, grey-eyed Athene, put a thought into his heart. He rushed in, and with both his hands clutched the rock, whereto he clung till the great wave went by. So he escaped that peril, but again with backward wash it leapt on him and smote him and cast him forth into the deep. And as when the cuttlefish is dragged forth from his chamber, the many pebbles clinging to his suckers, even so was the skin stript from his strong hand against the rocks, and the great wave closed over him. There of a truth would luckless Odysseus have perished beyond that which was ordained, had not grey-eyed Athene given him sure counsel. He rose from the line of the breakers that belch upon the shore, and swam outside, ever looking landwards, to find, if he might, spits that take the waves aslant, and havens of the sea. But when he came in his swimming over against the mouth of a fair-flowing river, whereby the place seemed best in his eyes, smooth of rocks, and withal there was a covert from the wind, Odysseus felt the river running, and prayed to him in his heart:

'Hear me, O king, whosoever thou art; unto thee am I come, as to one to whom prayer is made, while I flee the rebukes of Poseidon from the deep. Yea, reverend even to the deathless gods is that man who comes as a wanderer, even as I now have come to thy stream and to thy knees after much travail. Nay pity me, O king; for I avow myself thy suppliant.'

So spake he, and the god straightway stayed his stream and withheld his waves, and made the water smooth before him, and brought him safely to the mouths of the river. And his knees bowed and his stout hands fell, for his heart was broken by the brine. And his flesh was all swollen and a great stream of sea water gushed up through his mouth and nostrils. So he lay without breath or speech, swooning, such terrible weariness came upon him. But when now his breath returned and his spirit came to him again, he loosed from off him the veil of the goddess, and let it fall into the salt-flowing river. And the great wave bare it back down the stream, and lightly Ino caught it in her hands. Then Odysseus turned from the river, and fell back in the reeds, and kissed earth, the grain-giver, and heavily he spake unto his own brave spirit:

'Ah, woe is me! what is to betide me? what shall happen unto me at the last? If I watch in the river bed all through the careful night, I fear that the bitter frost and fresh dew may overcome me, as I breathe forth my life for faintness, for the river breeze blows cold betimes in the morning. But if I climb the hill-side up to the shady wood, and there take rest in the thickets, though perchance the cold and weariness leave hold of me, and sweet sleep may come over me, I fear lest of wild beasts I become the spoil and prey.'

So as he thought thereon this seemed to him the better way. He went up to the wood, and found it nigh the water in a place of wide prospect. So he crept beneath twin bushes that grew from one stem, both olive trees, one of them wild olive. Through these the force of the wet winds blew never, neither did the bright sun light on it with his rays, nor could the rain pierce through, so close were they twined either to other; and thereunder crept Odysseus, and anon he heaped together with his hands a broad couch; for of fallen leaves there was great plenty, enough to cover two or three men in winter time, however hard the weather. And the steadfast goodly Odysseus beheld it and rejoiced, and he laid him in the midst thereof and flung over him the fallen leaves. And as when a man hath hidden away a brand in the black embers at an upland farm, one that hath no neighbours nigh, and so saveth the seed of fire, that he may not have to seek a light otherwhere, even so did Odysseus cover him with the leaves. And Athene shed sleep upon his eyes, that so it might soon release him from his weary travail, overshadowing his eyelids.

BOOK VI

Nausicaa, going to a river near that place to wash the clothes of her father, mother, and brethren, while the clothes were drying played with her maids at ball; and Odysseus coming forth is fed and clothed, and led on his way to the house of her father, King Alcinous.

So there he lay asleep, the steadfast goodly Odysseus, fordone with toil and drowsiness. Meanwhile Athene went to the land and the city of the Phaeacians, who of old, upon a time, dwelt in spacious Hypereia; near the Cyclôpes they dwelt, men exceeding proud, who harried them continually, being mightier than they. Thence the godlike Nausithous made them depart, and he carried them away, and planted them in Scheria, far off from men that live by bread. And he drew a wall around the town, and builded houses and made temples for the gods and meted out the fields. Howbeit ere this had he been stricken by fate, and had gone down to the house of Hades, and now Alcinous was reigning, with wisdom granted by the gods. To his house went the goddess, grey-eyed Athene, devising a return for the great-hearted Odysseus. She betook her to the rich-wrought bower, wherein was sleeping a maiden like to the gods in form and comeliness, Nausicaa, the daughter of Alcinous, high of heart. Beside her on either hand of the pillars of the door were two handmaids, dowered with beauty from the Graces, and the shining doors were shut.

But the goddess, fleet as the breath of the wind, swept towards the couch of the maiden, and stood above her head, and spake to her in the semblance of the daughter of a famous seafarer, Dymas, a girl of like age with Nausicaa, who had found grace in her sight. In her shape the grey-eyed Athene spake to the princess, saying:

'Nausicaa, how hath thy mother so heedless a maiden to her daughter? Lo, thou hast shining raiment that lies by thee uncared for, and thy marriage-day is near at hand, when thou thyself must needs go beautifully clad, and have garments to give to them who shall lead thee to the house of the bridegroom! And, behold, these are the things whence a good report goes abroad among men, wherein a father and lady mother take delight. But come, let us arise and go a-washing with the breaking of the day, and I will follow with thee to be thy mate in the toil, that without delay thou mayst get thee ready, since truly thou art not long to be a maiden. Lo, already they are wooing thee, the noblest youths of all the Phaeacians, among that people whence thou thyself dost draw thy lineage. So come, beseech thy noble father betimes in the morning to furnish thee with mules and a wain to carry the men's raiment, and the robes, and the shining coverlets. Yea and for thyself it is seemlier far to go thus than on foot, for the places where we must wash are a great way off the town.'

So spake the grey-eyed Athene, and departed to Olympus, where, as they say, is the seat of the gods that standeth fast for ever. Not by winds is it shaken, nor ever wet with rain, nor doth the snow come nigh thereto, but most clear air is spread about it cloudless, and the white light floats over it. Therein the blessed gods are glad for all their days, and thither Athene went when she had shown forth all to the maiden.

Anon came the throned Dawn, and awakened Nausicaa of the fair robes, who straightway marvelled on the dream, and went through the halls to tell her parents, her father dear and her mother. And she found them within, her mother sitting by the hearth with the women her handmaids, spinning yarn of sea-purple stain, but her father she met as he was going forth to the renowned kings in their council, whither the noble Phaeacians called him. Standing close by her dear father she spake, saying: 'Father, dear, couldst thou not lend me a high waggon with strong wheels, that I may take the goodly raiment to the river to wash, so much as I have lying soiled? Yea and it is seemly that thou thyself, when thou art with the princes in council, shouldest have fresh raiment to wear. Also, there are five dear sons of thine in the halls, two married, but three are lusty bachelors, and these are always eager for new-washen garments wherein to go to the dances: for all these things have I taken thought.'

This she said, because she was ashamed to speak of glad marriage to her father; but he saw all and answered, saying:

'Neither the mules nor aught else do I grudge thee, my child. Go thy ways, and the thralls shall get thee ready a high waggon with good wheels, and fitted with an upper frame.'

Therewith he called to his men, and they gave ear, and without the palace they made ready the smooth-running mule-wain, and led the mules beneath the yoke, and harnessed them under the car, while the maiden brought forth from her bower the shining raiment. This she stored in the polished car, and her mother filled a basket with all manner of food to the heart's desire, dainties too she set therein, and she poured wine into a goat-skin bottle, while Nausicaa climbed into the wain. And her mother gave her soft olive oil also in a golden cruse, that she and her maidens might anoint themselves after the bath. Then Nausicaa took the whip and the shining reins, and touched the mules to start them; then there was a clatter of hoofs, and on they strained without flagging, with their load of the raiment and the maiden. Not alone did she go, for her attendants followed with her.

Now when they were come to the beautiful stream of the river, where truly were the unfailing cisterns, and bright water welled up free from beneath, and flowed past, enough to wash the foulest garments clean, there the girls unharnessed the mules from under the chariot, and turning them loose they drove them along the banks of the eddying river to graze on the honey-sweet clover. Then they took the garments from the wain, in their hands, and bore them to the black water, and briskly trod them down in the trenches, in busy rivalry. Now when they had washed and cleansed all the stains, they spread all out in order along the shore of the deep, even where the sea, in beating on the coast, washed the pebbles clean. Then having bathed and anointed them well with olive oil, they took their mid-day meal on the river's banks, waiting till the clothes should dry in the brightness of the sun. Anon, when they were satisfied with food, the maidens and the princess, they fell to playing at ball, casting away their tires, and among them Nausicaa of the white arms began the song. And even as Artemis, the archer, moveth down the mountain, either along the ridges of lofty Taygetus or Erymanthus, taking her pastime in the chase of boars and swift deer, and with her the wild wood-nymphs disport them, the daughters of Zeus, lord of the aegis, and Leto is glad at heart, while high over all she rears her head and brows, and easily may she be known,—but all are fair; even so the girl unwed outshone her maiden company.

But when now she was about going homewards, after yoking the mules and folding up the goodly raiment, then grey-eyed Athene turned to other thoughts, that so Odysseus might awake, and see the lovely maiden, who should be his guide to the city of the Phaeacian men. So then the princess threw the ball at one of her company; she missed the girl, and cast the ball into the deep eddying current, whereat they all raised a piercing cry. Then the goodly Odysseus awoke and sat up, pondering in his heart and spirit:

'Woe is me! to what men's land am I come now? say, are they froward, and wild, and unjust, or are they hospitable, and of God-fearing mind? How shrill a cry of maidens rings round me, of the nymphs that hold the steep hill-tops, and the river-springs, and the grassy water-meadows! It must be, methinks, that I am near men of human speech. Go to, I myself will make trial and see.'

Therewith the goodly Odysseus crept out from under the coppice, having broken with his strong hand a leafy bough from the thick wood, to hold athwart his body, that it might hide his nakedness withal. And forth he sallied like a lion mountain-bred, trusting in his strength, who fares out blown and rained upon, with flaming eyes; amid the kine he goes or amid the sheep or in the track of the wild deer; yea, his belly bids him go even to the good homestead to make assay upon the flocks. Even so Odysseus was fain to draw nigh to the fair-tressed maidens, all naked as he was, such need had come upon him. But he was terrible in their eyes, being marred with the salt sea foam, and they fled cowering here and there about the jutting spits of shore. And the daughter of Alcinous alone stood firm, for Athene gave her courage of heart, and took all trembling from her limbs. So she halted and stood over against him, and Odysseus considered whether he should clasp the knees of the lovely maiden, and so make his prayer, or should stand as he was, apart, and beseech her with smooth words, if haply she might show him the town, and give him raiment. And as he thought within himself, it seemed better to stand apart, and beseech her with smooth words, lest the maiden should be angered with him if he touched her knees: so straightway he spake a sweet and cunning word:

'I supplicate thee, O queen, whether thou art a goddess or a mortal! If indeed thou art a goddess of them that keep the wide heaven; to Artemis, then, the daughter of great Zeus, I mainly liken thee, for beauty and stature and shapeliness. But if thou art one of the daughters of men who dwell on earth, thrice blessed are thy father and thy lady mother, and thrice blessed thy brethren. Surely their souls ever glow with gladness for thy sake, each time they see thee entering the dance, so fair a flower of maidens. But he is of heart the most blessed beyond all other who shall prevail with gifts of wooing, and lead thee to his home. Never have mine eyes beheld such an one among mortals, neither man nor woman; great awe comes upon me as I look on thee. Yet in Delos once I saw as goodly a thing: a young sapling of a palm tree springing by the altar of Apollo. For thither too I went, and much people with me, on that path where my sore troubles were to be. Yea, and when I looked thereupon, long time I marvelled in spirit,—for never grew there yet so goodly a shoot from ground,—even in such wise as I wonder at thee, lady, and am astonied and do greatly fear to touch thy knees, though grievous sorrow is upon me. Yesterday, on the twentieth day, I escaped from the wine-dark deep, but all that time continually the wave bare me, and the vehement winds drave, from the isle Ogygia. And now some god has cast me on this shore, that here too, methinks, some evil may betide me; for I trow not that trouble will cease; the gods ere that time will yet bring many a thing to pass. But, queen, have pity on me, for after many trials and sore to thee first of all am I come, and of the other folk, who hold this city and land, I know no man. Nay show me the town, give me an old garment to cast about me, if thou hadst, when thou camest here, any wrap for the linen. And may the gods grant thee all thy heart's desire: a husband and a home, and a mind at one with his may they give—a good gift, for there is nothing mightier and nobler than when man and wife are of one heart and mind in a house, a grief to their foes, and to their friends great joy, but their own hearts know it best.'

Then Nausicaa of the white arms answered him, and said: 'Stranger, forasmuch as thou seemest no evil man nor foolish—and it is Olympian Zeus himself that giveth weal to men, to the good and to the evil, to each one as he will, and this thy lot doubtless is of him, and so thou must in anywise endure it:—and now, since thou hast come to our city and our land, thou shalt not lack raiment, nor aught else that is the due of a hapless suppliant, when he has met them who can befriend him. And I will show thee the town, and name the name of the people. The Phaeacians hold this city and land, and I am the daughter of Alcinous, great of heart, on whom all the might and force of the Phaeacians depend.'

Thus she spake, and called to her maidens of the fair tresses: 'Halt, my maidens, whither flee ye at the sight of a man? Ye surely do not take him for an enemy? That mortal breathes not, and never will be born, who shall come with war to the land of the Phaeacians, for they are very dear to the gods. Far apart we live in the wash of the waves, the outermost of men, and no other mortals are conversant with us. Nay, but this man is some helpless one come hither in his wanderings, whom now we must kindly entreat, for all strangers and beggars are from Zeus, and a little gift is dear. So, my maidens, give the stranger meat and drink, and bathe him in the river, where withal is a shelter from the winds.'

So she spake, but they had halted and called each to the other, and they brought Odysseus to the sheltered place, and made him sit down, as Nausicaa bade them, the daughter of Alcinous, high of heart. Beside him they laid a mantle, and a doublet for raiment, and gave him soft olive oil in the golden cruse, and bade him wash in the streams of the river. Then goodly Odysseus spake among the maidens, saying: 'I pray you stand thus apart, while I myself wash the brine from my shoulders, and anoint me with olive oil, for truly oil is long a stranger to my skin. But in your sight I will not bathe, for I am ashamed to make me naked in the company of fair-tressed maidens.'

Then they went apart and told all to their lady. But with the river water the goodly Odysseus washed from his skin the salt scurf that covered his back and broad shoulders, and from his head he wiped the crusted brine of the barren sea. But when he had washed his whole body, and anointed him with olive oil, and had clad himself in the raiment that the unwedded maiden gave him, then Athene, the daughter of Zeus, made him greater and more mighty to behold, and from his head caused deep curling locks to flow, like the hyacinth flower. And as when some skilful man overlays gold upon silver—one that Hephaestus and Pallas Athene have taught all manner of craft, and full of grace is his handiwork—even so did Athene shed grace about his head and shoulders.

Then to the shore of the sea went Odysseus apart, and sat down, glowing in beauty and grace, and the princess marvelled at him, and spake among her fair-tressed maidens, saying:

'Listen, my white-armed maidens, and I will say somewhat. Not without the will of all the gods who hold Olympus hath this man come among the godlike Phaeacians. Erewhile he seemed to me uncomely, but now he is like the gods that keep the wide heaven. Would that such an one might be called my husband, dwelling here, and that it might please him here to abide! But come, my maidens, give the stranger meat and drink.'

Thus she spake, and they gave ready ear and hearkened, and set beside Odysseus meat and drink, and the steadfast goodly Odysseus did eat and drink eagerly, for it was long since he had tasted food.

Now Nausicaa of the white arms had another thought. She folded the raiment and stored it in the goodly wain, and yoked the mules strong of hoof, and herself climbed into the car. Then she called on Odysseus, and spake and hailed him: 'Up now, stranger, and rouse thee to go to the city, that I may convey thee to the house of my wise father, where, I promise thee, thou shalt get knowledge of all the noblest of the Phaeacians. But do thou even as I tell thee, and thou seemest a discreet man enough. So long as we are passing along the fields and farms of men, do thou fare quickly with the maidens behind the mules and the chariot, and I will lead the way. But when we set foot within the city,—whereby goes a high wall with towers, and there is a fair haven on either side of the town, and narrow is the entrance, and curved ships are drawn up on either hand of the mole, for all the folk have stations for their vessels, each man one for himself. And there is the place of assembly about the goodly temple of Poseidon, furnished with heavy stones, deep bedded in the earth. There men look to the gear of the black ships, hawsers and sails, and there they fine down the oars. For the Phaeacians care not for bow nor quiver, but for masts, and oars of ships, and gallant barques, wherein rejoicing they cross the grey sea. Their ungracious speech it is that I would avoid, lest some man afterward rebuke me, and there are but too many insolent folk among the people. And some one of the baser sort might meet me and say: "Who is this that goes with Nausicaa, this tall and goodly stranger? Where found she him? Her husband he will be, her very own. Either she has taken in some ship-wrecked wanderer of strange men,—for no men dwell near us; or some god has come in answer to her instant prayer; from heaven has he descended, and will have her to wife for evermore. Better so, if herself she has ranged abroad and found a lord from a strange land, for verily she holds in no regard the Phaeacians here in this country, the many men and noble who are her wooers." So will they speak, and this would turn to my reproach. Yea, and I myself would think it blame of another maiden who did such things in despite of her friends, her father and mother being still alive, and was conversant with men before the day of open wedlock. But, stranger, heed well what I say, that as soon as may be thou mayest gain at my father's hands an escort and a safe return. Thou shalt find a fair grove of Athene, a poplar grove near the road, and a spring wells forth therein, and a meadow lies all around. There is my father's demesne, and his fruitful close, within the sound of a man's shout from the city. Sit thee down there and wait until such time as we may have come into the city, and reached the house of my father. But when thou deemest that we are got to the palace, then go up to the city of the Phaeacians, and ask for the house of my father Alcinous, high of heart. It is easily known, and a young child could be thy guide, for nowise like it are builded the houses of the Phaeacians, so goodly is the palace of the hero Alcinous. But when thou art within the shadow of the halls and the court, pass quickly through the great chamber, till thou comest to my mother, who sits at the hearth in the light of the fire, weaving yarn of sea-purple stain, a wonder to behold. Her chair is leaned against a pillar, and her maidens sit behind her. And there my father's throne leans close to hers, wherein he sits and drinks his wine, like an immortal. Pass thou by him, and cast thy hands about my mother's knees, that thou mayest see quickly and with joy the day of thy returning, even if thou art from a very far country. If but her heart be kindly disposed toward thee, then is there hope that thou shalt see thy friends, and come to thy well-builded house, and to thine own country.'

She spake, and smote the mules with the shining whip, and quickly they left behind them the streams of the river. And well they trotted and well they paced, and she took heed to drive in such wise that the maidens and Odysseus might follow on foot, and cunningly she plied the lash. Then the sun set, and they came to the famous grove, the sacred place of Athene; so there the goodly Odysseus sat him down. Then straightway he prayed to the daughter of mighty Zeus: 'Listen to me, child of Zeus, lord of the aegis, unwearied maiden; hear me even now, since before thou heardest not when I was smitten on the sea, when the renowned Earth-shaker smote me. Grant me to come to the Phaeacians as one dear, and worthy of pity.'

So he spake in prayer, and Pallas Athene heard him; but she did not yet appear to him face to face, for she had regard unto her father's brother, who furiously raged against the godlike Odysseus, till he should come to his own country.

BOOK VII

Odysseus being received at the house of the king Alcinous, the queen after supper, taking notice of his garments, gives him occasion to relate his passage thither on the raft. Alcinous promises him a convoy for the morrow.

So he prayed there, the steadfast goodly Odysseus, while the two strong mules bare the princess to the town. And when she had now come to the famous palace of her father, she halted at the gateway, and round her gathered her brothers, men like to the immortals, and they loosed the mules from under the car, and carried the raiment within. But the maiden betook her to her chamber; and an aged dame from Aperaea kindled the fire for her, Eurymedusa, the handmaid of the chamber, whom the curved ships upon a time had brought from Aperaea; and men chose her as a prize for Alcinous, seeing that he bare rule over all the Phaeacians, and the people hearkened to him as to a god. She waited on the white-armed Nausicaa in the palace halls; she was wont to kindle the fire and prepare the supper in the inner chamber.

At that same hour Odysseus roused him to go to the city, and Athene shed a deep mist about Odysseus for the favour that she bare him, lest any of the Phaeacians, high of heart, should meet him and mock him in sharp speech, and ask him who he was. But when he was now about to enter the pleasant city, then the goddess, grey-eyed Athene, met him, in the fashion of a young maiden carrying a pitcher, and she stood over against him, and goodly Odysseus inquired of her:

'My child, couldst thou not lead me to the palace of the lord Alcinous, who bears sway among this people? Lo, I am come here, a stranger travel-worn from afar, from a distant land; wherefore of the folk who possess this city and country I know not any man.'

Then the goddess, grey-eyed Athene, answered him saying: 'Yea now, father and stranger, I will show thee the house that thou bidst me declare, for it lies near the palace of my noble father; behold, be silent as thou goest, and I will lead the way. And look on no man, nor question any. For these men do not gladly suffer strangers, nor lovingly entreat whoso cometh from a strange land. They trust to the speed of their swift ships, wherewith they cross the great gulf, for the Earth-shaker hath vouchsafed them this power. Their ships are swift as the flight of a bird, or as a thought.'

Therewith Pallas Athene led the way swiftly, and he followed hard in the footsteps of the goddess. And it came to pass that the Phaeacians, mariners renowned, marked him not as he went down the city through their midst, for the fair-tressed Athene suffered it not, that awful goddess, who shed a wondrous mist about him, for the favour that she bare him in her heart. And Odysseus marvelled at the havens and the gallant ships, yea and the places of assembly of the heroes, and the long high walls crowned with palisades, a marvel to behold. But when they had now come to the famous palace of the king, the goddess, grey-eyed Athene, spake first and said:

'Lo, here, father and stranger, is the house that thou wouldst have me show thee: and thou shalt find kings at the feast, the fosterlings of Zeus; enter then, and fear not in thine heart, for the dauntless man is the best in every adventure, even though he come from a strange land. Thou shalt find the queen first in the halls: Arete is the name whereby men call her, and she came even of those that begat the king Alcinous. First Nausithous was son of Poseidon, the Earth-shaker, and of Periboea, the comeliest of women, youngest daughter of great-hearted Eurymedon, who once was king among the haughty Giants. Howbeit, he destroyed his infatuate people, and was himself destroyed; but Poseidon lay with Periboea and begat a son, proud Nausithous, who sometime was prince among the Phaeacians; and Nausithous begat Rhexenor and Alcinous. While Rhexenor had as yet no son, Apollo of the silver bow smote him, a groom new wed, leaving in his halls one only child Arete; and Alcinous took her to wife, and honoured her as no other woman in the world is honoured, of all that now-a-days keep house under the hand of their lords. Thus she hath, and hath ever had, all worship heartily from her dear children and from her lord Alcinous and from all the folk, who look on her as on a goddess, and greet her with reverend speech, when she goes about the town. Yea, for she too hath no lack of understanding. To whomso she shows favour, even if they be men, she ends their feuds. If but her heart be kindly disposed to thee, then is there good hope that thou mayest see thy friends, and come to thy high-roofed home and thine own country.'

Therewith grey-eyed Athene departed over the unharvested seas, and left pleasant Scheria, and came to Marathon and wide-wayed Athens, and entered the good house of Erechtheus. Meanwhile Odysseus went to the famous palace of Alcinous, and his heart was full of many thoughts as he stood there or ever he had reached the threshold of bronze. For there was a gleam as it were of sun or moon through the high-roofed hall of great-hearted Alcinous. Brazen were the walls which ran this way and that from the threshold to the inmost chamber, and round them was a frieze of blue, and golden were the doors that closed in the good house. Silver were the door-posts that were set on the brazen threshold, and silver the lintel thereupon, and the hook of the door was of gold. And on either side stood golden hounds and silver, which Hephaestus wrought by his cunning, to guard the palace of great-hearted Alcinous, being free from death and age all their days. And within were seats arrayed against the wall this way and that, from the threshold even to the inmost chamber, and thereon were spread light coverings finely woven, the handiwork of women. There the Phaeacian chieftains were wont to sit eating and drinking, for they had continual store. Yea, and there were youths fashioned in gold, standing on firm-set bases, with flaming torches in their hands, giving light through the night to the feasters in the palace. And he had fifty handmaids in the house, and some grind the yellow grain on the millstone, and others weave webs and turn the yarn as they sit, restless as the leaves of the tall poplar tree: and the soft olive oil drops off that linen, so closely is it woven. For as the Phaeacian men are skilled beyond all others in driving a swift ship upon the deep, even so are the women the most cunning at the loom, for Athene hath given them notable wisdom in all fair handiwork and cunning wit. And without the courtyard hard by the door is a great garden, of four ploughgates, and a hedge runs round on either side. And there grow tall trees blossoming, pear-trees and pomegranates, and apple-trees with bright fruit, and sweet figs, and olives in their bloom. The fruit of these trees never perisheth neither faileth, winter nor summer, enduring through all the year. Evermore the West Wind blowing brings some fruits to birth and ripen others. Pear upon pear waxes old, and apple on apple, yea and cluster ripens upon cluster of the grape, and fig upon fig. There too hath he a fruitful vineyard planted, whereof the one part is being dried by the heat, a sunny plot on level ground, while other grapes men are gathering, and yet others they are treading in the winepress. In the foremost row are unripe grapes that cast the blossom, and others there be that are growing black to vintaging. There too, skirting the furthest line, are all manner of garden beds, planted trimly, that are perpetually fresh, and therein are two fountains of water, whereof one scatters his streams all about the garden, and the other runs over against it beneath the threshold of the courtyard, and issues by the lofty house, and thence did the townsfolk draw water. These were the splendid gifts of the gods in the palace of Alcinous.

There the steadfast goodly Odysseus stood and gazed. But when he had gazed at all and wondered, he passed quickly over the threshold within the house. And he found the captains and the counsellors of the Phaeacians pouring forth wine to the keen-sighted god, the slayer of Argos; for to him they poured the last cup when they were minded to take rest. Now the steadfast goodly Odysseus went through the hall, clad in a thick mist, which Athene shed around him, till he came to Arete and the king Alcinous. And Odysseus cast his hands about the knees of Arete, and then it was that the wondrous mist melted from off him, and a silence fell on them that were within the house at the sight of him, and they marvelled as they beheld him. Then Odysseus began his prayer:

'Arete, daughter of god-like Rhexenor, after many toils am I come to thy husband and to thy knees and to these guests, and may the gods vouchsafe them a happy life, and may each one leave to his children after him his substance in his halls and whatever dues of honour the people have rendered unto him. But speed, I pray you, my parting, that I may come the more quickly to mine own country, for already too long do I suffer affliction far from my friends.'

Therewith he sat him down by the hearth in the ashes at the fire, and behold, a dead silence fell on all. And at the last the ancient lord Echeneus spake among them, an elder of the Phaeacians, excellent in speech and skilled in mucn wisdom of old time. With good will he made harangue and spake among them:

'Alcinous, this truly is not the more seemly way, nor is it fitting that the stranger should sit upon the ground in the ashes by the hearth, while these men refrain them, waiting thy word. Nay come, bid the stranger arise, and set him on a chair inlaid with silver, and command the henchmen to mix the wine, that we may pour forth likewise before Zeus, whose joy is in the thunder, who attendeth upon reverend suppliants. And let the housewife give supper to the stranger out of such stores as be within.'

Now when the mighty king Alcinous heard this saying, he took Odysseus, the wise and crafty, by the hand, and raised him from the hearth, and set him on a shining chair, whence he bade his son give place, valiant Laodamas, who sat next him and was his dearest. And a handmaid bare water for the hands in a goodly golden ewer, and poured it forth over a silver basin to wash withal, and drew to his side a polished table. And a grave dame bare wheaten bread and set it by him and laid upon the board many dainties, giving freely of such things as she had by her. So the steadfast goodly Odysseus did eat and drink; and then the mighty Alcinous spake unto the henchman:

'Pontonus, mix the bowl and serve out the wine to all in the hill, that we may pour forth likewise before Zeus, whose joy is in the thunder, who attendeth upon reverend suppliants.'

So spake he, and Pontonus mixed the honey-hearted wine, and served it out to all, when he had poured forth libation into each cup in turn. But when they had poured forth and had drunken to their hearts' content, Alcinous made harangue and spake among them:

'Hear me, ye captains and counsellors of the Phaeacians, that I may speak as my spirit bids me. Now that the feast is over, go ye home and lie down to rest; and in the morning we will call yet more elders together, and entertain the stranger in the halls and do fair sacrifice to the gods, and thereafter we will likewise bethink us of the convoy, that so without pain or grief yonder stranger may by our convoy reach his own country speedily and with joy, even though he be from very far away. So shall he suffer no hurt or harm in mid passage, ere he set foot on his own land; but thereafter he shall endure such things as Fate and the stern spinning women drew off the spindles for him at his birth when his mother bare him. But if he is some deathless god come down from heaven, then do the gods herein imagine some new device against us. For always heretofore the gods appear manifest amongst us, whensoever we offer glorious hecatombs, and they feast by our side, sitting at the same board; yea, and even if a wayfarer going all alone has met with them, they use no disguise, since we are near of kin to them, even as are the Cyclôpes and the wild tribes of the Giants.'

And Odysseus of many counsels answered him, saying: 'Alcinous, that thought be far from thee! for I bear no likeness either in form or fashion to the deathless gods, who keep wide heaven, but to men that die. Whomsoever ye know of human kind the heaviest laden with sorrow, to them might I liken myself in my griefs. Yea, and I might tell of yet other woes, even the long tale of toil that by the gods' will I endured. But as for me, suffer me to sup, afflicted as I am; for nought is there more shameless than a ravening belly, which biddeth a man perforce be mindful of him, though one be worn and sorrowful in spirit, even as I have sorrow of heart; yet evermore he biddeth me eat and drink and maketh me utterly to forget all my sufferings, and commandeth me to take my fill. But do ye bestir you at the breaking of the day, that so ye may set me, hapless as I am, upon my country's soil, albeit after much suffering. Ah, and may life leave me when I have had sight of mine own possessions, my thralls, and my dwelling that is great and high!'

So spake he, and they all assented thereto, and bade send the stranger on his way, for that he had spoken aright. Now when they had poured forth and had drunken to their hearts' content, they went each one to his house to lay them to rest. But goodly Odysseus was left behind in the hall, and by him sat Arete and godlike Alcinous; and the maids cleared away the furniture of the feast; and white-armed Arete first spake among them. For she knew the mantle and the doublet, when she saw the goodly raiment that she heresIf had wrought with the women her handmaids. So she uttered her voice and spake to him winged words:

'Sir, I am bold to ask thee first of this. Who art thou of the sons of men, and whence? Who gave thee this raiment? Didst thou not say indeed that thou camest hither wandering over the deep?'

Then Odysseus of many counsels answered her, and said: ''Tis hard, O queen, to tell my griefs from end to end, for that the gods of heaven have given me griefs in plenty. But this will I declare to thee, whereof thou dost question and inquire. There is an isle, Ogygia, that lies far off in the sea; there dwells the daughter of Atlas, crafty Calypso, of the braided tresses, an awful goddess, nor is any either of gods or mortals conversant with her. Howbeit, some god brought me to her hearth, wretched man that I am, all alone, for that Zeus with white bolt crushed my swift ship and cleft it in the midst of the wine-dark deep. There all the rest of my good company was lost, but I clung with fast embrace about the keel of the curved ship, and so was I borne for nine whole days. And on the tenth dark night the gods brought me nigh the isle Ogygia, where Calypso of the braided tresses dwells, an awful goddess. She took me in, and with all care she cherished me and gave me sustenance, and said that she would make me to know not death nor age for all my days; but never did she win my heart within me.

There I abode for seven years continually, and watered with my tears the imperishable raiment that Calypso gave me. But when the eighth year came round in his course, then at last she urged and bade me to be gone, by reason of a message from Zeus, or it may be that her own mind was turned. So she sent me forth on a well-bound raft, and gave me plenteous store, bread and sweet wine, and she clad me in imperishable raiment, and sent forth a warm and gentle wind to blow. For ten days and seven I sailed, traversing the deep, and on the eighteenth day the shadowy hills of your land showed in sight, and my heart was glad,—wretched that I was—for surely I was still to be the mate of much sorrow. For Poseidon, shaker of the earth, stirred up the same, who roused against me the winds and stopped my way, and made a wondrous sea to swell, nor did the wave suffer me to be borne upon my raft, as I made ceaseless moan. Thus the storm winds shattered the raft, but as for me I cleft my way through the gulf yonder, till the wind bare and the water brought me nigh your coast. Then as I strove to land upon the shore, the wave had overwhelmed me, dashing me against the great rocks and a desolate place, but at length I gave way and swam back, till I came to the river, where the place seemed best in mine eyes, smooth of rocks, and withal there was a shelter from the wind. And as I came out I sank down, gathering to me my spirit, and immortal night came on. Then I gat me forth and away from the heaven-fed river, and laid me to sleep in the bushes and strewed leaves about me, and the god shed over me infinite sleep. There among the leaves I slept, stricken at heart, all the night long, even till the morning and midday. And the sun sank when sweet sleep let me free. And I was aware of the company of thy daughter disporting them upon the sand, and there was she in the midst of them like unto the goddesses. To her I made my supplication, and she showed no lack of a good understanding, behaving so as thou couldst not hope for in chancing upon one so young; for the younger folk lack wisdom always. She gave me bread enough and red wine, and let me wash me in the river and bestowed on me these garments. Herein, albeit in sore distress, have I told thee all the truth.'

And Alcinous answered again, and spake saying: 'Sir, surely this was no right thought of my daughter, in that she brought thee not to our house with the women her handmaids, though thou didst first entreat her grace.'

And Odysseus of many counsels answered, and said unto him: 'My lord, chide not, I pray thee, for this the blameless maiden. For indeed she bade me follow with her company, but I would not for fear and very shame, lest perchance thine heart might be clouded at the sight; for a jealous race upon the earth are we, the tribes of men.'

And Alcinous answered yet again, and spake saying: 'Sir, my heart within me is not of such temper as to have been wroth without a cause: due measure in all things is best. Would to father Zeus, and Athene, and Apollo, would that so goodly a man as thou art, and like-minded with me, thou wouldst wed my daughter, and be called my son, here abiding: so would I give thee house and wealth, if thou wouldst stay of thine own will: but against thy will shall none of the Phaeacians keep thee: never be this well-pleasing in the eyes of father Zeus! And now I ordain an escort for thee on a certain day, that thou mayst surely know, and that day the morrow. Then shalt thou lay thee down overcome by sleep, and they the while shall smite the calm waters, till thou come to thy country and thy house, and whatsoever place is dear to thee, even though it be much farther than Euboea, which certain of our men say is the farthest of lands, they who saw it, when they carried Rhadamanthus of the fair hair, to visit Tityos, son of Gaia. Even thither they went, and accomplished the journey on the self-same day and won home again, and were not weary. And now shalt thou know for thyself how far my ships are the best, and how my young men excel at tossing the salt water with the oar-blade.'

So spake he, and the steadfast goodly Odysseus rejoiced; and then he uttered a word in prayer, and called aloud to Zeus: 'Father Zeus, oh that Alcinous may fulfil all that he hath said, so may his fame never be quenched upon the earth, the grain-giver, and I should come to mine own land!'

Thus they spake one to the other. And white-armed Arete bade her handmaids set out bedsteads beneath the gallery, and cast fair purple blankets over them, and spread coverlets above, and thereon lay thick mantles to be a clothing over all. So they went from the hall with torch in hand. But when they had busied them and spread the good bedstead, they stood by Odysseus and called unto him, saying:

'Up now, stranger, and get thee to sleep, thy bed is made.'

So spake they, and it seemed to him that rest was wondrous good. So he slept there, the steadfast goodly Odysseus, on the jointed bedstead, beneath the echoing gallery. But Alcinous laid him down in the innermost chamber of the high house, and by him the lady his wife arrayed bedstead and bedding.

BOOK VIII

The next day's entertainment of Odysseus, where he sees them contend in wrestling and other exercises, and upon provocation took up a greater stone than that which they were throwing, and overthrew them all. Alcinous and the lords give him presents. And how the king asked his name, his country, and his adventures.

Now when early Dawn shone forth, the rosy-fingered, then the mighty king Alcinous gat him up from his bed; and Odysseus, of the seed of Zeus, likewise uprose, the waster of cities. And the mighty king Alcinous led the way to the assembly place of the Phaeacians, which they had stablished hard by the ships. So when they had come thither, and sat them down on the polished stones close by each other, Pallas Athene went on her way through the town, in the semblance of the herald of wise Alcinous, devising a return for the great-hearted Odysseus. Then standing by each man she spake, saying:

'Hither now get ye to the assembly, ye captains and counsellors of the Phaeacians, that ye may learn concerning the stranger, who hath lately come to the palace of wise Alcinous, in his wanderings over the deep, and his form is like the deathless gods.'

Therewith she aroused the spirit and desire of each one, and speedily the meeting-places and seats were filled with men that came to the gathering: yea, and many an one marvelled at the sight of the wise son of Laertes, for wondrous was the grace Athene poured upon his head and shoulders, and she made him greater and more mighty to behold, that he might win love and worship and honour among all the Phaeacians, and that he might accomplish many feats, wherein the Phaeacians made trial of Odysseus. Now when they were gathered and come together, Alcinous made harangue and spake among them:

'Hearken, ye captains and counsellors of the Phaeacians, and I will say that which my spirit within me bids me utter. This stranger, I know not who he is, hath come to my house in his wandering, whether from the men of the dawning or the westward, and he presses for a convoy, and prays that it be assured to him. So let us, as in time past, speed on the convoy. For never, nay never, doth any man who cometh to my house, abide here long in sorrow for want of help upon his way. Nay, come let us draw down a black ship to the fair salt sea, for her first voyage, and let them choose fifty and two noble youths throughout the township, who have been proved heretofore the best. And when ye have made fast the oars upon the benches, step all ashore, and thereafter come to our house, and quickly fall to feasting; and I will make good provision for all. To the noble youths I give this commandment; but ye others, sceptred kings, come to my fair dwelling, that we may entertain the stranger in the halls, and let no man make excuse. Moreover, bid hither the divine minstrel, Demodocus, for the god hath given minstrelsy to him as to none other, to make men glad in what way soever his spirit stirs him to sing.'

He spake and led the way, and the sceptred kings accompanied him, while the henchman went for the divine minstrel. And chosen youths, fifty and two, departed at his command, to the shore of the unharvested sea. But after they had gone down to the ship and to the sea, first of all they drew the ship down to the deep water, and placed the mast and sails in the black ship, and fixed the oars in leathern loops, all orderly, and spread forth the white sails. And they moored her high out in the shore water, and thereafter went on their way to the great palace of the wise Alcinous. Now the galleries and the courts and the rooms were thronged with men that came to the gathering, for there were many, young and old. Then Alcinous sacrificed twelve sheep among them, and eight boars with flashing tusks, and two oxen with trailing feet. These they flayed and made ready, and dressed a goodly feast.

Then the henchman drew near, leading with him the beloved minstrel, whom the Muse loved dearly, and she gave him both good and evil; of his sight she reft him, but granted him sweet song. Then Pontonous, the henchman, set for him a high chair inlaid with silver, in the midst of the guests, leaning it against the tall pillar, and he hung the loud lyre on a pin, close above his head, and showed him how to lay his hands on it. And close by him he placed a basket, and a fair table, and a goblet of wine by his side, to drink when his spirit bade him. So they stretched forth their hands upon the good cheer spread before them. But after they had put from them the desire of meat and drink, the Muse stirred the minstrel to sing the songs of famous men, even that lay whereof the fame had then reached the wide heaven, namely, the quarrel between Odysseus and Achilles, son of Peleus; how once on a time they contended in fierce words at a rich festival of the gods, but Agamemnon, king of men, was inly glad when the noblest of the Achaeans fell at variance. For so Phoebus Apollo in his soothsaying had told him that it must be, in goodly Pytho, what time he crossed the threshold of stone, to seek to the oracle. For in those days the first wave of woe was rolling on Trojans and Danaans through the counsel of great Zeus.

This song it was that the famous minstrel sang; but Odysseus caught his great purple cloak with his stalwart hands, and drew it down over his head, and hid his comely face, for he was ashamed to shed tears beneath his brows in presence of the Phaeacians. Yea, and oft as the divine minstrel paused in his song, Odysseus would wipe away the tears, and draw the cloak from off his head, and take the two-handled goblet and pour forth before the gods. But whensoever he began again, and the chiefs of the Phaeacians stirred him to sing, in delight at the lay, again would Odysseus cover up his head and make moan. Now none of all the company marked him weeping, but Alcinous alone noted it and was ware thereof as he sat by him and heard him groaning heavily. And presently he spake among the Phaeacians, masters of the oar:

'Hearken, ye captains and counsellors of the Phaeacians, now have our souls been satisfied with the good feast, and with the lyre, which is the mate of the rich banquet. Let us go forth anon, and make trial of divers games, that the stranger may tell his friends, when home he returneth, how greatly we excel all men in boxing, and wrestling, and leaping, and speed of foot.'

He spake, and led the way, and they went with him. And the henchman hung the loud lyre on the pin, and took the hand of Demodocus, and led him forth from the hall, and guided him by the same way, whereby those others, the chiefs of the Phaeacians, had gone to gaze upon the games. So they went on their way to the place of assembly, and with them a great company innumerable; and many a noble youth stood up to play. There rose Acroneus, and Ocyalus, and Elatreus, and Nauteus, and Prymneus, and Anchialus, and Eretmeus, and Ponteus, and Proreus, Thoon, and Anabesineus, and Amphialus, son of Polyneus, son of Tekton, and likewise Euryalus, the peer of murderous Ares, the son of Naubolus, who in face and form was goodliest of all the Phaeacians next to noble Laodamas. And there stood up the three sons of noble Alcinous, Laodamas, and Halius, and godlike Clytoneus. And behold, these all first tried the issue in the foot race. From the very start they strained at utmost speed: and all together they fled forward swiftly, raising the dust along the plain. And noble Clytoneus was far the swiftest of them all in running, and by the length of the furrow that mules cleave in a fallow field, so far did he shoot to the front, and came to the crowd by the lists, while those others were left behind. Then they made trial of strong wrestling, and here in turn Euryalus excelled all the best. And in leaping Amphialus was far the foremost, and Elatreus in weight-throwing, and in boxing Laodamas, the good son of Alcinous. Now when they had all taken their pleasure in the games, Laodamas, son of Alcinous, spake among them:

'Come, my friends, let us ask the stranger whether he is skilled or practised in any sport. Ill fashioned, at least, he is not in his thighs and sinewy legs and hands withal, and his stalwart neck and mighty strength: yea and he lacks not youth, but is crushed by many troubles. For I tell thee there is nought else worse than the sea to confound a man, how hardy soever he may be.'

And Euryalus in turn made answer, and said: 'Laodamas, verily thou hast spoken this word in season. Go now thyself and challenge him, and declare thy saying.'

Now when the good son of Alcinous heard this, he went and stood in the midst, and spake unto Odysseus: 'Come, do thou too, father and stranger, try thy skill in the sports, if haply thou art practised in any; and thou art like to have knowledge of games, for there is no greater glory for a man while yet he lives, than that which he achieves by hand and foot. Come, then, make essay, and cast away care from thy soul: thy journey shall not now be long delayed; lo, thy ship is even now drawn down to the sea, and the men of thy company are ready.'

And Odysseus of many counsels answered him, saying: 'Laodamas, wherefore do ye mock me, requiring this thing of me? Sorrow is far nearer my heart than sports, for much have I endured and laboured sorely in time past, and now I sit in this your gathering, craving my return, and making my prayer to the king and all the people.'

And Euryalus answered, and rebuked him to his face: 'No truly, stranger, nor do I think thee at all like one that is skilled in games, whereof there are many among men, rather art thou such an one as comes and goes in a benched ship, a master of sailors that are merchantmen, one with a memory for his freight, or that hath the charge of a cargo homeward bound, and of greedily gotten gains; thou seemest not a man of thy hands.'

Then Odysseus of many counsels looked fiercely on him and said: 'Stranger, thou hast not spoken well; thou art like a man presumptuous. So true it is that the gods do not give every gracious gift to all, neither shapeliness, nor wisdom, nor skilled speech. For one man is feebler than another in presence, yet the god crowns his words with beauty, and men behold him and rejoice, and his speech runs surely on his way with a sweet modesty, and he shines forth among the gathering of his people, and as he passes through the town men gaze on him as a god. Another again is like the deathless gods for beauty, but his words have no crown of grace about them; even as thou art in comeliness pre-eminent, nor could a god himself fashion thee for the better, but in wit thou art a weakling. Yea, thou hast stirred my spirit in my breast by speaking thus amiss. I am not all unversed in sports, as thy words go, but methinks I was among the foremost while as yet I trusted in my youth and my hands, but now am I holden in misery and pains: for I have endured much in passing through the wars of men and the grievous waves of the sea. Yet even so, for all my affliction, I will essay the games, for thy word hath bitten to the quick, and thou hast roused me with thy saying.'

He spake, and clad even as he was in his mantle leaped to his feet, and caught up a weight larger than the rest, a huge weight heavier far than those wherewith the

Phaeacians contended in casting. With one whirl he sent it from his stout hand, and the stone flew hurtling: and the Phaeacians, of the long oars, those mariners renowned, crouched to earth beneath the rushing of the stone. Beyond all the marks it flew, so lightly it sped from his hand, and Athene in the fashion of a man marked the place, and spake and hailed him:

'Yea, even a blind man, stranger, might discern that token if he groped for it, for it is in no wise lost among the throng of the others, but is far the first; for this bout then take heart: not one of the Phaeacians shall attain thereunto or overpass it.'

So spake she; and the steadfast goodly Odysseus rejoiced and was glad, for that he saw a true friend in the lists. Then with a lighter heart he spake amid the Phaeacians:

'Now reach ye this throw, young men, if ye may; and soon, methinks, will I cast another after it, as far or yet further. And whomsoever of the rest his heart and spirit stir thereto, hither let him come and try the issue with me, in boxing or in wrestling or even in the foot race, I care not which, for ye have greatly angered me: let any of all the Phaeacians come save Laodamas alone, for he is mine host: who would strive with one that entreated him kindly? Witless and worthless is the man, whoso challengeth his host that receiveth him in a strange land, he doth but maim his own estate. But for the rest, I refuse none and hold none lightly, but I fain would know and prove them face to face. For I am no weakling in all sports, even in the feats of men. I know well how to handle the polished bow, and ever the first would I be to shoot and smite my man in the press of foes, even though many of my company stood by, and were aiming at the enemy. Alone Philoctetes in the Trojan land surpassed me with the bow in our Achaean archery. But I avow myself far more excellent than all besides, of the mortals that are now upon the earth and live by bread. Yet with the men of old time I would not match me, neither with Heracles nor with Eurytus of Oechalia, who contended even with the deathless gods for the prize of archery. Wherefore the great Eurytus perished all too soon, nor did old age come on him in his halls, for Apollo slew him in his wrath, seeing that he challenged him to shoot a match. And with the spear I can throw further than any other man can shoot an arrow. Only I doubt that in the foot race some of the Phaeacians may outstrip me, for I have been shamefully broken in many waters, seeing that there was no continual sustenance on board; wherefore my knees are loosened.'

So spake he and all kept silence; and Alcinous alone answered him, saying:

'Stranger, forasmuch as these thy words are not ill-taken in our gathering, but thou wouldest fain show forth the valour which keeps thee company, being angry that yonder man stood by thee in the lists, and taunted thee, in such sort as no mortal would speak lightly of thine excellence, who had knowledge of sound words; nay now, mark my speech; so shalt thou have somewhat to tell another hero, when with thy wife and children thou suppest in thy halls, and recallest our prowess, what deeds Zeus bestoweth even upon us from our fathers' days even until now. For we are no perfect boxers, nor wrestlers, but speedy runners, and the best of seamen; and dear to us ever is the banquet, and the harp, and the dance, and changes of raiment, and the warm bath, and love, and sleep. Lo, now arise, ye dancers of the Phaeacians, the best in the land, and make sport, that so the stranger may tell his friends, when he returneth home, how far we surpass all men besides in seamanship, and speed of foot, and in the dance and song. And let one go quickly, and fetch for Demodocus the loud lyre which is lying somewhere in our halls.'

So spake Alcinous the godlike, and the henchman rose to bear the hollow lyre from the king's palace. Then stood up nine chosen men in all, the judges of the people, who were wont to order all things in the lists aright. So they levelled the place for the dance, and made a fair ring and a wide. And the henchman drew near bearing the loud lyre to Demodocus, who gat him into the midst, and round him stood boys in their first bloom, skilled in the dance, and they smote the good floor with their feet. And Odysseus gazed at the twinklings of the feet, and marvelled in spirit.

Now as the minstrel touched the lyre, he lifted up his voice in sweet song, and he sang of the love of Ares and Aphrodite, of the fair crown, how at the first they lay together in the house of Hephaestus privily; and Ares gave her many gifts, and dishonoured the marriage bed of the lord Hephaestus. And anon there came to him one to report the thing, even Helios, that had seen them at their pastime. Now when Hephaestus heard the bitter tidings, he went his way to the forge, devising evil in the deep of his heart, and set the great anvil on the stithy, and wrought fetters that none might snap or loosen, that the lovers might there unmoveably remain. Now when he had forged the crafty net in his anger against Ares, he went on his way to the chamber where his marriage bed was set out, and strewed his snares all about the posts of the bed, and many too were hung aloft from the main beam, subtle as spiders' webs, so that none might see them, even of the blessed gods: so cunningly were they forged. Now after he had done winding the snare about the bed, he made as though he would go to Lemnos, that stablished castle, and this was far the dearest of all lands in his sight. But Ares of the golden rein kept no blind watch, what time he saw Hephaestus, the famed craftsman, depart afar. So he went on his way to the house of renowned Hephaestus, eager for the love of crowned Cytherea. Now she was but newly come from her sire, the mighty Cronion, and as it chanced had sat her down; and Ares entered the house, and clasped her hand, and spake, and hailed her:

'Come, my beloved, let us to bed, and take our pleasure of love, for Hephaestus is no longer among his own people; methinks he is already gone to Lemnos, to the Sintians, men of savage speech.'

So spake he, and a glad thing it seemed to her to lie with him. So they twain went to the couch, and laid them to sleep, and around them clung the cunning bonds of skilled Hephaestus, so that they could not move nor raise a limb. Then at the last they knew it, when there was no way to flee. Now the famous god of the strong arms drew near to them, having turned him back ere he reached the land of Lemnos. For Helios had kept watch, and told him all. So heavy at heart he went his way to his house, and stood at the entering in of the gate, and wild rage gat hold of him, and he cried terribly, and shouted to all the gods:

'Father Zeus, and ye other blessed gods, that live for ever, come hither, that ye may see a mirthful thing and a cruel, for that Aphrodite, daughter of Zeus, ever dishonours me by reason of my lameness, and sets her heart on Ares the destroyer, because he is fair and straight of limb, but as for me, feeble was I born. Howbeit, there is none to blame but my father and mother,—would they had never begotten me! But now shall ye see where these have gone up into my bed, and sleep together in love; and I am troubled at the sight. Yet, methinks, they will not care to lie thus even for a little while longer, despite their great love. Soon will they have no desire to sleep together, but the snare and the bond shall hold them, till her sire give back to me the gifts of wooing, one and all, those that I bestowed upon him for the hand of his shameless girl; for that his daughter is fair, but without discretion.'

So spake he; and lo, the gods gathered together to the

house of the brazen floor. Poseidon came, the girdler of the earth, and Hermes came, the bringer of luck, and prince Apollo came, the archer. But the lady goddesses abode each within her house for shame. So the gods, the givers of good things, stood in the porch: and laughter unquenchable arose among the blessed gods, as they beheld the sleight of cunning Hephaestus. And thus would one speak, looking to his neighbour.

'Ill deed, ill speed! The slow catcheth the swift! Lo, how Hephaestus, slow as he is, hath overtaken Ares, albeit he is the swiftest of the gods that hold Olympus, by his craft hath he taken him despite his lameness; wherefore surely Ares oweth the fine of the adulterer.' Thus they spake one to the other. But the lord Apollo, son of Zeus, spake to Hermes:

'Hermes, son of Zeus, messenger and giver of good things, wouldst thou be fain, aye, pressed by strong bonds though it might be, to lie on the couch by golden Aphrodite?'

Then the messenger, the slayer of Argos, answered him: 'I would that this might be, Apollo, my prince of archery! So might thrice as many bonds innumerable encompass me about, and all ye gods be looking on and all the goddesses, yet would I lie by golden Aphrodite.'

So spake he, and laughter rose among the deathless gods. Howbeit Poseidon laughed not, but was instant with Hephaestus, the renowned artificer, to loose the bonds of Ares: and he uttered his voice, and spake to him winged words:

'Loose him, I pray thee, and I promise even as thou biddest me, that he shall himself pay all fair forfeit in the presence of the deathless gods.'

Then the famous god of the strong arms answered him: 'Require not this of me, Poseidon, girdler of the earth. Evil are evil folk's pledges to hold. How could I keep thee bound among the deathless gods, if Ares were to depart, avoiding the debt and the bond?'

Then Poseidon answered him, shaker of the earth: 'Hephaestus, even if Ares avoid the debt and flee away, I myself will pay thee all.'

Then the famous god of the strong arms answered him: 'It may not be that I should say thee nay, neither is it meet.'

Therewith the mighty Hephaestus loosed the bonds, and the twain, when they were freed from that strong bond, sprang up straightway, and departed, he to Thrace, but laughter-loving Aphrodite went to Paphos of Cyprus, where is her precinct and fragrant altar. There the Graces bathed and anointed her with oil imperishable, such as is laid upon the everlasting gods. And they clad her in lovely raiment, a wonder to see.

This was the song the famous minstrel sang; and Odysseus listened and was glad at heart, and likewise did the Phaeacians, of the long oars, those mariners renowned.

Then Alcinous bade Halius and Laodamas dance alone, for none ever contended with them. So when they had taken in their hands the goodly ball of purple hue, that cunning Polybus had wrought for them, the one would bend backwards, and throw it towards the shadowy clouds; and the other would leap upward from the earth, and catch it lightly in his turn, before his feet touched the ground. Now after they had made trial of throwing the ball straight up, the twain set to dance upon the bounteous earth, tossing the ball from hand to hand, and the other youths stood by the lists and beat time, and a great din uprose.

Then it was that goodly Odysseus spake unto Alcinous: 'My lord Alcinous, most notable among all the people, thou didst boast thy dancers to be the best in the world, and lo, thy words are fulfilled; I wonder as I look on them.'

So spake he, and the mighty king Alcinous rejoiced and spake at once among the Phaeacians, masters of the oar:

'Hearken ye, captains and counsellors of the Phaeacians,

this stranger seems to me a wise man enough. Come then, let us give him a stranger's gift, as is meet. Behold, there are twelve glorious princes who rule among this people and bear sway, and I myself am the thirteenth. Now each man among you bring a fresh robe and a doublet, and a talent of fine gold, and let us speedily carry all these gifts together, that the stranger may take them in his hands, and go to supper with a glad heart. As for Euryalus let him yield amends to the man himself with soft speech and with a gift, for his was no gentle saying.'

So spake he, and they all assented thereto, and would have it so. And each one sent forth his henchman to fetch his gift, and Euryalus answered the king and spake, saying:

'My lord Alcinous, most notable among all the people, I will make atonement to thy guest according to thy word. I will give him a hanger all of bronze, with a silver hilt thereto, and a sheath of fresh-sawn ivory covers it about, and it shall be to him a thing of price.'

Therewith he puts into his hands the hanger dight with silver, and uttering his voice spake to him winged words: 'Hail, stranger and father; and if aught grievous hath been spoken, may the storm-winds soon snatch and bear it away. But may the gods grant thee to see thy wife and to come to thine own country, for all too long hast thou endured affliction away from thy friends.'

And Odysseus of many counsels answered him saying: 'Thou too, my friend, all hail; and may the gods vouchsafe thee happiness, and mayst thou never miss this sword which thou hast given me, thou that with soft speech hast yielded me amends.'

He spake and hung about his shoulders the silver-studded sword. And the sun sank, and the noble gifts were brought him. Then the proud henchmen bare them to the palace of Alcinous, and the sons of noble Alcinous took the fair gifts, and set them by their reverend mother. And the mighty king Alcinous led the way, and they came in and sat them down on the high seats. And the mighty Alcinous spake unto Arete:

'Bring me hither, my lady, a choice coffer, the best thou hast, and thyself place therein a fresh robe and a doublet, and heat for our guest a cauldron on the fire, and warm water, that after the bath the stranger may see all the gifts duly arrayed which the noble Phaeacians bare hither, and that he may have joy in the feast, and in hearing the song of the minstrelsy. Also I will give him a beautiful golden chalice of mine own, that he may be mindful of me all the days of his life when he poureth the drink-offering to Zeus and to the other gods.'

So spake he, and Arete bade her handmaids to set a great cauldron on the fire with what speed they might. And they set the cauldron for the filling of the bath on the blazing fire, and poured water therein, and took faggots and kindled them beneath. So the fire began to circle round the belly of the cauldron, and the water waxed hot. Meanwhile Arete brought forth for her guest the beautiful coffer from the treasure chamber, and bestowed fair gifts therein, raiment and gold, which the Phaeacians gave him. And with her own hands she placed therein a robe and goodly doublet, and uttering her voice spake to him winged words:

'Do thou now look to the lid, and quickly tie the knot, lest any man spoil thy goods by the way, when presently thou fallest on sweet sleep travelling in thy black ship.'

Now when the steadfast goodly Odysseus heard this saying, forthwith he fixed on the lid, and quickly tied the curious knot, which the lady Circé on a time had taught him. Then straightway the housewife bade him go to the bath and bathe him; and he saw the warm water and was glad, for he was not wont to be so cared for, from the day that he left the house of fair-tressed Calypso, but all that while he had comfort continually as a god.

Now after the maids had bathed him and anointed him with olive oil, and had cast a fair mantle and a doublet upon him, he stept forth from the bath, and went to be with the chiefs at their wine. And Nausicaa, dowered with beauty by the gods, stood by the pillar of the well-builded roof, and marvelled at Odysseus, beholding him before her eyes, and she uttered her voice and spake to him winged words:

'Farewell, stranger, and even in thine own country bethink thee of me upon a time, for that to me first thou owest the ransom of life.'

And Odysseus of many counsels answered her saying: 'Nausicaa, daughter of great-hearted Alcinous, yea, may Zeus, the thunderer, the lord of Here, grant me to reach my home and see the day of my returning; so would I, even there, do thee worship as to a god, all my days for evermore, for thou, lady, hast given me my life."

He spake and sat him in the high seat by king Alcinous. And now they were serving out the portions and mixing the wine. Then the henchman drew nigh leading the sweet minstrel, Demodocus, that was had in honour of the people. So he set him in the midst of the feasters, and made him lean against a tall column. Then to the henchman spake Odysseus of many counsels, for he had cut off a portion of the chine of a white-toothed boar, whereon yet more was left, with rich fat on either side:

'Lo, henchman, take this mess, and hand it to Demodocus, that he may eat, and I will bid him hail, despite my sorrow. For minstrels from all men on earth get their meed of honour and worship; inasmuch as the Muse teacheth them the paths of song, and loveth the tribe of minstrels.'

Thus he spake, and the henchman bare the mess, and set it upon the knees of the lord Demodocus, and he took it, and was glad at heart. Then they stretched forth their hands upon the good cheer set before them. Now after they had put from them the desire of meat and drink, then

Odysseus of many counsels spake to Demodocus, saying: 'Demodocus, I praise thee far above all mortal men, whether it be the Muse, the daughter of Zeus, that taught thee, or even Apollo, for right duly dost thou chant the faring of the Achaeans, even all that they wrought and suffered, and all their travail, as if, methinks, thou hadst been present, or heard the tale from another. Come now, change thy strain, and sing of the fashioning of the horse of wood, which Epeius made by the aid of Athene, even the guileful thing, that goodly Odysseus led up into the citadel, when he had laden it with the men who wasted Ilios. If thou wilt indeed rehearse me this aright, so will I be thy witness among all men, how the god of his grace hath given thee the gift of wondrous song.'

So spake he, and the minstrel, being stirred by the god, began and showed forth his minstrelsy. He took up the tale where it tells how the Argives of the one part set fire to their huts, and went aboard their decked ships and sailed away, while those others, the fellowship of renowned Odysseus, were now seated in the assembly-place of the Trojans, all hidden in the horse, for the Trojans themselves had dragged him to the citadel. So the horse stood there, while seated all around him the people spake many things confusedly and three ways their counsel looked; either to cleave the hollow timber with the pitiless spear, or to drag it to the brow of the hill, and hurl it from the rocks, or to leave it as a mighty offering to appease the gods. And on this wise it was to be at the last. For the doom was on them to perish when their city should have closed upon the great horse of wood, wherein sat all the bravest of the Argives, bearing to the Trojans death and destiny. And he sang how the sons of the Achaeans poured forth from the horse, and left the hollow lair, and sacked the burg. And he sang how and where each man wasted the town, and of Odysseus, how he went like Ares to the house of Deiphobus with godlike Menelaus. It was there, the said, that Odysseus adventured the most grievous battle, and in the end prevailed, by grace of great-hearted Athene.

This was the song that the famous minstrel sang. But the heart of Odysseus melted, and the tear wet his cheeks beneath the eyelids. And as a woman throws herself wailing about her dear lord, who hath fallen before his city and the host, warding from his town and his children the pitiless day; and she beholds him dying and drawing difficult breath, and embracing his body wails aloud, while the foemen behind smite her with spears on back and shoulders and lead her up into bondage, to bear labour and trouble, and with the most pitiful grief her cheeks are wasted; even so pitifully fell the tears beneath the brows of Odysseus. Now none of all the company marked him weeping; but Alcinous alone noted it, and was aware thereof, as he sat nigh him and heard him groaning heavily. And presently he spake among the Phaeacians, masters of the oar:

'Hearken, ye captains and counsellors of the Phaeacians, and now let Demodocus hold his hand from the loud lyre, for this song of his is nowise pleasing alike to all. From the time that we began to sup, and that the divine minstrel was moved to sing, ever since hath yonder stranger never ceased from woeful lamentation; sore grief, methinks, hath encompassed his heart. Nay, but let the minstrel cease, that we may all alike make merry, hosts and guest, since it is far meeter so. For all these things are ready for the sake of the honourable stranger, even the convoy and the loving gifts which we give him out of our love. In a brother's place stand the stranger and the suppliant, to him whose wits have even a little range. Wherefore do thou too hide not now with crafty purpose aught whereof I ask thee; it were more meet for thee to tell it out. Say, what is the name whereby they called thee at home, even thy father and thy mother, and others thy townsmen and the dwellers round about? For there is none of all mankind nameless, neither the mean man nor yet the noble, from first hour of his birth, but parents bestow a name on every man so soon as he is born. Tell me too of thy land, thy township, and thy city, that our ships may conceive of their course to bring thee thither. For the Phaeacians have no pilots nor any rudders after the manner of other ships, but their barques themselves understand the thoughts and intents of men; they know the cities and fat fields of every people, and most swiftly they traverse the gulf of the salt sea, shrouded in mist and cloud, and never do they go in fear of wreck or ruin. Howbeit I heard upon a time this word thus spoken by my father Nausithous, who was wont to say that Poseidon was jealous of us for that we give safe escort to all men. He said that the god would some day smite a well-wrought ship of the Phaeacians as she came home from a convoy over the misty deep, and would overshadow our city with a great mountain. Thus that ancient one would speak, and thus the god may bring it about, or leave it undone, according to the good pleasure of his will. But come now, declare me this and plainly tell it all; whither wast thou borne wandering, and to what shores of men thou camest; tell me of the people and of their fair-lying cities, of those whoso are hard and wild and unjust, and of those likewise who are hospitable and of a god-fearing mind. Declare, too, wherefore thou dost weep and mourn in spirit at the tale of the faring of the Argive Danaans and the lay of Ilios. All this the gods have fashioned, and have woven the skein of death for men, that there might be a song in the ears even of the folk of aftertime. Hadst thou even a kinsman by marriage that fell before Ilios, a true man, a daughter's husband or wife's father, such as are nearest us after those of our own stock and blood? Or else, may be, some loving friend, a good man and true; for a friend with an understanding heart is no whit worse than a brother.'

BOOK IX

Odysseus relates, first, what befell him amongst the Cicones at Ismarus; secondly, amongst the Lotophagi; thirdly, how he was used by the Cyclops Polyphemus.

And Odysseus of many counsels answered him saying: 'King Alcinous, most notable of all the people, verily it is a good thing to list to a minstrel such as this one, like to the gods in voice. Nay, as for me, I say that there is no more gracious or perfect delight than when a whole people makes merry, and the men sit orderly at feast in the halls and listen to the singer, and the tables by them are laden with bread and flesh, and a wine-bearer drawing the wine serves it round and pours it into the cups. This seems to me well-nigh the fairest thing in the world. But now thy heart was inclined to ask of my grievous troubles, that I may mourn for more exceeding sorrow. What then shall I tell of first, what last, for the gods of heaven have given me woes in plenty? Now, first, will I tell my name, that ye too may know it, and that I, when I have escaped the pitiless day, may yet be your host, though my home is in a far country. I am Odysseus, son of Laertes, who am in men's minds for all manner of wiles, and my fame reaches unto heaven. And I dwell in clear-seen Ithaca, wherein is a mountain Neriton, with trembling forest leaves, standing manifest to view, and many islands lie around, very near one to the other, Dulichium and Same, and wooded Zacynthus. Now Ithaca lies low, furthest up the sea-line toward the darkness, but those others face the dawning and the sun; a rugged isle, but a good nurse of noble youths; and for myself I can see nought beside sweeter than a man's own country. Verily Calypso, the fair goddess, would fain have kept me with her in her hollow caves, longing to have me for her lord; and likewise too, guileful Circé of Aia, would have stayed me in her halls, longing to have me for her lord. But never did they prevail upon my heart within my breast. So surely is there nought sweeter than a man's own country and his parents, even though he dwell far off in a rich home, in a strange land, away from them that begat him. But come, let me tell thee too of the troubles of my journeying, which Zeus laid on me as I came from Troy.

'The wind that bare me from Ilios brought me nigh to the Cicones, even to Ismarus, whereupon I sacked their city and slew the people. And from out the city we took their wives and much substance, and divided them amongst us, that none through me might go lacking his proper share. Howbeit, thereafter I commanded that we should flee with a swift foot, but my men in their great folly hearkened not. There was much wine still a drinking, and still they slew many flocks of sheep by the seashore and kine with trailing feet and shambling gait. Meanwhile the Cicones went and raised a cry to other Cicones their neighbours, dwelling inland, who were more in number than they and braver withal: skilled they were to fight with men from chariots, and when need was on foot. So they gathered in the early morning as thick as leaves and flowers that spring in their season—yea and in that hour an evil doom of Zeus stood by us, ill-fated men, that so we might be sore afflicted. They set their battle in array by the swift ships, and the hosts cast at one another with their bronze-shod spears. So long as it was morn and the sacred day waxed stronger, so long we abode their assault and beat them off, albeit they outnumbered us. But when the sun was wending to the time of the loosing of cattle, then at last the Cicones drave in the Achaeans and overcame them, and six of my goodly-greaved company perished from each ship: but the remnant of us escaped death and destiny.

'Thence we sailed onward stricken at heart, yet glad as men saved from death, albeit we had lost our dear companions. Nor did my curved ships move onward ere we had called thrice on each of those our hapless fellows, who died at the hands of the Cicones on the plain. Now Zeus, gatherer of the clouds, aroused the North Wind against our ships with a terrible tempest, and covered land and sea alike with clouds, and down sped night from heaven. Thus the ships were driven headlong, and their sails were torn to shreds by the might of the wind. So we lowered the sails into the hold, in fear of death, but rowed the ships landward apace. There for two nights and two days we lay continually, consuming our hearts with weariness and sorrow. But when the fair-tressed Dawn had at last brought the full light of the third day, we set up the masts and hoisted the white sails and sat us down, while the wind and the helmsman guided the ships. And now I should have come to mine own country all unhurt, but the wave and the stream of the sea and the North Wind swept me from my course as I was doubling Malea, and drave me wandering past Cythera.

'Thence for nine whole days was I borne by ruinous winds over the teeming deep; but on the tenth day we set foot on the land of the lotus-eaters, who eat a flowery food. So we stepped ashore and drew water, and straightway my company took their midday meal by the swift ships. Now when we had tasted meat and drink I sent forth certain of my company to go and make search what manner of men they were who here live upon the earth by bread, and I chose out two of my fellows, and sent a third with them as herald. Then straightway they went and mixed with the men of the lotus-eaters, and so it was that the lotus-eaters devised not death for our fellows, but gave them of the lotus to taste. Now whosoever of them did eat the honey-sweet fruit of the lotus, had no more wish to bring tidings nor to come back, but there he chose to abide with the lotus-eating men, ever feeding on the lotus, and forgetful of his homeward way. Therefore I led them back to the ships weeping, and sore against their will, and dragged them beneath the benches, and bound them in the hollow barques. But I commanded the rest of my well-loved company to make speed and go on board the swift ships, lest haply any should eat of the lotus and be forgetful of returning. Right soon they embarked and sat upon the benches, and sitting orderly they smote the grey sea water with their oars.

'Thence we sailed onward stricken at heart. And we came to the land of the Cyclôpes, a froward and a lawless folk, who trusting to the deathless gods plant not aught with their hands, neither plough: but, behold, all these things spring for them in plenty, unsown and untilled, wheat, and barley, and vines, which bear great clusters of the juice of the grape, and the rain of Zeus gives them increase. These have neither gatherings for council nor oracles of law, but they dwell in hollow caves on the crests of the high hills, and each one utters the law to his children and his wives, and they reck not one of another.

'Now there is a waste isle stretching without the harbour of the land of the Cyclôpes, neither nigh at hand nor yet afar off, a woodland isle, wherein are wild goats unnumbered, for no path of men scares them, nor do hunters resort thither who suffer hardships in the wood, as they range the mountain crests. Moreover it is possessed neither by flocks nor by ploughed lands, but the soil lies unsown evermore and untilled, desolate of men, and feeds the bleating goats. For the Cyclôpes have by them no ships with vermilion cheek, not yet are there shipwrights in the island, who might fashion decked barques, which should accomplish all their desire, voyaging to the towns of men (as ofttimes men cross the sea to one another in ships), who might likewise have made of their isle a goodly settlement. Yea, it is in no wise a sorry land, but would bear all things in their season; for therein are soft water-meadows by the shores of the grey salt sea, and there the vines know no decay, and the land is level to plough; thence might they reap a crop exceeding deep in due season, for verily there is fatness beneath the soil. Also there is a fair haven, where is no need of moorings, either to cast anchor or to fasten hawsers, but men may run the ship on the beach, and tarry until such time as the sailors are minded to be gone, and favourable breezes blow. Now at the head of the harbour is a well of bright water issuing from a cave, and round it are poplars growing. Thither we sailed, and some god guided us through the night, for it was dark and there was no light to see, a mist lying deep about the ships, nor did the moon show her light from heaven, but was shut in with clouds. No man then beheld that island, neither saw we the long waves rolling to the beach, till we had run our decked ships ashore. And when our ships were beached, we took down all their sails, and ourselves too stept forth upon the strand of the sea, and there we fell into sound sleep and waited for the bright Dawn.

'So soon as early Dawn shone forth, the rosy-fingered, in wonder at the island we roamed over the length thereof: and the Nymphs, the daughters of Zeus, lord of the aegis, started the wild goats of the hills, that my company might have wherewith to sup. Anon we took to us our curved bows from out the ships and long spears, and arrayed in three bands we began shooting at the goats; and the god soon gave us game in plenty. Now twelve ships bare me company, and to each ship fell nine goats for a portion, but for me alone they set ten apart.

'Thus we sat there the livelong day until the going down of the sun, feasting on abundant flesh and on sweet wine. For the red wine was not yet spent from out the ships, but somewhat was yet therein, for we had each one drawn off large store thereof in jars, when we took the sacred citadel of the Cicones. And we looked across to the land of the Cyclôpes who dwell nigh, and to the smoke, and to the voice of the men, and of the sheep and of the goats. And when the sun had sunk and darkness had come on, then we laid us to rest upon the sea-beach. So soon as early Dawn shone forth, the rosy-fingered, then I called a gathering of my men, and spake among them all:

' "Abide here all the rest of you, my dear companions; but I will go with mine own ship and my ship's company, and make proof of these men, what manner of folk they are, whether froward, and wild, and unjust, or hospitable and of god-fearing mind."

'So I spake, and I climbed the ship's side, and bade my company themselves to mount, and to loose the hawsers. So they soon embarked and sat upon the benches, and sitting orderly smote the grey sea water with their oars. Now when we had come to the land that lies hard by, we saw a cave on the border near to the sea, lofty and roofed over with laurels, and there many flocks of sheep and goats were used to rest. And about it a high outer court was built with stones, deep bedded, and with tall pines and oaks with their high crown of leaves. And a man was wont to sleep therein, of monstrous size, who shepherded his flocks alone and afar, and was not conversant with others, but dwelt apart in lawlessness of mind. Yea, for he was a monstrous thing and fashioned marvellously, nor was he like to any man that lives by bread, but like a wooded peak of the towering hills, which stands out apart and alone from others.

'Then I commanded the rest of my well-loved company to tarry there by the ship, and to guard the ship, but I chose out twelve men, the best of my company, and sallied forth. Now I had with me a goat-skin of the dark wine and sweet, which Maron, son of Euanthes, had given me, the priest of Apollo, the god that watched over Ismarus.

And he gave it, for that we had protected him with his wife and child reverently; for he dwelt in a thick grove of Phoebus Apollo. And he made me splendid gifts; he gave me seven talents of gold well wrought, and he gave me a mixing bowl of pure silver, and furthermore wine which he drew off in twelve jars in all, sweet wine unmingled, a draught divine; nor did any of his servants or of his handmaids in the house know thereof, but himself and his dear wife and one house-dame only. And as often as they drank that red wine honey sweet, he would fill one cup and pour it into twenty measures of water, and a marvellous sweet smell went up from the mixing bowl; then truly it was no pleasure to refrain.

'With this wine I filled a great skin, and bare it with me, and corn too I put in a wallet, for my lordly spirit straightway had a boding that a man would come to me, a strange man, clothed in mighty strength, one that knew not judgment and justice.

'Soon we came to the cave, but we found him not within; he was shepherding his fat flocks in the pastures. So we went into the cave, and gazed on all that was therein. The baskets were well laden with cheeses, and the folds were thronged with lambs and kids; each kind was penned by itself, the firstlings apart, and the summer lambs apart, apart too the younglings of the flock. Now all the vessels swam with whey, the milk-pails and the bowls, the well-wrought vessels whereinto he milked. My company then spake and besought me first of all to take of the cheeses and to return, and afterwards to make haste and drive off the kids and lambs to the swift ships from out the pens, and to sail over the salt sea water. Howbeit I hearkened not (and far better would it have been), but waited to see the giant himself, and whether he would give me gifts as a stranger's due. Yet was not his coming to be with joy to my company.

'Then we kindled a fire, and made burnt-offering, and

ourselves likewise took of the cheeses, and did eat, and sat waiting for him within till he came back, shepherding his flocks. And he bore a grievous weight of dry wood, against supper time. This log he cast down with a din inside the cave, and in fear we fled to the secret place of the rock. As for him, he drave his fat flocks into the wide cavern, even all that he was wont to milk; but the males both of the sheep and of the goats he left without in the deep yard. Thereafter he lifted a huge doorstone and weighty, and set it in the mouth of the cave, such an one as two and twenty good four-wheeled wains could not raise from the ground, so mighty a sheer rock did he set against the doorway. Then he sat down and milked the ewes and bleating goats all orderly, and beneath each ewe he placed her young. And anon he curdled one half of the white milk, and massed it together, and stored it in wicker-baskets, and the other half he let stand in pails, that he might have it to take and drink against supper time. Now when he had done all his work busily then he kindled the fire anew, and espied us, and made question:

' "Strangers, who are ye? Whence sail ye over the wet ways? On some trading enterprise or at adventure do ye rove, even as sea-robbers over the brine, for at hazard of their own lives they wander, bringing bale to alien men."

'So spake he, but as for us our heart within us was broken for terror of the deep voice and his own monstrous shape; yet despite all I answered and spake unto him, saying:

' "Lo, we are Achaeans, driven wandering from Troy, by all manner of winds over the great gulf of the sea; seeking our homes we fare, but another path have we come, by other ways: even such, methinks, was the will and the counsel of Zeus. And we avow us to be the men of Agamemnon, son of Atreus, whose fame is even now the mightiest under heaven, so great a city did he sack, and destroyed many people; but as for us we have lighted here, and come to these thy knees, if perchance thou wilt give us a stranger's gift, or make any present, as is the due of strangers. Nay, lord, have regard to the gods, for we are thy suppliants; and Zeus is the avenger of suppliants and sojourners, Zeus, the god of the stranger, who fareth in the company of reverend strangers."

'So I spake, and anon he answered out of his pitiless heart: "Thou art witless, my stranger, or thou hast come from afar, who biddest me either to fear or shun the gods. For the Cyclôpes pay no heed to Zeus, lord of the aegis, nor to the blessed gods, for verily we are better men than they. Nor would I, to shun the enmity of Zeus, spare either thee or thy company, unless my spirit bade me. But tell me where thou didst stay thy well-wrought ship on thy coming? Was it perchance at the far end of the island, or hard by, that I may know?"

'So he spake tempting me, but he cheated me not, who knew full much, and I answered him again with words of guile:

'"As for my ship, Poseidon, the shaker of the earth, brake it to pieces, for he cast it upon the rocks at the border of your country, and brought it nigh the headland, and a wind bare it thither from the sea. But I with these my men escaped from utter doom."

'So I spake, and out of his pitiless heart he answered me not a word, but sprang up, and laid his hands upon my fellows, and clutching two together dashed them, as they had been whelps, to the earth, and the brain flowed forth upon the ground and the earth was wet. Then cut he them up piecemeal, and made ready his supper. So he ate even as a mountain-bred lion, and ceased not, devouring entrails and flesh and bones with their marrow. And we wept and raised our hands to Zeus, beholding the cruel deeds; and we were at our wits' end. And after the Cyclops had filled his huge maw with human flesh and the milk he drank thereafter, he lay within the cave, stretched out among his sheep.

'So I took counsel in my great heart, whether I should draw near, and pluck my sharp sword from my thigh, and stab him in the breast, where the midriff holds the liver, feeling for the place with my hand. But my second thought withheld me, for so should we too have perished even there with utter doom. For we should not have prevailed to roll away with our hands from the lofty door the heavy stone which he set there. So for that time we made moan, awaiting the bright Dawn.

'Now when early Dawn shone forth, the rosy-fingered, again he kindled the fire and milked his goodly flocks all orderly, and beneath each ewe set her lamb. Anon when he had done all his work busily, again he seized yet other two men and made ready his mid-day meal. And after the meal, lightly he moved away the great door-stone, and drave his fat flocks forth from the cave, and afterwards he set it in his place again, as one might set the lid on a quiver. Then with a loud whoop, the Cyclops turned his fat flocks towards the hills; but I was left devising evil in the deep of my heart, if in any wise I might avenge me, and Athene grant me renown.

'And this was the counsel that showed best in my sight. There lay by a sheep-fold a great club of the Cyclops, a club of olive wood, yet green, which he had cut to carry with him when it should be seasoned. Now when we saw it we likened it in size to the mast of a black ship of twenty oars, a wide merchant vessel that traverses the great sea gulf, so huge it was to view in bulk and length. I stood thereby and cut off from it a portion as it were a fathom's length, and set it by my fellows, and bade them fine it down, and they made it even, while I stood by and sharpened it to a point, and straightway I took it and hardened it in the bright fire. Then I laid it well away, and hid it beneath the dung, which was scattered in great heaps ii the depths of the cave. And I bade my company cast lots among them, which of them should risk the adventure with me, and lift the bar and turn it about in his eye, when sweet sleep came upon him. And the lot fell upon those four whom I myself would have been fain to choose, and I appointed myself to be the fifth among them. In the evening he came shepherding his flocks of goodly fleece, and presently he drave his fat flocks into the cave each and all, nor left he any without in the deep court-yard, whether through some foreboding, or perchance that the god so bade him do. Thereafter he lifted the huge door-stone and set it in the mouth of the cave, and sitting down he milked the ewes and bleating goats, all orderly, and beneath each ewe he placed her young. Now when he had done all his work busily, again he seized yet other two and made ready his supper. Then I stood by the Cyclops and spake to him, holding in my hands an ivy bowl of the dark wine:

'"Cyclops, take and drink wine after thy feast of man's meat, that thou mayest know what manner of drink this was that our ship held. And lo, I was bringing it thee as a drink offering, if haply thou mayest take pity and send me on my way home, but thy mad rage is past all sufferance. O hard of heart, how may another of the many men there be come ever to thee again, seeing that thy deeds have been lawless?"

'So I spake, and he took the cup and drank it off, and found great delight in drinking the sweet draught, and asked me for it yet a second time:

'"Give it me again of thy grace, and tell me thy name straightway, that I may give thee a stranger's gift, wherein thou mayest be glad. Yea for the earth, the grain-giver, bears for the Cyclôpes the mighty clusters of the juice of the grape, and the rain of Zeus gives them increase, but this is a rill of very nectar and ambrosia."

'So he spake, and again I handed him the dark wine.

Thrice I bare and gave it him, and thrice in his folly he drank it to the lees. Now when the wine had got about the wits of the Cyclops, then did I speak to him with soft words:

' "Cyclops, thou askest me my renowned name, and I will declare it unto thee, and do thou grant me a stranger's gift, as thou didst promise. Noman is my name, and Noman they call me, my father and my mother and all my fellows."

'So I spake, and straightway he answered me out of his pitiless heart:

' "Noman will I eat last in the number of his fellows, and the others before him: that shall be thy gift."

'Therewith he sank backwards and fell with face upturned, and there he lay with his great neck bent round, and sleep, that conquers all men, overcame him. And the wine and the fragments of men's flesh issued forth from his mouth, and he vomited, being heavy with wine. Then I thrust in that stake under the deep ashes, until it should grow hot, and I spake to my companions comfortable words, lest any should hang back from me in fear. But when that bar of olive wood was just about to catch fire in the flame, green though it was, and began to glow terribly, even then I came nigh, and drew it from the coals, and my fellows gathered about me, and some god breathed great courage into us. For their part they seized the bar of olive wood, that was sharpened at the point, and thrust it into his eye, while I from my place aloft turned it about, as when a man bores a ship's beam with a drill while his fellows below spin it with a strap, which they hold at either end, and the auger runs round continually. Even so did we seize the fiery-pointed brand and whirled it round in his eye, and the blood flowed about the heated bar. And the breath of the flame singed his eyelids and brows all about, as the ball of the eye burnt away, and the roots thereof crackled in the flame. And as when a smith dips an axe or adze in chill water with a great hissing, when he would temper it—for hereby anon comes the strength of iron—even so did his eye hiss round the stake of olive. And he raised a great and terrible cry, that the rock rang around, and we fled away in fear, while he plucked forth from his eye the brand bedabbled in much blood. Then maddened with pain he cast it from him with his hands, and called with a loud voice on the Cyclôpes, who dwelt about him in the caves along the windy heights. And they heard the cry and flocked together from every side, and gathering round the cave asked him what ailed him:

'"What hath so distressed thee, Polyphemus, that thou criest thus aloud through the immortal night, and makest us sleepless? Surely no mortal driveth off thy flocks against thy will: surely none slayeth thyself by force or craft?"

'And the strong Polyphemus spake to them again from out the cave: "My friends, Noman is slaying me by guile, nor at all by force."

'And they answered and spake winged words: "If then no man is violently handling thee in thy solitude, it can in no wise be that thou shouldest escape the sickness sent by mighty Zeus. Nay, pray thou to thy father, the lord Poseidon."

'On this wise they spake and departed; and my heart within me laughed to see how my name and cunning counsel had beguiled them. But the Cyclops, groaning and travailing in pain, groped with his hands, and lifted away the stone from the door of the cave, and himself sat in the entry, with arms outstretched to catch, if he might, any one that was going forth with his sheep, so witless, methinks, did he hope to find me. But I advised me how all might be for the very best, if perchance I might find a way of escape from death for my companions and myself, and I wove all manner of craft and counsel, as a man will for his life, seeing that great mischief was nigh. And this was the counsel that showed best in my sight. The rams of the flock were well nurtured and thick of fleece, great and goodly, with wool dark as the violet. Quietly I lashed them together with twisted withies, whereon the Cyclops slept, that lawless monster. Three together I took: now the middle one of the three would bear each a man, but the other twain went on either side, saving my fellows. Thus every three sheep bare their man. But as for me I laid hold of the back of a young ram who was far the best and the goodliest of all the flock, and curled beneath his shaggy belly there I lay, and so clung face upward, grasping the wondrous fleece with a steadfast heart. So for that time making moan we awaited the bright Dawn.

'So soon as early Dawn shone forth, the rosy-fingered, then did the rams of the flock hasten forth to pasture, but the ewes bleated unmilked about the pens, for their udders were swollen to bursting. Then their lord, sore stricken with pain, felt along the backs of all the sheep as they stood up before him, and guessed not in his folly how that my men were bound beneath the breasts of his thick-fleeced flocks. Last of all the sheep came forth the ram, cumbered with his wool, and the weight of me and my cunning. And the strong Polyphemus laid his hands on him and spake to him, saying:

' "Dear ram, wherefore, I pray thee, art thou the last of all the flocks to go forth from the cave, who of old wast not wont to lag behind the sheep, but wert ever the foremost to pluck the tender blossom of the pasture, faring with long strides, and wert still the first to come to the streams of the rivers, and first didst long to return to the homestead in the evening. But now art thou the very last. Surely thou art sorrowing for the eye of thy lord, which an evil man blinded, with his accursed fellows, when he had subdued my wits with wine, even Noman, whom I say hath not yet escaped destruction. Ah, if thou couldst feel as I, and be endued with speech, to tell me where he shifts about to shun my wrath; then should he be smitten, and his brains be dashed against the floor here and there about the cave, and my heart be lightened of the sorrows which Noman, nothing worth, hath brought me!"

'Therewith he sent the ram forth from him, and when we had gone but a little way from the cave and from the yard, first I loosed myself from under the ram and then I set my fellows free. And swiftly we drave on those stiff-shanked sheep, so rich in fat, and often turned to look about, till we came to the ship. And a glad sight to our fellows were we that had fled from death, but the others they would have bemoaned with tears; howbeit I suffered it not, but with frowning brows forbade each man to weep. Rather I bade them to cast on board the many sheep with goodly fleece, and to sail over the salt sea water. So they embarked forthwith, and sate upon the benches, and sitting orderly smote the grey sea water with their oars. But when I had not gone so far, but that a man's shout might be heard, then I spoke unto the Cyclops taunting him:

' "Cyclops, so thou wert not to eat the company of a weakling by main might in thy hollow cave! Thine evil deeds were very sure to find thee out, thou cruel man, who hadst no shame to eat thy guests within thy gates, wherefore Zeus hath requited thee, and the other gods."

'So I spake, and he was mightily angered at heart, and he brake off the peak of a great hill and threw it at us, and it fell in front of the dark-prowed ship. And the sea heaved beneath the fall of the rock, and the backward flow of the wave bare the ship quickly to the dry land, with the wash from the deep sea, and drave it to the shore. Then I caught up a long pole in my hands, and thrust the ship from off the land, and roused my company, and with a motion of the head bade them dash in with their oars, that so we might escape our evil plight. So they bent to their oars and rowed on. But when we had now made twice the distance over the brine, I would fain have spoken to the Cyclops, but my company stayed me on every side with soft words, saying:

'"Foolhardy that thou art, why wouldst thou rouse a wild man to wrath, who even now hath cast so mighty a throw towards the deep and brought our ship back to land, yea and we thought that we had perished even there? If he had heard any of us utter sound or speech he would have crushed our heads and our ship timbers with a cast of a rugged stone, so mightily he hurls."

'So spake they, but they prevailed not on my lordly spirit, and I answered him again from out an angry heart:

'"Cyclops, if any one of mortal men shall ask thee of the unsightly blinding of thine eye, say that it was Odysseus that blinded it, the waster of cities, son of Laertes, whose dwelling is in Ithaca."

'So I spake, and with a moan he answered me, saying:

'"Lo now, in very truth the ancient oracles have come upon me. There lived here a soothsayer, a noble man and a mighty, Telemus, son of Eurymus, who surpassed all men in soothsaying, and waxed old as a seer among the Cyclôpes. He told me that all these things should come to pass in the aftertime, even that I should lose my eyesight at the hand of Odysseus. But I ever looked for some tall and goodly man to come hither, clad in great might, but behold now one that is a dwarf, a man of no worth and a weakling, hath blinded me of my eye after subduing me with wine. Nay come hither, Odysseus, that I may set by thee a stranger's cheer, and speed thy parting hence, that so the Earth-shaker may vouchsafe it thee, for his son am I, and he avows him for my father. And he himself will heal me, if it be his will; and none other of the blessed gods or of mortal men."

'Even so he spake, but I answered him, and said: "Would god that I were as sure to rob thee of soul and life, and send thee within the house of Hades, as I am that not even the Earth-shaker will heal thine eye!"

'So I spake, and then he prayed to the lord Poseidon stretching forth his hands to the starry heaven: "Hear me, Poseidon, girdler of the earth, god of the dark hair, if indeed I be thine, and thou avowest thee my sire,—grant that he may never come to his home, even Odysseus, waster of cities, the son of Laertes, whose dwelling is in Ithaca; yet if he is ordained to see his friends and come unto his well-builded house, and his own country, late may he come in evil case, with the loss of all his company, in the ship of strangers, and find sorrows in his house."

'So he spake in prayer, and the god of the dark locks heard him. And once again he lifted a stone, far greater than the first, and with one swing he hurled it, and he put forth a measureless strength, and cast it but a little space behind the dark-prowed ship, and all but struck the end of the rudder. And the sea heaved beneath the fall of the rock, but the wave bare on the ship and drave it to the further shore.

'But when we had now reached that island, where all our other decked ships abode together, and our company were gathered sorrowing, expecting us nevermore, on our coming thither we ran our ship ashore upon the sand, and ourselves too stept forth upon the sea-beach. Next we took forth the sheep of the Cyclops from out the hollow ship, and divided them, that none through me might go lacking his proper share. But the ram for me alone my goodly-greaved company chose out, in the dividing of the sheep, and on the shore I offered him up to Zeus, even to the son of Cronos, who dwells in the dark clouds, and is lord of all, and I burnt the slices of the thighs. But he heeded not the sacrifice, but was devising how my decked ships and my dear company might perish utterly. Thus for that time we sat the livelong day, until the going down of the sun, feasting on abundant flesh and sweet wine. And when the sun had sunk and darkness had come on, then we laid us to rest upon the sea-beach. So soon as early Dawn shone forth, the rosy-fingered, I called to my company, and commanded them that they should themselves climb the ship and loose the hawsers. So they soon embarked and sat upon the benches, and sitting orderly smote the grey sea water with their oars.

'Thence we sailed onward stricken at heart, yet glad as men saved from death, albeit we had lost our dear companions.

BOOK X

Odysseus, his entertainment by Aeolus, of whom he received a fair wind for the present, and all the rest of the winds tied up in a bag; which his men untying, flew out, and carried him back to Aeolus, who refused to receive him. His adventure at Lestrygonia with Antiphates, where of twelve ships he lost eleven, men and all. How he went thence to the Isle of Aia, where half of his men were turned by Circé into swine, and how he went himself, and by the help of Hermes recovered them and stayed with Circé a year.

'THEN we came to the isle Aeolian, where dwelt Aeolus, son of Hippotas, dear to the deathless gods, in a floating island, and all about it is a wall of bronze unbroken, and the cliff runs up sheer from the sea. His twelve children too abide there in his halls, six daughters and six lusty sons; and, behold, he gave his daughters to his sons to wife. And they feast evermore by their dear father and their kind mother, and dainties innumerable lie ready to their hands. And the house is full of the savour of feasting, and the noise thereof rings round, yea in the courtyard, by day, and in the night they sleep each one by his chaste wife in coverlets and on jointed bedsteads. So then we came to their city and their goodly dwelling, and the king entreated me kindly for a whole month, and sought out each thing, Ilios and the ships of the Argives, and the return of the Achaeans. So I told him all the tale in order duly. But when I in turn took the word and asked of my journey, and bade him send me on my way, he too denied me not, but furnished an escort. He gave me a wallet, made of the hide of an ox of nine seasons old, which he let flay, and therein he bound the ways of all the noisy winds; for him the son of Cronos made keeper of the winds, either to lull or to rouse what blasts he will. And he made it fast in the hold of the ship with a shining silver thong, that not the faintest breath might escape. Then he sent forth the blast of the West Wind to blow for me, to bear our ships and ourselves upon our way; but this he was never to bring to pass, for we were undone through our own heedlessness.

'For nine whole days we sailed by night and day continually, and now on the tenth day my native land came in sight, and already we were so near that we beheld the folk tending the beacon fires. Then over me there came sweet slumber in my weariness, for all the time I was holding the sheet, nor gave it to any of my company, that so we might come quicker to our own country. Meanwhile my company held converse together, and said that I was bringing home for myself gold and silver, gifts from Aeolus the high-hearted son of Hippotas. And thus would they speak looking each man to his neighbour:

'"Lo now, how beloved he is and highly esteemed among all men, to the city and land of whomsoever he may come. Many are the goodly treasures he taketh with him out of the spoil from Troy, while we who have fulfilled like journeying with him return homeward bringing with us but empty hands. And now Aeolus hath given unto him these things freely in his love. Nay come, let us quickly see what they are, even what wealth of gold and silver is in the wallet."

'So they spake, and the evil counsel of my company prevailed. They loosed the wallet, and all the winds brake forth. And the violent blast seized my men, and bare them towards the high seas weeping, away from their own country; but as for me, I awoke and communed with my great heart, whether I should cast myself from the ship and perish in the deep, or endure in silence and abide yet among the living. Howbeit I hardened my heart to endure, and muffling my head I lay still in the ship. But the vessels were driven by the evil storm-wind back to the isle Aeolian, and my company made moan.

'There we stepped ashore and drew water, and my company presently took their midday meal by the swift ships. Now when we had tasted bread and wine, I took with me a herald and one of my company, and went to the famous dwelling of Aeolus: and I found him feasting with his wife and children. So we went in and sat by the pillars of the door on the threshold, and they all marvelled and asked us:

'"How hast thou come hither, Odysseus? What evil god assailed thee? Surely we sent thee on thy way with all diligence, that thou mightest get thee to thine own country and thy home, and whithersoever thou wouldest."

'Even so they said, but I spake among them heavy at heart: "My evil company hath been my bane, and sleep thereto remorseless. Come, my friends, do ye heal the harm, for yours is the power."

'So I spake, beseeching them in soft words, but they held their peace. And the father answered, saying: "Get thee forth from the island straightway, thou that art the most reprobate of living men. Far be it from me to help or to further that man whom the blessed gods abhor! Get thee forth, for lo, thy coming marks thee hated by the deathless gods."

'Therewith he sent me forth from the house making heavy moan. Thence we sailed onwards stricken at heart. And the spirit of the men was spent beneath the grievous rowing by reason of our vain endeavour, for there was no more any sign of a wafting wind. So for the space of six days we sailed by night and day continually, and on the seventh we came to the steep stronghold of Lamos, Telepylos of the Laestrygons, where herdsman hails herdsman as he drives in his flock, and the other who drives forth answers the call. There might a sleepless man have earned a double wage, the one as neatherd, the other shepherding white flocks: so near are the outgoings of the night and of the day. Thither when we had come to the fair haven, whereabout on both sides goes one steep cliff unbroken, and jutting headlands over against each other stretch forth at the mouth of the harbour, and strait is the entrance; thereinto all the others steered their curved ships. Now the vessels were bound within the hollow harbour each hard by other, for no wave ever swelled within it, great or small, but there was a bright calm all around. But I alone moored my dark ship without the harbour, at the uttermost point thereof, and made fast the hawser to a rock. And I went up a craggy hill, a place of outlook, and stood thereon: thence there was no sign of the labour of men or oxen, only we saw the smoke curling upward from the land. Then I sent forth certain of my company to go and search out what manner of men they were who here live upon the earth by bread, choosing out two of my company and sending a third with them as herald. Now when they had gone ashore, they went along a level road whereby wains were wont to draw down wood from the high hills to the town. And without the town they fell in with a damsel drawing water, the noble daughter of Laestrygonian Antiphates. She had come down to the clear-flowing spring Artacia, for thence it was custom to draw water to the town. So they stood by her and spake unto her, and asked who was king of that land, and who they were he ruled over. Then at once she showed them the high-roofed hall of her father. Now when they had entered the renowned house, they found his wife therein: she was huge of bulk as a mountain peak and was loathly in their sight. Straightway she called the renowned Antiphates, her lord, from the assembly-place, and he contrived a pitiful destruction for my men. Forthwith he clutched up one of my company and made ready his midday meal, but the other twain sprang up and came in flight to the ships. Then he raised the war-cry through the town, and the valiant Laestrygonians at the sound thereof, flocked together from every side, a host past number, not like men but like the Giants. They cast at us from the cliffs with great rocks, each of them a man's burden, and anon there arose from the fleet an evil din of men dying and ships shattered withal. And like folk spearing fishes they bare home their hideous meal. While as yet they were slaying my friends within the deep harbour, I drew my sharp sword from my thigh, and with it cut the hawsers of my dark-prowed ship. Quickly then I called to my company, and bade them dash in with the oars, that we might clean escape this evil plight. And all with one accord they tossed the sea water with the oar-blade, in dread of death, and to my delight my barque flew forth to the high seas away from the beetling rocks, but those other ships were lost there, one and all.

'Thence we sailed onward stricken at heart, yet glad as men saved from death, albeit we had lost our dear companions. And we came to the isle Aeaean, where dwelt Circé of the braided tresses, an awful goddess of mortal speech, own sister to the wizard Aeetes. Both were begotten of Helios, who gives light to all men, and their mother was Perse, daughter of Oceanus. There on the shore we put in with our ship into the sheltering haven silently, and some god was our guide. Then we stept ashore, and for two days and two nights lay there, consuming our own hearts for weariness and pain. But when now the fair-tressed Dawn had brought the full light of the third day, then did I seize my spear and my sharp sword, and quickly departing from the ship I went up unto a place of wide prospect, if haply I might see any sign of the labour of men and hear the sound of their speech. So I went up a craggy hill, a place of out-look, and I saw the smoke rising from the broad-wayed earth in the halls of Circé, through the thick coppice and the woodland. Then I mused in my mind and heart whether I should go and make discovery, for that I had seen the smoke and flame. And as I thought thereon this seemed to me the better counsel, to go first to the swift ship and to the sea-banks, and give my company their midday meal, and then send them to make search. But as I came and drew nigh to the curved ship, some god even then took pity on me in my loneliness, and sent a tall antlered stag across my very path. He was coming down from his pasture in the woodland to the river to drink, for verily the might of the sun was sore upon him. And as he came up from out of the stream, I smote him on the spine in the middle of the back, and the brazen shaft went clean through him, and with a moan he fell in the dust, and his life passed from him. Then I set my foot on him and drew forth the brazen shaft from the wound, and laid it hard by upon the ground and let it lie. Next I broke withies and willow twigs, and wove me a rope a fathom in length, well twisted from end to end, and bound together the feet of the huge beast, and went to the black ship bearing him across my neck, and leaning on a spear, for it was in no wise possible to carry him on my shoulder with the one hand, for he was a mighty quarry. And I threw him down before the ship and roused my company with soft words, standing by each man in turn:

' "Friends, for all our sorrows we shall not yet a while go down to the house of Hades, ere the coming of the day of destiny; go to then, while as yet there is meat and drink in the swift ship, let us take thought thereof, that we be not famished for hunger."

'Even so I spake, and they speedily hearkened to my words. They unmuffled their heads, and there on the shore of the unharvested sea gazed at the stag, for he was a mighty quarry. But after they had delighted their eyes with the sight of him, they washed their hands and got ready the glorious feast. So for that time we sat the livelong day till the going down of the sun, feasting on abundant flesh and sweet wine. But when the sun sank and darkness had come on, then we laid us to rest upon the sea beach. So soon as early Dawn shone forth, the rosy-fingered, I called a gathering of my men and spake in the ears of them all:

' "Hear my words, my fellows, despite your evil case. My friends, lo, now we know not where is the place of darkness or of dawning, nor where the Sun, that gives light to men, goes beneath the earth, nor where he rises; therefore let us advise us speedily if any counsel yet may be: as for me, I deem there is none. For I went up a craggy hill, a place of out-look, and saw the island crowned about with the circle of the endless sea, the isle itself lying low; and in the midst thereof mine eyes beheld the smoke through the thick coppice and the woodland."

'Even so I spake, but their spirit within them was broken, as they remembered the deeds of Antiphates the Laestrygonian, and all the evil violence of the haughty Cyclops, the man-eater. So they wept aloud shedding big tears. Howbeit no avail came of their weeping.

'Then I numbered my goodly-greaved company in two bands, and appointed a leader for each, and I myself took the command of the one part, and godlike Eurylochus of the other. And anon we shook the lots in a brazen-fitted helmet, and out leapt the lot of proud Eurylochus. So he went on his way, and with him two and twenty of my fellowship all weeping; and we were left behind making lament. In the forest glades they found the halls of Circé builded, of polished stone, in a place with wide prospect. And all around the palace mountain-bred wolves and lions were roaming, whom she herself had bewitched with evil drugs that she gave them. Yet the beasts did not set on my men, but lo, they ramped about them and fawned on them, wagging their long tails. And as when dogs fawn about their lord when he comes from the feast, for he always brings them the fragments that soothe their mood, even so the strong-clawed wolves and the lions fawned around them; but they were affrighted when they saw the strange and terrible creatures. So they stood at the outer gate of the fair-tressed goddess, and within they heard Circé singing in a sweet voice, as she fared to and fro before the great web imperishable, such as is the handiwork of goddesses, fine of woof and full of grace and splendour. Then Polites, a leader of men, the dearest to me and the trustiest of all my company, first spake to them:

'"Friends, forasmuch as there is one within that fares to and fro before a mighty web singing a sweet song, so that all the floor of the hall makes echo, a goddess she is or a woman; come quickly and cry aloud to her."

'He spake the word and they cried aloud and called to her. And straightway she came forth and opened the shining doors and bade them in, and all went with her in their heedlessness. But Eurylochus tarried behind, for he guessed that there was some treason. So she led them in and set them upon the chairs and high seats, and made them a mess of cheese and barley-meal and yellow honey with Pramnian wine, and mixed harmful drugs with the food to make them utterly forget their own country. Now when she had given them the cup and they had drunk it off, presently she smote them with a wand, and in the styes of the swine she penned them. So they had the head and voice, the bristles and the shape of swine, but their mind abode even as of old. Thus were they penned there weeping, and Circé flung them acorns and mast and fruit of the cornel tree to eat, whereon wallowing swine do always batten.

'Now Eurylochus came back to the swift black ship to bring tidings of his fellows, and of their unseemly doom. Not a word could he utter, for all his desire, so deeply smitten was he to the heart with grief, and his eyes were filled with tears and his soul was fain of lamentation. But when we all had pressed him with our questions in amazement, even then he told the fate of the remnant of our company.

'"We went, as thou didst command, through the coppice, noble Odysseus: we found within the forest glades the fair halls, builded of polished stone, in a place with wide prospect. And there was one that fared before a mighty web and sang a clear song, a goddess she was or a woman, and they cried aloud and called to her. And straightway she came forth, and opened the shining doors and bade them in, and they all went with her in their heedlessness. But I tarried behind, for I guessed that there was some treason. Then they vanished away one and all, nor did any of them appear again, though I sat long time watching."

'So spake he, whereon I cast about my shoulder my silver-studded sword, a great blade of bronze, and slung my bow about me and bade him lead me again by the way that he came. But he caught me with both hands, and by my knees he besought me, and bewailing him spake to me winged words:

'"Lead me not thither against my will, oh fosterling of Zeus, but leave me here! For well I know thou shalt thyself return no more, nor bring any one of all thy fellowship; nay, let us flee the swifter with those that be here, for even yet may we escape the evil day."

'On this wise he spake, but I answered him, saying: "Eurylochus, abide for thy part here in this place, eating and drinking by the black hollow ship: but I will go forth, for a strong constraint is laid on me."

'With that I went up from the ship and the sea-shore. But lo, when in my faring through the sacred glades I was now drawing near to the great hall of the enchantress Circé, then did Hermes, of the golden wand, meet me as

I approached the house, in the likeness of a young man with the first down on his lip, the time when youth is most gracious. So he clasped my hand and spake and hailed me:

'"Ah, hapless man, whither away again, all alone through the wolds, thou that knowest not this country? And thy company yonder in the hall of Circé are penned in the guise of swine, in their deep lairs abiding. Is it in hope to free them that thou art come hither? Nay, methinks, thou thyself shalt never return but remain there with the others. Come then, I will redeem thee from thy distress, and bring deliverance. Lo, take this herb of virtue, and go to the dwelling of Circé, that it may keep from thy head the evil day. And I will tell thee all the magic sleight of Circé. She will mix thee a potion and cast drugs into the mess; but not even so shall she be able to enchant thee; so helpful is this charmed herb that I shall give thee, and I will tell thee all. When it shall be that Circé smites thee with her long wand, even then draw thou thy sharp sword from thy thigh, and spring on her, as one eager to slay her. And she will shrink away and be instant with thee to lie with her. Thenceforth disdain not thou the bed of the goddess, that she may deliver thy company and kindly entertain thee. But command her to swear a mighty oath by the blessed gods, that she will plan nought else of mischief to thine own hurt, lest she make thee a dastard and unmanned, when she hath thee naked."

'Therewith the slayer of Argos gave me the plant that he had plucked from the ground, and he showed me the growth thereof. It was black at the root, but the flower was like to milk. Moly the gods call it, but it is hard for mortal men to dig; howbeit with the gods all things are possible.

'Then Hermes departed toward high Olympus, up through the woodland isle, but as for me I held on my way to the house of Circé, and my heart was darkly troubled as I went. So I halted in the portals of the fair-tressed goddess; there I stood and called aloud and the goddess heard my voice, who presently came forth and opened the shining doors and bade me in, and I went with her heavy at heart. So she led me in and set me on a chair with studs of silver, a goodly carven chair, and beneath was a footstool for the feet. And she made me a potion in a golden cup, that I might drink, and she also put a charm therein, in the evil counsel of her heart. Now when she had given it and I had drunk it off and was not bewitched, she smote me with her wand and spake and hailed me:

' "Go thy way now to the stye, couch thee there with the rest of thy company."

'So spake she, but I drew my sharp sword from my thigh and sprang upon Circé, as one eager to slay her. But with a great cry she slipped under, and clasped my knees, and bewailing herself spake to me winged words:

' "Who art thou of the sons of men, and whence? Where is thy city? Where are they that begat thee? I marvel to see how thou hast drunk of this charm, and wast nowise subdued. Nay, for there lives no man else that is proof against this charm, whoso hath drunk thereof, and once it hath passed his lips. But thou hast, methinks, a mind within thee that may not be enchanted. Verily thou art Odysseus, ready at need, whom he of the golden wand, the slayer of Argos, full often told me was to come hither, on his way from Troy with his swift black ship. Nay come, put thy sword into the sheath, and thereafter let us go up into my bed, that meeting in love and sleep we may trust each the other."

'So spake she, but I answered her, saying: "Nay, Circé, how canst thou bid me be gentle to thee, who hast turned my company into swine within thy halls, and holding me here with a guileful heart requirest me to pass within thy chamber and go up into thy bed, that so thou mayest make me a dastard and unmanned when thou hast me naked? Nay, never will I consent to go up into thy bed, except thou wilt deign, goddess, to swear a mighty oath, that thou wilt plan nought else of mischief to mine own hurt."

'So I spake, and she straightway swore the oath not to harm me, as I bade her. But when she had sworn and had done that oath, then at last I went up into the beautiful bed of Circé.

'Now all this while her handmaids busied them in the halls, four maidens that are her serving women in the house. They are born of the wells and of the woods and of the holy rivers, that flow forward into the salt sea. Of these one cast upon the chairs goodly coverlets of purple above, and spread a linen cloth thereunder. And lo, another drew up silver tables to the chairs, and thereon set for them golden baskets. And a third mixed sweet honey-hearted wine in a silver bowl, and set out cups of gold. And a fourth bare water, and kindled a great fire beneath the mighty cauldron. So the water waxed warm; but when it boiled in the bright brazen vessel, she set me in a bath and bathed me with water from out a great cauldron, pouring it over head and shoulders, when she had mixed it to a pleasant warmth, till from my limbs she took away the consuming weariness. Now after she had bathed me and anointed me well with olive oil, and cast about me a fair mantle and a doublet, she led me into the halls and set me on a chair with studs of silver, a goodly carven chair, and beneath was a footstool for the feet. And a handmaid bare water for the hands in a goodly golden ewer, and poured it forth over a silver basin to wash withal; and to my side she drew a polished table, and a grave dame bare wheaten bread and set it by me, and laid on the board many dainties, giving freely of such things as she had by her. And she bade me eat, but my soul found no pleasure therein. I sat with other thoughts, and my heart had a boding of ill.

'Now when Circé saw that I sat thus, and that I put not forth my hands to the meat, and that I was mightily afflicted, she drew near to me and spake to me winged words:

' "Wherefore thus, Odysseus, dost thou sit there like a speechless man, consuming thine own soul, and dost not touch meat nor drink? Dost thou indeed deem there is some further guile? Nay, thou hast no cause to fear, for already I have sworn thee a strong oath not to harm thee."

'So spake she, but I answered her, saying: "Oh, Circé, what righteous man would have the heart to taste meat and drink ere he had redeemed his company, and beheld them face to face? But if in good faith thou biddest me eat and drink, then let them go free, that mine eyes may behold my dear companions."

'So I spake, and Circé passed out through the hall with the wand in her hand, and opened the doors of the stye, and drave them forth in the shape of swine of nine seasons old. There they stood before her, and she went through their midst, and anointed each one of them with another charm. And lo, from their limbs the bristles dropped away, wherewith the venom had erewhile clothed them, that lady Circé gave them. And they became men again, younger than before they were, and goodlier far, and taller to behold. And they all knew me again and each one took my hands, and wistful was the lament that sank into their souls, and the roof around rang wondrously. And even the goddess herself was moved with compassion.

'Then standing nigh me the fair goddess spake unto me: "Son of Laertes, of the seed of Zeus, Odysseus of many devices, depart now to thy swift ship and the sea-banks. And first of all, draw ye up the ship ashore, and bestow the goods in the caves and all the gear. And thyself return again, and bring with thee thy dear companions."

'So spake she, and my lordly spirit consented thereto. So I went on my way to the swift ship and the sea-banks, and there I found my dear company on the swift ship lamenting piteously, shedding big tears. And as when calves of the homestead gather round the droves of kine that have returned to the yard, when they have had their fill of pasture, and all with one accord frisk before them, and the folds may no more contain them, but with a ceaseless lowing they skip about their dams, so flocked they all about me weeping, when their eyes beheld me. Yea, and to their spirit it was as though they had got to their dear country, and the very city of rugged Ithaca, where they were born and reared.

'Then making lament they spake to me winged words: "O fosterling of Zeus, we were none otherwise glad at thy returning, than if we had come to Ithaca, our own country. Nay come, of our other companions tell us the tale of their ruin."

'So spake they, but I answered them with soft words: "Behold, let us first of all draw up the ship ashore, and bestow our goods in the caves and all our gear. And do ye bestir you, one and all, to go with me, that ye may see your fellows in the sacred dwelling of Circé, eating and drinking, for they have continual store."

'So spake I, and at once they hearkened to my words, but Eurylochus alone would have holden all my companions, and uttering his voice he spake to them winged words:

' "Wretched men that we are! whither are we going? Why are your hearts so set on sorrow that ye should go down to the hall of Circé, who will surely change us all to swine, or wolves, or lions, to guard her great house perforce, according to the deeds that the Cyclops wrought, when certain of our company went to his inmost fold, and with them went Odysseus, ever hardy, for through the blindness of his heart did they too perish?"

'So spake he, but I mused in my heart whether to draw my long hanger from my stout thigh, and therewith smite off his head and bring it to the dust, albeit he was very near of kin to me; but the men of my company stayed me on every side with soothing words:

' "Prince of the seed of Zeus, as for this man, we will suffer him, if thou wilt have it so, to abide here by the ship and guard the ship; but as for us, be our guide to the sacred house of Circé."

So they spake and went up from the ship and the sea. Nay, nor yet was Eurylochus left by the hollow ship, but he went with us, for he feared my terrible rebuke.

'Meanwhile Circé bathed the rest of my company in her halls with all care, and anointed them well with olive oil; and cast thick mantles and doublets about them. And we found them all feasting nobly in the halls. And when they saw and knew each other face to face, they wept and mourned, and the house rang around. Then she stood near me, that fair goddess, and spake saying:

' "Son of Laertes, of the seed of Zeus, Odysseus of many devices, no more now wake this plenteous weeping: myself I know of all the pains ye endured upon the teeming deep, and the great despite done you by unkindly men upon the land. Nay come, eat ye meat and drink wine, till your spirit shall return to you again, as it was when first ye left your own country of rugged Ithaca; but now are ye wasted and wanting heart, mindful evermore of your sore wandering, nor has your heart ever been merry, for very grievous hath been your trial."

'So spake she, and our lordly spirit consented thereto. So there we sat day by day for the full circle of a year, feasting on abundant flesh and sweet wine. But when now a year had gone, and the seasons returned as the months waned, and the long days came in their course, then did my dear company call me forth, and say:

'"Good sir, now is it high time to mind thee of thy native land, if it is ordained that thou shalt be saved, and come to thy lofty house and thine own country."

'So spake they and my lordly spirit consented thereto. So for that time we sat the livelong day till the going down of the sun, feasting on abundant flesh and sweet wine. But when the sun sank and darkness came on, they laid them to rest throughout the shadowy halls.

'But when I had gone up into the fair bed of Circé, I besought her by her knees, and the goddess heard my speech, and uttering my voice I spake to her winged words: "Circé, fulfil for me the promise which thou madest me to send me on my homeward way. Now is my spirit eager to be gone, and the spirit of my company, that wear away my heart as they mourn around me, when haply thou art gone from us."

'So spake I, and the fair goddess answered me anon: "Son of Laertes, of the seed of Zeus, Odysseus of many devices, tarry ye now no longer in my house against your will; but first must ye perform another journey, and reach the dwelling of Hades and of dread Persephone to seek to the spirit of Theban Teiresias, the blind soothsayer, whose wits abide steadfast. To him Persephone hath given judgment, even in death, that he alone should have understanding; but the other souls sweep shadow-like around."

'Thus spake she, but as for me, my heart was broken, and I wept as I sat upon the bed, and my soul had no more care to live and to see the sunlight. But when I had my fill of weeping and grovelling, then at the last I answered and spake unto her saying: "And who, Circé, will guide us on this way? for no man ever yet sailed to hell in a black ship."

'So spake I, and the fair goddess answered me anon: "Son of Laertes, of the seed of Zeus, Odysseus of many devices, nay, trouble not thyself for want of a guide, by thy ship abiding, but set up the mast and spread abroad the white sails and sit thee down; and the breeze of the

North Wind will bear thy vessel on her way. But when thou hast now sailed in thy ship across the stream Oceanus, where is a waste shore and the groves of Persephone, even tall poplar trees and willows that shed their fruit before the season, there beach thy ship by deep eddying Oceanus, but go thyself to the dank house of Hades. Thereby into Acheron flows Pyriphlegethon, and Cocytus, a branch of the water of the Styx, and there is a rock, and the meeting of the two roaring waters. So, hero, draw nigh thereto, as I command thee, and dig a trench as it were a cubit in length and breadth, and about it pour a drink-offering to all the dead, first with mead and thereafter with sweet wine, and for the third time with water, and sprinkle white meal thereon; and entreat with many prayers the strengthless heads of the dead, and promise that on thy return to Ithaca thou wilt offer in thy halls a barren heifer, the best thou hast, and wilt fill the pyre with treasure, and wilt sacrifice apart, to Teiresias alone, a black ram without spot, the fairest of your flock. But when thou hast with prayers made supplication to the lordly races of the dead, then offer up a ram and a black ewe, bending their heads towards Erebus and thyself turn thy back, with thy face set for the shore of the river. Then will many spirits come to thee of the dead that be departed. Thereafter thou shalt call to thy company and command them to flay the sheep which even now lie slain by the pitiless sword, and to consume them with fire, and to make prayer to the gods, to mighty Hades and to dread Persephone. And thyself draw the sharp sword from thy thigh and sit there, suffering not the strengthless heads of the dead to draw nigh to the blood, ere thou hast word of Teiresias. Then the seer will come to thee quickly, leader of the people; he will surely declare to thee the way and the measure of thy path, and as touching thy returning, how thou mayst go over the teeming deep."

'So spake she, and anon came the golden throned Dawn.

Then she put on me a mantle and a doublet for raiment, and the nymph clad herself in a great shining robe, light of woof and gracious, and about her waist she cast a fair golden girdle, and put a veil upon her head. But I passed through the halls and roused my men with smooth words, standing by each one in turn:

'"Sleep ye now no more nor breathe the sweet slumber; but let us go on our way, for surely she hath shown me all, the lady Circé."

'So spake I, and their lordly soul consented thereto. Yet even thence I led not my company safe away. There was one, Elpenor, the youngest of us all, not very valiant in war neither steadfast in mind. He was lying apart from the rest of my men on the housetop of Circé's sacred dwelling, very fain of the cool air, as one heavy with wine. Now when he heard the noise of the voices and of the feet of my fellows as they moved to and fro, he leaped up of a sudden and minded him not to descend again by the way of the tall ladder, but fell right down from the roof, and his neck was broken from the bones of the spine, and his spirit went down to the house of Hades.

'Then I spake among my men as they went on their way, saying: "Ye deem now, I see, that ye are going to your own dear country; but Circé hath showed us another way, even to the dwelling of Hades and of dread Persephone, to seek to the spirit of Theban Teiresias."

'Even so I spake, but their heart within them was broken, and they sat them down even where they were, and made lament and tore their hair. Howbeit no help came of their weeping.

'But as we were now wending sorrowful to the swift ship and the sea-banks, shedding big tears, Circé meanwhile had gone her ways and made fast a ram and a black ewe by the dark ship, lightly passing us by: who may behold a god against his will, whether going to or fro?

BOOK XI

Odysseus, his descent into hell, and discourses with the ghosts of the deceased heroes.

'Now when we had gone down to the ship and to the sea, first of all we drew the ship unto the fair salt water, and placed the mast and sails in the black ship, and took those sheep and put them therein, and ourselves too climbed on board, sorrowing, and shedding big tears. And in the wake of our dark-prowed ship she sent a favouring wind that filled the sails, a kindly escort,—even Circé of the braided tresses, a dread goddess of human speech. And we set in order all the gear throughout the ship and sat us down; and the wind and the helmsman guided our barque. And all day long her sails were stretched in her seafaring; and the sun sank and all the ways were darkened.

'She came to the limits of the world, to the deep flowing Oceanus. There is the land and the city of the Cimmerians, shrouded in mist and cloud, and never does the shining sun look down on them with his rays, neither when he climbs up the starry heavens, nor when again he turns earthward from the firmament, but deadly night is outspread over miserable mortals. Thither we came and ran the ship ashore and took out the sheep; but for our part we held on our way along the stream of Oceanus, till we came to the place which Circé had declared to us.

'There Perimedes and Eurylochus held the victims, but I drew my sharp sword from my thigh, and dug a pit, as it were a cubit in length and breadth, and about it poured a drink-offering to all the dead, first with mead and thereafter with sweet wine, and for the third time with water. And I sprinkled white meal thereon, and entreated with many prayers the strengthless heads of the dead, and promised that on my return to Ithaca I would offer in my halls a barren heifer, the best I had, and fill the pyre with treasure, and apart unto Teiresias alone sacrifice a black ram without spot, the fairest of my flock. But when I had besought the tribes of the dead with vows and prayers, I took the sheep and cut their throats over the trench, and the dark blood flowed forth, and lo, the spirits of the dead that be departed gathered them from out of Erebus. Brides and youths unwed, and old men of many and evil days, and tender maidens with grief yet fresh at heart; and many there were, wounded with bronze-shod spears, men slain in fight with their bloody mail about them. And these many ghosts flocked together from every side about the trench with a wondrous cry, and pale fear gat hold on me. Then did I speak to my company and command them to flay the sheep that lay slain by the pitiless sword, and to consume them with fire, and to make prayer to the gods, to mighty Hades and to dread Persephone, and myself I drew the sharp sword from my thigh and sat there, suffering not the strengthless heads of the dead to draw nigh to the blood, ere I had word of Teiresias.

'And first came the soul of Elpenor, my companion, that had not yet been buried beneath the wide-wayed earth; for we left the corpse behind us in the hall of Circé, unwept and unburied, seeing that another task was instant on us. At the sight of him I wept and had compassion on him, and uttering my voice spake to him winged words: "Elpenor, how hast thou come beneath the darkness and the shadow? Thou hast come fleeter on foot than I in my black ship."

'So spake I, and with a moan he answered me, saying: "Son of Laertes, of the seed of Zeus, Odysseus of many devices, an evil doom of some god was my bane and wine out of measure. When I laid me down on the house-top of Circé I minded me not to descend again by the way of the tall ladder, but fell right down from the roof, and my neck was broken off from the bones of the spine, and my spirit went down to the house of Hades. And now I pray thee in the name of those whom we left, who are no more with us, thy wife, and thy sire who cherished thee when as yet thou wert a little one, and Telemachus, whom thou didst leave in thy halls alone; forasmuch as I know that on thy way hence from out the dwelling of Hades, thou wilt stay thy well-wrought ship at the isle Aeaean, even then, my lord, I charge thee to think on me. Leave me not unwept and unburied as thou goest hence, nor turn thy back upon me, lest haply I bring on thee the anger of the gods. Nay, burn me there with mine armour, all that is mine, and pile me a barrow on the shore of the grey sea, the grave of a luckless man, that even men unborn may hear my story. Fulfil me this and plant upon the barrow mine oar, wherewith I rowed in the days of my life, while yet I was among my fellows."

'Even so he spake, and I answered him saying: "All this, luckless man, will I perform for thee and do."

'Even so we twain were sitting holding sad discourse, I on the one side, stretching forth my sword over the blood, while on the other side the ghost of my friend told all his tale.

'Anon came up the soul of my mother dead, Anticleia, the daughter of Autolycus the great-hearted, whom I left alive when I departed for sacred Ilios. At the sight of her I wept, and was moved with compassion, yet even so, for all my sore grief, I suffered her not to draw nigh to the blood, ere I had word of Teiresias.

'Anon came the soul of Theban Teiresias, with a golden sceptre in his hand, and he knew me and spake unto me: "Son of Laertes, of the seed of Zeus, Odysseus of many devices, what seekest thou *now*, wretched man, wherefore hast thou left the sunlight and come hither to behold the dead and a land desolate of joy? Nay, hold off from the ditch and draw back thy sharp sword, that I may drink of the blood and tell thee sooth."

'So spake he and I put up my silver-studded sword into the sheath, and when he had drunk the dark blood, even then did the noble seer speak unto me, saying: "Thou art asking of thy sweet returning, great Odysseus, but that will the god make hard for thee; for methinks thou shalt not pass unheeded by the Shaker of the Earth, who hath laid up wrath in his heart against thee, for rage at the blinding of his dear son. Yet even so, through many troubles, ye may come home, if thou wilt restrain thy spirit and the spirit of thy men so soon as thou shalt bring thy well-wrought ship nigh to the isle Thrinacia, fleeing the sea of violet blue, when ye find the herds of Helios grazing and his brave flocks, of Helios who overseeth all and overheareth all things. If thou doest these no hurt, being heedful of thy return, so may ye yet reach Ithaca, albeit in evil case. But if thou hurtest them, I foreshow ruin for thy ship and for thy men, and even though thou shalt thyself escape, late shalt thou return in evil plight, with the loss of all thy company, on board the ship of strangers, and thou shalt find sorrows in thy house, even proud men that devour thy living, while they woo thy godlike wife and offer the gifts of wooing. Yet I tell thee, on thy coming thou shalt avenge their violence. But when thou hast slain the wooers in thy halls, whether by guile, or openly with the edge of the sword, thereafter go thy way, taking with thee a shapen oar, till thou shalt come to such men as know not the sea, neither eat meat savoured with salt; yea, nor have they knowledge of ships of purple cheek, nor shapen oars which serve for wings to ships. And I will give thee a most manifest token, which cannot escape thee. In the day when another wayfarer shall meet thee and say that thou hast a winnowing fan on thy stout shoulder, even then make fast thy shapen oar in the earth and do goodly sacrifice to the lord Poseidon, even with a ram and a bull and a boar, the mate of swine, and depart for home and offer holy hecatombs to the deathless gods that keep the wide heaven, to each in order due. And from the sea shall thine own death come, the gentlest death that may be, which shall end thee foredone with smooth old age, and the folk shall dwell happily around thee. This that I say is sooth."

'So spake he, and I answered him, saying: "Teiresias, all these threads, methinks, the gods themselves have spun. But come, declare me this and plainly tell me all. I see here the spirit of my mother dead; lo, she sits in silence near the blood, nor deigns to look her son in the face nor speak to him! Tell me, prince, how may she know me again that I am he?"

'So spake I, and anon he answered me, and said: "I will tell thee an easy saying, and will put it in thy heart. Whomsoever of the dead that be departed thou shalt suffer to draw nigh to the blood, he shall tell thee sooth; but if thou shalt grudge any, that one shall go to his own place again." Therewith the spirit of the prince Teiresias went back within the house of Hades, when he had told all his oracles. But I abode there steadfastly, till my mother drew nigh and drank the dark blood; and at once she knew me, and bewailing herself spake to me winged words:

' "Dear child, how didst thou come beneath the darkness and the shadow, thou that art a living man? Grievous is the sight of these things to the living, for between us and you are great rivers and dreadful streams; first, Oceanus, which can no wise be crossed on foot, but only if one have a well-wrought ship. Art thou but now come hither with thy ship and thy company in thy long wanderings from Troy? and hast thou not yet reached Ithaca, nor seen thy wife in thy halls?"

'Even so she spake, and I answered her, and said: "O my mother, necessity was on me to come down to the house of Hades to seek to the spirit of Theban Teiresias. For not yet have I drawn near to the Achaean shore, nor yet have I set foot on mine own country, but have been wandering evermore in affliction, from the day that first I went with goodly Agamemnon to Ilios of the fair steeds, to do battle with the Trojans. But come, declare me this and plainly tell it all. What doom overcame thee of death that lays men at their length? Was it a slow disease, or did Artemis the archer slay thee with the visitation of her gentle shafts? And tell me of my father and my son, that I left behind me; doth my honour yet abide with them, or hath another already taken it, while they say that I shall come home no more? And tell me of my wedded wife, of her counsel and her purpose, doth she abide with her son and keep all secure, or hath she already wedded the best of the Achaeans?"

'Even so I spake, and anon my lady mother answered me: "Yea verily, she abideth with steadfast spirit in thy halls; and wearily for her the nights wane always and the days in shedding of tears. But the fair honour that is thine no man hath yet taken; but Telemachus sits at peace on his demesne, and feasts at equal banquets, whereof it is meet that a judge partake, for all men bid him to their house. And thy father abides there in the field, and goes not down to the town, nor lies he on bedding or rugs or shining blankets, but all the winter he sleeps, where sleep the thralls in the house, in the ashes by the fire, and is clad in sorry raiment. But when the summer comes and the rich harvest-tide, his beds of fallen leaves are strewn lowly all about the knoll of his vineyard plot. There he lies sorrowing and nurses his mighty grief, for long desire of thy return, and old age withal comes heavy upon him. Yea and even so did I too perish and meet my doom. It was not the archer goddess of the keen sight, who slew me in my halls with the visitation of her gentle shafts, nor did any sickness come upon me, such as chiefly with a sad wasting draws the spirit from the limbs; nay, it was my sore longing for thee, and for thy counsels, great Odysseus, and for thy loving-kindness, that reft me of sweet life."

'So spake she, and I mused in my heart and would fain have embraced the spirit of my mother dead. Thrice I sprang towards her, and was minded to embrace her; thrice she flitted from my hands as a shadow or even as a dream, and sharp grief arose ever at my heart. And uttering my voice I spake to her winged words:

' "Mother mine, wherefore dost thou not abide me who am eager to clasp thee, that even in Hades we twain may cast our arms each about the other, and have our fill of chill lament? Is this but a phantom that the high goddess Persephone hath sent me, to the end that I may groan for more exceeding sorrow?"

'So spake I, and my lady mother answered me anon: "Ah me, my child, of all men most ill-fated, Persephone, the daughter of Zeus, doth in no wise deceive thee, but even on this wise it is with mortals when they die. For the sinews no more bind together the flesh and the bones, but the great force of burning fire abolishes these, so soon as the life hath left the white bones, and the spirit like a dream flies forth and hovers near. But haste with all thine heart toward the sunlight, and mark all this, that even hereafter thou mayest tell it to thy wife."

'Thus we twain held discourse together; and lo, the women came up, for the high goddess Persephone sent them forth, all they that had been the wives and daughters of mighty men. And they gathered and flocked about the black blood, and I took counsel how I might question them each one. And this was the counsel that showed best in my sight. I drew my long hanger from my stalwart thigh, and suffered them not all at one time to drink of the dark blood. So they drew nigh one by one, and each declared her lineage, and I made question of all.

'Then verily did I first see Tyro, sprung of a noble sire, who said that she was the child of noble Salmoneus, and declared herself the wife of Cretheus, son of Aeolus. She loved a river, the divine Enipeus, far the fairest of the floods that run upon the earth, and she would resort to the fair streams of Enipeus. And it came to pass that the girdler of the world, the Earth-shaker, put on the shape of the god, and lay by the lady at the mouths of the whirling stream. Then the dark wave stood around them like a hill-side bowed, and hid the god and the mortal woman. And he undid her maiden girdle, and shed a slumber over her. Now when the god had done the work of love, he clasped her hand and spake and hailed her.

' "Woman, be glad in our love, and when the year comes round thou shalt give birth to glorious children,—for not weak are the embraces of the gods,—and do thou keep and cherish them. And now go home and hold thy peace, and tell it not: but behold, I am Poseidon, shaker of the earth."

'Therewith he plunged beneath the heaving deep. And she conceived and bare Pelias and Neleus, who both grew to be mighty men, servants of Zeus. Pelias dwelt in wide Iolcos, and was rich in flocks; and that other abode in sandy Pylos. And the queen of women bare yet other sons to Cretheus, even Aeson and Pheres and Amythaon, whose joy was in chariots.

'And after her I saw Antiope, daughter of Asôpus, and her boast was that she had slept even in the arms of Zeus, and she bare two sons, Amphion and Zethus, who founded first the place of seven-gated Thebes, and they made of it a fenced city, for they might not dwell in spacious Thebes unfenced, for all their valiancy.

'Next to her I saw Alcmene, wife of Amphitryon, who lay in the arms of mighty Zeus, and bare Heracles of the lion-heart, steadfast in the fight. And I saw Megara, daughter of Creon, haughty of heart, whom the strong and tireless son of Amphitryon had to wife.

'And I saw the mother of Oedipodes, fair Epicaste, who wrought a dread deed unwittingly, being wedded to her own son, and he that had slain his own father wedded her, and straightway the gods made these things known to men. Yet he abode in pain in pleasant Thebes, ruling the Cadmaeans, by reason of the deadly counsels of the gods. But she went down to the house of Hades, the mighty warder; yea, she tied a noose from the high beam aloft, being fast holden in sorrow; while for him she left pains behind full many, even all that the Avengers of a mother bring to pass.

'And I saw lovely Chloris, whom Neleus wedded on a time for her beauty, and brought gifts of wooing past number. She was the youngest daughter of Amphion, son of Iasus, who once ruled mightily in Minyan Orchomenus. And she was queen of Pylos, and bare glorious children to her lord, Nestor and Chromius, and princely Periclymenus, and stately Pero too, the wonder of all men. All that dwelt around were her wooers; but Neleus would not give her, save to him who should drive off from Phylace the kine of mighty Iphicles, with shambling gait and broad of brow, hard cattle to drive. And none but the noble seer took in hand to drive them; but a grievous fate from the gods fettered him, even hard bonds and the herdsmen of the wild. But when at length the months and days were being fulfilled, as the year returned upon his course, and the seasons came round, then did mighty Iphicles set him free, when he had spoken out all the oracles; and herein was the counsel of Zeus being accomplished.

'And I saw Lede, the famous bed-fellow of Tyndareus, who bare to Tyndareus two sons, hardy of heart, Castor tamer of steeds, and Polydeuces the boxer. These twain yet live, but the quickening earth is over them; and even in the nether world they have honour at the hand of Zeus. And they possess their life in turn, living one day and dying the next, and they have gotten worship even as the gods.

'And after her I beheld Iphimedeia, bed-fellow of Aloeus, who said that she had lain with Poseidon, and she bare children twain, but short of life were they, godlike Otus and far-famed Ephialtes. Now these were the tallest men that earth, the grain-giver, ever reared, and far the goodliest after the renowned Orion. At nine seasons old they were of breadth nine cubits, and nine fathoms in height. They it was who threatened to raise even against the immortals in Olympus the din of stormy war. They strove to pile Ossa on Olympus, and on Ossa Pelion with the trembling forest leaves, that there might be a pathway to the sky. Yea, and they would have accomplished it, had they reached the full measure of manhood. But the son of Zeus, whom Leto of the fair locks bare, destroyed the twain, ere the down had bloomed beneath their temples, and darkened their chins with the blossom of youth.

'And Phaedra and Procris I saw, and fair Ariadne, the daughter of wizard Minos, whom Theseus on a time was bearing from Crete to the hill of sacred Athens, yet had he no joy of her; for Artemis slew her ere that in sea-girt Dia, by reason of the witness of Dionysus.

'And Maera and Clymene I saw, and hateful Eriphyle, who took fine gold for the price of her dear lord's life. But I cannot tell or name all the wives and daughters of the heroes that I saw; ere that, the immortal night would wane. Nay, it is even now time to sleep, whether I go to the swift ship to my company or abide here: and for my convoy you and the gods will care.'

So spake he, and dead silence fell on all, and they were spell-bound throughout the shadowy halls. Then Arete of the white arms first spake among them: 'Phaeacians, what think you of this man for comeliness and stature, and within for wisdom of heart? Moreover he is my guest, though every one of you hath his share in this honour. Wherefore haste not to send him hence, and stint not these your gifts for one that stands in such sore need of them; for ye have much treasure stored in your halls by the grace of the gods.'

Then too spake among them the old man, lord Echeneus, that was an elder among the Phaeacians: 'Friends, behold, the speech of our wise queen is not wide of the mark, nor far from our deeming, so hearken ye thereto. But on Alcinous here both word and work depend.'

Then Alcinous made answer, and spake unto him: 'Yea, the word that she hath spoken shall hold, if indeed I am yet to live and bear rule among the Phaeacians, masters of the oar. Howbeit let the stranger, for all his craving to return, nevertheless endure to abide until the morrow, till I make up the full measure of the gift; and men shall care for his convoy, all men, but I in chief, for mine is the lordship in the land.'

And Odysseus of many counsels answered him, saying: 'My lord Alcinous, most notable of all the people, if ye bade me tarry here even for a year, and would speed my convoy and give me splendid gifts, even that I would choose; and better would it be for me to come with a fuller hand to mine own dear country, so should I get more love and worship in the eyes of all men, whoso should see me after I was returned to Ithaca.'

And Alcinous answered him, saying: 'Odysseus, in no wise do we deem thee, we that look on thee, to be a knave or a cheat, even as the dark earth rears many such broadcast, fashioning lies whence none can even see his way therein. But beauty crowns thy words, and wisdom is within thee; and thy tale, as when a minstrel sings, thou hast told with skill, the weary woes of all the Argives and of thine own self. But come, declare me this and plainly tell it all. Didst thou see any of thy godlike company who went up at the same time with thee to Ilios and there met their doom? Behold, the night is of great length, unspeakable, and the time for sleep in the hall is not yet; tell me therefore of those wondrous deeds. I could abide even till the bright dawn, so long as thou couldst endure to rehearse me these woes of thine in the hall.'

And Odysseus of many counsels answered him, saying: 'My lord Alcinous, most notable of all the people, there is a time for many words and there is a time for sleep. But if thou art eager still to listen, I would not for my part grudge to tell thee of other things more pitiful still, even the woes of my comrades, those that perished afterward, for they had escaped with their lives from the dread war-cry of the Trojans, but perished in returning by the will of an evil woman.

'Now when holy Persephone had scattered this way and that the spirits of the women folk, thereafter came the soul of Agamemnon, son of Atreus, sorrowing; and round him others were gathered, the ghosts of them who had died with him in the house of Aegisthus and met their doom. And he knew me straightway when he had drunk the dark blood, yea, and he wept aloud, and shed big tears as he stretched forth his hands in his longing to reach me. But it might not be, for he had now no steadfast strength nor power at all in moving, such as was aforetime in his supple limbs.

'At the sight of him I wept and was moved with compassion, and uttering my voice, spake to him winged words: "Most renowned son of Atreus, Agamemnon, king of men, say what doom overcame thee of death that lays men at their length? Did Poseidon smite thee in thy ships, raising the dolorous blast of contrary winds, or did unfriendly men do thee hurt upon the land, whilst thou wert cutting off their oxen and fair flocks of sheep, or fighting to win a city and the women thereof?"

'So spake I, and straightway he answered, and said unto me: "Son of Laertes, of the seed of Zeus, Odysseus of many devices, it was not Poseidon that smote me in my ships, and raised the dolorous blast of contrary winds, nor did unfriendly men do me hurt upon the land, but Aegisthus it was that wrought me death and doom and slew me, with the aid of my accursed wife, as one slays an ox at the stall, after he had bidden me to his house, and entertained me at a feast. Even so I died by a death most pitiful, and round me my company likewise were slain without ceasing, like swine with glittering tusks which are slaughtered in the house of a rich and mighty man, whether at a wedding banquet or a joint-feast or a rich clan-drinking. Ere now hast thou been at the slaying of many a man, killed in single fight or in strong battle, yet thou wouldst have sorrowed the most at this sight, how we lay in the hall round the mixing-bowl and the laden boards, and the floor all ran with blood. And most pitiful of all that I heard was the voice of the daughter of Priam, of Cassandra, whom hard by me the crafty Clytemnestra slew. Then I strove to raise my hands as I was dying upon the sword, but to earth they fell. And that shameless one turned her back upon me, and had not the heart to draw down my eyelids with her fingers nor to close my mouth. So surely is there nought more terrible and shameless than a woman who imagines such evil in her heart, even as she too planned a foul deed, fashioning death for her wedded lord. Verily I had thought to come home most welcome to my children and my thralls; but she, out of the depth of her evil knowledge, hath shed shame on herself and on all womankind, which shall be for ever, even on the upright."

'Even so he spake, but I answered him, saying: "Lo now, in very sooth, hath Zeus of the far-borne voice wreaked wondrous hatred on the seed of Atreus through the counsels of woman from of old. For Helen's sake so many of us perished, and now Clytemnestra hath practised treason against thee, while yet thou wast afar off."

'Even so I spake, and anon he answered me, saying: "Wherefore do thou too, never henceforth be soft even to thy wife, neither show her all the counsel that thou knowest, but a part declare and let part be hid. Yet shalt not thou, Odysseus, find death at the hand of thy wife, for she is very discreet and prudent in all her ways, the wise Penelope, daughter of Icarius. Verily we left her a bride new wed when we went to the war, and a child was at her breast, who now, methinks, sits in the ranks of men, happy in his lot, for his dear father shall behold him on his company, and he shall embrace his sire as is meet. But as for my wife, she suffered me not so much as to have my fill of gazing on my son; ere that she slew me, even her lord. And yet another thing will I tell thee, and do thou ponder it in thy heart. Put thy ship to land in secret, and not openly, on the shore of thy dear country; for there is no more faith in woman. But come, declare me this and plainly tell it all, if haply ye hear of my son as yet living, either, it may be, in Orchomenus or in sandy Pylos, or perchance with Menelaus in wide Sparta, for goodly Orestes hath not yet perished on the earth."

'Even so he spake, but I answered him, saying: "Son of Atreus, wherefore dost thou ask me straitly of these things? Nay I know not at all, whether he be alive or dead; it is ill to speak words light as wind."

'Thus we twain stood sorrowing, holding sad discourse, while the big tears fell fast: and therewithal came the soul of Achilles, son of Peleus, and of Patroclus and of noble Antilochus and of Aias, who in face and form was goodliest of all the Danaans, after the noble son of Peleus. And the spirit of the son of Aeacus, fleet of foot, knew me again, and making lament spake to me winged words:

'"Son of Laertes, of the seed of Zeus, Odysseus of

many devices, man overbold, what new deed and hardier than this wilt thou devise in thy heart? How durst thou come down to the house of Hades, where dwell the senseless dead, the phantoms of men outworn?"

'So he spake, but I answered him: "Achilles, son of Peleus, mightiest far of the Achaeans, I am come hither to seek to Teiresias, if he may tell me any counsel, how I may come to rugged Ithaca. For not yet have I come nigh the Achaean land, nor set foot on mine own soil, but am still in evil case; while as for thee, Achilles, none other than thou wast heretofore the most blessed of men, nor shall any be hereafter. For of old, in the days of thy life, we Argives gave thee one honour with the gods, and now thou art a great prince here among the dead. Wherefore let not thy death be any grief to thee, Achilles."

'Even so I spake, and he straightway answered me, and said: "Nay, speak not comfortably to me of death, oh great Odysseus. Rather would I live on ground as the hireling of another, with a landless man who had no great livelihood, than bear sway among all the dead that be departed. But come, tell me tidings of that lordly son of mine—did he follow to the war to be a leader or not? And tell me of noble Peleus, if thou hast heard aught,—is he yet held in worship among the Myrmidons, or do they dishonour him from Hellas to Phthia, for that old age binds him hand and foot? For I am no longer his champion under the sun, so mighty a man as once I was, when in wide Troy I slew the best of the host, and succoured the Argives. Ah! could I but come for an hour to my father's house as then I was, so would I make my might and hands invincible, to be hateful to many an one of those who do him despite and keep him from his honour."

'Even so he spake, but I answered him saying: "As for noble Peleus, verily I have heard nought of him; but concerning thy dear son Neoptolemus, I will tell thee all the truth, according to thy word. It was I that led him up out of Scyros in my good hollow ship, in the wake of the goodly-greaved Achaeans. Now oft as we took counsel around Troy town, he was ever the first to speak, and no word missed the mark; the godlike Nestor and I alone surpassed him. But whensoever we Achaeans did battle on the plain of Troy, he never tarried behind in the throng or the press of men, but ran out far before us all, yielding to none in that might of his. And many men he slew in warfare dread; but I could not tell of all or name their names, even all the host he slew in succouring the Argives; but, ah, how he smote with the sword that son of Telephus, the hero Eurypylus, and many Ceteians of his company were slain around him, by reason of a woman's bribe. He truly was the comeliest man that ever I saw, next to goodly Memnon. And again when we, the best of the Argives, were about to go down into the horse which Epeus wrought, and the charge of all was laid on me, both to open the door of our good ambush and to shut the same, then did the other princes and counsellors of the Danaans wipe away the tears, and the limbs of each one trembled beneath him, but never once did I see thy son's fair face wax pale, nor did he wipe the tears from his cheeks: but he besought me often to let him go forth from the horse, and kept handling his sword-hilt, and his heavy bronze-shod spear, and he was set on mischief against the Trojans. But after we had sacked the steep city of Priam, he embarked unscathed with his share of the spoil, and with a noble prize; he was not smitten with the sharp spear, and got no wound in close fight: and many such chances there be in war, for Ares rageth confusedly."

'So I spake, and the spirit of the son of Aeacus, fleet of foot, passed with great strides along the mead of asphodel, rejoicing in that I had told him of his son's renown.

'But lo, other spirits of the dead that be departed stood sorrowing, and each one asked of those that were dear to them. The soul of Aias son of Telamon, alone stood apart being still angry for the victory wherein I prevailed against him, in the suit by the ships concerning the arms of Achilles, that his lady mother had set for a prize; and the sons of the Trojans made award and Pallas Athene. Would that I had never prevailed and won such a prize! So goodly a head hath the earth closed over, for the sake of those arms, even over Aias, who in beauty and in feats of war was of a mould above all the other Danaans, next to the noble son of Peleus. To him then I spake softly, saying:

' "Aias, son of noble Telamon, so art thou not even in death to forget thy wrath against me, by reason of those arms accursed, which the gods set to be the bane of the Argives? What a tower of strength fell in thy fall, and we Achaeans cease not to sorrow for thee, even as for the life of Achilles, son of Peleus! Nay, there is none other to blame, but Zeus, who hath borne wondrous hate to the army of the Danaan spearsmen, and laid on thee thy doom. Nay, come hither, my lord, that thou mayest hear my word and my speech; master thy wrath and thy proud spirit."

'So I spake, but he answered me not a word and passed to Erebus after the other spirits of the dead that be departed. Even then, despite his anger, would he have spoken to me or I to him, but my heart within me was minded to see the spirits of those others that were departed.

'There then I saw Minos, glorious son of Zeus, wielding a golden sceptre, giving sentence from his throne to the dead, while they sat and stood around the prince, asking his dooms through the wide-gated house of Hades.

'And after him I marked the mighty Orion driving the wild beasts together over the mead of asphodel, the very beasts that himself had slain on the lonely hills, with a strong mace all of bronze in his hands, that is ever unbroken.

'And I saw Tityos, son of renowned Earth, lying on a

levelled ground, and he covered nine roods as he lay, and vultures twain beset him one on either side, and gnawed at his liver, piercing even to the caul, but he drave them not away with his hands. For he had dealt violently with Leto, the famous bed-fellow of Zeus, as she went up to Pytho through the fair lawns of Paponeus.

'Moreover I beheld Tantalus in grievous torment, standing in a mere and the water came nigh unto his chin. And he stood straining as one athirst, but he might not attain to the water to drink of it. For often as that old man stooped down in his eagerness to drink, so often the water was swallowed up and it vanished away, and the black earth still showed at his feet, for some god parched it evermore. And tall trees flowering shed their fruit overhead, pears and pomegranates and apple trees with bright fruit, and sweet figs and olives in their bloom, whereat when that old man reached out his hands to clutch them, the wind would toss them to the shadowy clouds.

'Yea and I beheld Sisyphus in strong torment, grasping a monstrous stone with both his hands. He was pressing thereat with hands and feet, and trying to roll the stone upward toward the brow of the hill. But oft as he was about to hurl it over the top, the weight would drive him back, so once again to the plain rolled the stone, the shameless thing. And he once more kept heaving and straining, and the sweat the while was pouring down his limbs, and the dust rose upwards from his head.

'And after him I descried the mighty Heracles, his phantom, I say; but as for himself he hath joy at the banquet among the deathless gods, and hath to wife Hebe of the fair ankles, child of great Zeus, and of Here of the golden sandals. And all about him there was a clamour of the dead, as it were fowls flying every way in fear, and he like black Night, with bow uncased, and shaft upon the string, fiercely glancing around, like one in the act to shoot. And about his breast was an awful belt, a baldric of gold, whereon wondrous things were wrougnt, bears and wild boars and lions with flashing eyes, and strife and battles and slaughters and murders of men. Nay, now that he hath fashioned this, never another may he fashion, whoso stored in his craft the device of that belt! And anon he knew me when his eyes beheld me, and making lament he spake unto me winged words:

'"Son of Laertes, of the seed of Zeus, Odysseus of many devices: ah! wretched one, dost thou too lead such a life of evil doom, as I endured beneath the rays of the sun? I was the son of Zeus Cronion, yet had I trouble beyond measure, for I was subdued unto a man far worse than I. And he enjoined on me hard adventures, yea and on a time he sent me hither to bring back the hound of hell; for he devised no harder task for me than this. I lifted the hound and brought him forth from out of the house of Hades; and Hermes sped me on my way and the grey-eyed Athene."

'Therewith he departed again into the house of Hades, but I abode there still, if perchance some one of the hero folk besides might come, who died in old time. Yea and I should have seen the men of old, whom I was fain to look on, Theseus and Peirithous, renowned children of the gods. But ere that might be the myriad tribes of the dead thronged up together with wondrous clamour: and pale fear gat hold of me, lest the high goddess Persephone should send me the head of the Gorgon, that dread monster, from out of Hades.

'Straightway then I went to the ship, and bade my men mount the vessel, and loose the hawsers. So speedily they went on board, and sat upon the benches. And the wave of the flood bore the barque down the stream of Oceanus, we rowing first, and afterwards the fair wind was our convoy.

BOOK XII

Odysseus, his passage by the Sirens, and by Scylla and Charybdis. The sacrilege committed by his men in the isle Thrinacia. The destruction of his ships and men. How he swam on a plank nine days together, and came to Ogygia, where he stayed seven years with Calypso.

'Now after the ship had left the stream of the river Oceanus, and was come to the wave of the wide sea, and the isle Aeaean, where is the dwelling place of early Dawn and her dancing grounds, and the land of sunrising, upon our coming thither we beached the ship in the sand, and ourselves too stept ashore on the sea-beach. There we fell on sound sleep and awaited the bright Dawn.

'So soon as early Dawn shone forth, the rosy-fingered, I sent forth my fellows to the house of Circé to fetch the body of the dead Elpenor. And speedily we cut billets of wood and sadly we buried him, where the furthest headland runs out into the sea, shedding big tears. But when the dead man was burned and the arms of the dead, we piled a barrow and dragged up thereon a pillar, and on the topmost mound we set the shapen oar.

'Now all that task we finished, and our coming from out of Hades was not unknown to Circé, but she arrayed herself and speedily drew nigh, and her handmaids with her bare flesh and bread in plenty and dark red wine. And the fair goddess stood in the midst and spake in our ears, saying:

' "Men overbold, who have gone alive into the house of Hades, to know death twice, while all men else die once for all. Nay come, eat ye meat and drink wine here all day long; and with the breaking of the day ye shall set sail, and myself I will show you the path and declare each thing, that ye may not suffer pain or hurt through any grievous ill-contrivance by sea or on the land."

'So spake she, and our lordly souls consented thereto. Thus for that time we sat the livelong day, until the going down of the sun, feasting on abundant flesh and on sweet wine. Now when the sun sank and darkness came on, my company laid them to rest by the hawsers of the ship. Then she took me by the hand and led me apart from my dear company, and made me to sit down and laid herself at my feet, and asked all my tale. And I told her all in order duly. Then at the last the lady Circé spake unto me, saying:

' "Even so, now all these things have an end; do thou then hearken even as I tell thee, and the god himself shall bring it back to thy mind. To the Sirens first shalt thou come, who bewitch all men, whosoever shall come to them. Whoso draws nigh them unwittingly and hears the sound of the Sirens' voice, never doth he see wife or babes stand by him on his return, nor have they joy at his coming; but the Sirens enchant him with their clear song, sitting in the meadow, and all about is a great heap of bones of men, corrupt in death, and round the bones the skin is wasting. But do thou drive thy ship past, and knead honey-sweet wax, and anoint therewith the ears of thy company, lest any of the rest hear the song; but if thou thyself art minded to hear, let them bind thee in the swift ship hand and foot, upright in the mast-stead, and from the mast let rope-ends be tied, that with delight thou mayest hear the voice of the Sirens. And if thou shalt beseech thy company and bid them to loose thee, then let them bind thee with yet more bonds. But when thy friends have driven thy ship past these, I will not tell thee fully which path shall thenceforth be thine, but do thou thyself consider it, and I will speak to thee of either way. On the one side there are beetling rocks, and against them the great wave roars of dark-eyed Amphitrite. These, ye must know, are they the blessed gods call the Rocks Wandering. By this way even winged things may never pass, nay, not even the cowering doves that bear ambrosia to Father Zeus, but the sheer rock evermore takes away one even of these, and the Father sends in another to make up the tale. Thereby no ship of men ever escapes that comes thither, but the planks of ships and the bodies of men confusedly are tossed by the waves of the sea and the storms of ruinous fire. One ship only of all that fare by sea hath passed that way, even Argo, that is in all men's minds, on her voyage from Aeëtes. And even her the wave would lightly have cast there upon the mighty rocks, but Here sent her by for love of Iason.

'"On the other part are two rocks, whereof the one reaches with sharp peak to the wide heaven, and a dark cloud encompasses it; this never streams away, and there is no clear air about the peak neither in summer nor in harvest tide. No mortal man may scale it or set foot thereon, not though he had twenty hands and feet. For the rock is smooth, and sheer, as it were polished. And in the midst of the cliff is a dim cave turned to Erebus, towards the place of darkness, whereby ye shall even steer your hollow ship, noble Odysseus. Not with an arrow from a bow might a man in his strength reach from his hollow ship into that deep cave. And therein dwelleth Scylla, yelping terribly. Her voice indeed is no greater than the voice of a new-born whelp, but a dreadful monster is she, nor would any look on her gladly, not if it were a god that met her. Verily she hath twelve feet all dangling down, and six necks exceeding long, and on each a hideous head, and therein three rows of teeth set thick and close, full of black death. Up to her middle is she sunk far down in the hollow cave, but forth she holds her heads from the dreadful gulf, and there she fishes, swooping round the rock, for dolphins or sea-dogs, or whatso greater beast she may anywhere take, whereof the deep-voiced Amphitrite feeds countless flocks. Thereby no sailors boast that they had fled scatheless ever with their ship, for with each head she carries off a man, whom she hath snatched from out the dark-prowed ship.

'"But that other cliff, Odysseus, thou shalt note, lying lower, hard by the first: thou couldest send an arrow across. And thereon is a great fig-tree growing, in fullest leaf, and beneath it mighty Charybdis sucks down black water, for thrice a day she spouts it forth, and thrice a day she sucks it down in terrible wise. Never mayest thou be there when she sucks the water, for none might save thee then from thy bane, not even the Earth-shaker! But take heed and swiftly drawing nigh to Scylla's rock drive the ship past, since of a truth it is far better to mourn six of thy company in the ship, than all in the selfsame hour."

'So spake she, but I answered, and said unto her: "Come I pray thee herein, goddess, tell me true, if there be any means whereby I might escape from the deadly Charybdis and avenge me on that other, when she would prey upon my company."

'So spake I, and that fair goddess answered me: "Man overbold, lo, now again the deeds of war are in thy mind and the travail thereof. Wilt thou not yield thee even to the deathless gods? As for her, she is no mortal, but an immortal plague, dread, grievous, and fierce, and not to be fought with; and against her there is no defence; flight is the bravest way. For if thou tarry to do on thine armour by the cliff, I fear lest once again she sally forth and catch at thee with so many heads, and seize as many men as before. So drive past with all thy force, and call on Cratais, mother of Scylla, which bore her for a bane to mortals. And she will then let her from darting forth thereafter.

'"Then thou shalt come unto the isle Thrinacia; there are the many kine of Helios and his brave flocks feeding, seven herds of kine and as many goodly flocks of sheep, and fifty in each flock. They have no part in birth or in corruption, and there are goddesses to shepherd them, nymphs with fair tresses, Phaethusa and Lampetie whom bright Neaera bare to Helios Hyperion. Now when the lady their mother had borne and nursed them, she carried them to the isle Thrinacia to dwell afar, that they should guard their father's flocks and his kine with shambling gait. If thou doest these no hurt, being heedful of thy return, truly ye may even yet reach Ithaca, albeit in evil case. But if thou hurtest them, I foreshow ruin for thy ship and for thy men, and even though thou shouldest thyself escape, late shalt thou return in evil plight with the loss of all thy company."

'So spake she, and anon came the golden-throned Dawn. Then the fair goddess took her way up the island. But I departed to my ship and roused my men themselves to mount the vessel and loose the hawsers. And speedily they went aboard and sat upon the benches, and sitting orderly smote the grey sea water with their oars. And in the wake of our dark-prowed ship she sent a favouring wind that filled the sails, a kindly escort,—even Circé of the braided tresses, a dread goddess of human speech. And straightway we set in order the gear throughout the ship and sat us down, and the wind and the helmsman guided our barque.

'Then I spake among my company with a heavy heart: "Friends, forasmuch as it is not well that one or two alone should know of the oracles that Circé, the fair goddess, spake unto me, therefore will I declare them, that with foreknowledge we may die, or haply shunning death and destiny escape. First she bade us avoid the sound of the voice of the wondrous Sirens, and their field of flowers, and me only she bade listen to their voices. So bind ye me in a hard bond, that I may abide unmoved in my place, upright in the mast-stead, and from the mast let rope-ends be tied, and if I beseech and bid you to set me free, then do ye straiten me with yet more bonds."

'Thus I rehearsed these things one and all, and declared them to my company. Meanwhile our good ship quickly came to the island of the Sirens twain, for a gentle breeze sped her on her way. Then straightway the wind ceased, and lo, there was a windless calm, and some god lulled the waves. Then my company rose up and drew in the ship's sails, and stowed them in the hold of the ship, while they sat at the oars and whitened the water with their polished pine blades. But I with my sharp sword cleft in pieces a great circle of wax, and with my strong hands kneaded it. And soon the wax grew warm, for that my great might constrained it, and the beam of the lord Helios, son of Hyperion. And I anointed therewith the ears of all my men in their order, and in the ship they bound me hand and foot upright in the mast-stead, and from the mast they fastened rope-ends and themselves sat down, and smote the grey sea water with their oars. But when the ship was within the sound of a man's shout from the land, we fleeing swiftly on our way, the Sirens espied the swift ship speeding toward them, and they raised their clear-toned song:

' "Hither, come hither, renowned Odysseus, great glory of the Achaeans, here stay thy barque, that thou mayest listen to the voice of us twain. For none hath ever driven by this way in his black ship, till he hath heard from our lips the voice sweet as the honeycomb, and hath had joy thereof and gone on his way the wiser. For lo, we know all things, all the travail that in wide Troy-land the Argives and Trojans bare by the gods' designs, yea, and we know all that shall hereafter be upon the fruitful earth."

'So spake they uttering a sweet voice, and my heart was fain to listen, and I bade my company unbind me, nodding at them with a frown, but they bent to their oars and rowed on. Then straight uprose Perimedes and Eurylochus and bound me with more cords and straitened me yet the more. Now when we had driven past them, nor heard we any longer the sound of the Sirens or their song, forthwith my dear company took away the wax wherewith I had anointed their ears and loosed me from my bonds.

"But so soon as we left that isle, thereafter presently I saw smoke and a great wave, and heard the sea roaring. Then for very fear the oars flew from their hands, and down the stream they all splashed, and the ship was holden there, for my company no longer plied with their hands the tapering oars. But I paced the ship and cheered on my men, as I stood by each one and spake smooth words:

'"Friends, forasmuch as in sorrow we are not all unlearned, truly this is no greater woe that is upon us, than when the Cyclops penned us by main might in his hollow cave; yet even thence we made escape by my manfulness, even by my counsel and my wit, and some day I think that this adventure too we shall remember. Come now, therefore, let us all give ear to do according to my word. Do ye smite the deep surf of the sea with your oars, as ye sit on the benches, if peradventure Zeus may grant us to escape from and shun this death. And as for thee, helmsman, thus I charge thee, and ponder it in thine heart seeing that thou wieldest the helm of the hollow ship. Keep the ship well away from this smoke and from the wave and hug the rocks, lest the ship, ere thou art aware, start from her course to the other side, and so thou hurl us into ruin."

'So I spake, and quickly they hearkened to my words. But of Scylla I told them nothing more, a bane none might deal with, lest haply my company should cease from rowing for fear, and hide them in the hold. In that same hour I suffered myself to forget the hard behest of Circé in that she bade me in no wise be armed; but I did on my glorious harness and caught up two long lances in my hands, and went on to the decking of the prow, for thence methought that Scylla of the rock would first be seen, who was to bring woe on my company. Yet could I not spy her anywhere, and my eyes waxed weary for gazing all about toward the darkness of the rock.

'Next we began to sail up the narrow strait lamenting. For on the one hand lay Scylla, and on the other mighty Charybdis in terrible wise sucked down the salt sea water. As often as she belched it forth, like a cauldron on a great fire she would seethe up through all her troubled deeps, and overhead the spray fell on the tops of either cliff. But oft as she gulped down the salt sea water, within she was all plain to see through her troubled deeps, and the rock around roared horribly and beneath the earth was manifest swart with sand, and pale fear gat hold on my men. Toward her, then, we looked fearing destruction; but Scylla meanwhile caught from out my hollow ship six of my company, the hardiest of their hands and the chief in might. And looking into the swift ship to find my men, even then I marked their feet and hands as they were lifted on high, and they cried aloud in their agony, and called me by my name for that last time of all. Even as when a fisher on some headland lets down with a long rod his baits for a snare to the little fishes below, casting into the deep the horn of an ox of the homestead, and as he catches each flings it writhing ashore, so writhing were they borne upward to the cliff. And there she devoured them shrieking in her gates, they stretching forth their hands to me in the dread death-struggle. And the most pitiful thing was this that mine eyes have seen of all my travail in searching out the paths of the sea.

'Now when we had escaped the Rocks and dread Charybdis and Scylla, thereafter we soon came to the fair island of the god; where were the goodly kine, broad of brow, and the many brave flocks of Helios Hyperion. Then while as yet I was in my black ship upon the deep, I heard the lowing of the cattle being stalled and the bleating of the sheep, and on my mind there fell the saying of the blind seer, Theban Teiresias, and of Circé of Aia, who charged me very straitly to shun the isle of Helios, the gladdener of the world. Then I spake out among my company in sorrow of heart:

' "Hear my words, my men, albeit in evil plight, that I may declare unto you the oracles of Teiresias and of Circé of Aia, who very straitly charged me to shun the isle of Helios, the gladdener of the world. For there she said the most dreadful mischief would befall us. Nay, drive ye then the black ship beyond and past that isle."

'So spake I, and their heart was broken within them. And Eurylochus straightway answered me sadly, saying:

' "Hardy art thou, Odysseus, of might beyond measure, and thy limbs are never weary; verily thou art fashioned all of iron, that sufferest not thy fellows, foredone with toil and drowsiness, to set foot on shore, where we might presently prepare us a good supper in this sea-girt island. But even as we are thou biddest us fare blindly through the sudden night, and from the isle go wandering on the misty deep. And strong winds, the bane of ships, are born of the night. How could a man escape from utter doom, if there chanced to come a sudden blast of the South Wind, or of the boisterous West, which mainly wreck ships, beyond the will of the gods, the lords of all? Howbeit for this present let us yield to the black night, and we will make ready our supper abiding by the swift ship, and in the morning we will climb on board, and put out into the broad deep."

'So spake Eurylochus, and the rest of my company consented thereto. Then at the last I knew that some god was indeed imagining evil, and I uttered my voice and spake unto him winged words:

'"Eurylochus, verily ye put force upon me, being but one among you all. But come, swear me now a mighty oath, one and all, to the intent that if we light on a herd of kine or a great flock of sheep, none in the evil folly of his heart may slay any sheep or ox; but in quiet eat ye the meat which the deathless Circé gave."

'So I spake, and straightway they swore to refrain as I commanded them. Now after they had sworn and done that oath, we stayed our well-builded ship in the hollow harbour near to a well of sweet water, and my company went forth from out the ship and deftly got ready supper. But when they had put from them the desire of meat and drink, thereafter they fell a weeping as they thought upon their dear companions whom Scylla had snatched from out the hollow ship and so devoured. And deep sleep came upon them amid their weeping. And when it was the third watch of the night, and the stars had crossed the zenith, Zeus the cloud-gatherer roused against them an angry wind with wondrous tempest, and shrouded in clouds land and sea alike, and from heaven sped down the night. Now when early Dawn shone forth, the rosy-fingered, we beached the ship, and dragged it up within a hollow cave, where were the fair dancing grounds of the nymphs and the places of their session. Thereupon I ordered a gathering of my men and spake in their midst, saying:

'"Friends, forasmuch as there is yet meat and drink in the swift ship, let us keep our hands off those kine, lest some evil thing befall us. For these are the kine and the brave flocks of a dread god, even of Helios, who overseeth all and overheareth all things."

'So I spake, and their lordly spirit hearkened thereto. Then for a whole month the South Wind blew without ceasing, and no other wind arose, save only the East and the South.

'Now so long as my company still had corn and red

wine, they refrained them from the kine, for they were fain of life. But when the corn was now all spent from out the ship, and they went wandering with barbed hooks in quest of game, as needs they must, fishes and fowls, whatsoever might come to their hand, for hunger gnawed at their belly, then at last I departed up the isle, that I might pray to the gods, if perchance some one of them might show me a way of returning. And now when I had avoided my company on my way through the island, I laved my hands where was a shelter from the wind, and prayed to all the gods that hold Olympus. But they shed sweet sleep upon my eyelids. And Eurylochus the while set forth an evil counsel to my company:

'"Hear my words, my friends, though ye be in evil case. Truly every shape of death is hateful to wretched mortals, but to die of hunger and so meet doom is most pitiful of all. Nay come, we will drive off the best of the kine of Helios and will do sacrifice to the deathless gods who keep wide heaven. And if we may yet reach Ithaca, our own country, forthwith will we rear a rich shrine to Helios Hyperion, and therein would we set many a choice offering. But if he be somewhat wroth for his cattle with straight horns, and is fain to wreck our ship, and the other gods follow his desire, rather with one gulp at the wave would I cast my life away, than be slowly straitened to death in a desert isle."

'So spake Eurylochus, and the rest of the company consented thereto. Forthwith they drave off the best of the kine of Helios that were nigh at hand, for the fair kine of shambling gait and broad of brow were feeding no great way from the dark-prowed ship. Then they stood around the cattle and prayed to the gods, plucking the fresh leaves from an oak of lofty boughs, for they had no white barley on board the decked ship. Now after they had prayed and cut the throats of the kine and flayed them, they cut out slices of the thighs and wrapped them in the fat, making a double fold, and thereon they laid raw flesh. Yet had they no pure wine to pour over the flaming sacrifices, but they made libation with water and roasted the entrails over the fire. Now after the thighs were quite consumed and they had tasted the inner parts, they cut the rest up small and spitted it on spits. In the same hour deep sleep sped from my eyelids and I sallied forth to the swift ship and the sea-banks. But on my way as I drew near to the curved ship, the sweet savour of the fat came all about me; and I groaned and spake out before the deathless gods:

' "Father Zeus, and all ye other blessed gods that live for ever, verily to my undoing ye have lulled me with a ruthless sleep, and my company abiding behind have imagined a monstrous deed."

'Then swiftly to Helios Hyperion came Lampetie of the long robes, with the tidings that we had slain his kine. And straight he spake with angry heart amid the Immortals:

' "Father Zeus, and all ye other blessed gods that live for ever, take vengeance I pray you on the company of Odysseus, son of Laertes, that have insolently slain my cattle, wherein I was wont to be glad as I went toward the starry heaven, and when I again turned earthward from the firmament. And if they pay me not full atonement for the cattle, I will go down to Hades and shine among the dead."

'And Zeus the cloud-gatherer answered him, saying: "Helios, do thou, I say, shine on amidst the deathless gods, and amid mortal men upon the earth, the grain-giver. But as for me, I will soon smite their swift ship with my white bolt, and cleave it in pieces in the midst of the wine-dark deep."

'This I heard from Calypso of the fair hair; and she said that she herself had heard it from Hermes the Messenger.

'But when I had come down to the ship and to the sea, I went up to my companions and rebuked them one by one; but we could find no remedy, the cattle were dead and gone. And soon thereafter the gods showed forth signs and wonders to my company. The skins were creeping, and the flesh bellowing upon the spits, both the roast and raw, and there was a sound as the voice of kine.

'Then for six days my dear company feasted on the best of the kine of Helios which they had driven off. But when Zeus, son of Cronos, had added the seventh day thereto, thereafter the wind ceased to blow with a rushing storm, and at once we climbed the ship and launched into the broad deep, when we had set up the mast and hoisted the white sails.

'But now when we left that isle nor any other land appeared, but sky and sea only, even then the son of Cronos stayed a dark cloud above the hollow ship, and beneath it the deep darkened. And the ship ran on her way for no long while, for of a sudden came the shrilling West, with the rushing of a great tempest, and the blast of wind snapped the two forestays of the mast, and the mast fell backward and all the gear dropped into the bilge. And behold, on the hind part of the ship the mast struck the head of the pilot and brake all the bones of his skull together, and like a diver he dropt down from the deck, and his brave spirit left his bones. In that same hour Zeus thundered and cast his bolt upon the ship, and she reeled all over being stricken by the bolt of Zeus, and was filled with sulphur, and lo, my company fell from out the vessel. Like sea-gulls they were borne round the black ship upon the billows, and the god reft them of returning.

'But I kept pacing through my ship, till the surge loosened the sides from the keel, and the wave swept her along stript of her tackling, and brake her mast clean off at the keel. Now the backstay fashioned of an oxhide had been flung thereon; therewith I lashed together both keel and mast and sitting thereon I was borne by the ruinous winds.

'Then verily the West Wind ceased to blow with a rushing storm, and swiftly withal the South Wind came, bringing sorrow to my soul, that so I might again measure back that space of sea, the way to deadly Charybdis. All the night was I borne, but with the rising of the sun I came to the rock of Scylla, and to dread Charybdis. Now she had sucked down her salt sea water, when I was swung up on high to the tall fig tree whereto I clung like a bat, and could find no sure rest for my feet nor place to stand, for the roots spread far below and the branches hung aloft out of reach, long and large, and overshadowed Charybdis. Steadfast I clung till she should spew forth mast and keel again; and late they came to my desire. At the hour when a man rises up from the assembly and goes to supper, one who judges the many quarrels of the young men that seek to him for law, at that same hour those timbers came forth to view from out Charybdis. And I let myself drop down hands and feet, and plunged heavily in the midst of the waters beyond the long timbers, and sitting on these I rowed hard with my hands. But the father of gods and of men suffered me no more to behold Scylla, else I should never have escaped from utter doom.

'Thence for nine days was I borne, and on the tenth night the gods brought me nigh to the isle of Ogygia, where dwells Calypso of the braided tresses, an awful goddess of mortal speech, who took me in and entreated me kindly. But why rehearse all this tale? For even yesterday I told it to thee and to thy noble wife in thy house; and it liketh me not twice to tell a plain-told tale.'

BOOK XIII

Odysseus, sleeping, is set ashore at Ithaca by the Phaeacians, and waking knows it not. Pallas, in the form of a shepherd, helps to hide his treasure. The ship that conveyed him is turned into a rock, and Odysseus by Pallas is instructed what to do, and transformed into an old beggarman.

So spake he, and dead silence fell on all, and they were spell-bound throughout the shadowy halls. Thereupon Alcinous answered him, and spake, saying:

'Odysseus, now that thou hast come to my high house with floor of bronze, never, methinks, shalt thou be driven from thy way ere thou returnest, though thou hast been sore afflicted. And for each man among you, that in these halls of mine drink evermore the dark wine of the elders, and hearken to the minstrel, this is my word and command. Garments for the stranger are already laid up in a polished coffer, with gold curiously wrought, and all other such gifts as the counsellors of the Phaeacians bare hither. Come now, let us each of us give him a great tripod and a cauldron, and we in turn will gather goods among the people and get us recompense; for it were hard that one man should give without repayment.'

So spake Alcinous, and the saying pleased them well. Then they went each one to his house to lay him down to rest; but so soon as early Dawn shone forth, the rosy-fingered, they hastened to the ship and bare the bronze, the joy of men. And the mighty king Alcinous himself went about the ship and diligently bestowed the gifts beneath the benches, that they might not hinder any of the crew in their rowing, when they laboured at their oars. Then they betook them to the house of Alcinous and fell to feasting. And the mighty king Alcinous sacrificed before them an ox to Zeus, the son of Cronos, that dwells in the dark clouds, who is lord of all. And when they had burnt the pieces of the thighs, they shared the glorious feast and made merry, and among them harped the divine minstrel Demodocus, whom the people honoured. But Odysseus would ever turn his head toward the splendour of the sun, as one fain to hasten his setting: for verily he was most eager to return. And as when a man longs for his supper, for whom all day long two dark oxen drag through the fallow field the jointed plough, yea and welcome to such an one the sunlight sinketh, that so he may get him to supper, for his knees wax faint by the way, even so welcome was the sinking of the sunlight to Odysseus. Then straight he spake among the Phaeacians, masters of the oar, and to Alcinous in chief he made known his word, saying:

'My lord Alcinous, most notable of all the people, pour ye the drink offering, and send me safe upon my way, and as for you, fare ye well. For now have I all that my heart desired, an escort and loving gifts. May the gods of heaven give me good fortune with them, and may I find my noble wife in my home with my friends unharmed, while ye, for your part, abide here and make glad your wedded wives and children; and may the gods vouchsafe all manner of good, and may no evil come nigh the people!'

So spake he, and they all consented thereto and bade send the stranger on his way, in that he had spoken aright. Then the mighty Alcinous spake to the henchman: 'Pontonous, mix the bowl and serve out the wine to all in the hall, that we may pray to Father Zeus, and send the stranger on his way to his own country.'

So spake he, and Pontonous mixed the honey-hearted

wine, and served it to all in turn. And they poured forth before the blessed gods that keep wide heaven, even there as they sat. Then goodly Odysseus uprose, and placed in Arete's hand the two-handled cup, and uttering his voice spake to her winged words:

'Fare thee well, O queen, all the days of thy life, till old age come and death, that visit all mankind. But I go homeward, and do thou in this thy house rejoice in thy children and thy people and Alcinous the king.'

Therewith goodly Odysseus stept over the threshold. And with him the mighty Alcinous sent forth a henchman to guide him to the swift ship and the sea-banks. And Arete sent in his train certain maidens of her household, one bearing a fresh robe and a doublet, and another she joined to them to carry the strong coffer, and yet another bare bread and red wine. Now when they had come down to the ship and to the sea, straightway the good men of the escort took these things and laid them by in the hollow ship, even all the meat and drink. Then they strewed for Odysseus a rug and a sheet of linen, on the decks of the hollow ship in the hinder part thereof, that he might sleep sound. Then he too climbed aboard and laid him down in silence, while they sat upon the benches, every man in order, and unbound the hawser from the pierced stone. So soon as they leant backwards and tossed the sea water with the oar blade, a deep sleep fell upon his eyelids, a sound sleep, very sweet, and next akin to death. And even as on a plain a yoke of four stallions comes springing all together beneath the lash, leaping high and speedily accomplishing the way, so leaped the stern of that ship, and the dark wave of the sounding sea rushed mightily in the wake, and she ran ever surely on her way, nor could a circling hawk keep pace with her, of winged things the swiftest. Even thus she lightly sped and cleft the waves of the sea, bearing a man whose counsel was as the counsel of the gods, one that erewhile had suffered much sorrow of heart, in passing through the wars of men, and the grievous waves; but for that time he slept in peace, forgetful of all that he had suffered.

So when the star came up, that is brightest of all, and goes ever heralding the light of early Dawn, even then did the sea-faring ship draw nigh the island. There is in the land of Ithaca a certain haven of Phorcys, the ancient one of the sea, and thereby are two headlands of sheer cliff, which slope to the sea on the haven's side and break the mighty wave that ill winds roll without, but within, the decked ships ride unmoored when once they have reached the place of anchorage. Now at the harbour's head is a long-leaved olive tree, and hard by is a pleasant cave and shadowy, sacred to the nymphs, that are called the Naiads. And therein are mixing bowls and jars of stone, and there moreover do bees hive. And there are great looms of stone, whereon the nymphs weave raiment of purple stain, a marvel to behold, and therein are waters welling evermore. Two gates there are to the cave, the one set toward the North Wind whereby men may go down, but the portals toward the South pertain rather to the gods, whereby men may not enter; it is the way of the immortals.

Thither they, as having knowledge of that place, let drive their ship; and now the vessel in full course ran ashore, half her keel's length high; so well was she sped by the hands of the oarsmen. Then they alighted from the benched ship upon the land, and first they lifted Odysseus from out the hollow ship, all as he was in the sheet of linen and the bright rug, and laid him yet heavy with slumber on the sand. And they took forth the goods which the lordly Phaeacians had given him on his homeward way by grace of the great-hearted Athene. These they set in a heap by the trunk of the olive tree, a little aside from the road, lest some wayfaring man, before Odysseus awakened, should come and spoil them. Then themselves departed homeward again. But the shaker of the earth forgat not the threats, wherewith at the first he had threatened godlike Odysseus, and he inquired into the counsel of Zeus, saying:

'Father Zeus, I for one shall no longer be of worship among the deathless gods, when mortal men hold me in no regard, even Phaeacians, who moreover are of mine own lineage. Lo, now I said that after much affliction Odysseus should come home, for I had no mind to rob him utterly of his return, when once thou hadst promised it and given assent; but behold, in his sleep they have borne him in a swift ship over the sea, and set him down in Ithaca, and given him gifts out of measure, bronze and gold in plenty and woven raiment, much store, such as never would Odysseus have won for himself out of Troy; yea, though he had returned unhurt with the share of the spoil that fell to him.'

And Zeus, the cloud-gatherer, answered him saying: 'Lo now, shaker of the earth, of widest power, what a word hast thou spoken! The gods nowise dishonour thee; hard would it be to assail with dishonour our eldest and our best. But if any man, giving place to his own hardihood and strength, holds thee not in worship, thou hast always thy revenge for the same, even in the time to come. Do thou as thou wilt, and as seems thee good.'

Then Poseidon, shaker of the earth, answered him: 'Straightway would I do even as thou sayest, O god of the dark clouds; but thy wrath I always hold in awe and avoid. Howbeit, now I fain would smite a fair ship of the Phaeacians, as she comes home from a convoy on the misty deep, that thereby they may learn to hold their hands, and cease from giving escort to men; and I would overshadow their city with a great mountain.'

And Zeus the gatherer of the clouds, answered him, saying: 'Friend, learn now what seems best in my sight. At an hour when the folk are all looking forth from the city at the ship upon her way, smite her into a stone hard by the land; a stone in the likeness of a swift ship, that all mankind may marvel, and do thou overshadow their city with a great mountain.'

Now when Poseidon, shaker of the earth, heard this saying, he went on his way to Scheria, where the Phaeacians dwell. There he abode awhile; and lo, she drew near, the seafaring ship, lightly sped upon her way. Then nigh her came the shaker of the earth, and he smote her into a stone, and rooted her far below with the down-stroke of his hand; and he departed thence again.

Then one to the other they spake winged words, the Phaeacians, of the long oars, mariners renowned. And thus would they speak, looking each man to his neighbour:

'Ah me! who is this that fettered our swift ship on the deep as she drave homewards? Even now she stood full in sight.'

Even so they would speak; but they knew not how these things were ordained. And Alcinous made harangue and spake among them:

'Lo now, in very truth the ancient oracles of my father have come home to me. He was wont to say that Poseidon was jealous of us, for that we give safe escort to all men. He said that the day would come when the god would smite a fair ship of the Phaeacians, as she came home from a convoy on the misty deep, and overshadow our city with a great mountain. Thus that ancient one would speak; and lo, all these things now have an end. But come, let us all give ear and do according to my word. Cease ye from the convoy of mortals, whensoever any shall come unto our town, and let us sacrifice to Poseidon twelve choice bulls, if perchance he may take pity, neither overshadow our city with a great mountain.'

So spake he, and they were dismayed and got ready the bulls. Thus were they praying to the lord Poseidon, the princes and counsellors of the land of the Phaeacians, as they stood about the altar.

Even then the goodly Odysseus awoke where he slept on his native land; nor knew he the same again, having now been long afar, for around him the goddess had shed a mist, even Pallas Athene, daughter of Zeus, to the end that she might make him undiscovered for that he was, and might expound to him all things, that so his wife should not know him neither his townsmen and kinsfolk, ere the wooers had paid for all their transgressions. Wherefore each thing showed strange to the lord of the land, the long paths and the sheltering havens and the steep rocks and the trees in their bloom. So he started up, and stood and looked upon his native land, and then he made moan withal, and smote on both his thighs with the down-stroke of his hands, and making lament, he spake, saying:

'Oh, woe is me, unto what mortals' land am I now come? Say, are they froward, and wild, and unjust, or hospitable and of a god-fearing mind? Whither do I bear all this treasure? Yea, where am I wandering myself? Oh that the treasure had remained with the Phaeacians where it was, so had I come to some other of the mighty princes, who would have entreated me kindly and sent me on my way. But now I know not where to bestow these things, nor yet will I leave them here behind, lest haply other men make spoil of them. Ah then, they are not wholly wise or just, the princes and counsellors of the Phaeacians, who carried me to a strange land. Verily they promised to bring me to clear-seen Ithaca, but they performed it not. May Zeus requite them, the god of suppliants, seeing that he watches over all men and punishes the transgressor! But come, I will reckon up these goods and look to them, lest the men be gone, and have taken ought away upon their hollow ship.'

Therewith he set to number the fair tripods and the cauldrons and the gold and the goodly woven raiment; and of all these he lacked not aught, but he bewailed him for his own country, as he walked downcast by the shore of the sounding sea, and made sore lament. Then Athene came nigh him in the guise of a young man, the herdsman of a flock, a young man most delicate, such as are the sons of kings. And she had a well-wrought mantle that fell in two folds about her shoulders, and beneath her smooth feet she had sandals bound, and a javelin in her hands. And Odysseus rejoiced as he saw her, and came over against her, and uttering his voice spake to her winged words:

'Friend, since thou art the first that I have chanced on in this land, hail to thee, and with no ill-will mayest thou meet me! Nay, save this my substance and save me too, for to thee as to a god I make prayer, and to thy dear knees have I come. And herein tell me true, that I may surely know. What land, what people is this? what men dwell therein? Surely, methinks, it is some clear seen isle, or a shore of the rich mainland that lies and leans upon the deep.'

Then the goddess, grey-eyed Athene, spake to him again: 'Thou art witless, stranger, or thou art come from afar, if indeed thou askest of this land; nay, it is not so very nameless but that many men know it, both all those who dwell toward the dawning and the sun, and they that abide over against the light toward the shadowy west. Verily it is rough and not fit for the driving of horses, yet is it not a very sorry isle, though narrow withal. For herein is corn past telling, and herein too wine is found, and the rain is on it evermore, and the fresh dew. And it is good for feeding goats and feeding kine; all manner of wood is here, and watering-places unfailing are herein. Wherefore, stranger, the name of Ithaca hath reached even unto Troy-land, which men say is far from this Achaean shore.'

So spake she, and the steadfast goodly Odysseus was glad, and had joy in his own country, according to the word of Pallas Athene, daughter of Zeus, lord of the aegis. And he uttered his voice and spake unto her winged words; yet he did not speak the truth, but took back the word that was on his lips, for quick and crafty was his wit within his breast:

'Of Ithaca have I heard tell, even in broad Crete, far over the seas; and now have I come hither myself with these my goods. And I left as much again to my children, when I turned outlaw for the slaying of the dear son of Idomeneus, Orsilochus, swift of foot, who in wide Crete was the swiftest of all men that live by bread. Now he would have despoiled me of all that booty of Troy, for the which I had endured pain of heart, in passing through the wars of men, and the grievous waves of the sea, for this cause that I would not do a favour to his father, and made me his squire in the land of the Trojans, but commanded other fellowship of mine own. So I smote him with a bronze-shod spear as he came home from the field, lying in ambush for him by the wayside, with one of my companions. And dark midnight held the heavens, and no man marked us, but privily I took his life away. Now after I had slain him with the sharp spear, straightway I went to a ship and besought the lordly Phoenicians, and gave them spoil to their hearts' desire. I charged them to take me on board, and land me at Pylos or at goodly Elis where the Epeans bear rule. Howbeit of a truth, the might of the wind drave them out of their course, sore against their will, nor did they wilfully play me false. Thence we were driven wandering, and came hither by night. And with much ado we rowed onward into harbour, nor took we any thought of supper, though we stood sore in need thereof, but even as we were we stept ashore and all lay down. Then over me there came sweet slumber in my weariness, but they took forth my goods from the hollow ship, and set them by me where I myself lay upon the sands. Then they went on board, and departed for the fair-lying land of Sidon; while as for me I was left stricken at heart.'

So spake he and the goddess, grey-eyed Athene, smiled, and caressed him with her hand; and straightway she changed to the semblance of a woman, fair and tall, and skilled in splendid handiwork. And uttering her voice she spake unto him winged words:

'Crafty must he be, and knavish, who would outdo thee in all manner of guile, even if it were a god encountered thee. Hardy man, subtle of wit, of guile insatiate, so thou wast not even in thine own country to cease from thy sleights and knavish words, which thou lovest from the bottom of thine heart! But come, no more let us tell of these things, being both of us practised in deceits, for that thou art of all men far the first in counsel and in discourse, and I in the company of all the gods win renown for my wit and wile. Yet thou knewest not me, Pallas Athene, daughter of Zeus, who am always by thee and guard thee in all adventures. Yea, and I made thee to be beloved of all the Phaeacians. And now am I come hither to contrive a plot with thee and to hide away the goods, that by my counsel and design the noble Phaeacians gave thee on thy homeward way. And I would tell thee how great a measure of trouble thou art ordained to fulfil within thy well-builded house. But do thou harden thy heart, for so it must be, and tell none neither man nor woman of all the folk, that thou hast indeed returned from wandering, but in silence endure much sorrow, submitting thee to the despite of men.'

And Odysseus of many counsels answered her saying: 'Hard is it, goddess, for a mortal man that meets thee to discern thee, howsoever wise he be; for thou takest upon thee every shape. But this I know well, that of old thou wast kindly to me, so long as we sons of the Achaeans made war in Troy. But so soon as we had sacked the steep city of Priam and had gone on board our ships, and the god had scattered the Achaeans, thereafter I have never beheld thee, daughter of Zeus, nor seen thee coming on board my ship, to ward off sorrow from me—but I wandered evermore with a stricken heart, till the gods delivered me from my evil case—even till the day when, within the fat land of the men of Phaeacia, thou didst comfort me with thy words, and thyself didst lead me to their city. And now I beseech thee in thy father's name to tell me: for I deem not that I am come to clear-seen Ithaca, but I roam over some other land, and methinks that thou speakest thus to mock me and beguile my mind. Tell me whether in very deed I am come to mine own dear country.'

Then the goddess, grey-eyed Athene, answered him: 'Yea, such a thought as this is ever in thy breast. Wherefore I may in no wise leave thee in thy grief, so courteous art thou, so ready of wit and so prudent. Right gladly would any other man on his return from wandering have hasted to behold his children and his wife in his halls; but thou hast no will to learn or to hear aught, till thou hast furthermore made trial of thy wife, who sits as ever in her halls, and wearily for her the nights wane always and the days, in shedding of tears. But of this I never doubted, but ever knew it in my heart that thou wouldest come home with the loss of all thy company. Yet, I tell thee, I had no mind to be at strife with Poseidon, my own father's brother, who laid up wrath in his heart against thee, being angered at the blinding of his dear son. But come, and I will show thee the place of the dwelling of Ithaca, that thou mayst be assured. Lo, here is the haven of Phorcys, the ancient one of the sea, and here at the haven's head is the olive tree with spreading leaves, and hard by it is the pleasant cave and shadowy, sacred to the nymphs that are called the Naiads. Yonder, behold, is the roofed cavern, where thou offeredst many an acceptable sacrifice of hecatombs to the nymphs; and lo, this hill is Neriton, all clothed in forest.'

Therewith the goddess scattered the mist, and the land appeared. Then the steadfast goodly Odysseus was glad rejoicing in his own land, and he kissed the earth, the grain-giver. And anon he prayed to the nymphs, and lifted up his hands, saying:

'Ye Naiad nymphs, daughters of Zeus, never did I think to look on you again, but now be ye greeted in my loving prayers: yea and gifts as aforetime I will give, if the daughter of Zeus, driver of the spoil, suffer me of her grace myself to live, and bring my dear son to manhood.'

Then the goddess, grey-eyed Athene, spake to him again: 'Be of good courage, and let not thy heart be careful about these things. But come, let us straightway set thy goods in the secret place of the wondrous cave, that there they may abide for thee safe. And let us for ourselves advise us how all may be for the very best.'

Therewith the goddess plunged into the shadowy cave, searching out the chambers of the cavern. Meanwhile Odysseus brought up his treasure, the gold and the unyielding bronze and fair woven raiment, which the Phaeacians gave him. And these things he laid by with care, and Pallas Athene, daughter of Zeus, lord of the aegis, set a stone against the door of the cave. Then they twain sat down by the trunk of the sacred olive tree, and devised death for the froward wooers. And the goddess, grey-eyed Athene, spake first, saying:

'Son of Laertes, of the seed of Zeus, Odysseus of many devices, advise thee how thou mayest stretch forth thine hands upon the shameless wooers, who now these three years lord it through thy halls, as they woo thy godlike wife and proffer the gifts of wooing. And she, that is ever bewailing her for thy return, gives hope to all and makes promises to every man and sends them messages, but her mind is set on other things.'

And Odysseus of many counsels answered her, saying:

'Lo now, in very truth I was like to have perished in my halls by the evil doom of Agamemnon, son of Atreus, hadst not thou, goddess, declared me each thing aright.

Come then, weave some counsel whereby I may requite them; and thyself stand by me, and put great boldness of spirit within me, even as in the day when we loosed the shining coronal of Troy. If but thou wouldest stand by me with such eagerness, thou grey-eyed goddess, I would war even with three hundred men, with thee my lady and goddess, if thou of thy grace didst succour me the while.'

Then the goddess, grey-eyed Athene, answered him: 'Yea, verily I will be near thee nor will I forget thee, whensoever we come to this toil: and methinks that certain of the wooers that devour thy livelihood shall bespatter the boundless earth with blood and brains. But come, I will make thee such-like that no man shall know thee. Thy fair skin I will wither on thy supple limbs, and make waste thy yellow hair from off thy head, and wrap thee in a foul garment, such that one would shudder to see a man therein. And I will dim thy two eyes, erewhile so fair, in such wise that thou mayest be unseemly in the sight of all the wooers and of thy wife and son, whom thou didst leave in thy halls. And do thou thyself first of all go unto the swineherd, who tends thy swine, loyal and at one with thee, and loves thy son and constant Penelope. Him shalt thou find sitting by the swine, as they are feeding near the rock of Corax and the spring Arethusa, and there they eat abundance of acorns and drink the black water, things whereby swine grow fat and well-liking. There do thou abide and sit by the swine, and find out all, till I have gone to Sparta, the land of fair women, to call Telemachus thy dear son, Odysseus, who hath betaken himself to spacious Lacedaemon, to the house of Menelaus to seek tidings of thee, whether haply thou art yet alive.'

And Odysseus of many counsels answered her saying: 'Nay, wherefore then didst thou not tell him, seeing thou hast knowledge of all? Was it, perchance, that he too may wander in sorrow over the unharvested seas, and that others may consume his livelihood?'

Then the goddess, grey-eyed Athene, answered him: 'Nay, let him not be heavy on thy heart. I myself was his guide, that by going thither he might win a good report. Lo, he knows no toil, but he sits in peace in the palace of the son of Atreus, and has boundless store about him. Truly the young men with their black ship they lie in wait, and are eager to slay him ere he come to his own country. But this, methinks, shall never be. Yea, sooner shall the earth close over certain of the wooers that devour thy livelihood.'

Therewith Athene touched him with her wand. His fair flesh she withered on his supple limbs, and made waste his yellow hair from off his head, and over all his limbs she cast the skin of an old man, and dimmed his two eyes, erewhile so fair. And she changed his raiment to a vile wrap and a doublet, torn garments and filthy, stained with foul smoke. And over all she clad him with the great bald hide of a swift stag, and she gave him a staff and a mean tattered scrip, and a cord therewith to hang it.

And after they twain had taken this counsel together, they parted; and she now went to goodly Lacedaemon to fetch the son of Odysseus.

BOOK XIV

Odysseus, in the form of a beggar, goes to Eumaeus, the master of his swine, where he is well used and tells a feigned story, and informs himself of the behaviour of the wooers.

BUT Odysseus fared forth from the haven by the rough track, up the wooded country and through the heights, where Athene had showed him that he should find the goodly swineherd, who cared most for his substance of all the thralls that goodly Odysseus had gotten.

Now he found him sitting at the vestibule of the house, where his courtyard was builded high, in a place with wide prospect; a great court it was and a fair, with free range round it. This the swineherd had builded by himself for the swine of his lord who was afar, and his mistress and the old man Laertes knew not of it. With stones from the quarry had he builded it, and coped it with a fence of white thorn, and he had split an oak to the dark core, and without he had driven stakes the whole length thereof on either side, set thick and close; and within the courtyard he made twelve styes hard by one another to be beds for the swine, and in each stye fifty grovelling swine were penned, brood swine; but the boars slept without. Now these were far fewer in number, the godlike wooers minishing them at their feasts, for the swineherd ever sent in the best of all the fatted hogs. And their tale was three hundred and three-score. And by them always slept four dogs, as fierce as wild beasts, which the swineherd had bred, a master of men. Now he was fitting sandals to his feet, cutting a good brown oxhide, while the rest of his fellows, three in all, were abroad this way and that, with the droves of swine; while the fourth he had sent to the city to take a boar to the proud wooers, as needs he must, that they might sacrifice it and satisfy their soul with flesh.

And of a sudden the baying dogs saw Odysseus, and they ran at him yelping, but Odysseus in his wariness sat him down, and let the staff fall from his hand. There by his own homestead would he have suffered foul hurt, but the swineherd with quick feet hasted after them, and sped through the outer door, and let the skin fall from his hand. And the hounds he chid and drave them this way and that, with a shower of stones, and he spake unto his lord, saying:

'Old man, truly the dogs went nigh to be the death of thee all of a sudden, so shouldest thou have brought shame on me. Yea, and the gods have given me other pains and griefs enough. Here I sit, mourning and sorrowing for my godlike lord, and foster the fat swine for others to eat, while he craving, perchance, for food, wanders over some land and city of men of a strange speech, if haply he yet lives and beholds the sunlight. But come with me, let us to the inner steading, old man, that when thy heart is satisfied with bread and wine, thou too mayest tell thy tale and declare whence thou art, and how many woes thou hast endured.'

Therewith the goodly swineherd led him to the steading, and took him in and set him down, and strewed beneath him thick brushwood, and spread thereon the hide of a shaggy wild goat, wide and soft, which served himself for a mattress. And Odysseus rejoiced that he had given him such welcome, and spake and hailed him:

'May Zeus, O stranger, and all the other deathless gods grant thee thy dearest wish, since thou hast received me heartily!'

Then, O swineherd Eumaeus, didst thou answer him, saying: 'Guest of mine, it were an impious thing for me to slight a stranger, even if there came a meaner man than thou; for from Zeus are all strangers and beggars; and a little gift from such as we, is dear; for this is the way with thralls, who are ever in fear when young lords like ours bear rule over them. For surely the gods have stayed the returning of my master, who would have loved me diligently, and given me somewhat of my own, a house and a parcel of ground, and a comely wife, such as a kind lord gives to his man, who hath laboured much for him and the work of whose hands God hath likewise increased, even as he increaseth this work of mine whereat I abide. Therefore would my lord have rewarded me greatly, had he grown old at home. But he hath perished, as I would that all the stock of Helen had perished utterly, forasmuch as she hath caused the loosening of many a man's knees. For he too departed to Ilios of the goodly steeds, to get atonement for Agamemnon, that so he might war with the Trojans.'

Therewith he quickly bound up his doublet with his girdle, and went his way to the styes, where the tribes of the swine were penned. Thence he took and brought forth two, and sacrificed them both, and singed them and cut them small, and spitted them. And when he had roasted all, he bare and set it by Odysseus, all hot as it was upon the spits, and he sprinkled thereupon white barley-meal. Then in a bowl of ivywood he mixed the honey-sweet wine, and himself sat over against him and bade him fall to:

'Eat now, stranger, such fare as thralls have to hand, even flesh of sucking pigs; but the fatted hogs the wooers devour, for they know not the wrath of the gods nor any pity. Verily the blessed gods love not froward deeds, but they reverence justice and the righteous acts of men. Yet even foes and men unfriendly, that land on a strange coast, and Zeus grants them a prey, and they have laden their ships and depart for home; yea, even on their hearts falls strong fear of the wrath of the gods. But lo you, these men know somewhat,—for they have heard an utterance of a god,—even the tidings of our lord's evil end, seeing that they are not minded justly to woo, nor to go back to their own, but at ease they devour our wealth with insolence, and now there is no sparing. For every day and every night that comes from Zeus, they make sacrifice not of one victim only, nor of two, and wine they draw and waste it riotously. For surely his livelihood was great past telling, no lord in the dark mainland had so much, nor any in Ithaca itself; nay, not twenty men together have wealth so great, and I will tell thee the sum thereof. Twelve herds of kine upon the mainland, as many flocks of sheep, as many droves of swine, as many ranging herds of goats, that his own shepherds and strangers pasture. And ranging herds of goats, eleven in all, graze here by the extremity of the island with trusty men to watch them. And day by day each man of these ever drives one of the flock to the wooers, whichsoever seems the best of the fatted goats. But as for me I guard and keep these swine and I choose out for them, as well as I may, the best of the swine and send it hence.'

So spake he, but Odysseus ceased not to eat flesh and drink wine right eagerly and in silence, and the while was sowing the seeds of evil for the wooers. Now when he had well eaten and comforted his heart with food, then the herdsman filled him the bowl out of which he was wont himself to drink, and he gave it him brimming with wine, and he took it and was glad at heart, and uttering his voice spake to him winged words:

'My friend, who was it then that bought thee with his wealth, a man so exceeding rich and mighty as thou declarest? Thou saidest that he perished to get atonement for Agamemnon; tell me, if perchance I may know him, being such an one as thou sayest. For Zeus, methinks, and the other deathless gods know whether I may bring tidings of having seen him; for I have wandered far.'

Then the swineherd, a master of men, answered him: 'Old man, no wanderer who may come hither and bring tidings of him can win the ear of his wife and his dear son; but lightly do vagrants lie when they need entertainment, and care not to tell truth. Whosoever comes straying to the land of Ithaca, goes to my mistress and speaks words of guile. And she receives him kindly and lovingly and inquires of all things, and the tears fall from her eyelids for weeping, as is meet for a woman when her lord hath died afar. And quickly enough wouldst thou too, old man, forge a tale, if any would but give thee a mantle and a doublet for raiment. But as for him, dogs and swift fowls are like already to have torn his skin from the bones, and his spirit hath left him. Or the fishes have eaten him in the deep, and there lie his bones swathed in sand-drift on the shore. Yonder then hath he perished, but for his friends nought is ordained but care, for all, but for me in chief. For never again shall I find a lord so gentle, how far soever I may go, not though again I attain unto the house of my father and my mother, where at first I was born and they nourished me themselves and with their own hands they reared me. Nor henceforth it is not for these that I sorrow so much, though I long to behold them with mine eyes in mine own country, but desire comes over me for Odysseus who is afar. His name, stranger, even though he is not here, it shameth me to speak, for he loved me exceedingly, and cared for me at heart; nay, I call him "worshipful," albeit he is far hence.'

Then the steadfast goodly Odysseus spake to him again: 'My friend, forasmuch as thou gainsayest utterly, and sayest that henceforth he will not come again, and thine heart is ever slow to believe, therefore will I tell thee not lightly but with an oath, that Odysseus shall return. And let me have the wages of good tidings as soon as ever he in his journeying shall come hither to his home. Then clothe me in a mantle and a doublet, goodly raiment. But ere that, albeit I am sore in need I will not take aught, for hateful to me even as the gates of hell, is that man, who under stress of poverty speaks words of guile. Now be Zeus my witness before any god, and the hospitable board and the hearth of noble Odysseus whereunto I am come, that all these things shall surely be accomplished even as I tell thee. In this same year Odysseus shall come hither; as the old moon wanes and the new is born shall he return to his home, and shall take vengeance on all who here dishonour his wife and noble son.'

Then didst thou make answer, swineherd Eumaeus: 'Old man, it is not I then, that shall ever pay thee these wages of good tidings, nor henceforth shall Odysseus ever come to his home. Nay drink in peace, and let us turn our thoughts to other matters, and bring not these to my remembrance, for surely my heart within me is sorrowful whenever any man puts me in mind of my true lord. But as for thine oath, we will let it go by; yet, oh that Odysseus may come according to my desire, and the desire of Penelope and of that old man Laertes and godlike Telemachus! But now I make a comfortless lament for the boy begotten of Odysseus, even for Telemachus. When the gods had reared him like a young sapling, and I thought that he would be no worse man among men than his dear father, glorious in form and face, some god or some man marred his good wits within him, and he went to fair Pylos after tidings of his sire. And now the lordly wooers lie in wait for him on his way home, that the race of godlike Arceisius may perish nameless out of Ithaca. Howbeit, no more of him now, whether he shall be taken or whether he shall escape, and Cronion stretch out his hand to shield him. But come, old man, do thou tell me of thine own troubles. And herein tell me true, that I may surely know. Who art thou of the sons of men, and whence? Where is thy city, where are they that begat thee? Say on what manner of ship didst thou come, and how did sailors bring thee to Ithaca, and who did they avow them to be? For in no wise do I deem that thou camest hither by land.'

And Odysseus of many counsels answered him saying: 'Yea now, I will tell thee all most plainly. Might we have food and sweet wine enough to last for long, while we abide within thy hut to feast thereon in quiet, and others betake them to their work; then could I easily speak for a whole year, nor yet make a full end of telling all the troubles of my spirit, all the travail I have wrought by the will of the gods.

'I avow that I come by lineage from wide Crete, and am the son of a wealthy man. And many other sons he had born and bred in the halls, lawful-born of a wedded wife; but the mother that bare me was a concubine bought with a price. Yet Castor son of Hylax, of whose blood I avow me to be, gave me no less honour than his lawful sons. Now he at that time got worship even as a god from the Cretans in the land, for wealth and riches and sons renowned. Howbeit the fates of death bare him away to the house of Hades, and his gallant sons divided among them his living and cast lots for it. But to me they gave a very small gift and assigned me a dwelling, and I took unto me a wife, the daughter of men that had wide lands, by reason of my valour, for that I was no weakling nor a dastard; but now all my might has failed me, yet even so I deem that thou mightest guess from seeing the stubble what the grain has been, for of trouble I have plenty and to spare. But then verily did Ares and Athene give me boldness and courage to hurl through the press of men, whensoever I chose the best warriors for an ambush, sowing the seeds of evil for my foes; no boding of death was ever in my lordly heart, but I would leap out the foremost and slay with the spear whoso of my foes was less fleet of foot than I. Such an one was I in war, but the labour of the field I never loved, nor homekeeping thrift, that breeds brave children, but galleys with their oars were dear to me, and wars and polished shafts and darts—baneful things whereat others use to shudder. But that, methinks, was dear to me which the god put in my heart, for divers men take delight in divers deeds. For ere ever the sons of the Achaeans had set foot on the land of Troy, I had nine times been a leader of men and of swift-faring ships against a strange people, and wealth fell ever to my hands. Of the booty I would choose out for me all that I craved, and much thereafter I won by lot. So my house got increase speedily, and thus I waxed dread and honourable among the Cretans. But when Zeus, of the far-borne voice, devised at the last that hateful path which loosened the knees of many a man in death, then the people called on me and on renowned Idomeneus to lead the ship to Ilios, nor was there any way whereby to refuse, for the people's voice bore hard upon us. There we sons of the Achaeans warred for nine whole years, and then in the tenth year we sacked the city of Priam, and departed homeward with our ships, and a god scattered the Achaeans. But Zeus, the counsellor, devised mischief against me, wretched man that I was! For one month only I abode and had joy in my children and my wedded wife, and all that I had; and thereafter my spirit bade me fit out ships in the best manner and sail to Egypt with my godlike company. Nine ships I fitted out and the host was gathered quickly; and then for six days my dear company feasted, and I gave them many victims that they might sacrifice to the gods and prepare a feast for themselves. But on the seventh day we set sail from wide Crete, with a North Wind fresh and fair, and lightly we ran as it were down stream, yea and no harm came to any ship of mine, but we sat safe and hale, while the wind and the pilots guided the barques. And on the fifth day we came to the fair-flowing Aegyptus, and in the river Aegyptus I stayed my curved ships. Then verily I bade my dear companions to abide there by the ships and to guard them, and I sent forth scouts to range the points of outlook. But my men gave place to wantonness, being the fools of their own force, and soon they fell to wasting the fields of the Egyptians, exceeding fair, and led away their wives and infant children and slew the men. And the cry came quickly to the city, and the people hearing the shout came forth at the breaking of the day, and all the plain was filled with footmen and chariots and with the glitter of bronze. And Zeus, whose joy is in the thunder, sent an evil panic upon my company, and none durst stand and face the foe, for danger encompassed us on every side. There they slew many of us with the edge of the sword, and others they led up with them alive to work for them perforce. But as for me, Zeus himself put a thought into my heart; would to God that I had rather died, and met my fate there in Egypt, for sorrow was still mine host! Straightway I put off my well-wrought helmet from my head, and the shield from off my shoulders, and I cast away my spear from my hand, and I came over against the chariots of the king, and clasped and kissed his knees, and he saved me and delivered me, and setting me on his own chariot took me weeping to his home. Truly many an one made at me with their ashen spears, eager to slay me, for verily they were sore angered. But the king kept them off and had respect unto the wrath of Zeus, the god of strangers, who chiefly hath displeasure at evil deeds. So for seven whole years I abode with their king, and gathered much substance among the Egyptians, for they all gave me gifts. But when the eighth year came in due season, there arrived a Phoenician practised in deceit, a greedy knave, who had already done much mischief among men. He wrought on me with his cunning, and took me with him until he came to Phoenicia, where was his house and where his treasures lay. There I abode with him for the space of a full year. But when now the months and days were fulfilled, as the year came round and the seasons returned, he set me aboard a seafaring ship for Libya under colour as though I was to convey a cargo thither with him, but his purpose was to sell me in Libya, and get a great price. So I went with him on board, perforce, yet boding evil. And the ship ran before a North Wind fresh and fair, through the mid sea over above Crete, and Zeus contrived the destruction of the crew. But when we left Crete, and no land showed in sight but sky and sea only, even then the son of Cronos stayed a dark cloud over the hollow ship, and the deep grew dark beneath it. And in the same moment Zeus thundered and smote his bolt into the ship, and she reeled all over being stricken by the bolt of Zeus, and was filled with fire and brimstone, and all the crew fell overboard. And like sea-gulls they were borne hither and thither on the waves about the black ship, and the god cut off their return. But in this hour of my affliction Zeus himself put into my hands the huge mast of the dark-prowed ship, that even yet I might escape from harm. So I clung round the mast and was borne by the ruinous winds. For nine days was I borne, and on the tenth black night the great rolling wave brought me nigh to the land of the Thesprotians. There the king of the Thesprotians, the lord Pheidon, took me in freely, for his dear son lighted on me and raised me by the hand and led me to his house, foredone with toil and the keen air, till he came to his father's palace. And he clothed me in a mantle and a doublet for raiment.

'There I heard tidings of Odysseus, for the king told me that he had entertained him, and kindly entreated him on his way to his own country; and he showed me all the wealth that Odysseus had gathered, bronze and gold and well-wrought iron; yea it would suffice for his children after him even to the tenth generation, so great were the treasures he had stored in the chambers of the king. He had gone, he said, to Dodona to hear the counsel of Zeus, from the high leafy oak tree of the god, how he should return to the fat land of Ithaca after long absence, whether openly or by stealth. Moreover, he sware, in mine own presence, as he poured the drink offering in his house, that the ship was drawn down to the sea and his company were ready, who were to convey him to his own dear country. But ere that, he sent me off, for it chanced that a ship of the Thesprotians was starting for Dulichium, a land rich in grain. Thither he bade them bring me with all diligence to the king Acastus. But an evil counsel concerning me found favour in their sight, that even yet I might reach the extremity of sorrow. When the seafaring ship had sailed a great way from the land, anon they sought how they might compass for me the day of slavery. They stript me of my garments, my mantle and a doublet, and changed my raiment to a vile wrap and doublet, tattered garments, even those thou seest now before thee; and in the evening they reached the fields of clear-seen Ithaca. There in the decked ship they bound me closely with a twisted rope, and themselves went ashore, and hasted to take supper by the sea-banks. Meanwhile the gods themselves lightly unclasped my bands, and muffling my head with the wrap I slid down the smooth lading-plank, and set my breast to the sea and rowed hard with both hands as I swam, and very soon I was out of the water and beyond their reach. Then I went up where there was a thicket, a wood in full leaf, and lay there crouching. And they went hither and thither making great moan; but when now it seemed to them little avail to go further on their quest, they departed back again aboard their hollow ship. And the gods themselves hid me easily and brought me nigh to the homestead of a wise man; for still, methinks, I am ordained to live on.'

Then didst thou make answer to him, swineherd Eumaeus: 'Ah! wretched guest, verily thou hast stirred my heart with the tale of all these things, of thy sufferings and thy wanderings. Yet herein, methinks, thou speakest not aright, and never shalt thou persuade me with the tale about Odysseus; why should one in thy plight lie vainly? Well I know of mine own self, as touching my lord's return, that he was utterly hated by all the gods, in that they smote him not among the Trojans nor in the arms of his friends, when he had wound up the clew of war. So should the whole Achaean host have builded him a barrow; yea and for his son would he have won great glory in the after days; but now all ingloriously the spirits of the storm have snatched him away. But as for me I dwell apart by the swine and go not to the city, unless perchance wise Penelope summons me thither, when tidings of my master are brought I know not whence. Now all the people sit round and straitly question the news-bearer, both such as grieve for their lord that is long gone, and such as rejoice in devouring his living without atonement. But I have no care to ask or to inquire, since the day that an Aetolian cheated me with his story, one who had slain his man and wandered over wide lands and came to my steading, and I dealt lovingly with him. He said that he had seen my master among the Cretans at the house of Idomeneus, mending his ships which the storms had broken. And he said that he would come home either by the summer or the harvest-tide, bringing much wealth with the godlike men of his company. And thou too, old man of many sorrows, seeing that some god hath brought thee to me, seek not my grace with lies, nor give me any such comfort; not for this will I have respect to thee or hold thee dear, but only for the fear of Zeus, the god of strangers, and for pity of thyself.'

And Odysseus of many counsels answered him saying: 'Verily thy heart within thee is slow to believe, seeing that even with an oath I have not won thee, nor find credence with thee. But come now, let us make a covenant; and we will each one have for witnesses the gods above, who hold Olympus. If thy lord shall return to this house, put on me a mantle and doublet for raiment, and send me on my way to Dulichium, whither I had a desire to go. But if thy lord return not according to my word, set thy thralls upon me, and cast me down from a mighty rock, that another beggar in his turn may beware of deceiving.'

And the goodly swineherd answered him, saying: 'Yea stranger, even so should I get much honour and good luck among men both now and ever hereafter, if after bringing thee to my hut and giving thee a stranger's cheer, I should turn again and slay thee and take away thy dear life. Eager indeed thereafter should I be to make a prayer to Zeus the son of Cronos! But now it is supper-time, and would that my fellows may speedily be at home, that we may make ready a dainty supper within the hut.'

Thus they spake one to the other. And lo, the swine and the swineherds drew nigh. And the swine they shut up to sleep in their lairs, and a mighty din arose as the swine were being stalled. Then the goodly swineherd called to his fellows, saying:

'Bring the best of the swine, that I may sacrifice it for a guest of mine from a far land: and we too will have good cheer therewith, for we have long suffered and toiled by reason of the white-tusked swine, while others devour the fruit of our labour without atonement.'

Therewithal he cleft logs with the pitiless axe, and the others brought in a well-fatted boar of five years old; and they set him by the hearth, nor did the swineherd forget the deathless gods, for he was of an understanding heart. But for a beginning of sacrifice he cast bristles from the head of the white-tusked boar upon the fire, and prayed to all the gods that wise Odysseus might return to his own house. Then he stood erect, and smote the boar with a billet of oak which he had left in the cleaving, and the boar yielded up his life. Then they cut the throat and singed the carcase and quickly cut it up, and the swineherd took a first portion from all the limbs, and laid the raw flesh on the rich fat. And some pieces he cast into the fire after sprinkling them with bruised barley-meal, and they cut the rest up small, and pierced it, and spitted and roasted it carefully, and drew it all off from the spits, and put the whole mess together on trenchers. Then the swineherd stood up to carve, for well he knew what was fair, and he cut up the whole and divided it into seven portions. One, when he had prayed, he set aside for the nymphs and for Hermes son of Maia, and the rest he distributed to each. And he gave Odysseus the portion of honour, the long back of the white-tusked boar, and the soul of his lord rejoiced at this renown, and Odysseus of many counsels hailed him saying:

'Eumaeus, oh that thou mayest so surely be dear to father Zeus, as thou art to me, seeing that thou honourest me with a good portion, such an one as I am!'

Then didst thou make answer, swineherd Eumaeus:

'Eat, luckless stranger, and make merry with such fare as is here. And one thing the god will give and another withhold, even as he will, for with him all things are possible.'

So he spake, and made burnt offering of the hallowed parts to the everlasting gods, and poured the dark wine for a drink offering, and set the cup in the hands of Odysseus, the waster of cities, and sat down by his own mess. And Mesaulius bare them wheaten bread, a thrall that the swineherd had gotten all alone, while his lord was away, without the knowledge of his mistress and the old Laertes: yea he had bought him of the Taphians with his own substance. So they stretched forth their hands upon the good cheer spread before them. Now after they had put from them the desire of meat and drink, Mesaulius cleared away the bread, and they, now that they had eaten enough of bread and flesh, were moved to go to rest.

Now it was so that night came on foul with a blind moon, and Zeus rained the whole night through, and still the great West Wind, the rainy wind, was blowing. Then Odysseus spake among them that he might make trial of the swineherd, and see whether he would take off his own mantle and give it to him or bid one of his company strip, since he cared for him so greatly:

'Listen now, Eumaeus, and all of you his companions, with a prayer will I utter my word; so bids me witless wine, which drives even the wisest to sing and to laugh softly, and rouses him to dance, yea and makes him to speak out a word which were better unspoken. Howbeit, now that I have broken into speech, I will not hide aught. Oh that I were young, and my might were steadfast, as in the day when we arrayed our ambush and led it beneath Troy town! And Odysseus, and Menelaus son of Atreus, were leaders and with them I was a third in command; for so they bade me. Now when we had come to the city and the steep wall, we lay about the citadel in the thick brushwood, crouching under our arms among the reeds and the marsh land, and behold, the night came on foul, with frost, as the North Wind went down, while the snow fell from above, and crusted like rime, bitter cold, and the ice set thick about our shields. Now the others all had mantles and doublets, and slept in peace with their shields buckled close about their shoulders; but I as I went forth had left my mantle behind with my men, in my folly, thinking that even so I should not be cold: so I came with only my shield and bright leathern apron. But when it was now the third watch of the night and the stars had passed the zenith, in that hour I spake unto Odysseus who was nigh me, and thrust him with my elbow, and he listened straightway:

' "Son of Laertes, of the seed of Zeus, Odysseus of many devices, verily I shall cease from among living men, for this wintry cold is slaying me, seeing that I have no mantle. Some god beguiled me to wear a doublet only, and henceforth is no way of escape."

'So I spake, and he apprehended a thought in his heart, such an one as he was in counsel and in fight. So he whispered and spake to me, saying:

' "Be silent now, lest some other Achaeans hear thee." Therewith he raised his head upon his elbow, and spake, saying: "Listen, friends, a vision from a god came to me in my sleep. Lo, we have come very far from the ships; I would there were one to tell it to Agamemnon, son of Atreus, shepherd of the host, if perchance he may send us hither a greater company from the ships."

'So spake he, and Thoas, son of Andraemon, rose up quickly and cast off his purple mantle. And he started to run unto the ships, but I lay gladly in his garment, and the golden-throned Dawn showed her light. Oh! that I were young as then and my might steadfast! Then should some of the swineherds in the homestead give me a mantle, alike for love's sake and for pity of a good warrior. But now they scorn me for that sorry raiment is about my body.'

Then didst thou make answer, O swineherd Eumaeus: 'Old man, the tale that thou hast told in his praise is very good, and so far thou hast not misspoken aught, nor uttered a word unprofitably. Wherefore for this night thou shalt lack neither raiment nor aught else that is the due of hapless suppliant, when he has met them that can befriend him. But in the morning thou shalt go shuffling in thine own rags, for there are not many mantles here or changes of doublet; for each man hath but one coat. But when the dear son of Odysseus comes, he himself will give thee a mantle and doublet for raiment, and send thee whithersoever thy heart and spirit bid.'

With that he sprang up and set a bed for Odysseus near the fire, and thereon he cast skins of sheep and goats. There Odysseus laid him down and Eumaeus cast a great thick mantle over him, which he had ever by him for a change of covering, when any terrible storm should arise.

So there Odysseus slept, and the young men slept beside him. But the swineherd had no mind to lie there in a bed away from the boars. So he made him ready to go forth and Odysseus was glad, because he had a great care for his master's substance while he was afar. First he cast his sharp sword about his strong shoulders, then he clad him in a very thick mantle, to keep the wind away; and he caught up the fleece of a great and well-fed goat, and seized his sharp javelin, to defend him against dogs and men. Then he went to lay him down even where the white-tusked boars were sleeping, beneath the hollow of the rock, in a place of shelter from the North Wind.

BOOK XV

Pallas sends home Telemachus from Lacedaemon with the presents given him by Menelaus. Telemachus landed, goes first to Eumaeus.

Now Pallas Athene went to the wide land of Lacedaemon, to put the noble son of the great-hearted Odysseus in mind of his return, and to make him hasten his coming. And she found Telemachus, and the glorious son of Nestor, couched at the vestibule of the house of famous Menelaus. The son of Nestor truly was overcome with soft sleep, but sweet sleep gat not hold of Telemachus, but, through the night divine, careful thoughts for his father kept him wakeful. And grey-eyed Athene stood nigh him and spake to him, saying:

'Telemachus, it is no longer meet that thou shouldest wander far from thy home, leaving thy substance behind thee, and men in thy house so wanton, lest they divide and utterly devour all thy wealth, and thou shalt have gone on a vain journey. But come, rouse with all haste Menelaus, of the loud war-cry, to send thee on thy way, that thou mayest even yet find thy noble mother in her home. For even now her father and her brethren bid her wed Eurymachus, for he outdoes all the wooers in his presents, and hath been greatly increasing his gifts of wooing. So shall she take no treasure from thy house despite thy will. Thou knowest of what sort is the heart of a woman within her; all her desire is to increase the house of the man who takes her to wife, but of her former children and of her own dear lord she has no more memory once he is dead, and she asks concerning him no more. Go then, and thyself place all thy substance in the care of the handmaid who seems to thee the best, till the day when the gods shall show thee a glorious bride. Now another word will I tell thee, and do thou lay it up in thine heart. The noblest of the wooers lie in wait for thee of purpose, in the strait between Ithaca and rugged Samos, eager to slay thee before thou come to thine own country. But this, methinks, will never be; yea, sooner shall the earth close over certain of the wooers that devour thy livelihood. Nay, keep thy well-wrought ship far from those isles, and sail by night as well as day, and he of the immortals who hath thee in his keeping and protection will send thee a fair breeze in thy wake. But when thou hast touched the nearest shore of Ithaca, send thy ship and all thy company forward to the city, but for thy part seek first the swineherd who keeps thy swine, loyal and at one with thee. There do thou rest the night, and bid him go to the city to bear tidings of thy coming to the wise Penelope, how that she hath got thee safe, and thou art come up out of Pylos.'

Therewith she departed to high Olympus. But Telemachus woke the son of Nestor out of sweet sleep, touching him with his heel, and spake to him, saying:

'Awake, Peisistratus, son of Nestor, bring up thy horses of solid hoof, and yoke them beneath the car, that we may get forward on the road.'

Then Peisistratus, son of Nestor, answered him, saying: 'Telemachus, we may in no wise drive through the dark night, how eager soever to be gone; nay, soon it will be dawn. Tarry then, till the hero, the son of Atreus, spear-famed Menelaus, brings gifts, and sets them on the car, and bespeaks thee kindly, and sends thee on thy way. For of him a guest is mindful all the days of his life, even of the host that shows him loving-kindness.'

So spake he, and anon came the golden-throned Dawn.

And Menelaus, of the loud war-cry, drew nigh to them, new risen from his bed, by fair-haired Helen. Now when the dear son of Odysseus marked him, he made haste and girt his shining doublet about him, and the hero cast a great mantle over his mighty shoulders, and went forth at the door, and Telemachus, dear son of divine Odysseus, came up and spake to Menelaus, saying:

'Menelaus, son of Atreus, fosterling of Zeus, leader of the people, even now do thou speed me hence, to mine own dear country; for even now my heart is fain to come home again.'

Then Menelaus, of the loud war-cry, answered him: 'Telemachus, as for me, I will not hold thee a long time here, that art eager to return; nay, I think it shame even in another host, who loves overmuch or hates overmuch. Measure is best in all things. He does equal wrong who speeds a guest that would fain abide, and stays one who is in haste to be gone. Men should lovingly entreat the present guest and speed the parting. But abide till I bring fair gifts and set them on the car and thine own eyes behold them, and I bid the women to prepare the midday meal in the halls, out of the good store they have within. Honour and glory it is for us, and gain withal for thee, that ye should have eaten well ere ye go on your way, over vast and limitless lands. What and if thou art minded to pass through Hellas and mid Argos? So shall I too go with thee, and yoke thee horses and lead thee to the towns of men, and none shall send us empty away, but will give us some one thing to take with us, either a tripod of goodly bronze or a cauldron, or two mules or a golden chalice.'

Then wise Telemachus answered him, saying: 'Menelaus, son of Atreus, fosterling of Zeus, leader of the people, rather would I return even now to mine own land, for I left none behind to watch over my goods when I departed. I would not that I myself should perish on the quest of my godlike father, nor that any good heir-loom should be lost from my halls.'

Now when Menelaus, of the loud war-cry, heard this saying, straightway he bade his wife and maids to prepare the midday meal in the halls, out of the good store they had by them. Then Eteoneus, son of Boethous, came nigh him, just risen from his bed, for he abode not far from him. Him Menelaus of the loud war-cry bade kindle the fire and roast of the flesh; and he hearkened and obeyed. Then the prince went down into the fragrant treasure chamber, not alone, for Helen went with him, and Megapenthes. Now, when they came to the place where the treasures were stored, then Atrides took a two-handled cup, and bade his son Megapenthes to bear a mixing bowl of silver. And Helen stood by the coffers, wherein were her robes of curious needlework which she herself had wrought. Then Helen, the fair lady, lifted one and brought it out, the widest and most beautifully embroidered of all, and it shone like a star, and lay far beneath the rest.

Then they went forth through the house till they came to Telemachus; and Menelaus, of the fair hair, spake to him saying:

'Telemachus, may Zeus the thunderer, and the lord of Here, in very truth, bring about thy return according to the desire of thy heart. And of the gifts, such as are treasures stored in my house, I will give thee the goodliest and greatest of price. I will give thee a mixing bowl beautifully wrought; it is all of silver and the lips thereof are finished with gold, the work of Hephaestus; and the hero Phaedimus the king of the Sidonians, gave it to me when his house sheltered me, on my coming thither. This cup I would give to thee.'

Therewith the hero Atrides set the two-handled cup in his hands. And the strong Megapenthes bare the shining silver bowl and set it before him. And Helen came up, beautiful Helen, with the robe in her hands, and spake and hailed him:

'Lo! I too give thee this gift, dear child, a memorial of the hands of Helen, against the day of thy desire, even of thy bridal, for thy bride to wear it. But meanwhile let it lie by thy dear mother in her chamber. And may joy go with thee to thy well-builded house, and thine own country.'

With that she put it into his hands, and he took it and was glad. And the hero Peisistratus took the gifts and laid them in the chest of the car, and gazed on all and wondered. Then Menelaus of the fair hair led them to the house. Then they twain sat them down on chairs and high seats, and a handmaid bare water for the hands in a goodly golden ewer, and poured it forth over a silver basin to wash withal, and drew to their side a polished table. And a grave dame bare wheaten bread and set it by them, and laid on the board many dainties, giving freely of such things as she had by her. And the son of Boethous carved by the board and divided the messes, and the son of renowned Menelaus poured forth the wine. So they stretched forth their hands upon the good cheer set before them. Now when they had put from them the desire of meat and drink, then did Telemachus and the glorious son of Nestor yoke the horses and climb into the inlaid car. And they drave forth from the gateway and the echoing gallery. After these Menelaus, of the fair hair, the son of Atreus, went forth bearing in his right hand a golden cup of honey-hearted wine, that they might pour a drink-offering ere they departed. And he stood before the horses and spake his greeting:

'Farewell, knightly youths, and salute in my name Nestor, the shepherd of the people; for truly he was gentle to me as a father, while we sons of the Achaeans warred in the land of Troy.'

And wise Telemachus answered him, saying: 'Yea verily,

O fosterling of Zeus, we will tell him all on our coming even as thou sayest. Would God that when I return to Ithaca I may find Odysseus in his home and tell him all, so surely as now I go on my way having met with all loving-kindness at thy hands, and take with me treasures many and goodly!'

And even as he spake a bird flew forth at his right hand, an eagle that bare in his claws a great white goose, a tame fowl from the yard, and men and women followed shouting. But the bird drew near them and flew off to the right, across the horses, and they that saw it were glad, and their hearts were all comforted within them. And Peisistratus, son of Nestor, first spake among them:

'Consider, Menelaus, fosterling of Zeus, leader of the people, whether god hath showed forth this sign for us twain, or for thee thyself.'

So spake he, and the warrior Menelaus pondered thereupon, how he should take heed to answer, and interpret it aright.

And long-robed Helen took the word and spake, saying: 'Hear me, and I will prophesy as the immortals put it into my heart, and as I deem it will be accomplished. Even as yonder eagle came down from the hill, the place of his birth and kin, and snatched away the goose that was fostered in the house, even so shall Odysseus return home after much trial and long wanderings and take vengeance; yea, or even now is he at home and sowing the seeds of evil for all the wooers.'

Then wise Telemachus answered her, saying: 'Now may Zeus ordain it so, Zeus the thunderer and the lord of Here. Then would I do thee worship, as to a god, even in my home afar.'

He spake and smote the horses with the lash, and they sped quickly towards the plain, in eager course through the city. So all day long they swayed the yoke they bore upon their necks. And the sun sank, and all the ways were darkened. And they came to Pherae, to the house of Diocles, son of Orsilochus, the child begotten of Alpheus. There they rested for the night, and by them he set the entertainment of strangers.

Now so soon as early Dawn shone forth, the rosy-fingered, they yoked the horses and mounted the inlaid car. And forth they drave from the gateway and the echoing gallery. And he touched the horses with the whip to start them, and the pair flew onward nothing loth. And soon thereafter they reached the steep hold of Pylos. Then Telemachus spake unto the son of Nestor, saying:

'Son of Nestor, in what wise mightest thou make me a promise and fulfil my bidding? For we claim to be friends by reason of our fathers' friendship from of old. Moreover we are equals in age, and this journey shall turn to our greater love. Take me not hence past my ship, O fosterling of Zeus, but leave me there, lest that old man keep me in his house in my despite, out of his eager kindness, for I must go right quickly home.'

So spake he, and the son of Nestor communed with his own heart how he might make promise, and duly fulfil the same. So as he thought thereon, in this wise it seemed to him best. He turned back his horses toward the swift ship and the sea-banks, and took forth the fair gifts and set them in the hinder part of the ship, the raiment and the gold which Menelaus gave him. And he called to Telemachus and spake to him winged words:

'Now climb the ship with all haste, and bid all thy company do likewise, ere I reach home and bring the old man word. For well I know in my mind and heart that, being so wilful of heart, he will not let thee go, but he himself will come hither to bid thee to his house, and methinks that he will not go back without thee; for very wroth will he be despite thine excuse.'

Thus he spake, and drave the horses with the flowing manes back to the town of the Pylians, and came quickly to the halls. And Telemachus called to his companions and commanded them saying:

'Set ye the gear in order, my friends, in the black ship, and let us climb aboard that we may make way upon our course.'

So spake he, and they gave good heed and hearkened. Then straightway they embarked and sat upon the benches.

Thus was he busy hereat and praying and making burnt-offering to Athene, by the stern of the ship, when there drew nigh him one from a far country, that had slain his man and was fleeing from out of Argos. He was a soothsayer, and by his lineage he came of Melampus, who of old time abode in Pylos, mother of flocks, a rich man and one that had an exceeding goodly house among the Pylians, but afterward he had come to the land of strangers, fleeing from his country and from Neleus, the great-hearted, the proudest of living men, who kept all his goods for a full year by force. All that time Melampus lay bound with hard bonds in the halls of Phylacus, suffering strong pains for the sake of the daughter of Neleus, and for the dread blindness of soul which the goddess, the Erinnys of the dolorous stroke, had laid on him. Howsoever he escaped his fate, and drave away the lowing kine from Phylace to Pylos, and avenged the foul deed upon godlike Neleus, and brought the maiden home to his own brother to wife. As for him, he went to a country of other men, to Argos, the pastureland of horses; for there truly it was ordained that he should dwell, bearing rule over many of the Argives. There he wedded a wife, and builded him a lofty house, and begat Antiphates and Mantius, two mighty sons. Now Antiphates begat Oïcles, the great-hearted, and Oïcles Amphiaraus, the rouser of the host, whom Zeus, lord of the aegis, and Apollo loved with all manner of love. Yet he reached not the threshold of old age, but died in Thebes by reason of a woman's gifts. And the sons born to him were Alcmaeon and Amphilochus. But Mantius begat Polypheides and Cleitus; but it came to pass that the golden-throned Dawn snatched away Cleitus for his very beauty's sake, that he might dwell with the Immortals.

And Apollo made the high-souled Polypheides a seer, far the chief of human kind, Amphiaraus being now dead. He removed his dwelling to Hypheresia, being angered with his father, and here he abode and prophesied to all men.

This man's son it was, Theoclymenus by name, that now drew nigh and stood by Telemachus. And he found him pouring a drink-offering and praying by the swift black ship, and uttering his voice he spake to him winged words:

'Friend, since I find thee making burnt-offering in this place, I pray thee, by thine offerings and by the god, and thereafter by thine own head, and in the name of the men of thy company answer my question truly and hide it not. Who art thou of the sons of men and whence? Where is thy city, where are they that begat thee?'

And wise Telemachus answered him, saying: 'Yea now, stranger, I will plainly tell thee all. Of Ithaca am I by lineage, and my father is Odysseus, if ever such an one there was, but now hath he perished by an evil fate. Wherefore I have taken my company and a black ship, and have gone forth to hear word of my father that has been long afar.'

Then godlike Theoclymenus spake to him again: 'Even so I too have fled from my country, for the manslaying of one of mine own kin. And many brethren and kinsmen of the slain are in Argos, the pastureland of horses, and rule mightily over the Achaeans. Wherefore now am I an exile to shun death and black fate at their hands, for it is my doom yet to wander among men. Now set me on board ship, since I supplicate thee in my flight, lest they slay me utterly; for methinks they follow hard after me.'

And wise Telemachus answered him, saying: 'Surely I will not drive thee away from our good ship, if thou art fain to come. Follow thou with us then, and in Ithaca thou shalt be welcome to such things as we have.'

Therewith he took from him his spear of bronze, and laid it along the deck of the curved ship, and himself too climbed the seafaring ship. Then he sat him down in the stern and made Theoclymenus to sit beside him; and his company loosed the hawsers. Then Telemachus called unto his company, and bade them lay hands on the tackling, and speedily they hearkened to his call. So they raised the mast of pine tree, and set it in the hole of the cross plank and made it fast with forestays, and hauled up the white sails with twisted ropes of ox-hide. And grey-eyed Athene sent them a favouring breeze, rushing violently through the clear sky that the ship might speedily finish her course over the salt water of the sea. So they passed by Crouni and Chalcis, a land of fair streams.

And the sun set and all the ways were darkened. And the vessel drew nigh to Pheae, being sped before the breeze of Zeus, and then passed goodly Elis where the Epeans bear rule. From thence he drave on again to the Pointed Isles, pondering whether he should escape death or be cut off.

Now Odysseus and the goodly swineherd were supping in the hut, and the other men sat at meat with them. So when they had put from them the desire of meat and drink, Odysseus spake among them, to prove the swineherd, whether he would still entertain him diligently, and bid him abide there in the steading or send him forward to the city:

'Listen now, Eumaeus, and all the others of the company. In the morning I would fain be gone to the town to go a begging, that I be not ruinous to thyself and thy fellows. Now advise me well, and lend me a good guide by the way to lead me thither; and through the city will I wander alone as needs I must, if perchance one may give me a cup of water and a morsel of bread. Moreover I would go to the house of divine Odysseus and bear tidings to the wise Penelope, and consort with the wanton wooers, if haply they might grant me a meal out of the boundless store that they have by them. Lightly might I do good service among them, even all that they would. For lo! I will tell thee and do thou mark and listen. By the favour of Hermes, the messenger, who gives grace and glory to all men's work, no mortal may vie with me in the business of a serving-man, in piling well a fire, in cleaving dry faggots, and in carving and roasting flesh and in pouring of wine, those offices wherein meaner men serve their betters.'

Then didst thou speak to him in heaviness of heart, swineherd Eumaeus: 'Ah! wherefore, stranger, hath such a thought arisen in thine heart? Surely thou art set on perishing utterly there, if thou wouldest indeed go into the throng of the wooers, whose outrage and violence reacheth even to the iron heaven! Not such as thou are their servants; they that minister to them are young and gaily clad in mantles and in doublets, and their heads are anointed with oil and they are fair of face, and the polished boards are laden with bread and flesh and wine. Nay, abide here, for none is vexed by thy presence, neither I nor any of my fellows that are with me. But when the dear son of Odysseus comes, he himself will give thee a mantle and a doublet for raiment, and will send thee whithersoever thy heart and spirit bid thee go.'

Then the steadfast goodly Odysseus answered him: 'Oh, that thou mayst so surely be dear to father Zeus as thou art to me, in that thou didst make me to cease from wandering and dread woe! For there is no other thing more mischievous to men than roaming; yet for their cursed belly's need men endure sore distress, to whom come wandering and tribulation and pain. But behold now, since thou stayest me here, and biddest me wait his coming, tell me of the mother of divine Odysseus, and of the father whom at his departure he left behind him on the threshold of old age; are they, it may be, yet alive beneath the sunlight, or already dead and within the house of Hades?'

Then spake to him the swineherd, a master of men: 'Yea now, stranger, I will plainly tell thee all. Laertes yet lives, and prays evermore to Zeus that his life may waste from out his limbs within his halls. For he has wondrous sorrow for his son that is far away, and for the wedded lady his wise wife, whose death afflicted him in chief and brought him to old age before his day. Now she died of very grief for her son renowned, by an evil death, so may no man perish who dwells here and is a friend to me in word and deed! So long as she was on earth, though in much sorrow, I was glad to ask and inquire concerning her, for that she herself had reared me along with long-robed Ctimene, her noble daughter, the youngest of her children. With her I was reared, and she honoured me little less than her own. But when we both came to the time of our desire, to the flower of age, thereupon they sent her to Same, and got a great bride-price; but my lady clad me in a mantle and a doublet, raiment very fair, and gave me sandals for my feet and sent me forth to the field, and right dear at heart she held me. But of these things now at last am I lacking; yet the blessed gods prosper the work of mine own hands, whereat I abide. Of this my substance I have eaten and drunken and given to reverend strangers. But from my lady I may hear nought pleasant, neither word nor deed, for evil hath fallen on her house, a plague of froward men: yet thralls have a great desire to speak before their mistress and find out all and eat and drink, and moreover to carry off somewhat with them to the field, such things as ever comfort the heart of a thrall.'

And Odysseus of many counsels answered him saying: 'Ah, Eumaeus, how far then didst thou wander from thine own country and thy parents while as yet thou wast but a child! But come, declare me this and plainly tell it all. Was a wide-wayed town of men taken and sacked, wherein dwelt thy father and thy lady mother, or did unfriendly men find thee lonely, tending sheep or cattle, and shipped thee thence, and sold thee into the house of thy master here, who paid for thee a goodly price?'

Then spake to him the swineherd, a master of men: 'Stranger, since thou askest and questionest me hereof, give heed now in silence and make merry, and abide here drinking wine. Lo, the nights now are of length untold. Time is there to sleep, and time to listen and be glad; thou needest not turn to bed before the hour; even too much sleep is vexation of spirit. But for the rest, let him whose heart and mind bid him, go forth and slumber, and at the dawning of the day let him break his fast, and follow our master's swine. But let us twain drink and feast within the steading, and each in his neighbour's sorrows take delight, recalling them, for even the memory of griefs is a joy to a man who hath been sore tried and wandered far. Wherefore I will tell thee that whereof thou askest and dost question me.

'There is a certain isle called Syria, if haply thou hast heard tell of it, over above Ortygia, and there are the turning-places of the sun. It is not very great in compass, though a goodly isle, rich in herds, rich in flocks, with plenty of corn and wine. Dearth never enters the land, and no hateful sickness falls on wretched mortals. But when the tribes of men grow old in that city, then comes Apollo of the silver bow, with Artemis, and slays them with the visitation of his gentle shafts. In that isle are two cities, and the whole land is divided between them, and my father was king over the twain, Ctesius son of Ormenus, a man like to the Immortals.

'Thither came the Phoenicians, mariners renowned, greedy merchant men, with countless gauds in a black ship. Now in my father's house was a Phoenician woman, tall and fair and skilled in bright handiwork; this woman the Phoenicians with their sleights beguiled. First as she was washing clothes, one of them lay with her in love by the hollow ship, for love beguiles the minds of womankind, even of the upright. Then he asked her who she was and whence she came, and straightway she showed him the lofty home of my father, saying:

' "From out of Sidon I avow that I come, a land rich in bronze, and I am the daughter of Arybas, the deeply wealthy. But Taphians, who were sea-robbers, laid hands on me and snatched me away as I came in from the fields, and brought me hither and sold me into the house of my master, who paid for me a goodly price."

'Then the man who had lain with her privily, answered: "Say, wouldst thou now return home with us, that thou mayst look again on the lofty house of thy father and mother and on their faces? For truly they yet live, and have a name for wealth."

'Then the woman answered him and spake, saying: "Even this may well be, if ye sailors will pledge me an oath to bring me home in safety."

'So spake she, and they all swore thereto as she bade them. Now when they had sworn and done that oath, again the woman spake among them and answered, saying:

' "Hold your peace now, and let none of your fellows speak to me and greet me, if they meet me in the street, or even at the well, lest one go and tell it to the old man at home, and he suspect somewhat and bind me in hard bonds and devise death for all of you. But keep ye the matter in mind, and speed the purchase of your homeward freight. And when your ship is freighted with stores, let a message come quickly to me at the house; for I will likewise bring gold, all that comes under my hand. Yea and there is another thing that I would gladly give for my fare. I am nurse to the child of my lord in the halls, a most cunning little boy, that runs out and abroad with me. Him would I bring on board ship, and he should fetch you a great price, wheresoever ye take him for sale among men of strange speech."

'Therewith she went her way to the fair halls. But they abode among us a whole year, and got together much wealth in their hollow ship. And when their hollow ship was now laden to depart, they sent a messenger to tell the tidings to the woman. There came a man versed in craft to my father's house, with a golden chain strung here and there with amber beads. Now the maidens in the hall and my lady mother were handling the chain and gazing on it, and offering him their price; but he had signed silently to the woman, and therewithal gat him away to the hollow ship. Then she took me by the hand and led me forth from the house. And at the vestibule of the house she found the cups and tables of the guests that had been feasting, who were in waiting on my father. They had gone forth to the session and the place of parley of the people. And she straightway hid three goblets in her bosom, and bare them away, and I followed in my innocence. Then the sun sank and all the ways were darkened. And we went quickly and came to the good haven, where was the swift ship of the Phoenicians. So they climbed on board and took us up with them, and sailed over the wet ways, and Zeus sent us a favouring wind. For six days we sailed by day and night continually; but when Zeus, son of Cronos, added the seventh day thereto, then Artemis, the archer, smote the woman that she fell, as a sea-swallow falls, with a plunge into the hold. And they cast her forth to be the prey of seals and fishes, but I was left stricken at heart. And wind and water bare them and brought them to Ithaca, where Laertes bought me with his possessions. And thus it chanced that mine eyes beheld this land.'

Then Odysseus, of the seed of Zeus, answered him saying:

'Eumaeus, verily thou hast stirred my heart within me with the tale of all these things, of all the sorrow of heart thou hast endured. Yet surely Zeus hath given thee good as well as evil, since after all these adventures thou hast come to the house of a kindly man, who is careful to give thee meat and drink and right well thou livest. But I have come hither still wandering through the many towns of men.'

Thus they spake one with the other. Then they laid them down to sleep for no long while, but for a little space, for soon came the throned Dawn. But on the shore the company of Telemachus were striking their sails, and took down the mast quickly and rowed the ship on to anchorage. And they cast anchors and made fast the hawsers, and themselves too stept forth upon the strand of the sea, and made ready the midday meal, and mixed the dark wine. Now when they had put from them the desire of meat and drink, wise Telemachus first spake among them:

'Do ye now drive the black ship to the city, while I will go to the fields and to the herdsmen, and at even I will return to the city, when I have seen my lands. And in the morning I will set by you the wages of the voyage, a good feast of flesh and of sweet wine.'

Then godlike Theoclymenus answered him: 'And whither shall I go, dear child? To what man's house shall I betake me, of such as are lords in rocky Ithaca? Shall I get me straight to thy mother and to thy home?'

Then wise Telemachus answered him, saying: 'In other case I would bid thee go even to our own house; for there is no lack of cheer for strangers, but now would it be worse for thyself, forasmuch as I shall be away nor would my mother see thee. For she comes not often in sight of the wooers in the house, but abides apart from them in her upper chamber, and weaves at her web. Yet there is one whom I will tell thee of, to whom thou mayst go, Eurymachus the glorious son of wise Polybus, whom now the men of Ithaca look on, even as if he were a god. For he is far the best man of them all, and is most eager to wed my mother and to have the sovereignty of Odysseus. Howbeit, Olympian Zeus, that dwells in the clear sky, knows hereof, whether or no he will fulfil for them the evil day before their marriage.'

Now even as he spake, a bird flew out on the right, a hawk, the swift messenger of Apollo. In his talons he held a dove and plucked her, and shed the feathers down to the earth, midway between the ship and Telemachus himself. Then Theoclymenus called him apart from his fellows, and clasped his hand and spake and hailed him:

'Telemachus, surely not without the god's will hath the bird flown out on the right, for I knew when I saw him that he was a bird of omen. There is no other house more kingly than yours in the land of Ithaca; nay, ye have ever the mastery.'

And wise Telemachus answered him, saying: 'Ah, stranger, would that this word may be accomplished! Soon shouldest thou be aware of kindness and many a gift at my hands, so that whoso met with thee would call thee blessed.'

Then he spake to Piraeus, his trusty companion: 'Piraeus, son of Clytius, thou that at other seasons hearkenest to me above all my company who went with me to Pylos, even now, I pray, lead this stranger home with thee, and give heed to treat him lovingly and with worship in thy house till I come.'

Then Piraeus, spearsman renowned, answered him saying: 'Telemachus, why, even if thou shouldest tarry here long, yet will I entertain this man, and he shall have no lack of stranger's cheer.'

Therewith he went on board, and bade his men themselves to mount and loose the hawsers. And quickly they embarked and sat upon the benches. And Telemachus bound his goodly sandals beneath his feet, and seized a mighty spear, shod with sharp bronze, from the deck of the ship and his men loosed the hawsers. So they thrust off and sailed to the city, as Telemachus bade them, the dear son of divine Odysseus. But swiftly his feet bore him on his forward way, till he came to the court, where were his swine out of number; and among them the good swineherd slept, a man loyal to his lords.

BOOK XVI

Telemachus sends Eumaeus to the city to tell his mother of his return. And how, in the meantime, Odysseus discovers himself to his son.

Now these twain, Odysseus and the goodly swineherd, within the hut had kindled a fire, and were making ready breakfast at the dawn, and had sent forth the herdsmen with the droves of swine. And round Telemachus the hounds, that love to bark, fawned and barked not, as he drew nigh. And goodly Odysseus took note of the fawning of the dogs, and the noise of footsteps fell upon his ears. Then straight he spake to Eumaeus winged words:

'Eumaeus, verily some friend or some other of thy familiars will soon be here, for the dogs do not bark but fawn around, and I catch the sound of footsteps.'

While the word was yet on his lips, his own dear son stood at the entering in of the gate. Then the swineherd sprang up in amazement, and out of his hands fell the vessels wherewith he was busied in mingling the dark wine. And he came over against his master and kissed his head and both his beautiful eyes and both his hands, and he let a great tear fall. And even as a loving father welcomes his son that has come in the tenth year from a far country, his only son and well-beloved, for whose sake he has had great sorrow and travail, even so did the goodly swineherd fall upon the neck of godlike Telemachus, and kiss him all over as one escaped from death, and he wept aloud and spake to him winged words:

'Thou art come, Telemachus, a sweet light in the dark;

methought I should see thee never again, after thou hadst gone in thy ship to Pylos. Nay now enter, dear child, that my heart may be glad at the sight of thee in mine house, who hast newly come from afar. For thou dost not often visit the field and the herdsmen, but abidest in the town; so it seems has thy good pleasure been, to look on the ruinous throng of the wooers.'

Then wise Telemachus answered him, saying: 'So be it, father, as thou sayest; and for thy sake am I come hither to see thee with mine eyes, and to hear from thy lips whether my mother yet abides in the halls or another has already wedded her, and the couch of Odysseus, perchance, lies in lack of bedding and deep in foul spider-webs.'

Then the swineherd, a master of men, answered him: 'Yea verily, she abides with patient spirit in thy halls, and wearily for her the nights wane always and the days, in shedding of tears.'

So he spake and took from him the spear of bronze. Then Telemachus passed within and crossed the threshold of stone. As he came near, his father Odysseus arose from his seat to give him place; but Telemachus, on his part, stayed him and spake saying:

'Be seated, stranger, and we will find a seat some other where in our steading, and there is a man here to set it for us.'

So he spake, and Odysseus went back and sat him down again. And the swineherd strewed for Telemachus green brushwood below, and a fleece thereupon, and there presently the dear son of Odysseus sat him down. Next the swineherd set by them platters of roast flesh, the fragments that were left from the meal of yesterday. And wheaten bread he briskly heaped up in baskets, and mixed the honey-sweet wine in a goblet of ivy wood, and himself sat down over against divine Odysseus. So they stretched forth their hands upon the good cheer set before them. Now when they had put from them the desire of meat and drink, Telemachus spake to the goodly swineherd, saying:

'Father, whence came this stranger to thee? How did sailors bring him to Ithaca? and who did they avow them to be? For in no wise, I deem, did he come hither by land.'

Then didst thou make answer, swineherd Eumaeus: 'Yea now, my son, I will tell thee all the truth. Of wide Crete he avows him to be by lineage, and he says that round many cities of mortals he has wandered at adventure; even so has some god spun for him the thread of fate. But now, as a runaway from the ship of the Thesprotians, has he come to my steading, and I will give him to thee for thy man; do with him as thou wilt; he avows him for thy suppliant.'

Then wise Telemachus answered him, saying: 'Eumaeus, verily a bitter word is this that thou speakest. How indeed shall I receive this guest in my house? Myself I am young, and trust not yet to my strength of hands to defend me against the man who does violence without a cause. And my mother has divisions of heart, whether to abide here with me and keep the house, respecting the bed of her lord and the voice of the people, or straightway to go with whomsoever of the Achaeans that woo her in the halls is the best man, and gives most bridal gifts. But behold, as for this guest of thine, now that he has come to thy house, I will clothe him in a mantle and a doublet, goodly raiment, and I will give him a two-edged sword, and shoes for his feet, and send him on his way, whithersoever his heart and his spirit bid him go. Or, if thou wilt, hold him here in the steading and take care of him, and raiment I will send hither, and all manner of food to eat, that he be not ruinous to thee and to thy fellows. But thither into the company of the wooers would I not suffer him to go, for they are exceedingly full of infatuate insolence, lest they mock at him, and that would be a sore grief to me. And hard it is for one man, how valiant soever, to achieve aught among a multitude, for verily they are far the stronger.'

Then the steadfast goodly Odysseus answered him: 'My friend, since it is indeed my right to answer thee withal, of a truth my heart is rent as I hear your words, such infatuate deeds ye say the wooers devise in the halls, in despite of thee, a man so noble. Say, dost thou willingly submit thee to oppression, or do the people through the township hate thee, obedient to the voice of a god? Or hast thou cause to blame thy brethren, in whose battle a man puts trust, even if a great feud arise? Ah, would that I had the youth, as now I have the spirit, and were either the son of noble Odysseus or Odysseus' very self, straightway then might a stranger sever my head from off my neck, if I went not to the halls of Odysseus, son of Laertes, and made myself the bane of every man among them! But if they should overcome me by numbers, being but one man against so many, far rather would I die slain in mine own halls, than witness for ever these unseemly deeds, strangers shamefully entreated, and men haling the handmaidens in foul wise through the fair house, and wine drawn wastefully, and the wooers devouring food all recklessly without avail, at a work that knows no ending.'

Then wise Telemachus answered him, saying: 'Yea now, stranger, I will plainly tell thee all. There is no grudge and hatred borne me by the whole people, neither have I cause to blame my brethren, in whose battle a man puts trust, even if a great feud arise. For thus, as thou seest, Cronion has made us a house of but one heir. Arceisius got him one only son Laertes, and one only son Odysseus was begotten of his father, and Odysseus left me the only child of his getting in these halls, and had no joy of me; wherefore now are foemen innumerable in the house. For all the noblest that are princes in the islands, in Dulichium and Same and wooded Zacynthus, and as many as lord it in rocky Ithaca, all these woo my mother and waste my house.

But as for her she neither refuseth the hated bridal, nor hath the heart to make an end; so they devour and minish my house; and ere long will they make havoc likewise of myself. Howbeit these things surely lie on the knees of the gods. Nay, father, but do thou go with haste and tell the constant Penelope that she hath got me safe and that I am come up out of Pylos. As for me, I will tarry here, and do thou return hither when thou hast told the tidings to her alone; but of the other Achaeans let no man learn it, for there be many that devise mischief against me.'

Then didst thou make answer, swineherd Eumaeus: 'I mark, I heed, all this thou speakest to one with understanding. But come, declare me this and tell it plainly; whether or no I shall go the same road with tidings to Laertes, that hapless man, who till lately, despite his great sorrow for Odysseus' sake, yet had oversight of the tillage, and did eat and drink with the thralls in his house, as often as his heart within him bade him. But now, from the day that thou wentest in thy ship to Pylos, never to this hour, they say, hath he so much as eaten and drunken, nor looked to the labours of the field, but with groaning and lamentation he sits sorrowing, and the flesh wastes away about his bones.'

Then wise Telemachus answered him, saying: 'All the more grievous it is! yet will we let him be, though we sorrow thereat. For if men might in any wise have all their will, we should before ought else choose the day of my father's returning. But do thou when thou hast told the tidings come straight back, and go not wandering through the fields after Laertes. But speak to my mother that with all speed she send forth the house-dame her handmaid, secretly, for she might bear tidings to the old man.'

With that word he roused the swineherd, who took his sandals in his hands and bound them beneath his feet and departed for the city. Now Athene noted Eumaeus the swineherd pass from the steading, and she drew nigh in the semblance of a woman fair and tall, and skilled in splendid handiwork. And she stood in presence manifest to Odysseus over against the doorway of the hut; but it was so that Telemachus saw her not before him and marked her not; for the gods in no wise appear visibly to all. But Odysseus was ware of her and the dogs likewise, which barked not, but with a low whine shrank cowering to the far side of the steading. Then she nodded at him with bent brows, and goodly Odysseus perceived it, and came forth from the room, past the great wall of the yard, and stood before her, and Athene spake to him, saying:

'Son of Laertes, of the seed of Zeus, Odysseus of many devices, now is the hour to reveal thy word to thy son, and hide it not, that ye twain having framed death and doom for the wooers, may fare to the famous town. Nor will I, even I, be long away from you, being right eager for battle.'

Therewith Athene touched him with her golden wand. First she cast about his breast a fresh linen robe and a doublet, and she increased his bulk and bloom. Dark his colour grew again, and his cheeks filled out, and the black beard spread thick around his chin.

Now she, when she had so wrought, withdrew again, but Odysseus went into the hut, and his dear son marvelled at him and looked away for very fear lest it should be a god, and he uttered his voice and spake to him winged words:

'Even now, stranger, thou art other in my sight than that thou wert a moment since, and other garments thou hast, and the colour of thy skin is no longer the same. Surely thou art a god of those that keep the wide heaven. Nay then, be gracious, that we may offer to thee well-pleasing sacrifices and golden gifts, beautifully wrought; and spare us I pray thee.'

Then the steadfast goodly Odysseus answered him, saying: 'Behold, no god am I; why likenest thou me to the immortals? nay, thy father am I, for whose sake thou sufferest many pains and groanest sore, and submittest thee to the despite of men.'

At the word he kissed his son, and from his cheeks let a tear fall to earth: before, he had stayed the tears continually. But Telemachus (for as yet he believed not that it was his father) answered in turn and spake, saying:

'Thou art not Odysseus my father, but some god beguiles me, that I may groan for more exceeding sorrow. For it cannot be that a mortal man should contrive this by the aid of his own wit, unless a god were himself to visit him, and lightly of his own will to make him young or old. For truly, but a moment gone, thou wert old and foully clad, but now thou art like the gods who keep the wide heaven.'

Then Odysseus of many counsels answered him saying:

'Telemachus, it fits thee not to marvel overmuch that thy father is come home, or to be amazed. Nay for thou shalt find no other Odysseus come hither any more; but lo, I, all as I am, after sufferings and much wandering have come in the twentieth year to mine own country. Behold, this is the work of Athene, driver of the spoil, who makes me such manner of man as she will,—for with her it is possible,—now like a beggar, and now again like a young man, and one clad about in rich raiment. Easy it is for the gods who keep the wide heaven to glorify or to abase a mortal man.'

With this word then he sat down again; but Telemachus, flinging himself upon his noble father's neck, mourned and shed tears, and in both their hearts arose the desire of lamentation. And they wailed aloud, more ceaselessly than birds, sea-eagles or vultures of crooked claws, whose younglings the country folk have taken from the nest, ere yet they are fledged. Even so pitifully fell the tears beneath their brows. And now would the sunlight have gone down upon their sorrowing, had not Telemachus spoken to his father suddenly:

'And in what manner of ship, father dear, did sailors at length bring thee hither to Ithaca? and who did they avow them to be? For in no wise, I deem, didst thou come hither by land.'

And the steadfast goodly Odysseus answered him: 'Yea now, my child, I will tell thee all the truth. The Phaeacians brought me hither, mariners renowned, who speed other men too upon their way, whosoever comes to them. Asleep in the swift ship they bore me over the seas and set me down in Ithaca, and gave me splendid gifts, bronze and gold in plenty and woven raiment. And these treasures are lying by the gods' grace in the caves. But now I am come hither by the promptings of Athene, that we may take counsel for the slaughter of the foemen. But come, tell me all the tale of the wooers and their number, that I may know how many and what men they be, and that so I may commune with my good heart and advise me, whether we twain shall be able alone to make head against them without aid, or whether we should even seek succour of others.'

Then wise Telemachus answered him, saying: 'Verily, father, I have ever heard of thy great fame, for a warrior hardy of thy hands, and sage in counsel. But this is a hard saying of thine: awe comes over me; for it may not be that two men should do battle with many men and stalwart. For of the wooers there are not barely ten nor twice ten only, but many a decade more: and straight shalt thou learn the tale of them ere we part. From Dulichium there be two and fifty chosen lords, and six serving men go with them; and out of Same four and twenty men; and from Zacynthus there are twenty lords of the Achaeans; and from Ithaca itself full twelve men of the best, and with them Medon the henchman, and the divine minstrel, and two squires skilled in carving viands. If we shall encounter all these within the halls, see thou to it, lest bitter and baneful for us be the vengeance thou takest on their violence at thy coming. But do thou, if thou canst think of some champion, advise thee of any that may help us with all his heart.'

Then the steadfast goodly Odysseus answered him, saying:

'Yea now, I will tell thee, and do thou mark and listen to me, and consider whether Athene with Father Zeus will suffice for us twain, or whether I shall cast about for some other champion.'

Then wise Telemachus answered him, saying: 'Valiant helpers, in sooth, are these two thou namest, whose seat is aloft in the clouds, and they rule among all men and among the deathless gods!'

Then the steadfast goodly Odysseus answered him: 'Yet will the twain not long keep aloof from the strong tumult of war, when between the wooers and us in my halls is held the trial of the might of Ares. But as now, do thou go homeward at the breaking of the day, and consort with the proud wooers. As for me, the swineherd will lead me to the town later in the day, in the likeness of a beggar, a wretched man and an old. And if they shall evil entreat me in the house, let thy heart harden itself to endure while I am shamefully handled, yea even if they drag me by the feet through the house to the doors, or cast at me and smite me: still do thou bear the sight. Howbeit thou shalt surely bid them cease from their folly, exhorting them with smooth words; yet no whit will they hearken, nay for the day of their doom is at hand. Yet another thing will I tell thee, and do thou ponder in thy heart. When Athene, of deep counsel, shall put it into my heart, I will nod to thee with my head and do thou note it, and carry away all thy weapons of war that lie in the halls, and lay them down every one in the secret place of the lofty chamber. And when the wooers miss them and ask thee concerning them, thou shalt beguile them with soft words, saying:

'"Out of the smoke I laid them by, since they were no longer like those that Odysseus left behind him of old when he went to Troy, but they are wholly marred: so mightily hath passed upon them the vapour of fire. Moreover Cronion hath put into my heart this other and greater care, that perchance, when ye are heated with wine, ye set a quarrel between you and wound one the other and thereby shame the feast and the wooing; for iron of itself draws a man thereto." But for us twain alone leave two swords and two spears and two shields of oxhide to grasp, that we may rush upon the arms and seize them; and then shall Pallas Athene and Zeus the counsellor enchant the wooers to their ruin. Yet another thing will I tell thee, and do thou ponder it in thy heart. If in very truth thou art my son and of our blood, then let no man hear that Odysseus is come home; neither let Laertes know it, nor the swineherd nor any of the household nor Penelope herself, but let me and thee alone discover the intent of the women. Yea, and we would moreover make trial of certain of the men among the thralls, and learn who of them chances to honour us and to fear us heartily, and who regards us not at all and holds even thee in no esteem, so noble a man as thou art.'

Then his renowned son answered him, and said: 'O my father, of a truth thou shalt learn, methinks, even hereafter what spirit I am of, for no whit doth folly possess me. But I deem not that this device of thine will be gainful to us twain, so I bid thee to give heed. For thou shalt be long time on thy road to little purpose, making trial of each man, while thou visitest the farm lands; but at ease in thy halls the wooers devour thy goods with insolence, and now there is no sparing. Howbeit I would have thee take knowledge of the women who they be that dishonour thee, and who are guiltless. But of the men I would not that we should make trial in the steadings, but that we should see to this task afterwards, if indeed thou knowest some sign from Zeus, lord of the aegis.'

Thus they spake one to the other. And now the well-builded ship was being brought to land at Ithaca, the ship that bare Telemachus from Pylos with all his company. When they were now come within the deep harbour, the men drew up the black ship on the shore, while squires, haughty of heart, bare away their weapons, and straightway carried the glorious gifts to the house of Clytius. Anon they sent forward a herald to the house of Odysseus to bear the tidings to prudent Penelope, namely, how Telemachus was in the field, and had bidden the ship sail to the city, lest the noble queen should be afraid, and let the round tears fall. So these two met, the herald and the goodly swineherd, come on the same errand to tell all to the lady. Now when they were got to the house of the divine king, the herald spake out among all the handmaids saying:

'Verily, O queen, thy son hath come out of Pylos.'

But the swineherd went up to Penelope, and told her all that her dear son had bidden him say. So, when he had declared all that had been enjoined him, he went on his way to the swine and left the enclosure and the hall.

Now the wooers were troubled and downcast in spirit, and forth they went from the hall past the great wall of the court, and there in front of the gates they held their session. And Eurymachus son of Polybus first spake among them saying:

'Verily, friends, a proud deed hath Telemachus accomplished with a high hand, even this journey, and we said that he should never bring it to pass. But come, launch we a black ship, the best there is, and let us get together oarsmen of the sea, who shall straightway bear word to our friends to return home with speed.'

The word was yet on his lips, when Amphinomus turned in his place and saw the ship within the deep harbour, and the men lowering the sails and with the oars in their hands. Then sweetly he laughed out and spake among his fellows:

'Nay, let us now send no message any more, for lo, they are come home. Either some god has told them all or they themselves have seen the ship of Telemachus go by, and have not been able to catch her.'

Thus he spake, and they arose and went to the sea-banks. Swiftly the men drew up the black ship on the shore, and squires, haughty of heart, bare away their weapons. And the wooers all together went to the assembly-place, and suffered none other to sit with them, either of the young men or of the elders. Then Antinous spake among them, the son of Eupeithes:

'Lo now, how the gods have delivered this man from his evil case! All day long did scouts sit along the windy headlands, ever in quick succession, and at the going down of the sun we never rested for a night upon the shore, but sailing with our swift ship on the high seas we awaited the bright Dawn, as we lay in wait for Telemachus, that we might take and slay the man himself; but meanwhile some god has brought him home. But even here let us devise an evil end for him, even for Telemachus, and let him not escape out of our hands, for methinks that while he lives we shall never achieve this task of ours. For he himself has understanding in counsel and wisdom, and the people no longer show us favour in all things. Nay come, before he assembles all the Achaeans to the gathering; for methinks that he will in no wise be slack, but will be exceeding wroth, and will stand up and speak out among them all, and tell how we plotted against him sheer destruction but did not overtake him. Then will they not approve us, when they hear these evil deeds. Beware then lest they do us a harm, and drive us forth from our country, and we come to the land of strangers. Nay, but let us be beforehand and take him in the field far from the city, or by the way; and let us ourselves keep his livelihood and his possessions, making fair division among us, but the house we would give to his mother to keep and to whomsoever marries her. But if this saying likes you not, but ye chose rather that he should live and keep the heritage of his father, no longer then let us gather here and eat all his store of pleasant substance, but let each one from his own hall woo her with his bridal gifts and seek to win her; so should she wed the man that gives the most and comes as the chosen of fate.'

So he spake, and they all held their peace. Then Amphinomus made harangue and spake out among them; he was the famous son of Nisus the prince, the son of Aretias, and he led the wooers that came from out Dulichium, a land rich in wheat and in grass, and more than all the rest his words were pleasing to Penelope, for he was of an understanding mind. And now of his good will he made harangue, and spake among them:

'Friends, I for one would not choose to kill Telemachus; it is a fearful thing to slay one of the stock of kings! Nay, first let us seek to the counsel of the gods, and if the oracles of great Zeus approve, myself I will slay him and bid all the rest to aid. But if the gods are disposed to avert it, I bid you to refrain.'

So spake Amphinomus, and his saying pleased them well. Then straightway they arose and went to the house of Odysseus, and entering in sat down on the polished seats.

Then the wise Penelope had a new thought, namely, to show herself to the wooers, so despiteful in their insolence; for she had heard of the death of her son that was to be in the halls, seeing that Medon the henchman had told her of it, who heard their counsels. So she went on her way to the hall, with the women her handmaids. Now when that fair lady had come unto the wooers, she stood by the pillar of the well-builded roof, holding up her glistening tire before her face, and rebuked Antinous and spake and hailed him:

'Antinous, full of all insolence, deviser of mischief! and yet they say that in the land of Ithaca thou art chiefest among thy peers in counsel and in speech. Nay, no such man dost thou show thyself. Fool! why indeed dost thou contrive death and doom for Telemachus, and hast no regard unto suppliants who have Zeus to witness? Nay but it is an impious thing to contrive evil one against another. What! knowest thou not of the day when thy father fled to this house in fear of the people, for verily they were exceeding wroth against him, because he had followed with Taphian sea-robbers and harried the Thesprotians, who were at peace with us? So they wished to destroy thy father and wrest from him his dear life, and utterly to devour all his great and abundant livelihood; but Odysseus stayed and withheld them, for all their desire. His house thou now consumest without atonement, and his wife thou wooest, and wouldst slay his son, and dost greatly grieve me. But I bid thee cease, and command the others to do likewise.'

Then Eurymachus, son of Polybus, answered her saying: 'Daughter of Icarius, wise Penelope, take courage, and let not thy heart be careful for these things. The man is not, nor shall be, nor ever shall be born, that shall stretch forth his hands against Telemachus, thy son, while I live and am on earth and see the light. For thus will I declare to thee, and it shall surely come to pass. Right quickly shall the black blood of such an one flow about our spear; for Odysseus, waster of cities, of a truth did many a time set me too upon his knees, and gave me roasted flesh into my hand, and held the red wine to my lips. Wherefore Telemachus is far the dearest of all men to me, and I bid him have no fear of death, not from the wooers' hands; but from the gods none may avoid it.'

Thus he spake comforting her, but was himself the while framing death for her son.

Now she ascended to her shining upper chamber, and then

was bewailing Odysseus, her dear lord, till grey-eyed Athene cast sweet sleep upon her eyelids.

And in the evening the goodly swineherd came back to Odysseus and his son, and they made ready and served the supper, when they had sacrificed a swine of a year old. Then Athene drew near Odysseus, son of Laertes, and smote him with her wand, and made him into an old man again. In sorry raiment she clad him about his body, lest the swineherd should look on him and know him, and depart to tell the constant Penelope, and not keep the matter in his heart.

Then Telemachus spake first to the swineherd, saying: 'Thou hast come, goodly Eumaeus. What news is there in the town? Are the lordly wooers now come in from their ambush, or do they still watch for me as before on my homeward way?'

Then didst thou make answer, swineherd Eumaeus: 'I had no mind to go down the city asking and inquiring hereof; my heart bade me get me home again, as quick as might be, when once I had told the tidings. And the swift messenger from thy company joined himself unto me, the henchman, who was the first to tell the news to thy mother. Yet this, too, I know, if thou wouldest hear; for I beheld it with mine eyes. Already had I come in my faring above the city, where is the hill Hermaean, when I marked a swift ship entering our haven, and many men there were in her, and she was laden with shields and two-headed spears, and methought they were the wooers, but I know not at all.'

So spake he, and the mighty prince Telemachus smiled, and glanced at his father, while he shunned the eye of the swineherd.

Now when they had ceased from the work and got supper ready, they fell to feasting, and their hearts lacked not ought of the equal banquet. But when they had put from them the desire of meat and drink, they bethought them of rest, and took the boon of sleep.

BOOK XVII

Telemachus relates to his mother what he had heard at Pylos and Sparta.

So soon as early Dawn shone forth, the rosy-fingered, then Telemachus, the dear son of divine Odysseus, bound beneath his feet his goodly sandals, and took up his mighty spear that fitted his grasp, to make for the city; and he spake to his swineherd, saying:

'Verily, father, I am bound for the city, that my mother may see me, for methinks that she will not cease from grievous wailing and tearful lament, until she beholds my very face. But this command I give thee: Lead this stranger, the hapless one, to the city, that there he may beg his meat, and whoso chooses will give him a morsel of bread and a cup of water. As for myself, I can in no wise suffer every guest who comes to me, so afflicted am I in spirit. But if the stranger be sore angered hereat, the more grievous will it be for himself; howbeit I for one love to speak the truth.'

And Odysseus of many counsels answered him saying: 'I too, my friend, have no great liking to be left behind here. It is better that a beggar should beg his meat in the town than in the fields, and whoso chooses will give it me. For I am not now of an age to abide at the steading, and to obey in all things the word of the master. Nay go, and this man that thou biddest will lead me, so soon as I shall be warmed with the fire, and the sun waxes hot. For woefully poor are these garments of mine, and I fear lest the hoar frost of the dawn overcome me; moreover ye say the city is far away.'

So he spake, and Telemachus passed out through the steading, stepping forth at a quick pace, and was sowing the seeds of evil for the wooers. Now when he was come to the fair-lying house, he set his spear against the tall pillar and leaned it there, and himself went in and crossed the threshold of stone.

And the nurse Eurycleia saw him far before the rest, as she was strewing skin coverlets upon the carven chairs, and straightway she drew near him, weeping, and all the other maidens of Odysseus, of the hardy heart, were gathered about him, and kissed him lovingly on the head and shoulders. Now wise Penelope came forth from her chamber, like Artemis or golden Aphrodite, and cast her arms about her dear son, and fell a weeping, and kissed his face and both his beautiful eyes, and wept aloud, and spake to him winged words:

'Thou art come, Telemachus, a sweet light in the dark; methought I should see thee never again, after thou hadst gone in thy ship to Pylos, secretly and without my will, to seek tidings of thy dear father. Come now, tell me, what sight thou didst get of him?'

And wise Telemachus answered her, saying: 'Mother mine, wake not wailing in my soul, nor stir the heart within the breast of me, that have but now fled from utter death. Nay, but wash thee in water, and take to thee fresh raiment, and go aloft to thine upper chamber with the women thy handmaids, and vow to all the gods an acceptable sacrifice of hecatombs, if haply Zeus may grant that deeds of requital be made. But I will go to the assembly-place to bid a stranger to our house, one that accompanied me as I came hither from Pylos. I sent him forward with my godlike company, and commanded Piraeus to lead him home, and to take heed to treat him lovingly and with worship till I should come.'

Thus he spake, and wingless her speech remained. And she washed her in water, and took to her fresh raiment, and vowed to all the gods an acceptable sacrifice of hecatombs, if haply Zeus might grant that deeds of requital should be made.

Now Telemachus went out through the hall with the spear in his hand: and two swift hounds bare him company. And Athene shed on him a wondrous grace, and all the people marvelled at him as he came. And the lordly wooers gathered about him with fair words on their lips, but brooding evil in the deep of their heart. Then he avoided the great press of the wooers, but where Mentor sat, and Antiphus, and Halitherses, who were friends of his house from of old, there he went and sat down; and they asked him of all his adventures. Then Piraeus, the famed spearsman, drew nigh, leading the stranger to the assembly-place by the way of the town; and Telemachus kept not aloof from him long, but went up to him.

Then Piraeus first spake to him, saying: 'Bestir the women straightway to go to my house, that I may send thee the gifts that Menelaus gave thee.'

Then wise Telemachus answered him, saying: 'Piraeus, we know not how these matters will fall out. If the lordly wooers shall slay me by guile in the halls, and divide among them the heritage of my father, then I should wish thee to keep and enjoy the gifts thyself, rather than any of these. But if I shall sow the seeds of death and fate for the wooers, then gladly bring me to the house the gifts that I will gladly take.'

Therewith he led the travel-worn stranger to the house. Now when they came to the fair-lying palace, they laid aside their mantles on the chairs and high seats, and went to the polished baths, and bathed them. So when the maidens had bathed them and anointed them with olive oil, and cast about them thick mantles and doublets, they came forth from the baths, and sat upon the seats. Then the handmaid bare water for the hands in a goodly golden ewer, and poured it forth over a silver basin to wash withal, and drew to their side a polished table. And the grave dame bare wheaten bread, and set it by them, and laid on the board many dainties, giving freely of such things as she had by her. And the mother of Telemachus sat over against him by the pillar of the hall, leaning against a chair, and spinning the slender threads from the yarn. And they stretched forth their hands upon the good cheer set before them. Now when they had put from them the desire of meat and drink, the wise Penelope first spake among them:

'Telemachus, verily I will go up to my upper chamber, and lay me in my bed, the place of my groanings, that is ever watered by my tears, since the day that Odysseus departed with the sons of Atreus for Ilios. Yet thou hadst no care to tell me clearly, before the lordly wooers came to this house, concerning the returning of thy father, if haply thou hast heard thereof.'

And wise Telemachus answered her, saying: 'Yea now, mother, I will tell thee all the truth. We went to Pylos and to Nestor, the shepherd of the people, and he received me in his lofty house, and was diligent to entreat me lovingly, as a father might his son that had but newly come from strange lands after many years; even so diligently he cared for me with his renowned sons. Yet he said that he had heard no word from any man on earth concerning Odysseus, of the hardy heart, whether alive or dead. But he sent me forward on my way with horses and a chariot, well compact, to Menelaus, son of Atreus, spearman renowned. There I saw Argive Helen, for whose sake the Argives and Trojans bore much travail by the gods' designs. Then straightway Menelaus, of the loud war-cry, asked me on what quest I had come to goodly Lacedaemon. And I told him all the truth. Then he made answer, and spake, saying:

'"Out upon them, for truly in the bed of a brave-hearted man were they minded to lie, very cravens as they are! Even as when a hind hath couched her newborn fawns unweaned in a strong lion's lair, and searcheth out the mountain-knees and grassy hollows, seeking pasture; and afterward the lion cometh back to his bed, and sendeth forth unsightly death upon that pair, even so shall Odysseus send forth unsightly death upon the wooers. Would to our father Zeus, and Athene, and Apollo, would that in such might as when of old in stablished Lesbos he rose up in strife and wrestled with Philomeleides, and threw him mightily, and all the Achaeans rejoiced; would that in such strength Odysseus might consort with the wooers; then should they all have swift fate and bitter wedlock! But for that whereof thou askest and entreatest me, be sure I will not swerve from the truth in aught that I say, nor deceive thee; but of all that the ancient one of the sea, whose speech is sooth, declared to me, not a word will I hide or keep from thee. He said that he saw Odysseus in an island, suffering strong pains in the halls of the nymph Calypso, who holds him there perforce; so that he may not come to his own country, for he has by him no ships with oars, and no companions to send him on his way over the broad back of the sea." So spake Menelaus, son of Atreus, spearsman renowned. Then having fulfilled all, I set out for home, and the deathless gods gave me a fair wind, and brought me swiftly to mine own dear country.'

So he spake, and stirred her heart within her breast. And next the godlike Theoclymenus spake among them:

'O wife revered of Odysseus, son of Laertes, verily he hath no clear knowledge; but my word do thou mark, for I will prophesy to thee most truly and hide nought. Now Zeus be witness before any god, and this hospitable board and this hearth of noble Odysseus, whereunto I am come, that Odysseus is even now of a surety in his own country, resting or faring, learning of these evil deeds, and sowing the seeds of evil for all the wooers. So clear was the omen of the bird that I saw as I sat on the decked ship, and I proclaimed it to Telemachus.'

Then wise Penelope answered him, saying: 'Ah, stranger, would that this thy word may be accomplished! Soon shouldest thou be aware of kindness and of many a gift at my hands, so that whoso met with thee would call thee blessed.'

Thus they spake one to the other. But the wooers meantime were before the palace of Odysseus, taking their pleasure in casting of weights and of spears on a levelled place, as heretofore, in their insolence. But when it was now the hour for supper, and the flocks came home from the fields all around, and the men led them whose custom it was, then Medon, who of all the henchmen was most to their mind, and was ever with them at the feast, spake to them, saying:

'Noble youths, now that ye have had sport to your hearts' content, get you into the house, that we may make ready a feast; for truly it is no bad thing to take meat in season.'

Even so he spake, and they rose up and departed, and were obedient to his word. Now when they were come into the fair-lying house, they laid aside their mantles on the chairs and high seats, and they sacrificed great sheep and stout goats, yea, and the fatlings of the boars and an heifer of the herd, and got ready the feast.

Now all this while Odysseus and the goodly swineherd were bestirring them to go from the field to the city; and the swineherd, a master of men, spake first saying:

'Well, my friend, forasmuch as I see thou art eager to be going to the city to-day, even as my master gave command;—though myself I would well that thou shouldest be left here to keep the steading, but I hold him in reverence and fear, lest he chide me afterwards, and grievous are the rebukes of masters—come then, let us go on our way, for lo, the day is far spent, and soon wilt thou find it colder toward evening.'

Then Odysseus of many counsels answered him saying: 'I mark, I heed: all this thou speakest to one with understanding. But let us be going, and be thou my guide withal to the end. And if thou hast anywhere a staff ready cut, give it me to lean upon, for truly ye said that slippery was the way.'

Therewith he cast about his shoulders a mean scrip, all tattered, and a cord withal to hang it, and Eumaeus gave him a staff to his mind. So these twain went on their way, and the dogs and the herdsmen stayed behind to guard the steading. And the swineherd led his lord to the city in the guise of a beggar, a wretched man and an old, leaning on a staff; and sorry was the raiment wherewith he was clothed upon. But as they fared along the rugged path they drew near to the town, and came to the fair flowing spring, with a basin fashioned, whence the people of the city drew water. This well Ithacus and Neritus and Polyctor had builded. And around it was a thicket of alders that grow by the waters, all circlewise, and down the cold stream fell from a rock on high, and above was reared an altar to the Nymphs, whereat all wayfarers made offering. In that place Melanthius, son of Dolius, met them, leading his goats to feast the wooers, the best goats that were in all the herds; and two herdsmen bare him company. Now when he saw them he reviled them, and spake and hailed them, in terrible and evil fashion, and stirred the heart of Odysseus, saying:

'Now in very truth the vile is leading the vile, for God brings ever like to like! Say, whither art thou leading this glutton,—thou wretched swineherd,—this plaguy beggar, a kill-joy of the feast? He is one to stand about and rub his shoulders against many doorposts, begging for scraps of meat, not for swords or cauldrons. If thou wouldst give me the fellow to watch my steading and sweep out the stalls, and carry fresh fodder to the kids, then he might drink whey and get him a stout thigh. Howbeit, since he is practised only in evil, he will not care to betake him to the labour of the farm, but rather chooses to go louting through the land asking alms to fill his insatiate belly. But now I will speak out and my word shall surely be accomplished. If ever he fares to the house of divine Odysseus, many a stool that men's hands hurl shall fly about his head, and break upon his ribs, as they pelt him through the house.'

Therewith, as he went past, he kicked Odysseus on the hip, in his witlessness, yet he drave him not from the path, but he abode steadfast. And Odysseus pondered whether he should rush upon him and take away his life with the staff, or lift him in his grasp and smite his head to the earth. Yet he hardened his heart to endure and refrained himself. And the swineherd looked at the other and rebuked him, and lifting up his hands prayed aloud:

'Nymphs of the well-water, daughters of Zeus, if ever Odysseus burned on your altars pieces of the thighs of rams or kids, in their covering of rich fat, fulfil for me this wish:—oh that he, even he, may come home, and that some god may bring him! Then would he scatter all thy bravery, which now thou flauntest insolently, wandering ever about the city, while evil shepherds destroy the flock.'

Then Melanthius, the goatherd, answered: 'Lo now, what a word has this evil-witted dog been saying! Some day I will take him in a black decked ship far from Ithaca, that he may bring me in much livelihood. Would God that Apollo, of the silver bow, might smite Telemachus to-day in the halls, or that he might fall before the wooers, so surely as for Odysseus the day of returning has in a far land gone by!'

So he spake and left them there as they walked slowly

on. But Melanthius stepped forth, and came very speedily to the house of the prince, and straightway he went in and sat down among the wooers, over against Eurymachus, who chiefly showed him kindness. And they that ministered set by him a portion of flesh, and the grave dame brought wheaten bread and set it by him to eat. Now Odysseus and the goodly swineherd drew near and stood by, and the sound of the hollow lyre rang around them, for Phemius was lifting up his voice amid the company in song, and Odysseus caught the swineherd by the hand, and spake, saying:

'Eumaeus, verily this is the fair house of Odysseus, and right easily might it be known and marked even among many. There is building beyond building, and the court of the house is cunningly wrought with a wall and battlements, and well-fenced are the folding doors; no man may hold it in disdain. And I see that many men keep revel within, for the savour of the fat rises upward, and the voice of the lyre is heard there, which the gods have made to be the mate of the feast.'

Then didst thou make answer, swineherd Eumaeus: 'Easily thou knowest it, for indeed thou never lackest understanding. But come, let us advise us, how things shall fall out here. Either do thou go first within the fair-lying halls, and join the company of the wooers, so will I remain here, or if thou wilt, abide here, and I will go before thy face, and tarry not long, lest one see thee without, and hurl at thee or strike thee. Look well to this, I bid thee.'

Then the steadfast goodly Odysseus answered him, saying: 'I mark, I heed, all this thou speakest to one with understanding. Do thou then go before me, and I will remain here, for well I know what it is to be smitten and hurled at. My heart is full of hardiness, for much evil have I suffered in perils of waves and war; let this be added to the tale of those. But a ravening belly may none conceal, a thing accursed, that works much ill for men. For this cause too the benched ships are furnished, that bear mischief to foemen over the unharvested seas.'

Thus they spake one to the other. And lo, a hound raised up his head and pricked his ears, even where he lay, Argos, the hound of Odysseus, of the hardy heart, which of old himself had bred, but had got no joy of him, for ere that, he went to sacred Ilios. Now in time past the young men used to lead the hound against wild goats and deer and hares; but as then, despised he lay (his master being afar) in the deep dung of mules and kine, whereof an ample bed was spread before the doors, till the thralls of Odysseus should carry it away to dung therewith his wide demesne. There lay the dog Argos, full of vermin. Yet even now when he was ware of Odysseus standing by, he wagged his tail and dropped both his ears, but nearer to his master he had not now the strength to draw. But Odysseus looked aside and wiped away a tear that he easily hid from Eumaeus, and straightway he asked him, saying:

'Eumaeus, verily this is a great marvel, this hound lying here in the dung. Truly he is goodly of growth, but I know not certainly if he have speed with this beauty, or if he be comely only, like as are men's trencher dogs that their lords keep for the pleasure of the eye.'

Then didst thou make answer, swineherd Eumaeus: 'In very truth this is the dog of a man that has died in a far land. If he were what once he was in limb and in the feats of the chase, when Odysseus left him to go to Troy, soon wouldst thou marvel at the sight of his swiftness and his strength. There was no beast that could flee from him in the deep places of the wood, when he was in pursuit; for even on a track he was the keenest hound. But now he is holden in an evil case, and his lord hath perished far from his own country, and the careless women take no charge of him. Nay, thralls are no more inclined to honest service when their masters have lost the dominion, for Zeus, of the far-borne voice, takes away the half of a man's virtue, when the day of slavery comes upon him.'

Therewith he passed within the fair-lying house, and went straight to the hall, to the company of the proud wooers. But upon Argos came the fate of black death even in the hour that he beheld Odysseus again, in the twentieth year.

Now godlike Telemachus was far the first to behold the swineherd as he came into the hall, and straightway then he beckoned and called him to his side. So Eumaeus looked about and took a settle that lay by him, where the carver was wont to sit dividing much flesh among the wooers that were feasting in the house. This seat he carried and set by the table of Telemachus over against him, and there sat down himself. And the henchman took a mess and served it him, and wheaten bread out of the basket.

And close behind him Odysseus entered the house in the guise of a beggar, a wretched man and an old, leaning on his staff, and clothed on with sorry raiment. And he sat down on the ashen threshold within the doorway, leaning against a pillar of cypress wood, which the carpenter on a time had deftly planed, and thereon made straight the line. And Telemachus called the swineherd to him, and took a whole loaf out of the fair basket, and of flesh so much as his hands could hold in their grasp, saying:

'Take and give this to the stranger, and bid him go about and beg himself of all the wooers in their turn, for shame is an ill mate of a needy man.'

So he spake, and the swineherd went when he heard that saying, and stood by and spake to him winged words:

'Stranger, Telemachus gives thee these and bids thee

go about and beg of all the wooers in their turn, for, he says, "shame ill becomes a beggar man."'

Then Odysseus of many counsels answered him and said: 'King Zeus, grant me that Telemachus may be happy among men, and may he have all his heart's desire!'

Therewith he took the gift in both hands, and set it there before his feet on his unsightly scrip. Then he ate meat so long as the minstrel was singing in the halls. When he had done supper, and the divine minstrel was ending his song, then the wooers raised a clamour through the halls; but Athene stood by Odysseus, son of Laertes, and moved him to go gathering morsels of bread among the wooers, and learn which were righteous and which unjust. Yet not even so was she fated to redeem one man of them from an evil doom. So he set out, beginning on the right, to ask of each man, stretching out his hand on every side, as though he were a beggar from of old. And they in pity gave him somewhat, and were amazed at the man, asking one another who he was and whence he came?

Then Melanthius, the goatherd, spake among them:

'Listen, ye wooers of the renowned queen, concerning this stranger, for verily I have seen him before. The swineherd truly was his guide hither, but of him I have no certain knowledge, whence he avows him to be born.'

So spake he, but Antinous rebuked the swineherd, saying: 'Oh notorious swineherd, wherefore, I pray thee, didst thou bring this man to the city? Have we not vagrants enough besides, plaguy beggars, kill-joys of the feast? Dost thou count it a light thing that they assemble here and devour the living of thy master, but thou must needs call in this man too?'

Then didst thou make answer, swineherd Eumaeus: 'Antinous, no fair words are these of thine, noble though thou art. For who ever himself seeks out and bids to the feast a stranger from afar, save only one of those that are craftsmen of the people, a prophet or a healer of ills, or a shipwright, or even a godlike minstrel, who can delight all with his song? Nay, these are the men that are welcome over all the wide earth. But none would call a beggar to the banquet, to waste his substance. But thou art ever hard above all the other wooers to the servants of Odysseus, and, beyond all, to me; but behold, I care not, so long as my mistress, the constant Penelope, lives in the halls and godlike Telemachus.'

Then wise Telemachus answered him, saying: 'Be silent, answer him not, I pray thee, with many words, for Antinous is wont ever to chide us shamefully with bitter speech, yea, and urges the others thereto.'

Therewithal he spake winged words to Antinous: 'Antinous, verily thou hast a good care for me, as it were a father for his son, thou that biddest me drive our guest from the hall with a harsh command. God forbid that such a thing should be! Take somewhat and give it him: lo, I grudge it not; nay, I charge thee to do it. And herein regard not my mother, nor any of the thralls that are in the house of divine Odysseus. Nay, but thou hast no such thought in thy heart, for thou art far more fain to eat thyself than to give to another.'

Then Antinous answered him and spake, saying: 'Telemachus, proud of speech, and unrestrained in fury, what word hast thou spoken? If all the wooers should vouchsafe him as much as I, this house would keep him far enough aloof even for three months' space.'

So he spake, and seized the footstool whereon he rested his sleek feet as he sat at the feast, and showed it from beneath the table where it lay. But all the others gave somewhat and filled the wallet with bread and flesh; yea, and even now, Odysseus as he returned to the threshold, was like to escape scot free, making trial of the Archaeans, but he halted by Antinous, and spake to him, saying:

'Friend, give me somewhat; for methinks thou art not

the basest of the Achaeans, but the best man of them all, for thou art like a king. Wherefore thou shouldest give me a portion of bread, and that a better than the others; so would I make thee renowned over all the wide earth. For I too, once had a house of mine own among men, a rich man with a wealthy house, and many a time would I give to a wanderer, what manner of man soever he might be, and in whatsoever need he came. And I had thralls out of number, and all else in plenty, wherewith folk live well and have a name for riches. But Zeus, the son of Cronos, made me desolate of all,—for surely it was his will,—who sent me with wandering sea-robbers to go to Egypt, a far road, to my ruin. And in the river Aegyptus I stayed my curved ships. Then verily I bade my loved companions to abide there by the ships, and to guard the ship, and I sent forth scouts to range the points of outlook. Now they gave place to wantonness, being the fools of their own force, and soon they fell to wasting the fields of the Egyptians, exceeding fair, and carried away their wives and infant children, and slew the men. And the cry came quickly to the city, and the people heard the shout and came forth at the breaking of the day; and all the plain was filled with footmen and horsemen and with the glitter of bronze. And Zeus, whose joy is in the thunder, sent an evil panic upon my company, and none durst stand and face the foe: for danger encompassed us on every side. There they slew many of us with the edge of the sword, and others they led up with them alive to work for them perforce. But they gave me to a friend who met them, to take to Cyprus, even to Dmetor son of Iasus, who ruled mightily over Cyprus; and thence, behold, am I now come hither in sore distress.'

Then Antinous answered, and spake, saying: 'What god hath brought this plague hither to trouble the feast? Stand forth thus in the midst, away from my table, lest thou come soon to a bitter Egypt and a sad Cyprus; for a bold beggar art thou and a shameless. Thou standest by all in turn and recklessly they give to thee, for they hold not their hand nor feel any ruth in giving freely of others' goods, for that each man has plenty by him.'

Then Odysseus of many counsels drew back and answered him: 'Lo now, I see thou hast not wisdom with thy beauty! From out of thine own house thou wouldest not give even so much as a grain of salt to thy suppliant, thou who now even at another's board dost sit, and canst not find it in thy heart to take of the bread and give it me, where there is plenty to thy hand.'

He spake, and Antinous was mightily angered at heart, and looked fiercely on him and spake winged words:

'Henceforth, methinks, thou shalt not get thee out with honour from the hall, seeing thou dost even rail upon me.'

Therewith he caught up the footstool and smote Odysseus at the base of the right shoulder by the back. But he stood firm as a rock, nor reeled he beneath the blow of Antinous, but shook his head in silence, brooding evil in the deep of his heart. Then he went back to the threshold, and sat him there, and laid down his well-filled scrip, and spake among the wooers:

'Hear me, ye wooers of the renowned queen, and I will say what my spirit within me bids me. Verily there is neither pain nor grief of heart, when a man is smitten in battle fighting for his own possessions, whether cattle or white sheep. But now Antinous hath stricken me for my wretched belly's sake, a thing accursed, that works much ill for men. Ah, if indeed there be gods and Avengers of beggars, may the issues of death come upon Antinous before his wedding!'

Then Antinous, son of Eupeithes, answered him: 'Sit and eat thy meat in quiet, stranger, or get thee elsewhere, lest the young men drag thee by hand or foot through the house for thy evil words, and strip all thy flesh from off thee.'

Even so he spake, and they were all exceedingly wroth at his word. And on this wise would one of the lordly young men speak:

'Antinous, thou didst ill to strike the hapless wanderer, doomed man that thou art,—if indeed there be a god in heaven. Yea and the gods, in the likeness of strangers from far countries, put on all manner of shapes, and wander through the cities, beholding the violence and the righteousness of men.'

So the wooers spake, but he heeded not their words. Now Telemachus nursed in his heart a mighty grief at the smiting of Odysseus, yet he let no tear fall from his eyelids to the ground, but shook his head in silence, brooding evil in the deep of his heart.

Now when wise Penelope heard of the stranger being smitten in the halls, she spake among her maidens, saying: 'Oh that Apollo, the famed archer, may so smite thee thyself, Antinous!'

And the house-dame, Eurynome, answered her, saying: 'Oh that we might win fulfilment of our prayers! So should not one of these men come to the fair-throned Dawn.'

And wise Penelope answered her: 'Nurse, they are all enemies, for they all devise evil continually, but of them all Antinous is the most like to black fate. Some hapless stranger is roaming about the house, begging alms of the men, as his need bids him; and all the others filled his wallet and gave him somewhat, but Antinous smote him at the base of the right shoulder with a stool.'

So she spake among her maidens, sitting in her chamber, while goodly Odysseus was at meat. Then she called to her the goodly swineherd and spake, saying:

'Go thy way, goodly Eumaeus, and bid the stranger come hither, that I may speak him a word of greeting, and ask him if haply he has heard tidings of Odysseus of the hardy heart, or seen him with his eyes; for he seems like one that has wandered far.'

Then didst thou make answer, swineherd Eumaeus: 'Queen, oh that the Achaeans would hold their peace! so would he charm thy very heart, such things doth he say. For I kept him three nights and three days I held him in the steading, for to me he came first when he fled from the ship, yet he had not made an end of the tale of his affliction. Even as when a man gazes on a singer, whom the gods have taught to sing words of yearning joy to mortals, and they have a ceaseless desire to hear him, so long as he will sing; even so he charmed me, sitting by me in the halls. He says that he is a friend of Odysseus and of his house, one that dwells in Crete, where is the race of Minos. Thence he has come hither even now, with sorrow by the way, onward and yet onward wandering; and he stands to it that he has heard tidings of Odysseus nigh at hand and yet alive in the fat land of the men of Thesprotia; and he is bringing many treasures to his home.'

Then wise Penelope answered him, saying: 'Go, call him hither, that he may speak to me face to face. But let these men sit in the doorway and take their pleasure, or even here in the house, since their heart is glad. For their own wealth lies unspoiled at home, bread and sweet wine, and thereon do their servants feed. But they resorting to our house day by day sacrifice oxen and sheep and fat goats, and keep revel and drink the dark wine recklessly; and, lo, our great wealth is wasted, for there is no man now alive, such as Odysseus was, to keep ruin from the house. Oh, if Odysseus might come again to his own country; soon would he and his son avenge the violence of these men!'

Even so she spake, and Telemachus sneezed loudly, and around the roof rang wondrously. And Penelope laughed, and straightway spake to Eumaeus winged words:

'Go, call me the stranger, even so, into my presence.

Dost thou not mark how my son has sneezed a blessing on all my words? Wherefore no half-wrought doom shall befall the wooers every one, nor shall any avoid death and the fates. Yet another thing will I say, and do thou ponder it in thy heart. If I shall find that he himself speaks nought but truth, I will clothe him with a mantle and a doublet, goodly raiment.'

So she spake, and the swineherd departed when he heard that saying, and stood by the stranger and spake winged words:

'Father and stranger, wise Penelope, the mother of Telemachus, is calling for thee, and her mind bids her inquire as touching her lord, albeit she has sorrowed much already. And if she shall find that thou dost speak nought but truth, she will clothe thee in a mantle and a doublet, whereof thou standest most in need. Moreover thou shalt beg thy bread through the land and shalt fill thy belly, and whosoever will, shall give to thee.'

Then the steadfast goodly Odysseus answered him, saying: 'Eumaeus, soon would I tell all the truth to the daughter of Icarius, wise Penelope, for well I know his story, and we have borne our travail together. But I tremble before the throng of the froward wooers, whose outrage and violence reach even to the iron heaven. For even now, as I was going through the house, when this man struck and pained me sore, and that for no ill deed, neither Telemachus nor any other kept off the blow. Wherefore now, bid Penelope tarry in the chambers, for all her eagerness, till the going down of the sun, and then let her ask me concerning her lord, as touching the day of his returning, and let her give me a seat yet nearer to the fire, for behold, I have sorry raiment, and thou knowest it thyself, since I made my supplication first to thee.'

Even so he spake, and the swineherd departed when he heard that saying. And as he crossed the threshold Penelope spake to him:

'Thou bringest him not, Eumaeus: what means the wanderer hereby? Can it be that he fears some one out of measure, or is he even ashamed of tarrying in the house? A shamefaced man makes a bad beggar.'

Then didst thou make answer, swineherd Eumaeus: 'He speaks aright, and but as another would deem, in that he shuns the outrage of overweening men. Rather would he have thee wait till the going down of the sun. Yea, and it is far meeter for thyself, O queen, to utter thy word to the stranger alone, and to listen to his speech.'

Then the wise Penelope answered: 'Not witless is the stranger; even as he deems, so it well may be. For there are no mortal men, methinks, so wanton as these, and none that devise such infatuate deeds.'

So she spake, and the goodly swineherd departed into the throng of the wooers, when he had showed her all his message. And straightway he spake to Telemachus winged words, holding his head close to him, that the others might not hear:

'Friend, I am going hence to look after thy swine and the things of the farm, thy livelihood and mine; but do thou take charge of all that is here. Yet first look to thyself and take heed that no evil comes nigh thee, for many of the Achaeans have ill will against us, whom may Zeus confound before their mischief falls on us!'

And wise Telemachus answered him, and said: 'Even so shall it be, father; and do thou get thee on thy way, when thou hast supped. And in the morning come again, and bring fair victims for sacrifice. And all these matters will be a care to me and to the deathless gods.'

Thus he spake, and the other sat down again on the polished settle; and when he had satisfied his heart with meat and drink, he went on his way to the swine, leaving the courts and the hall full of feasters; and they were making merry with dance and song, for already it was close on eventide.

BOOK XVIII

The fighting at fists of Odysseus with Irus. His admonitions to Amphinomus. Penelope appears before the wooers, and draws presents from them.

THEN up came a common beggar, who was wont to beg through the town of Ithaca, one that was known among all men for ravening greed, for his endless eating and drinking, yet he had no force or might, though he was bulky enough to look on. Arnaeus was his name, for so had his good mother given it him at his birth, but all the young men called him Irus, because he ran on errands, whensoever any might bid him. So now he came, and would have driven Odysseus from his own house, and began reviling him, and spake winged words:

'Get thee hence, old man, from the doorway, lest thou be even haled out soon by the foot. Seest thou not that all are now giving me the wink, and bidding me drag thee forth? Nevertheless, I feel shame of the task. Nay get thee up, lest our quarrel soon pass even to blows.'

Then Odysseus of many counsels looked fiercely on him, and spake saying: 'Sir, neither in deed nor word do I harm thee, nor do I grudge that any should give to thee, yea though it were a good handful. But this threshold will hold us both, and thou hast no need to be jealous for the sake of other men's goods. Thou seemest to me to be a wanderer, even as I am, and the gods it is that are like to give us gain. Only provoke me not overmuch to buffeting, lest thou anger me, and old though I be I defile thy breast and lips with blood. Thereby should I have the greater quiet to-morrow, for methinks that thou shalt never again come to the hall of Odysseus, son of Laertes.'

Then the beggar Irus spake unto him in anger: 'Lo now, how trippingly and like an old cinder-wife this glutton speaks, on whom I will work my evil will, and smite him right and left, and drive all the teeth from his jaws to the ground, like the tusks of a swine that spoils the corn. Gird thyself now, that even these men all may know our mettle in fight. Nay, how shouldst thou do battle with a younger man than thou?'

Thus did they whet each the other's rage right manfully before the lofty doors upon the polished threshold. And the mighty prince Antinous heard the twain, and sweetly he laughed out, and spake among the wooers:

'Friends, never before has there been such a thing; such goodly game has a god brought to this house. The stranger yonder and Irus are bidding each other to buffets. Quick, let us match them one against the other.'

Then all at the word leaped up laughing, and gathered round the ragged beggars, and Antinous, son of Eupeithes, spake among them saying: 'Hear me, ye lordly wooers, and I will say somewhat. Here are goats' bellies lying at the fire, that we laid by at supper-time and filled with fat and blood. Now whichsoever of the twain wins, and shows himself the better man, let him stand up and take his choice of these puddings. And further, he shall always eat at our feasts, nor will we suffer any other beggar to come among us and ask for alms.'

So spake Antinous, and the saying pleased them well. Then Odysseus of many counsels spake among them craftily:

'Friends, an old man and foredone with travail may in no wise fight with a younger. But my belly's call is urgent on me, that evil-worker, to the end that I may be subdued with stripes. But come now, swear me all of you a strong oath, so that none, for the sake of shewing a favour to Irus, may strike me a foul blow with heavy hand and subdue me by violence to my foe.'

So he spake, and they all swore not to strike him, as he bade them. Now when they had sworn and done that oath, the mighty prince Telemachus once more spake among them:

'Stranger, if thy heart and lordly spirit urge thee to rid thee of this fellow, then fear not any other of the Achaeans, for whoso strikes thee shall have to fight with many. Thy host am I, and the princes consent with me, Antinous and Eurymachus, men of wisdom both.'

So spake he and they all consented thereto. Then Odysseus girt his rags about his loins, and let his thighs be seen, goodly and great, and his broad shoulders and breast and mighty arms were manifest. And Athene came nigh and made greater the limbs of the shepherd of the people. Then the wooers were exceedingly amazed, and thus would one speak looking to his neighbour:

'Right soon will Irus, un-Irused, have a bane of his own bringing, such a thing as that old man shows from out his rags!"

So they spake, and the mind of Irus was pitifully stirred; but even so the servants girded him and led him out perforce in great fear, his flesh trembling on his limbs. Then Antinous chid him, and spake and hailed him:

'Thou lubber, better for thee that thou wert not now, nor ever hadst been born, if indeed thou tremblest before this man, and art so terribly afraid; an old man too he is, and foredone with the travail that is come upon him. But I will tell thee plainly, and it shall surely be accomplished. If this man prevail against thee and prove thy master, I will cast thee into a black ship, and send thee to the mainland to Echetus the king, the maimer of all mankind, who will cut off thy nose and ears with the pitiless steel, and draw out thy vitals and give them raw to dogs to rend.'

So he spake, and yet greater trembling gat hold of the limbs of Irus, and they led him into the ring, and the twain put up their hands. Then the steadfast goodly Odysseus mused in himself whether he should smite him in such wise that his life should leave his body, even there where he fell, or whether he should strike him lightly, and stretch him on the earth. And as he thought thereon, this seemed to him the better way, to strike lightly, that the Achaeans might not take note of him, who he was. Then the twain put up their hands, and Irus struck at the right shoulder, but the other smote him on his neck beneath the ear, and crushed in the bones, and straightway the red blood gushed up through his mouth, and with a moan he fell in the dust, and drave together his teeth as he kicked the ground. But the proud wooers threw up their hands, and died outright for laughter. Then Odysseus, seized him by the foot, and dragged him forth through the doorway, till he came to the courtyard and the gates of the gallery, and he set him down and rested him against the courtyard wall, and put his staff in his hands, and uttering his voice spake to him winged words:

'Sit thou there now, and scare off swine and dogs, and let not such an one as thou be lord over strangers and beggars, pitiful as thou art, lest haply some worse thing befall thee.'

Thus he spake, and cast about his shoulders his mean scrip all tattered, and the cord therewith to hang it, and he gat him back to the threshold, and sat him down there again. Now the wooers went within laughing sweetly, and greeted him, saying:

'May Zeus, stranger, and all the other deathless gods give thee thy dearest wish, even all thy heart's desire, seeing that thou hast made that insatiate one to cease from his begging in the land! Soon will we take him over to the mainland, to Echetus the king, the maimer of all mankind.'

So they spake, and goodly Odysseus rejoiced in the omen of the words. And Antinous set by him the great pudding, stuffed with fat and blood, and Amphinomus took up two loaves from the basket, and set them by him and pledged him in a golden cup, and spake saying:

'Father and stranger, hail! may happiness be thine in the time to come; but as now, thou art fast holden in befall thee.'

And Odysseus of many counsels answered him saying: 'Amphinomus, verily thou seemest to me a prudent man enough; for such too was the father of whom thou art sprung, for I have heard the fair fame of him, how that Nisus of Dulichium was a good man and a rich, and his son they say thou art, and thou seemest a man of understanding. Wherefore I will tell thee, and do thou mark and listen to me. Nought feebler doth the earth nurture than man, of all the creatures that breathe and move upon the face of the earth. Lo, he thinks that he shall never suffer evil in time to come, while the gods give him happiness, and his limbs move lightly. But when again the blessed gods have wrought for him sorrow, even so he bears it, as he must, with a steadfast heart. For the spirit of men upon the earth is even as their day, that comes upon them from the father of gods and men. Yea, and I too once was like to have been prosperous among men, but many an infatuate deed I did, giving place to mine own hardihood and strength, and trusting to my father and my brethren. Wherefore let no man for ever be lawless any more, but keep quietly the gifts of the gods, whatsoever they may give. Such infatuate deeds do I see the wooers devising, as they waste the wealth, and hold in no regard the wife of a man, who, methinks, will not much longer be far from his friends and his own land; nay, he is very near. But for thee, may some god withdraw thee hence to thy home, and mayst thou not meet him in the day when he returns to his own dear country! For not without blood, as I deem, will they be sundered, the wooers and Odysseus, when once he shall have come beneath his own roof.'

Thus he spake, and pouring an offering and then drank of the honey-sweet wine, and again set the cup in the hands of the arrayer of the people. But the other went back through the hall, sad at heart and bowing his head; for verily his soul boded evil. Yet even so he avoided not his fate, for Athene had bound him likewise to be slain outright at the hands and by the spear of Telemachus. So he sat down again on the high seat whence he had arisen.

Now the goddess, grey-eyed Athene, put it into the heart of the daughter of Icarius, wise Penelope, to show herself to the wooers, that she might make their heart all flutter with hope, and that she might win yet more worship from her lord and her son than heretofore. So she laughed an idle laugh, and spake to the nurse, and hailed her, saying:

'Eurynome, my heart yearns, though before I had no such desire, to show myself to the wooers, hateful as they are. I would also say a word to my son, that will be for his weal, namely, that he should not for ever consort with the proud wooers, who speak friendly with their lips, but imagine evil in the latter end.'

Then the housewife, Eurynome, spake to her saying: 'Yea, my child, all this thou hast spoken as is meet. Go then, and declare thy word to thy son and hide it not, but first wash thee and anoint thy face, and go not as thou art with thy cheeks all stained with tears. Go, for it is little good to sorrow always, and never cease. And lo, thy son is now of an age to hear thee, he whom thou hast above all things prayed the gods that thou mightest see with a beard upon his chin.'

Then wise Penelope answered her, saying: "Eurynome, speak not thus comfortably to me, for all thy love, bidding me to wash and be anointed with ointment. For the gods that keep Olympus destroyed my bloom, since the day that he departed in the hollow ships. But bid Autonoe and Hippodameia come to me, to stand by my side in the halls. Alone I will not go among men for I am ashamed.'

So she spake, and the old woman passed through the chamber to tell the maidens, and hasten their coming.

Thereon the goddess, grey-eyed Athene, had another thought. She shed a sweet slumber over the daughter of Icarius, who sank back in sleep, and all her joints were loosened as she lay in the chair, and the fair goddess the while was giving her gifts immortal, that all the Achaeans might marvel at her. Her fair face first she steeped with beauty imperishable, such as that wherewith the crowned Cytherea is anointed, when she goes to the lovely dances of the Graces. And she made her taller and greater to behold, and made her whiter than new-sawn ivory. Now when she had wrought thus, that fair goddess departed, and the white-armed handmaidens came forth from the chamber and drew nigh with a sound of voices. Then sweet sleep left hold of Penelope, and she rubbed her cheeks with her hands, and said:

'Surely soft slumber wrapped me round, most wretched though I be. Oh! that pure Artemis would give me so soft a death even now, that I might no more waste my life in sorrow of heart, and longing for the manifold excellence of my dear lord, for that he was foremost of the Achaeans.'

With this word she went down from the shining upper chamber, not alone, for two handmaidens likewise bare her company. But when the fair lady had now come to the wooers, she stood by the pillar of the well-builded roof, holding her glistening tire before her face, and on either side of her stood a faithful handmaiden. And straightway the knees of the wooers were loosened, and their hearts were enchanted with love, and each one uttered a prayer that he might be her bed-fellow. But she spake to Telemachus, her dear son:

'Telemachus, thy mind and thy thoughts are no longer stable as they were. While thou wast still a child, thou hadst a yet quicker and more crafty wit, but now that thou art great of growth, and art come to the measure of manhood, and a stranger looking to thy stature and thy beauty might say that thou must be some rich man's son, thy mind and thy thoughts are no longer right as of old. For lo, what manner of deed has been done in these halls, in that thou hast suffered thy guest to be thus shamefully dealt with! How would it be now, if the stranger sitting thus in our house, were to come to some harm all through this evil handling? Shame and disgrace would be thine henceforth among men.'

Then wise Telemachus answered her: 'Mother mine, as to this matter I count it no blame that thou art angered. Yet have I knowledge and understanding of each thing, of the good and of the evil; but heretofore I was a child. Howbeit I cannot devise all things according to wisdom, for these men in their evil counsel drive me from my wits, on this side and on that, and there is none to aid me. Howsoever this battle between Irus and the stranger did not fall out as the wooers would have had it, but the stranger proved the better man. Would to Father Zeus and Athene and Apollo, that the wooers in our halls were even now thus vanquished, and wagging their heads, some in the court, and some within the house, and that the limbs of each man were loosened in such fashion as Irus yonder sits now, by the courtyard gates wagging his head, like a drunken man, and cannot stand upright on his feet, nor yet get him home to his own place, seeing that his limbs are loosened!'

Thus they spake one to another. But Eurymachus spake to Penelope, saying:

'Daughter of Icarius, wise Penelope, if all the Achaeans

in Iasian Argos could behold thee, even a greater press of wooers would feast in your halls from to-morrow's dawn, since thou dost surpass all women in beauty and stature, and within in wisdom of mind.'

Then wise Penelope answered him: 'Eurymachus, surely my excellence, both of face and form, the gods destroyed in the day when the Argives embarked for Ilios, and with them went my lord Odysseus. If but he might come and watch over this my life, greater thus would be my fame and fairer! But now am I in sorrow; such a host of ills some god has sent against me. Ah, well do I remember, when he set forth and left his own country, how he took me by the right hand at the wrist and spake, saying:

' "Lady, methinks that all the goodly-greaved Achaeans will not win a safe return from Troy; for the Trojans too, they say, are good men at arms, as spearsmen, and bowmen, and drivers of fleet horses, such as ever most swiftly determine the great strife of equal battle. Wherefore I know not if the gods will suffer me to return, or whether I shall be cut off there in Troy; so do thou have a care for all these things. Be mindful of my father and my mother in the halls, even as now thou art, or yet more than now, while I am far away. But when thou seest thy son a bearded man, marry whom thou wilt and leave thine own house."

'Even so did he speak, and now all these things have an end. The night shall come when a hateful marriage shall find me out, me most luckless, whose good hap Zeus has taken away. But furthermore this sore trouble has come on my heart and soul; for this was not the manner of wooers in time past. Whoso wish to woo a good lady and the daughter of a rich man, and vie one with another, themselves bring with them oxen of their own and goodly flocks, a banquet for the friends of the bride, and they give the lady splendid gifts, but do not devour another's livelihood without atonement.'

Thus she spake, and the steadfast goodly Odysseus rejoiced because she drew from them gifts, and beguiled their souls with soothing words, while her heart was set on other things.

Then Antinous, son of Eupeithes, answered her again: 'Daughter of Icarius, wise Penelope, the gifts which any of the Achaeans may choose to bring hither, do thou take; for it were ill to withhold a gift. But we for our part will neither go to our lands nor otherwise, before thou art wedded to the best man of the Achaeans.'

So spake Antinous, and the saying pleased them well, and each man sent a henchman to bring his gifts. For Antinous his henchman bare a broidered robe, great and very fair, wherein were golden brooches, twelve in all, fitted with well bent clasps. And the henchman straightway bare Eurymachus a golden chain of curious work, strung with amber beads, shining like the sun. And his squires bare for Eurydamas a pair of ear-rings, with three drops well wrought, and much grace shone from them. And out of the house of Peisander the prince, the son of Polyctor, the squire brought a necklet, a very lovely jewel. And likewise the Achaeans brought each one some other beautiful gift.

Then the fair lady went aloft to her upper chamber, and her attendant maidens bare for her the lovely gifts, while the wooers turned to dancing and the delight of song, and therein took their pleasure, and awaited the coming of eventide. And dark evening came on them at their pastime. Anon they set up three braziers in the halls, to give them light, and on these they laid firewood all around, faggots seasoned long since and sere, and new split with the axe. And midway by the braziers they placed torches, and the maids of Odysseus, of the hardy heart, held up the lights in turn. Then the prince Odysseus of many counsels himself spake among them saying:

'Ye maidens of Odysseus, the lord so long afar, get ye

into the chambers where the honoured queen abides, and twist the yarn at her side, and gladden her heart as ye sit in the chamber, or card the wools with your hands; but I will minister light to all these that are here. For even if they are minded to wait the throned Dawn, they shall not outstay me, so long enduring am I.'

So he spake, but they laughed and looked one at the other. And the fair Melantho chid him shamefully, Melantho that Dolius begat, but Penelope reared, and entreated her tenderly as she had been her own child, and gave her playthings to her heart's desire. Yet, for all that, sorrow for Penelope touched not her heart, but she loved Eurymachus and was his paramour. Now she chid Odysseus with railing words:

'Wretched guest, surely thou art some brain-struck man, seeing that thou dost not choose to go and sleep at a smithy, or at some place of common resort, but here thou pratest much and boldly among many lords and hast no fear at heart. Verily wine has got about thy wits, or perchance thou art always of this mind, and so thou dost babble idly. Art thou beside thyself for joy, because thou hast beaten the beggar Irus? Take heed lest a better man than Irus rise up presently against thee, to lay his mighty hands about thy head and bedabble thee with blood, and send thee hence from the house.'

Then Odysseus of many counsels looked fiercely on her, and said: 'Yea, straight will I go yonder and tell Telemachus hereof, thou shameless thing, for this thy speech, that forthwith he may cut thee limb from limb.'

So he spake, and with his saying scared away the women, who fled through the hall, and the knees of each were loosened for fear, for they deemed that his words were true. But Odysseus took his stand by the burning braziers, tending the lights, and gazed on all the men: but far other matters he pondered in his heart, things not to be unfulfilled.

Now Athene would in no wise suffer the lordly wooers to abstain from biting scorn, that the pain might sink yet the deeper into the heart of Odysseus, son of Laertes. So Eurymachus, son of Polybus, began to speak among them, girding at Odysseus, and so made mirth for his friends:

'Hear me, ye wooers of the queen renowned, that I may say that which my spirit within bids me. Not without the gods' will has this man come to the house of Odysseus; methinks at least that the torchlight flares forth from that head of his, for there are no hairs on it, nay never so thin.'

He spake and withal addressed Odysseus, waster of cities: 'Stranger, wouldest thou indeed be my hireling, if I would take thee for my man, at an upland farm, and thy wages shall be assured thee, and there shalt thou gather stones for walls and plant tall trees? There would I provide thee bread continual, and clothe thee with raiment, and give thee shoes for thy feet. Howbeit, since thou art practised only in evil, thou wilt not care to go to the labours of the field, but wilt choose rather to go louting through the land, that thou mayst have wherewithal to feed thine insatiate belly.'

Then Odysseus of many counsels answered him and said: 'Eurymachus, would that there might be a trial of labour between us twain, in the season of spring, when the long days begin! In the deep grass might it be, and I should have a crooked scythe, and thou another like it, that we might try each the other in the matter of labour, fasting till late eventide, and grass there should be in plenty. Or would again, that there were oxen to drive, the best there may be, large and tawny, both well filled with fodder, of equal age and force to bear the yoke and of strength untiring! And it should be a field of four ploughgates, and the clod should yield before the ploughshare. Then shouldest thou see me, whether or no I would cut a clean furrow unbroken before me. Or would that this very day Cronion might waken war whence he would, and that I had a shield and two spears, and a helmet all of bronze, close fitting on my temples! Then shouldest thou see me mingling in the forefront of the battle, nor speak and taunt me with this my belly. Nay, thou art exceeding wanton and thy heart is hard, and thou thinkest thyself some great one and mighty, because thou consortest with few men and feeble. Ah, if Odysseus might but return and come to his own country, right soon would yonder doors, full wide as they are, prove all too strait for thee in thy flight through the doorway!'

Thus he spake, and Eurymachus waxed yet the more wroth at heart, and looking fiercely on him spake to him winged words:

'Ah, wretch that thou art, right soon will I work thee mischief, so boldly thou pratest among many lords, and hast no fear at heart. Verily wine has got about thy wits, or perchance thou art always of this mind, and so thou dost babble idly. Art thou beside thyself for joy, because thou hast beaten the beggar Irus?'

Therewith he caught up a footstool, but Odysseus sat him down at the knees of Amphinomus of Dulichium, in dread of Eurymachus. And Eurymachus cast and smote the cup-bearer on the right hand, and the ladle cup dropped to the ground with a clang, while the young man groaned and fell backwards in the dust. Then the wooers clamoured through the shadowy halls, and thus one would say looking to his neighbour:

'Would that our wandering guest had perished otherwhere, or ever he came hither; so should he never have made all this tumult in our midst! But now we are all at strife about beggars, and there will be no more joy of the good feast, for worse things have their way.'

Then the mighty prince Telemachus spake among them:

'Sirs, ye are mad; now doth your mood betray that ye

have eaten and drunken; some one of the gods is surely moving you. Nay, now that ye have feasted well, go home and lay you to rest, since your spirit so bids; for as for me, I drive no man hence.'

Thus he spake, and they all bit their lips and marvelled at Telemachus, in that he spake boldly. Then Amphinomus made harangue, and spake among them, Amphinomus, the famous son of Nisus the prince, the son of Aretias:

'Friends, when a righteous word has been spoken, none surely would rebuke another with hard speech and be angry. Misuse ye not this stranger, neither any of the thralls that are in the house of godlike Odysseus. But come, let the wine-bearer pour for libation into each cup in turn, that after the drink-offering we may get us home to bed. But the stranger let us leave in the halls of Odysseus for a charge to Telemachus: for to his home has he come.'

Thus he spake, and his word was well-pleasing to them all. Then the lord Mulius mixed for them the bowl, the henchman out of Dulichium, who was squire of Amphinomus. And he stood by all and served it to them in their turn; and they poured forth before the blessed gods, and drank the honey-sweet wine. Now when they had poured forth and had drunken to their hearts' content, they departed to lie down, each one to his own house.

BOOK XIX

Telemachus removes the arms out of the hall. Odysseus discourseth with Penelope. And is known by his nurse, but concealed. And the hunting of the boar upon that occasion related.

Now the goodly Odysseus was left behind in the hall, devising with Athene's aid the slaying of the wooers, and straightway he spake winged words to Telemachus:

'Telemachus, we must needs lay by the weapons of war within, every one; and when the wooers miss them and ask thee concerning them, thou shalt beguile them with soft words, saying:

'Out of the smoke I laid them by, since they were no longer like those that Odysseus left behind him of old, when he went to Troy, but they are wholly marred, so mightily hath passed upon them the vapour of fire. Moreover some god hath put into my heart this other and greater care, that perchance when ye are heated with wine, ye set a quarrel between you and wound one the other, and thereby shame the feast and the wooing; for iron of itself draws a man thereto.'

Thus he spake, and Telemachus hearkened to his dear father, and called forth to him the nurse Eurycleia and spake to her, saying:

'Nurse, come now I pray thee, shut up the women in their chambers till I shall have laid by in the armoury the goodly weapons of my father, which all uncared for the smoke dims in the hall, since my father went hence, and I was still but a child. Now I wish to lay them by where the vapour of the fire will not reach them.'

Then the good nurse Eurycleia answered him, saying: 'Ah, my child, if ever thou wouldest but take careful thought in such wise as to mind the house, and guard all this wealth! But come, who shall fetch the light and bear it, if thou hast thy way, since thou wouldest not that the maidens, who might have given light, should go before thee?'

Then wise Telemachus made answer to her: 'This stranger here, for I will keep no man in idleness who eats of my bread, even if he have come from afar.'

Thus he spake, and wingless her speech remained, and she closed the doors of the fair-lying chambers. Then they twain sprang up, Odysseus and his renowned son, and set to carry within the helmets and the bossy shields, and the sharp-pointed spears; and before them Pallas Athene bare a golden cresset and cast a most lovely light. Thereon Telemachus spake to his father suddenly:

'Father, surely a great marvel is this that I behold with mine eyes; meseems, at least, that the walls of the hall and the fair main-beams of the roof and the cross-beams of pine, and the pillars that run aloft, are bright as it were with flaming fire. Verily some god is within, of those that hold the wide heaven.'

And Odysseus of many counsels answered him and said: 'Hold thy peace and keep thy thoughts in check and ask not hereof. Lo, this is the wont of the gods that hold Olympus. But do thou go and lay thee down, and I will abide here, that I may yet further provoke the maids and thy mother to answer; and she in her sorrow will ask me concerning each thing, one by one.'

So he spake, and Telemachus passed out through the hall to his chamber to lie down, by the light of the flaming torches, even to the chamber where of old he took his rest, when sweet sleep came over him. There now too he lay down and awaited the bright Dawn. But goodly Odysseus was left behind in the hall, devising with Athene's aid the slaying of the wooers.

Now forth from her chamber came the wise Penelope, like Artemis or golden Aphrodite, and they set a chair for her hard by before the fire, where she was wont to sit, a chair well-wrought and inlaid with ivory and silver, which on a time the craftsman Icmalius had fashioned, and had joined thereto a footstool, that was part of the chair, whereon a great fleece was used to be laid. Here, then, the wise Penelope sat her down, and next came white-armed handmaids from the women's chamber, and began to take away the many fragments of food, and the tables and the cups whence the proud lords had been drinking, and they raked out the fire from the braziers on to the floor, and piled many fresh logs upon them, to give light and warmth.

Then Melantho began to revile Odysseus yet a second time, saying: 'Stranger, wilt thou still be a plague to us here, circling round the house in the night, and spying the women? Nay, get thee forth, thou wretched thing, and be thankful for thy supper, or straightway shalt thou even be smitten with a torch and so fare out of the doors.'

Then Odysseus of many counsels looked fiercely on her, and said: 'Good woman, what possesses thee to assail me thus out of an angry heart? Is it because I go filthy and am clothed about in sorry raiment, and beg through the land, for necessity is laid on me? This is the manner of beggars and of wandering men. For I too once had a house of mine own among men, a rich man with a wealthy house, and many a time would I give to a wanderer, what manner of man soever he might be, and in whatsoever need he came. And I had countless thralls, and all else in plenty, whereby folk live well and have a name for riches. But Zeus, the son of Cronos, made me desolate of all, for surely it was his will. Wherefore, woman, see lest some day thou too lose all thy fine show wherein thou now excellest among the handmaids, as well may chance, if thy mistress be provoked to anger with thee, or if Odysseus come home, for there is yet a place for hope. And even if he hath perished as ye deem, and is never more to return, yet by Apollo's grace he hath a son like him, Telemachus, and none of the women works wantonness in his halls without his knowledge, for he is no longer of an age not to mark it.'

Thus he spake, and the wise Penelope heard him, and rebuked the handmaid, and spake and hailed her:

'Thou reckless thing and unabashed, be sure thy great sin is not hidden from me, and thy blood shall be on thine own head for the same! For thou knewest right well, in that thou hadst heard it from my lips, how that I was minded to ask the stranger in my halls for tidings of my lord; for I am grievously afflicted.'

Therewith she spake likewise to the housedame, Eurynome, saying:

'Eurynome, bring hither a settle with a fleece thereon, that the stranger may sit and speak with me and hear my words, for I would ask him all his story.'

So she spake, and the nurse made haste and brought a polished settle, and cast a fleece thereon; and then the steadfast goodly Odysseus sat him down there, and the wise Penelope spake first, saying:

'Stranger, I will make bold first to ask thee this: who art thou of the sons of men, and whence? Where is thy city, and where are they that begat thee?'

And Odysseus of many counsels answered her and said: 'Lady, no one of mortal men in the wide world could find fault with thee, for lo, thy fame goes up to the wide heaven, as doth the fame of a blameless king, one that fears the gods and reigns among many men and mighty, maintaining right, and the black earth bears wheat and barley, and the trees are laden with fruit, and the sheep bring forth and fail not, and the sea gives store of fish, and all out of his good guidance, and the people prosper under him. Wherefore do thou ask me now in thy house all else that thou wilt, but inquire not concerning my race and mine own country, lest as I think thereupon thou fill my heart the more with pains, for I am a man of many sorrows. Moreover it beseems me not to sit weeping and wailing in another's house, for it is little good to mourn always without ceasing, lest perchance one of the maidens, or even thyself, be angry with me and say that I swim in tears, as one that is heavy with wine.'

Then wise Penelope answered him, and said: 'Stranger, surely my excellence, both of face and form, the gods destroyed in the day when the Argives embarked for Ilios, and with them went my lord Odysseus. If but he might come and watch over this my life, greater and fairer thus would be my fame! But now am I in sorrow, such a host of ills some god has sent against me. For all the noblest that are princes in the isles, in Dulichium and Same and wooded Zacynthus, and they that dwell around even in clear-seen Ithaca, these are wooing me against my will, and devouring the house. Wherefore I take no heed of strangers, nor suppliants, nor at all of heralds, the craftsmen of the people. But I waste my heart away in longing for Odysseus; so they speed on my marriage and I weave a web of wiles. First some god put it into my heart to set up a great web in the halls, and thereat to weave a robe fine of woof and very wide; and anon I spake among them, saying: "Ye princely youths, my wooers, now that goodly Odysseus is dead, do ye abide patiently, how eager soever to speed on this marriage of mine, till I finish the robe. I would not that the threads perish to no avail, even this shroud for the hero Laertes, against the day when the ruinous doom shall bring him low, of death that lays men at their length. So shall none of the Achaean women in the land count it blame in me, as well might be, were he to lie without a winding sheet, a man that had gotten great possessions."

'So spake I, and their high hearts consented thereto. So then in the daytime I would weave the mighty web, and in the night unravel the same, when I had let place the torches by me. Thus for the space of three years I hid the thing by craft and beguiled the minds of the Achaeans. But when the fourth year arrived, and the seasons came round as the months waned, and many days were accomplished, then it was that by help of the handmaids, shameless things and reckless, the wooers came and trapped me, and chid me loudly. Thus did I finish the web by no will of mine, for so I must. And now I can neither escape the marriage nor devise any further counsel, and my parents are instant with me to marry, and my son chafes that these men devour his livelihood, as he takes note of all; for by this time he has come to man's estate, and is full able to care for a household, for one to which Zeus vouchsafes honour. But even so tell me of thine own stock, whence thou art, for thou art not sprung of oak or rock, whereof old tales tell.'

And Odysseus of many counsels answered her and said:

'O wife revered of Odysseus, son of Laertes, wilt thou never have done asking me about mine own race? Nay, but I will tell thee: yet surely thou wilt give me over to sorrows yet more than those wherein I am holden, for so it ever is when a man has been afar from his own country, so long as now I am, wandering in sore pain to many cities of mortals. Yet even so I will tell thee what thou askest and inquirest. There is a land called Crete in the midst of the wine-dark sea, a fair land and a rich, begirt with water, and therein are many men innumerable, and ninety cities. And all have not the same speech, but there is confusion of tongues; there dwell Achaeans and there too Cretans of Crete, high of heart, and Cydonians there and Dorians of waving plumes and goodly Pelasgians. And among these cities is the mighty city Cnosus, wherein Minos when he was nine years old began to rule, he who held converse with great Zeus, and was the father of my father, even of Deucalion, high of heart. Now Deucalion begat me and Idomeneus the prince. Howbeit, he had gone in his beaked ships up into Ilios, with the sons of Atreus; but my famed name is Aethon, being the younger of the twain and he was the first born and the better man. There I saw Odysseus, and gave him guest-gifts, for the might of the wind bare him too to Crete, as he was making for Troy-land, and had driven him wandering past Malea. So he stayed his ships in Amnisus, whereby is the cave of Eilithyia, in havens hard to win, and scarce he escaped the tempest. Anon he came up to the city and asked for Idomeneus, saying that he was his friend and held by him in love and honour. But it was now the tenth or the eleventh dawn since Idomeneus had gone in his beaked ships up into Ilios. Then I led him to the house, and gave him good entertainment with all loving-kindness out of the plenty in my house, and for him and for the rest of his company, that went with him, I gathered and gave barleymeal and dark wine out of the public store, and oxen to sacrifice to his heart's desire. There the goodly Achaeans abode twelve days, for the strong North Wind penned them there, and suffered them not to stay upon the coast, for some angry god had roused it. On the thirteenth day the wind fell, and then they lifted anchor.'

So he told many a false tale in the likeness of truth, and her tears flowed as she listened, and her flesh melted. And even as the snow melts in the high places of the hills, the snow that the South-East wind has thawed, when the West has scattered it abroad, and as it wastes the river streams run full, even so her fair cheeks melted beneath her tears, as she wept her own lord, who even then was sitting by her. Now Odysseus had compassion of heart upon his wife in her lamenting, but his eyes kept steadfast between his eyelids as it were horn or iron, and craftily he hid his tears. But she, when she had taken her fill of tearful lamentation, answered him in turn and spake, saying:

'Friend as thou art, even now I think to make trial of thee, and learn whether in very truth thou didst entertain my lord there in thy halls with his godlike company, as thou sayest. Tell me what manner of raiment he was clothed in about his body, and what manner of man he was himself, and tell me of his fellows that went with him.'

Then Odysseus of many counsels answered her saying: 'Lady, it is hard for one so long parted from him to tell thee all this, for it is now the twentieth year since he went thither and left my country. Yet even so I will tell thee as I see him in spirit. Goodly Odysseus wore a thick purple mantle, twofold, which had a brooch fashioned in gold, with two sheaths for the pins, and on the face of it was a curious device: a hound in his forepaws held a dappled fawn and gazed on it as it writhed. And all men marvelled at the workmanship, how, wrought as they were in gold, the hound was gazing on the fawn and strangling it, and the fawn was writhing with his feet and striving to flee. Moreover, I marked the shining doublet about his body, like the gleam over the skin of a dried onion, so smooth it was, and glistening as the sun; truly many women looked thereon and wondered. Yet another thing will I tell thee, and do thou ponder it in thy heart. I know not if Odysseus was thus clothed upon at home, or if one of his fellows gave him the raiment as he went on board the swift ship, or even it may be some stranger, seeing that to many men was Odysseus dear, for few of the Achaeans were his peers. I, too, gave him a sword of bronze, and a fair purple mantle with double fold, and a tasselled doublet, and I sent him away with all honour on his decked ship. Moreover, a henchman bare him company, somewhat older than he, and I will tell thee of him too, what manner of man he was. He was round-shouldered, black-skinned, and curly-headed, his name Eurybates; and Odysseus honoured him above all his company, because in all things he was like-minded with himself.'

So he spake, and in her heart he stirred yet more the desire of weeping, as she knew the certain tokens that Odysseus showed her. So when she had taken her fill of tearful lament, then she answered him, and spake saying: 'Now verily, stranger, thou that even before wert held in pity, shalt be dear and honourable in my halls, for it was I who gave him these garments, as judging from thy words, and folded them myself, and brought them from the chamber, and added besides the shining brooch to be his jewel. But him I shall never welcome back, returned home to his own dear country. Wherefore with an evil fate it was that Odysseus went hence in the hollow ship to see that evil Ilios, never to be named!'

And Odysseus of many counsels answered her saying: 'Wife revered of Odysseus, son of Laertes, destroy not now thy fair flesh any more, nor waste thy heart with weeping for thy lord;—not that I count it any blame in thee, for many a woman weeps that has lost her wedded lord, to whom she has borne children in her love,—albeit a far other man than Odysseus, who, they say, is like the gods. Nay, cease from thy lamenting, and lay up my word in thy heart; for I will tell thee without fail, and will hide nought, how but lately I heard tell of the return of Odysseus, that he is nigh at hand, and yet alive in the fat land of the men of Thesprotia, and is bringing with him many choice treasures, as he begs through the land. But he has lost his dear companions and his hollow ship on the wine-dark sea, on his way from the isle Thrinacia: for Zeus and Helios had a grudge against him, because his company had slain the kine of Helios. They for their part all perished in the wash of the sea, but the wave cast him on the keel of the ship out upon the coast, on the land of the Phaeacians that are near of kin to the gods, and they did him all honour heartily as unto a god, and gave him many gifts, and themselves would fain have sent him scatheless home. Yea and Odysseus would have been here long since, but he thought it more profitable to gather wealth, as he journeyed over wide lands; so truly is Odysseus skilled in gainful arts above all men upon earth, nor may any mortal men contend with him. So Pheidon king of the Thesprotians told me. Moreover he sware, in mine own presence, as he poured the drink-offering in his house, that the ship was drawn down to the sea and his company were ready, who were to convey him to his own dear country. But me he first sent off, for it chanced that a ship of the Thesprotians was on her way to Dulichium, a land rich in grain. And he showed me all the wealth that Odysseus had gathered, yea, it would suffice for his children after him, even to the tenth generation, so great were the treasures he had stored in the chambers of the king. As for him he had gone, he said, to Dodona to hear the counsel of Zeus, from the high leafy oak tree of the god, how he should return to his own dear country, having now been long afar, whether openly or by stealth.

'In this wise, as I tell thee, he is safe and will come shortly, and very near he is and will not much longer be far from his friends and his own country; yet withal I will give thee my oath on it. Zeus be my witness first, of gods the highest and best, and the hearth of noble Odysseus whereunto I am come, that all these things shall surely be accomplished even as I tell thee. In this same year Odysseus shall come hither, as the old moon wanes and the new is born.'

Then wise Penelope answered him: 'Ah! stranger, would that this word may be accomplished. Soon shouldst thou be aware of kindness and many a gift at my hands, so that whoso met with thee would call thee blessed. But on this wise my heart has a boding, and so it shall be. Neither shall Odysseus come home any more, nor shalt thou gain an escort hence, since there are not now such masters in the house as Odysseus was among men,—if ever such an one there was,—to welcome guests revered and speed them on their way. But do ye, my handmaids, wash this man's feet and strew a couch for him, bedding and mantles and shining blankets, that well and warmly he may come to the time of golden throned Dawn. And very early in the morning bathe him and anoint him, that within the house beside Telemachus he may eat meat, sitting quietly in the hall. And it shall be the worse for any hurtful man of the wooers, that vexes the stranger, yea, he shall not henceforth profit himself here, for all his sore anger. For how shalt thou learn concerning me, stranger, whether indeed I excel all women in wit and thrifty device, if all unkempt and evil clad thou sittest at supper in my halls? Man's life is brief enough! And if any be a hard man and hard at heart, all men cry evil on him for the time to come, while yet he lives, and all men mock him when he is dead. But if any be a blameless man and blameless of heart, his guests spread abroad his fame over the whole earth, and many people call him noble.'

Then Odysseus of many counsels answered her and said: 'O wife revered of Odysseus, son of Laertes, mantles verily and shining blankets are hateful to me, since first I left behind me the snowy hills of Crete, voyaging in the long-oared galley; nay, I will lie as in time past I was used to rest through the sleepless nights. For full many a night I have lain on an unsightly bed, and awaited the bright throned Dawn. And baths for the feet are no longer my delight, nor shall any women of those who are serving maidens in thy house touch my foot, unless there chance to be some old wife, true of heart, one that has borne as much trouble as myself; I would not grudge such an one to touch my feet.'

Then wise Penelope answered him: 'Dear stranger, for never yet has there come to my house, of strangers from afar, a dearer man or so discreet as thou, uttering so heedfully the words of wisdom. I have an ancient woman of an understanding heart, that diligently nursed and tended that hapless man my lord, she took him in her arms in the hour when his mother bare him. She will wash thy feet, albeit her strength is frail. Up now, wise Eurycleia, and wash this man, whose years are the same as thy master's. Yea and perchance such even now are the feet of Odysseus, and such too his hands, for quickly men age in misery.'

So she spake, and the old woman covered her face with her hands and shed hot tears, and spake a word of lamentation, saying:

'Ah, woe is me, child, for thy sake, all helpless that I am! Surely Zeus hated thee above all men, though thou hadst a god-fearing spirit! For never yet did any mortal burn so many fat pieces of the thigh and so many choice hecatombs to Zeus, whose joy is in the thunder, as thou didst give to him, praying that so thou mightest grow to a smooth old age and near thy renowned son. But now from thee alone hath Zeus wholly cut off the day of thy returning. Haply at him too did the women mock in a strange land afar, whensoever he came to the famous palace of any lord, even as here these shameless ones all mock at thee. To shun their insults and many taunts it is that thou sufferest them not to wash thy feet, but the daughter of Icarius, wise Penelope, hath bidden me that am right willing to this task. Wherefore I will wash thy feet, both for Penelope's sake and for thine own, for that my heart within me is moved and troubled. But come, mark the word that I shall speak. Many strangers travel-worn have ere now come hither, but I say that I have never seen any so like another, as thou art like Odysseus, in fashion in voice and in feet.'

Then Odysseus of many counsels answered her saying: 'Old wife, even so all men declare, that have beheld us twain, that we favour each other exceedingly, even as thou dost mark and say.'

Thereupon the crone took the shining cauldron, wherefrom she set to wash his feet, and poured in much cold water and next mingled therewith the warm. Now Odysseus sat aloof from the hearth, and of a sudden he turned his face to the darkness, for anon he had a misgiving of heart lest when she handled him she might know the scar again, and all should be revealed. Now she drew near her lord to wash him, and straightway she knew the scar of the wound, that the boar had dealt him with his white tusk long ago, when Odysseus went to Parnassus to see Autolycus, and the son of Autolycus, his mother's noble father, who outdid all men in thievery and skill in swearing. This skill was the gift of the god himself, even Hermes, for that he burned to him the well-pleasing sacrifice of the thighs of lambs and kids; wherefore Hermes abetted him gladly. Now Autolycus once had gone to the rich land of Ithaca, and found his daughter's son a child new-born, and when he was making an end of supper, behold, Eurycleia set the babe on his knees, and spake and hailed him: 'Autolycus, find now a name thyself to give thy child's own son; for lo, he is a child of many prayers.'

Then Autolycus made answer and spake: 'My daughter and my daughter's lord, give ye him whatsoever name I tell you. Forasmuch as I am come hither in wrath against many a one, both man and woman, over the fruitful earth, wherefore let the child's name be "a man of wrath," Odysseus. But when the child reaches his full growth, and comes to the great house of his mother's kin at Parnassus, whereby are my possessions, I will give him a gift out of these and send him on his way rejoicing.'

Therefore it was that Odysseus went to receive the splendid gifts. And Autolycus and the sons of Autolycus grasped his hands and greeted him with gentle words, and Amphithea, his mother's mother, clasped him in her arms and kissed his face and both his fair eyes. Then Autolycus called to his renowned sons to get ready the meal, and they hearkened to the call. So presently they led in a five-year-old bull, which they flayed and busily prepared, and cut up all the limbs and deftly chopped them small, and pierced them with spits and roasted them cunningly, dividing the messes. So for that livelong day they feasted till the going down of the sun, and their soul lacked not ought of the equal banquet. But when the sun sank and darkness came on, then they laid them to rest and took the boon of sleep.

Now so soon as early Dawn shone forth, the rosy-fingered, they all went forth to the chase, the hounds and the sons of Autolycus, and with them went the goodly Odysseus. So they fared up the steep hill of wood-clad Parnassus, and quickly they came to the windy hollows. Now the sun was but just striking on the fields, and was come forth from the soft flowing stream of deep Oceanus. Then the beaters reached a glade of the woodland, and before them went the hounds tracking a scent, but behind came the sons of Autolycus, and among them goodly Odysseus followed close on the hounds, swaying a long spear. Thereby in a thick lair was a great boar lying, and through the coppice the force of the wet winds blew never, neither did the bright sun light on it with his rays, nor could the rain pierce through, so thick it was, and of fallen leaves there was great plenty therein. Then the tramp of the men's feet and of the dogs' came upon the boar, as they pressed on in the chase, and forth from his lair he sprang towards them with crest well bristled and fire shining in his eyes, and stood at bay before them all. Then Odysseus was the first to rush in, holding his spear aloft in his strong hand, most eager to stab him; but the boar was too quick and drave a gash above the knee, ripping deep into the flesh with his tusk as he charged sideways, but he reached not to the bone of the man. Then Odysseus aimed well and smote him on his right shoulder, so that the point of the bright spear went clean through, and the boar fell in the dust with a cry, and his life passed from him. Then the dear sons of Autolycus began to busy them with the carcase, and as for the wound of the noble godlike Odysseus, they bound it up skilfully, and stayed the black blood with a song of healing, and straightway returned to the house of their dear father. Then Autolycus and the sons of Autolycus got him well healed of his hurt, and gave him splendid gifts, and quickly sent him with all love to Ithaca, gladly speeding a glad guest. There his father and lady mother were glad of his returning, and asked him of all his adventures, and of his wound how he came by it, and duly he told them all, namely, how the boar gashed him with his white tusk in the chase, when he had gone to Parnassus with the sons of Autolycus.

Now the old woman took the scarred limb and passed her hands down it, and knew it by the touch and let the foot drop suddenly, so that the knee fell into the bath, and the brazen vessel rang, being turned over on the other side, and behold, the water was spilled on the ground. Then joy and anguish came on her in one moment, and both her eyes filled up with tears, and the voice of her utterance was stayed, and touching the chin of Odysseus she spake to him, saying:

'Yea verily, thou art Odysseus my dear child, and I knew thee not before, till I had handled all the body of my lord.'

Therewithal she looked towards Penelope, as minded to make a sign that her husband was now home. But Penelope could not meet her eyes nor take note of her, for Athene had bent her thoughts to other things. But Odysseus feeling for the old woman's throat gript it with his right hand and with the other drew her closer to him and spake saying:

'Woman, why wouldest thou indeed destroy me? It was thou that didst nurse me there at thine own breast, and now after travail and much pain I am come in the twentieth year to mine own country. But since thou art ware of me, and the god has put this in thy heart, be silent, lest another learn the matter in the halls. For on this wise I will declare it, and it shall surely be accomplished:—if the gods subdue the lordly wooers unto me, I will not hold my hand from thee, my nurse though thou art, when I slay the other handmaids in my halls.'

Then wise Eurycleia answered, saying: 'My child, what word hath escaped the door of thy lips? Thou knowest how firm is my spirit and unyielding, and I will keep me fast as stubborn stone or iron. Yet another thing will I tell thee, and do thou ponder it in thine heart. If the gods subdue the lordly wooers to thy hand, then will I tell thee all the tale of the women in the halls, which of them dishonour thee and which be guiltless.'

Then Odysseus of many counsels answered her saying: 'Nurse, wherefore I pray thee wilt thou speak of these? Thou needest not, for even I myself will mark them well and take knowledge of each. Nay, do thou keep thy saying to thyself, and leave the rest to the gods.'

Even so he spake, and the old woman passed forth from the hall to bring water for his feet, for the first water was all spilled. So when she had washed him and anointed him well with olive-oil, Odysseus again drew up his settle nearer to the fire to warm himself, and covered up the scar with his rags. Then the wise Penelope spake first, saying: 'Stranger, there is yet a little thing I will make bold to ask thee, for soon will it be the hour for pleasant rest, for him on whomsoever sweet sleep falls, though he be heavy with care. But to me has the god given sorrow, yea sorrow measureless, for all the day I have my fill of wailing and lamenting, as I look to mine own housewiferies and to the tasks of the maidens in the house. But when night comes and sleep takes hold of all, I lie on my couch, and shrewd cares, thick thronging about my inmost heart, disquiet me in my sorrowing. Even as when the daughter of Pandareus, the nightingale of the greenwood, sings sweet in the first season of the spring, from her place in the thick leafage of the trees, and with many a turn and trill she pours forth her full-voiced music bewailing her child, dear Itylus, whom on a time she slew with the sword unwitting, Itylus the son of Zethus the prince; even as her song, my troubled soul sways to and fro. Shall I abide with my son, and keep all secure, all the things of my getting, my thralls and great high-roofed home, having respect unto the bed of my lord and the voice of the people, or even now follow with the best of the Achaeans that wooes me in the halls, and gives a bride-price beyond reckoning? Now my son, so long as he was a child and light of heart, suffered me not to marry and leave the house of my husband; but now that he is great of growth, and is come to the full measure of manhood, lo now he prays me to go back home from these walls, being vexed for his possessions that the Achaeans devour before his eyes. But come now, hear a dream of mine and tell me the interpretation thereof. Twenty geese I have in the house, that eat wheat, coming forth from the water, and I am gladdened at the sight. Now a great eagle of crooked beak swooped from the mountain, and brake all their necks and slew them; and they lay strewn in a heap in the halls, while he was borne aloft to the bright air. Thereupon I wept and wailed, in a dream though it was, and around me were gathered the fair-tressed Achaean women as I made piteous lament, for that the eagle had slain my geese. But he came back and sat him down on a jutting point of the roof-beam, and with the voice of a man he spake, and stayed my weeping:

'"Take heart, O daughter of renowned Icarius; this is no dream but a true vision, that shall be accomplished for thee. The geese are the wooers, and I that before was the eagle am now thy husband come again, who will let slip unsightly death upon all the wooers." With that word sweet slumber let me go, and I looked about, and beheld the geese in the court pecking their wheat at the trough, where they were wont before.'

Then Odysseus of many counsels answered her and said: 'Lady, none may turn aside the dream to interpret it otherwise, seeing that Odysseus himself hath showed thee how he will fulfil it. For the wooers destruction is clearly boded, for all and every one; not a man shall avoid death and the fates.'

Then wise Penelope answered him: 'Stranger, verily dreams are hard, and hard to be discerned; nor are all things therein fulfilled for men. Twain are the gates of shadowy dreams, the one is fashioned of horn and one of ivory. Such dreams as pass through the portals of sawn ivory are deceitful, and bear tidings that are unfulfilled. But the dreams that come forth through the gates of polished horn bring a true issue, whosoever of mortals beholds them. Yet methinks my strange dream came not thence; of a truth that would be most welcome to me and to my son. But another thing will I tell thee, and do thou ponder it in thy heart. Lo, even now draws nigh the morn of evil name, that is to sever me from the house of Odysseus, for now I am about to ordain for a trial those axes that he would set up in a row in his halls, like stays of oak in ship-building, twelve in all, and he would stand far apart and shoot his arrow through them all. And now I will offer this contest to the wooers: whoso shall most easily string the bow in his hands, and shoot through all twelve axes, with him will I go and forsake this house, this house of my wedlock, so fair and filled with all livelihood, which methinks I shall yet remember, aye, in a dream.'

Then Odysseus of many counsels answered her and said: 'Wife revered of Odysseus, son of Laertes, no longer delay this contest in thy halls; for, lo, Odysseus of many counsels will be here, before these men, for all their handling of this polished bow, shall have strung it, and shot the arrow through the iron.'

Then the wise Penelope answered him: 'Stranger, if only thou wert willing still to sit beside me in the halls and to delight me, not upon my eyelids would sleep be shed. But men may in no wise abide sleepless ever, for the immortals have made a time for all things for mortals on the grain-giving earth. Howbeit I will go aloft to my upper chamber, and lay me on my bed, the place of my groanings, that is ever watered by my tears, since the day that Odysseus went to see that evil Ilios, never to be named. There will I lay me down, but do thou lie in this house; either strew thee somewhat on the floor, or let them lay bedding for thee.'

Therewith she ascended to her shining upper chamber, not alone, for with her likewise went her handmaids. So she went aloft to her upper chamber with the women her handmaids, and there was bewailing Odysseus, her dear lord, till grey-eyed Athene cast sweet sleep upon her eyelids.

BOOK XX

Pallas and Odysseus consult of the killing of the wooers.

BUT the goodly Odysseus laid him down to sleep in the vestibule of the house. He spread an undressed bull's hide on the ground and above it many fleeces of sheep, that the Achaeans were wont to slay in sacrifice, and Eurynome threw a mantle over him where he lay. There Odysseus lay wakeful, with evil thoughts against the wooers in his heart. And the women came forth from their chamber, that aforetime were wont to lie with the wooers, making laughter and mirth among themselves. Then the heart of Odysseus was stirred within his breast, and much he communed with his mind and soul, whether he should leap forth upon them and deal death to each, or suffer them to lie with the proud wooers, now for the last and latest time. And his heart growled sullenly within him. And even as a bitch stands over her tender whelps growling, when she spies a man she knows not, and she is eager to assail him, so growled his heart within him in his wrath at their evil deeds. Then he smote upon his breast and rebuked his own heart, saying:

'Endure, my heart; yea, a baser thing thou once didst bear, on that day when the Cyclops, unrestrained in fury, devoured the mighty men of my company; but still thou didst endure till thy craft found a way for thee forth from out the cave, where thou thoughtest to die.'

So spake he, chiding his own spirit within him, and his heart verily abode steadfast in obedience to his word. But Odysseus himself lay tossing this way and that. And as when a man by a great fire burning takes a paunch full of fat and blood, and turns it this way and that and longs to have it roasted most speedily, so Odysseus tossed from side to side, musing how he might stretch forth his hands upon the shameless wooers, being but one man against so many. Then down from heaven came Athene and drew nigh him, fashioned in the likeness of a woman. And she stood over his head and spake to him, saying:

'Lo now again, wherefore art thou watching, most luckless of all men living? Is not this thy house and is not thy wife there within and thy child, such a son as men wish to have for their own?'

Then Odysseus of many counsels answered her saying: 'Yea, goddess, all this thou hast spoken as is meet. But my heart within me muses in some measure upon this, how I may stretch forth my hands upon the shameless wooers, being but one man, while they abide ever in their companies within. Moreover this other and harder matter I ponder in my heart: even if I were to slay them by thy will and the will of Zeus, whither should I flee from the avengers? Look well to this, I pray thee.'

Then answered the goddess, grey-eyed Athene: 'O hard of belief! yea, many there be that trust even in a weaker friend than I am, in one that is a mortal and knows not such craft as mine; but I am a god, that preserve thee to the end, in all manner of toils. And now I will tell thee plainly; even should fifty companies of mortal men compass us about eager to slay us in battle, even their kine shouldst thou drive off and their brave flocks. But let sleep in turn come over thee; to wake and to watch all night, this too is vexation of spirit; and soon shalt thou rise from out of thy troubles.'

So she spake and poured slumber upon his eyelids, but for her part the fair goddess went back to Olympus.

While sleep laid hold of him loosening the cares of his soul, sleep that loosens the limbs of men, his good wife awoke and wept as she sat on her soft bed. But when she had taken her fill of weeping, to Artemis first the fair lady made her prayer:

'Artemis, lady and goddess, daughter of Zeus, would that even now thou wouldst plant thy shaft within my breast and take my life away, even in this hour! Or else, would that the stormwind might snatch me up, and bear me hence down the dusky ways, and cast me forth where the back-flowing Oceanus mingles with the sea. It should be even as when the stormwinds bare away the daughters of Pandareus. Their father and their mother the gods had slain, and the maidens were left orphans in the halls, and fair Aphrodite cherished them with curds and sweet honey and delicious wine. And Here gave them beauty and wisdom beyond the lot of women, and holy Artemis dowered them with stature, and Athene taught them skill in all famous handiwork. Now while fair Aphrodite was wending to high Olympus, to pray that a glad marriage might be accomplished for the maidens,—and to Zeus she went whose joy is in the thunder, for he knows all things well, what the fates give and deny to mortal men—in the meanwhile the spirits of the storm snatched away these maidens, and gave them to be handmaids to the hateful Erinyes. Would that in such wise they that hold the mansions of Olympus would take me from the sight of men, or that fair-tressed Artemis would strike me, that so with a vision of Odysseus before mine eyes I might even pass beneath the dreadful earth, nor ever make a baser man's delight! But herein is an evil that may well be borne, namely, when a man weeps all the day long in great sorrow of heart, but sleep takes him in the night, for sleep makes him forgetful of all things, of good and evil, when once it has overshadowed his eyelids. But as for me, even the dreams that the gods send upon me are evil. For furthermore, this very night one seemed to lie by my side, in the likeness of my lord, as he was when he went with the host, and then was my heart glad, since methought it was no vain dream but a clear vision at the last.'

So she spake, and anon came the golden throned Dawn. Now goodly Odysseus caught the voice of her weeping, and then he fell a musing, and it seemed to him that even now she knew him and was standing by his head. So he took up the mantle and the fleeces whereon he was lying, and set them on a high seat in the hall, and bare out the bull's hide out of doors and laid it there, and lifting up his hands he prayed to Zeus:

'Father Zeus, if ye gods of your good will have led me over wet and dry, to mine own country, after ye had plagued me sore, let some one I pray of the folk that are waking show me a word of good omen within, and without let some sign also be revealed to me from Zeus.'

So he spake in prayer, and Zeus, the counsellor, heard him. Straightway he thundered from shining Olympus, from on high from the place of clouds; and goodly Odysseus was glad. Moreover a woman, a grinder at the mill, uttered a voice of omen from within the house hard by, where stood the mills of the shepherd of the people. At these handmills twelve women in all plied their task, making meal of barley and of wheat, the marrow of men. Now all the others were asleep, for they had ground out their task of grain, but one alone rested not yet, being the weakest of all. She now stayed her quern and spake a word, a sign to her lord:

'Father Zeus, who rulest over gods and men, loudly hast thou thundered from the starry sky, yet nowhere is there a cloud to be seen: this surely is a portent thou art showing to some mortal. Fulfil now, I pray thee, even to miserable me, the word that I shall speak. May the wooers, on this day, for the last and latest time make their sweet feasting in the halls of Odysseus! They that have loosened my knees with cruel toil to grind their barleymeal, may they now sup their last!'

Thus she spake, and goodly Odysseus was glad in the omen of the voice and in the thunder of Zeus; for he thought that he had gotten his vengeance on the guilty.

Now the other maidens in the fair halls of Odysseus had gathered, and were kindling on the hearth the never-resting fire. And Telemachus rose from his bed, a godlike man, and put on his raiment, and slung a sharp sword about his shoulders, and beneath his shining feet he bound his goodly sandals. And he caught up his mighty spear shod with sharp bronze, and went and stood by the threshold, and spake to Eurycleia:

'Dear nurse, have ye honoured our guest in the house with food and couch, or does he lie uncared for, as he may? For this is my mother's way, wise as she is: blindly she honours one of mortal men, even the worse, but the better she sends without honour away.'

Then the prudent Eurycleia answered: 'Nay, my child, thou shouldst not now blame her where no blame is. For the stranger sat and drank wine, so long as he would, and of food he said he was no longer fain, for thy mother asked him. Moreover, against the hour when he should bethink him of rest and sleep, she bade the maidens strew for him a bed. But he, as one utterly wretched and ill-fated, refused to lie on a couch and under blankets, but on an undressed hide and on the fleeces of sheep he slept in the vestibule, and we cast a mantle over him.'

So she spake, and Telemachus passed out through the hall with his lance in his hand, and two fleet dogs bare him company. He went on his way to the assembly-place to join the goodly-greaved Achaeans. But the good lady Eurycleia, daughter of Ops son of Peisenor, called aloud to her maidens:

'Come hither, let some of you go busily and sweep the hall, and sprinkle it, and on the fair-fashioned seats throw purple coverlets, and others with sponges wipe all the tables clean, and cleanse the mixing bowls and well-wrought double beakers, and others again go for water to the well, and return with it right speedily. For the wooers will not long be out of the hall but will return very early, for it is a feast day, yea for all the people.'

So she spake, and they all gave ready ear and hearkened. Twenty of them went to the well of dark water, and the others there in the halls were busy with skilful hands.

Then in came the serving-men of the Achaeans. Thereon they cleft the faggots well and cunningly, while, behold, the women came back from the well. Then the swineherd joined them leading three fatted boars, the best in all the flock. These he left to feed at large in the fair courts, but as for him he spake to Odysseus gently, saying:

"Tell me, stranger, do the Achaeans at all look on thee with more regard, or do they dishonour thee in the halls, as heretofore?'

Then Odysseus of many counsels answered him saying:

'Oh, that the gods, Eumaeus, may avenge the scorn wherewith these men deal insolently, and devise infatuate deeds in another's house, and have no place for shame!'

On such wise they spake one to another. And Melanthius drew near them, the goatherd, leading the goats that were most excellent in all the herds to be a dinner for the wooers, and two shepherds bare him company. So he tethered the goats beneath the echoing gallery, and himself spake to Odysseus and taunted him, saying:

'Stranger, wilt thou still be a plague to us here in the hall, with thy begging of men, and wilt not get thee gone? In no wise do I think we twain will be sundered, till we taste each the other's fists, for thy begging is out of all order. Also there are elsewhere other feasts of the Achaeans.'

So he spake, but Odysseus of many counsels answered him not a word, but in silence he shook his head, brooding evil in the deep of his heart.

Moreover a third man came up, Philoetius, a master of

men, leading a barren heifer for the wooers and fatted goats. Now ferrymen had brought them over from the mainland, boatmen who send even other folks on their way, whosoever comes to them. The cattle he tethered carefully beneath the echoing gallery, and himself drew close to the swineherd, and began to question him:

'Swineherd, who is this stranger but newly come to our house? From what men does he claim his birth? Where are his kin and his native fields? Hapless is he, yet in fashion he is like a royal lord; but the gods mar the goodliness of wandering men, when even for kings they have woven the web of trouble.'

So he spake, and came close to him offering his right hand in welcome, and uttering his voice spake to him winged words:

'Father and stranger, hail! may happiness be thine in the time to come; but as now, thou art fast holden in many sorrows! Father Zeus, none other god is more baneful than thou; thou hast no compassion on men, that are of thine own begetting, but makest them to have fellowship with evil and with bitter pains. The sweat brake out on me when I beheld him, and mine eyes stand full of tears for memory of Odysseus, for he too, methinks, is clad in such vile raiment as this, and is wandering among men, if haply he yet lives and sees the sunlight. But if he be dead already and in the house of Hades, then woe is me for the noble Odysseus, who set me over his cattle while I was but a lad in the land of the Cephallenians. And now these wax numberless; in no better wise could the breed of broad-browed cattle of any mortal increase, even as the ears of corn. But strangers command me to be ever driving these for themselves to devour, and they care nothing for the heir in the house, nor tremble at the vengeance of the gods, for they are eager even now to divide among themselves the posssessions of our lord who is long afar. Now my heart within my breast often revolves this thing.

Truly it were an evil deed, while a son of the master is yet alive, to get me away to the land of strangers, and go off, with cattle and all, to alien men. But this is more grievous still, to abide here in affliction watching over the herds of other men. Yea, long ago I would have fled and gone forth to some other of the proud kings, for things are now past sufferance; but still my thought is of that hapless one, if he might come I know not whence, and make a scattering of the wooers in the halls.'

Then Odysseus of many counsels answered him saying:

'Neatherd, seeing thou art not like to an evil man or a foolish, and of myself I mark how that thou hast gotten understanding of heart, therefore I will tell thee somewhat, and swear a great oath to confirm it. Be Zeus now my witness before any god, and the hospitable board and the hearth of noble Odysseus, whereunto I am come, that while thou art still in this place Odysseus shall come home, and thou shalt see with thine eyes, if thou wilt, the slaying of the wooers who lord it here.'

Then the neatherd made answer, saying:

'Ah, would, stranger, that Cronion may accomplish this word! So shouldst thou know what my might is, and how my hands follow to obey.'

In like manner Eumaeus prayed to all the gods, that wise Odysseus might return to his own home.

On such wise they spake one to the other, but the wooers at that time were framing death and doom for Telemachus. Even so there came by them a bird on their left, an eagle of lofty flight, with a cowering dove in his clutch. Then Amphinomus made harangue and spake among them:

'Friends, this counsel of ours will not go well, namely, the slaying of Telemachus; rather let us bethink us of the feast.'

So spake Amphinomus, and his saying pleased them well. They passed into the halls of godlike Odysseus and laid by their mantles on the chairs and high seats, and sacrificed great sheep and stout goats and the fatlings of the boars and the heifer of the herd; then they roasted the entrails and served them round and mixed wine in the bowl, and the swineherd set a cup by each man. And Philoetius, a master of men, handed them wheaten bread in beautiful baskets, and Melanthius poured out the wine. So they put forth their hands on the good cheer set before them.

Now Telemachus, in his crafty purpose, made Odysseus to sit down within the stablished hall by the threshold of stone, and placed for him a mean settle and a little table. He set by him his mess of the entrails, and poured wine into a golden cup and spake to him, saying:

'There, sit thee down, drinking thy wine among the lords, and the taunts and buffets of all the wooers I myself will ward off from thee, for this is no house of public resort, but the very house of Odysseus, and for me he won it. But, ye wooers, refrain your minds from rebukes and your hands from buffets, that no strike and feud may arise.'

So he said, and they all bit their lips and marvelled at Telemachus, in that he spake boldly. Then Antinous, son of Eupeithes, spake among them, saying:

'Hard though the word be, let us accept it, Achaeans, even the word of Telemachus, though mightily he threatens us in his speech. For Zeus Cronion hath hindered us of our purpose, else would we have silenced him in our halls, shrill orator as he is.'

So spake Antinous, but Telemachus took no heed of his words. Now the henchmen were leading through the town the holy hecatomb of the gods, and lo, the long-haired Achaeans were gathered beneath the shady grove of Apollo, the prince of archery.

Now when they had roasted the outer flesh and drawn it off the spits, they divided the messes and shared the glorious feast. And beside Odysseus they that waited set an equal share, the same as that which fell to themselves, for so Telemachus commanded, the dear son of divine Odysseus.

Now Athene would in no wise suffer the lordly wooers to abstain from biting scorn, that the pain might sink yet the deeper into the heart of Odysseus, son of Laertes. There was among the wooers a man of a lawless heart, Ctesippus was his name, and in Same was his home, who trusting, forsooth, to his vast possessions, was wooing the wife of Odysseus the lord long afar. And now he spake among the proud wooers:

'Hear me, ye lordly wooers, and I will say somewhat. The stranger verily has long had his due portion, as is meet, an equal share; for it is not fair nor just to rob the guests of Telemachus of their right, whosoever they may be that come to this house. Go to then, I also will bestow on him a stranger's gift, that he in turn may give a present either to the bath-woman, or to any other of the thralls within the house of godlike Odysseus.'

Therewith he caught up an ox's foot from the dish, where it lay, and hurled it with strong hand. But Odysseus lightly avoided it with a turn of his head, and smiled right grimly in his heart, and the ox's foot smote the well-builded wall. Then Telemachus rebuked Ctesippus, saying:

'Verily, Ctesippus, it has turned out happier for thy heart's pleasure as it is! Thou didst not smite the stranger, for he himself avoided that which was cast at him, else surely would I have struck thee through the midst with the sharp spear, and in place of wedding banquet thy father would have had to busy him about a funeral feast in this place. Wherefore let no man make show of unseemly deeds in this my house, for now I have understanding to discern both good and evil, but in time past I was yet a child. But as needs we must, we still endure to see these deeds, while sheep are slaughtered and wine drunken and bread devoured, for hard it is for one man to restrain many. But come, no longer work me harm out of an evil heart; but if ye be set on slaying me, even me, with the sword, even that would I rather endure, and far better would it be to die than to witness for ever these unseemly deeds—strangers shamefully entreated, and men haling the handmaidens in foul wise through the fair house.'

So he spake, and they were all hushed in silence. And late and at last spake among them Agelaus, son of Damastor:

'Friends, when a righteous word has been spoken, none surely would rebuke another with hard speech and be angry. Misuse ye not this stranger, nor any of the thralls that are in the house of godlike Odysseus. But to Telemachus himself I would speak a soft word and to his mother, if perchance it may find favour with the mind of those twain. So long as your hearts within you had hope of the wise Odysseus returning to his own house, so long none could be wroth that ye waited and held back the wooers in the halls, for so had it been better, if Odysseus had returned and come back to his own home. But now the event is plain, that he will return no more. Go then, sit by thy mother and tell her all, namely, that she must wed the best man that wooes her, and whoso gives most gifts; so shalt thou with gladness live on the heritage of thy father, eating and drinking, while she cares for another's house.'

Then wise Telemachus answered, and said: 'Nay by Zeus, Agelaus, and by the griefs of my father, who far away methinks from Ithaca has perished or goes wandering, in no wise do I delay my mother's marriage; nay, I bid her be married to what man she will, and withal I offer gifts without number. But I do indeed feel shame to drive her forth from the hall, despite her will, by a word of compulsion; God forbid that ever this should be.'

So spake Telemachus, but among the wooers Pallas Athene roused laughter unquenchable, and drave their wits wandering. And now they were laughing with alien lips, and blood-bedabbled was the flesh they ate, and their eyes were filled with tears and their soul was fain of lamentation. Then the godlike Theoclymenus spake among them:

'Ah, wretched men, what woe is this ye suffer? Shrouded in night are your heads and your faces and your knees, and kindled is the voice of wailing, and all cheeks are wet with tears, and the walls and the fair main-beams of the roof are sprinkled with blood. And the porch is full, and full is the court, of ghosts that hasten hellwards beneath the gloom, and the sun has perished out of heaven, and an evil mist has overspread the world.'

So spake he, and they all laughed sweetly at him. Then Eurymachus, son of Polybus, began to speak to them, saying:

'The guest that is newly come from a strange land is beside himself. Quick, ye young men, and convey him forth out of doors, that he may go to the place of the gathering, since here he finds it dark as night.'

Then godlike Theoclymenus answered him: 'Eurymachus, in no wise do I seek guides of thee to send me on my way. Eyes have I, and ears, and both my feet, and a stable mind in my breast of no mean fashioning. With these I will go forth, for I see evil coming on you, which not one man of the wooers may avoid or shun, of all you who in the house of divine Odysseus deal insolently with men and devise infatuate deeds.'

Therewith he went forth from out the fair-lying halls, and came to Piraeus who received him gladly. Then all the wooers, looking one at the other, provoked Telemachus to anger, laughing at his guests. And thus some one of the haughty youths would speak:

'Telemachus, no man is more luckless than thou in his guests, seeing thou keepest such a filthy wanderer, whosoever he be, always longing for bread and wine, and skilled in no peaceful work nor any deed of war, but a mere burden of the earth. And this other fellow again must stand up to play the seer! Nay, but if thou wouldest listen to me, much better it were. Let us cast these strangers on board a benched ship, and send them to the Sicilians, whence they would fetch thee their price.'

So spake the wooers, but he heeded not their words; in silence he looked towards his father, expecting evermore the hour when he should stretch forth his hands upon the shameless wooers.

Now the daughter of Icarius, wise Penelope, had set her fair chair over against them, and heard the words of each one of the men in the halls. For in the midst of laughter they had got ready the midday meal, a sweet meal and abundant, for they had sacrificed many cattle. But never could there be a banquet less gracious than that supper, such an one as the goddess and the brave man were soon to spread for them; for that they had begun the devices of shame.

BOOK XXI

Penelope bringeth forth her husband's bow, which the suitors could not bend, but was bent by Odysseus.

Now the goddess, grey-eyed Athene, put it into the heart of the daughter of Icarius, wise Penelope, to set the bow and the axes of grey iron, for the wooers in the halls of Odysseus, to be the weapons of the contest, and the beginning of death. So she descended the tall staircase of her chamber, and took the well-bent key in her strong hand, a goodly key of bronze, whereon was a handle of ivory. And she betook her, with her handmaidens, to the treasure-chamber in the uttermost part of the house, where lay the treasures of her lord, bronze and gold and well-wrought iron. And there lay the back-bent bow and the quiver for the arrows, and many shafts were therein, winged for death, gifts of a friend of Odysseus, that met with him in Lacedaemon, Iphitus son of Eurytus, a man like to the gods. These twain fell in with one another in Messene, in the house of wise Ortilochus. Now Odysseus had gone thither to recover somewhat that was owing to him from all the people, for the men of Messene had lifted three hundred sheep in benched ships from out of Ithaca, with the shepherds of the flock. In quest of these it was that Odysseus went on a far embassy, being yet a lad; for his father and the other elders sent him forth. Moreover, Iphitus came thither in his search for twelve brood mares, which he had lost, with sturdy mules at the teat. These same it was that brought him death and destiny in the latter end, when he came to the child of Zeus, hardy of heart, the man Heracles, that had knowledge of great adventures, who smote Iphitus though his guest in his house, in his frowardness, and had no regard for the vengeance of the gods, nor for the table which he spread before him; for after the meal he slew him, his guest though he was, and kept for himself in the halls the horses strong of hoof. After these was Iphitus asking, when he met with Odysseus, and he gave him the bow, which of old great Eurytus bare and had left at his death to his son in his lofty house. And Odysseus gave Iphitus a sharp sword and a mighty spear, for the beginning of a loving friendship; but never had they acquaintance one of another at the board; ere that might be, the son of Zeus slew Iphitus son of Eurytus, a man like to the immortals, the same that gave Odysseus the bow. But goodly Odysseus would never take it with him on the black ships, as he went to the wars, but the bow was laid by at home in the halls as a memorial of a dear guest, and he carried it on his own land.

Now when the fair lady had come even to the treasure-chamber, and had stept upon the threshold of oak, which the carpenter had on a time planed cunningly, and over it had made straight the line,—doorposts also had he fitted thereby, whereon he set shining doors,—anon she quickly loosed the strap from the handle of the door, and thrust in the key, and with a straight aim shot back the bolts. And even as a bull roars that is grazing in a meadow, so mightily roared the fair doors smitten by the key; and speedily they flew open before her. Then she stept on to the high floor, where the coffers stood, wherein the fragrant raiment was stored. Thence she stretched forth her hand, and took the bow from off the pin, all in the bright case which sheathed it around. And there she sat down, and set the case upon her knees, and cried aloud and wept, and took out the bow of her lord. Now when she had her fill of tearful lament, she set forth to go to the hall to the company of the proud wooers, with the back-bent bow in her hands, and the quiver for the arrows, and many shafts were therein winged for death. And her maidens along with her bare a chest, wherein lay much store of iron and bronze, the gear of combat of their lord. Now when the fair lady had come unto the wooers, she stood by the pillar of the well-builded roof, holding up her glistening tire before her face; and a faithful maiden stood on either side of her, and straightway she spake out among the wooers and declared her word, saying:

'Hear me, ye lordly wooers, who have vexed this house, that ye might eat and drink here evermore, forasmuch as the master is long gone, nor could ye find any other mark for your speech, but all your desire was to wed me and take me to wife. Nay come now, ye wooers, seeing that this is the prize that is put before you. I will set forth for you the great bow of divine Odysseus, and whoso shall most easily string the bow in his hands, and shoot through all twelve axes, with him will I go and forsake this house, this house of my wedlock, so fair and filled with all livelihood, which methinks I shall yet remember, aye, in a dream.'

So spake she, and commanded Eumaeus, the goodly swineherd, to set the bow for the wooers and the axes of grey iron. And Eumaeus took them with tears, and laid them down; and otherwhere the neatherd wept, when he beheld the bow of his lord. Then Antinous rebuked them, and spake and hailed them:

'Foolish boors, whose thoughts look not beyond the day, ah, wretched pair, wherefore now do ye shed tears, and stir the soul of the lady within her, when her heart already lies low in pain, for that she has lost her dear lord? Nay sit, and feast in silence, or else get ye forth and weep, and leave the bow here behind, to be a terrible contest for the wooers, for methinks that this polished bow does not lightly yield itself to be strung. For there is no man among all these present such as Odysseus was, and I myself saw him, yea I remember it well, though I was still but a child.'

So spake he, but his heart within him hoped that he would string the bow, and shoot through the iron. Yet verily, he was to be the first that should taste the arrow at the hands of the noble Odysseus, whom but late he was dishonouring as he sat in the halls, and was inciting all his fellows to do likewise.

Then the mighty prince Telemachus spake among them, saying: 'Lo now, in very truth, Cronion has robbed me of my wits! My dear mother, wise as she is, declares that she will go with a stranger and forsake this house; yet I laugh and in my silly heart I am glad. Nay come now, ye wooers, seeing that this is the prize which is set before you, a lady, the like of whom there is not now in the Achaean land, neither in sacred Pylos, nor in Argos, nor in Mycenae, nor yet in Ithaca, nor in the dark mainland. Nay but ye know all this yourselves,—why need I praise my mother? Come therefore, delay not the issue with excuses, nor hold much longer aloof from the drawing of the bow, that we may see the thing that is to be. Yea and I myself would make trial of this bow. If I shall string it, and shoot through the iron, then should I not sorrow if my lady mother were to quit these halls and go with a stranger, seeing that I should be left behind, well able now to lift my father's goodly gear of combat.'

Therewith he cast from off his neck his cloak of scarlet, and sprang to his full height, and put away the sword from his shoulders. First he dug a good trench and set up the axes, one long trench for them all, and over it he made straight the line and round about stamped in the earth. And amazement fell on all that beheld how orderly he set the axes, though never before had he seen it so. Then he went and stood by the threshold and began to prove the bow. Thrice he made it to tremble in his great desire to draw it, and thrice he rested from his effort, though still he hoped in his heart to string the bow, and shoot through the iron. And now at last he might have strung it, mightily straining thereat for the fourth time, but Odysseus nodded frowning and stayed him, for all his eagerness. Then the strong prince Telemachus spake among them again:

'Lo you now, even to the end of my days I shall be a coward and a weakling, or it may be I am too young, and have as yet no trust in my hands to defend me from such an one as does violence without a cause. But come now, ye who are mightier men than I, essay the bow and let us make an end of the contest.'

Therewith he put the bow from him on the ground, leaning it against the smooth and well-compacted doors, and the swift shaft he propped hard by against the fair bow-tip, and then he sat down once more on the high seat, whence he had risen.

Then Antinous, son of Eupeithes, spake among them, saying: 'Rise up in order, all my friends, beginning from the left, even from the place whence the wine is poured.'

So spake Antinous, and the saying pleased them well. Then first stood up Leiodes, son of Oenops, who was their soothsayer and ever sat by the fair mixing bowl at the extremity of the hall; he alone hated their infatuate deeds and was indignant with all the wooers. He now first took the bow and the swift shaft, and he went and stood by the threshold, and began to prove the bow; but he could not bend it; or ever that might be, his hands grew weary with the straining, his unworn, delicate hands; so he spake among the wooers, saying:

'Friends, of a truth I cannot bend it, let some other take it. Ah, many of our bravest shall this bow rob of spirit and of life, since truly it is far better for us to die, than to live on and to fail of that for which we assemble evermore in this place, day by day expecting the prize. Many there be even now that hope in their hearts and desire to wed Penelope, the bed-fellow of Odysseus: but when such an one shall make trial of the bow and see the issue, thereafter let him woo some other fair-robed Achaean woman with his bridal gifts and seek to win her. So may our lady wed the man that gives most gifts, and comes as the chosen of fate.'

So he spake, and put from him the bow leaning it against the smooth and well-compacted doors, and the swift shaft he propped hard by against the fair bow-tip, and then he sat down once more on the high seat, whence he had risen.

But Antinous rebuked him, and spake and hailed him: 'Leiodes, what word hath escaped the door of thy lips; a hard word, and a grievous? Nay, it angers me to hear it, and to think that a bow such as this shall rob our bravest of spirit and of life, and all because thou canst not draw it. For I tell thee that thy lady mother bare thee not of such might as to draw a bow and shoot arrows: but there be others of the proud wooers that shall draw it soon.'

So he spake, and commanded Melanthius, the goatherd, saying: 'Up now, light a fire in the halls, Melanthius; and place a great settle by the fire and a fleece thereon, and bring forth a great ball of lard that is within, that we young men may warm and anoint the bow therewith and prove it, and make an end of the contest.'

So he spake, and Melanthius soon kindled the never-resting fire, and drew up a settle and placed it near, and put a fleece thereon, and he brought forth a great ball of lard that was within. Therewith the young men warmed the bow, and made essay, but could not string it, for they were greatly lacking of such might. And Antinous still held to the task and godlike Eurymachus, chief men among the wooers, who were far the most excellent of all.

But those other twain went forth both together from the house, the neatherd and the swineherd of godlike Odysseus; and Odysseus passed out after them. But when they were now gotten without the gates and the courtyard, he uttered his voice and spake to them in gentle words:

'Neatherd and thou swineherd, shall I say somewhat or

keep it to myself? Nay, my spirit bids me declare it. What manner of men would ye be to help Odysseus, if he should come thus suddenly, I know not whence, and some god were to bring him? Would ye stand on the side of the wooers or of Odysseus? Tell me even as your heart and spirit bid you.'

Then the neatherd answered him, saying: 'Father Zeus, if but thou wouldst fulfil this wish:—oh, that that man might come, and some god lead him hither! So shouldest thou know what my might is, and how my hands follow to obey.'

In like manner Eumaeus prayed to all the gods that wise Odysseus might return to his own home.

Now when he knew for a surety what spirit they were of, once more he answered and spake to them, saying:

'Behold, home am I come, even I; after much travail and sore am I come in the twentieth year to mine own country. And I know how that my coming is desired by you alone of all my thralls, for from none besides have I heard a prayer that I might return once more to my home. And now I will tell you all the truth, even as it shall come to pass. If the god shall subdue the proud wooers to my hands, I will bring you each one a wife, and will give you a heritage of your own and a house builded near to me, and ye twain shall be thereafter in mine eyes as the brethren and companions of Telemachus. But behold, I will likewise show you a most manifest token, that ye may know me well and be certified in heart, even the wound that the boar dealt me with his white tusk long ago, when I went to Parnassus with the sons of Autolycus.'

Therewith he drew aside the rags from the great scar. And when the twain had beheld it and marked it well, they cast their arms about the wise Odysseus, and fell a weeping; and kissed him lovingly on head and shoulders. And in like manner Odysseus too kissed their heads and hands. And now would the sunlight have gone down upon their sorrowing, had not Odysseus himself stayed them saying:

'Cease ye from weeping and lamentation, lest some one come forth from the hall and see us, and tell it likewise in the house. Nay, go ye within one by one and not both together, I first and you following, and let this be the token between us. All the rest, as many as are proud wooers, will not suffer that I should be given the bow and quiver; do thou then, goodly Eumaeus, as thou bearest the bow through the hall, set it in my hands and speak to the women that they bar the well-fitting doors of their chamber. And if any of them hear the sound of groaning or the din of men within our walls, let them not run forth but abide where they are in silence at their work. But on thee, goodly Philoetius, I lay this charge, to bolt and bar the outer gate of the court and swiftly to tie the knot.'

Therewith he passed within the fair-lying halls, and went and sat upon the settle whence he had risen. And likewise the two thralls of divine Odysseus went within.

And now Eurymachus was handling the bow, warming it on this side and on that at the light of the fire; yet even so he could not string it, and in his great heart he groaned mightily; and in heaviness of spirit he spake and called aloud, saying:

'Lo you now, truly am I grieved for myself and for you all! Not for the marriage do I mourn so greatly, afflicted though I be; there are many Achaean women besides, some in sea-begirt Ithaca itself and some in other cities. Nay, but I grieve, if indeed we are so far worse than godlike Odysseus in might, seeing that we cannot bend the bow. It will be a shame even for men unborn to hear thereof.'

Then Antinous, son of Eupeithes, answered him: "Eurymachus, this shall not be so, and thou thyself too knowest it. For to-day the feast of the archer god is held in the land, a holy feast. Who at such a time would be bending bows? Nay, set it quietly by; what and if we should let the axes all stand as they are? None methinks will come to the hall of Odysseus, son of Laertes, and carry them away. Go to now, let the wine-bearer pour for libation into each cup in turn, that after the drink-offering we may set down the curved bow. And in the morning bid Melanthius, the goatherd, to lead hither the very best goats in all his herds, that we may lay pieces of the thighs on the altar of Apollo the archer, and essay the bow and make an end of the contest.'

So spake Antinous, and the saying pleased them well. Then the henchmen poured water on their hands, and pages crowned the mixing-bowls with drink, and served out the wine to all, when they had poured for libation into each cup in turn. But when they had poured forth and had drunken to their hearts' desire, Odysseus of many counsels spake among them out of a crafty heart, saying:

'Hear me, ye wooers of the renowned queen, that I may say that which my heart within me bids. And mainly to Eurymachus I make my prayer and to the godlike Antinous, forasmuch as he has spoken even this word aright, namely, that for this present ye cease from your archery and leave the issue to the gods; and in the morning the god will give the victory to whomsoever he will. Come therefore, give me the polished bow, that in your presence I may prove my hands and strength, whether I have yet any force such as once was in my supple limbs, or whether my wanderings and needy fare have even now destroyed it.'

So spake he and they all were exceeding wroth, for fear lest he should string the polished bow. And Antinous rebuked him, and spake and hailed him:

'Wretched stranger, thou hast no wit, nay never so little. Art thou not content to feast at ease in our high company, and to lack not thy share of the banquet, but to listen to our speech and our discourse, while no guest and beggar beside thee hears our speech? Wine it is that wounds thee, honey-sweet wine, that is the bane of others too, even of all who take great draughts and drink out of measure. Wine it was that darkened the mind even of the Centaur, renowned Eurytion, in the hall of high-hearted Peirithous, when he went to the Lapithae; and after that his heart was darkened with wine, he wrought foul deeds in his frenzy, in the house of Peirithous. Then wrath fell on all the heroes, and they leaped up and dragged him forth through the porch, when they had shorn off his ears and nostrils with the pitiless sword, and then with darkened mind he bare about with him the burden of his sin in foolishness of heart. Thence was the feud begun between the Centaurs and mankind; but first for himself gat he hurt, being heavy with wine. And even so I declare great mischief unto thee if thou shalt string the bow, for thou shalt find no courtesy at the hand of any one in our land, and anon we will send thee in a black ship to Echetus, the maimer of all men, and thence thou shalt not be saved alive. Nay then, drink at thine ease, and strive not still with men that are younger than thou.'

Then wise Penelope answered him: 'Antinous, truly it is not fair nor just to rob the guests of Telemachus of their due, whosoever he may be that comes to this house. Dost thou think if yonder stranger strings the great bow of Odysseus, in the pride of his might and of his strength of arm, that he will lead me to his home and make me his wife? Nay he himself, methinks, has no such hope in his breast; so, as for that, let not any of you fret himself while feasting in this place; that were indeed unmeet.'

Then Eurymachus, son of Polybus, answered her, saying: 'Daughter of Icarius, wise Penelope, it is not that we deem that he will lead thee to his home,—far be such a thought from us,—but we dread the speech of men and women, lest some day one of the baser sort among the

Achaeans say: "Truly men far too mean are wooing the wife of one that is noble, nor can they string the polished bow. But a stranger and a beggar came in his wanderings, and lightly strung the bow, and shot through the iron." Thus will they speak, and this will turn to our reproach.'

Then wise Penelope answered him: 'Eurymachus, never can there be fair fame in the land for those that devour and dishonour the house of a prince, but why make ye this thing into a reproach? But, behold, our guest is great of growth and well-knit, and avows him to be born the son of a good father. Come then, give ye him the polished bow, that we may see that which is to be. For thus will I declare my saying, and it shall surely come to pass. If he shall string the bow and Apollo grant him renown, I will clothe him in a mantle and a doublet, goodly raiment, and I will give him a sharp javelin to defend him against dogs and men, and a two-edged sword and sandals to bind beneath his feet, and I will send him whithersoever his heart and spirit bid him go.'

Then wise Telemachus answered her, saying: 'My mother, as for the bow, no Achaean is mightier than I to give or to deny it to whomso I will, neither as many as are lords in rocky Ithaca nor in the isles on the side of Elis, the pastureland of horses. Not one of these shall force me in mine own despite, if I choose to give this bow, yea once and for all, to the stranger to bear away with him. But do thou go to thine own chamber and mind thine own housewiferies, the loom and distaff, and bid thine handmaids ply their tasks. But the bow shall be for men, for all, but for me in chief, for mine is the lordship in the house.'

Then in amaze she went back to her chamber, for she laid up the wise saying of her son in her heart. She ascended to her upper chamber with the women her handmaids, and then was bewailing Odysseus, her dear lord, till grey-eyed Athene cast sweet sleep upon her eyelids.

Now the goodly swineherd had taken the curved bow, and was bearing it, when the wooers all cried out upon him in the halls. And thus some one of the haughty youths would speak: 'Whither now art thou bearing the curved bow, thou wretched swineherd, crazed in thy wits? Lo, soon shall the swift hounds of thine own breeding eat thee hard by thy swine, alone and away from men, if Apollo will be gracious to us and the other deathless gods.'

Even so they spake, and he took and set down the bow in that very place, being affrighted because many cried out on him in the halls. Then Telemachus from the other side spake threateningly, and called aloud:

'Father, bring hither the bow, soon shalt thou rue it that thou servest many masters. Take heed, lest I that am younger than thou pursue thee to the field, and pelt thee with stones, for in might I am the better. If only I were so much mightier in strength of arm than all the wooers that are in the halls, soon would I send many an one forth on a woeful way from out our house, for they imagine mischief against us.'

So he spake, and all the wooers laughed sweetly at him, and ceased now from their cruel anger toward Telemachus. Then the swineherd bare the bow through the hall, and went up to wise Odysseus, and set it in his hands. And he called forth the nurse Eurycleia from the chamber and spake to her:

'Wise Eurycleia, Telemachus bids thee bar the well-fitting doors of thy chamber, and if any of the women hear the sound of groaning or the din of men within our walls, let them not go forth, but abide where they are in silence at their work.'

So he spake, and wingless her speech remained, and she barred the doors of the fair-lying chambers.

Then Philoetius hasted forth silently from the house, and barred the outer gates of the fenced court. Now there lay beneath the gallery the cable of a curved ship, fashioned of the byblus plant, wherewith he made fast the gates, and then himself passed within. Then he went and sat on the settle whence he had risen, and gazed upon Odysseus. He already was handling the bow, turning it every way about, and proving it on this side and on that, lest the worms might have eaten the horns when the lord of the bow was away. And thus men spake looking each one to his neighbour:

'Verily he has a good eye, and a shrewd turn for a bow! Either, methinks, he himself has such a bow lying by at home or else he is set on making one, in such wise does he turn it hither and thither in his hands, this evil-witted beggar.'

And another again of the haughty youths would say: 'Would that the fellow may have profit thereof, just so surely as he shall ever prevail to bend this bow!'

So spake the wooers, but Odysseus of many counsels had lifted the great bow and viewed it on every side, and even as when a man that is skilled in the lyre and in minstrelsy, easily stretches a cord about a new peg, after tying at either end the twisted sheep-gut, even so Odysseus straightway bent the great bow, all without effort, and took it in his right hand and proved the bow-string, which rang sweetly at the touch, in tone like a swallow. Then great grief came upon the wooers, and the colour of their countenance was changed, and Zeus thundered loud showing forth his tokens. And the steadfast goodly Odysseus was glad thereat, in that the son of deep-counselling Cronos had sent him a sign. Then he caught up a swift arrow which lay by his table, bare, but the other shafts were stored within the hollow quiver, those whereof the Achaeans were soon to taste. He took and laid it on the bridge of the bow, and held the notch and drew the string, even from the settle whereon he sat, and with straight aim shot the shaft and missed not one of the axes, beginning from the first axe-handle, and the bronze-weighted shaft passed clean through and out at the last. Then he spake to Telemachus, saying:

'Telemachus, thy guest that sits in the halls does thee no shame. In no wise did I miss my mark, nor was I wearied with long bending of the bow. Still is my might steadfast—not as the wooers say scornfully to slight me. But now is it time that supper too be got ready for the Achaeans, while it is yet light, and thereafter must we make other sport with the dance and the lyre, for these are the crown of the feast.'

Therewith he nodded with bent brows, and Telemachus, the dear son of divine Odysseus, girt his sharp sword about him and took the spear in his grasp, and stood by his high seat at his father's side, armed with the gleaming bronze.

BOOK XXII

The killing of the wooers.

THEN Odysseus of many counsels stripped him of his rags and leaped on to the great threshold with his bow and quiver full of arrows, and poured forth all the swift shafts there before his feet, and spake among the wooers: 'Lo, now is this terrible trial ended at last; and now will I know of another mark, which never yet man has smitten, if perchance I may hit it and Apollo grant me renown.'

With that he pointed the bitter arrow at Antinous. Now he was about raising to his lips a fair twy-eared chalice of gold, and behold, he was handling it to drink of the wine, and death was far from his thoughts. For who among men at feast would deem that one man amongst so many, how hardy soever he were, would bring on him foul death and black fate? But Odysseus aimed and smote him with the arrow in the throat, and the point passed clean out through his delicate neck, and he fell sidelong and the cup dropped from his hand as he was smitten, and at once through his nostrils there came up a thick jet of slain man's blood, and quickly he spurned the table from him with his foot, and spilt the food on the ground, and the bread and the roast flesh were defiled. Then the wooers raised a clamour through the halls when they saw the man fallen, and they leaped from their high seats, as men stirred by fear, all through the hall, peering everywhere along the well-builded walls, and nowhere was there a shield or mighty spear to lay hold on. Then they reviled Odysseus with angry words:

'Stranger, thou shootest at men to thy hurt. Never again shalt thou enter other lists, now is utter doom assured thee. Yea, for now hast thou slain the man that was far the best of all the noble youths in Ithaca; wherefore vultures shall devour thee here.'

So each one spake, for indeed they thought that Odysseus had not slain him wilfully; but they knew not in their folly that on their own heads, each and all of them, the bands of death had been made fast. Then Odysseus of many counsels looked fiercely on them, and spake:

'Ye dogs, ye said in your hearts that I should never more come home from the land of the Trojans, in that ye wasted my house, and lay with the maidservants by force, and traitorously wooed my wife while I was yet alive, and ye had no fear of the gods, that hold the wide heaven, nor of the indignation of men hereafter. But now the bands of death have been made fast upon you one and all.'

Even so he spake, and pale fear gat hold on the limbs of all, and each man looked about, where he might shun utter doom. And Eurymachus alone answered him, and spake: 'If thou art indeed Odysseus of Ithaca, come home again, with right thou speakest thus, of all that the Achaeans have wrought, many infatuate deeds in thy halls and many in the field. Howbeit, he now lies dead that is to blame for all, Antinous; for he brought all these things upon us, not as longing very greatly for the marriage nor needing it sore, but with another purpose, that Cronion has not fulfilled for him, namely, that he might himself be king over all the land of stablished Ithaca, and he was to have lain in wait for thy son and killed him. But now he is slain after his deserving, and do thou spare thy people, even thine own; and we will hereafter go about the township and yield thee amends for all that has been eaten and drunken in thy halls, each for himself bringing atonement of twenty oxen worth, and requiting thee in gold and bronze till thy heart is softened, but till then none may blame thee that thou art angry.'

Then Odysseus of many counsels looked fiercely on him, and said: 'Eurymachus, not even if ye gave me all your heritage, all that ye now have, and whatsoever else ye might in any wise add thereto, not even so would I henceforth hold my hands from slaying, ere the wooers had paid for all their transgressions. And now the choice lies before you, whether to fight in fair battle or to fly, if any may avoid death and the fates. But there be some, methinks, that shall not escape from utter doom.'

He spake, and their knees were straightway loosened and their hearts melted within them. And Eurymachus spake among them yet again:

'Friends, it is plain that this man will not hold his unconquerable hands, but now that he has caught up the polished bow and quiver, he will shoot from the smooth threshold, till he has slain us all; wherefore let us take thought for the delight of battle. Draw your blades, and hold up the tables to ward off the arrows of swift death, and let us all have at him with one accord, and drive him, if it may be, from the threshold and the doorway and then go through the city, and quickly would the cry be raised. Thereby should this man soon have shot his latest bolt.'

Therewith he drew his sharp two-edged sword of bronze, and leapt on Odysseus with a terrible cry, but in the same moment goodly Odysseus shot the arrow forth and struck him on the breast by the pap, and drave the swift shaft into his liver. So he let the sword fall from his hand, and grovelling over the table he bowed and fell, and spilt the food and the two-handled cup on the floor. And in his agony he smote the ground with his brow, and spurning with both his feet he overthrew the high seat, and the mist of death was shed upon his eyes.

Then Amphinomus made at renowned Odysseus, setting straight at him, and drew his sharp sword, if perchance he might make him give ground from the door. But Telemachus was beforehand with him, and cast and smote him from behind with a bronze-shod spear between the shoulders, and drave it out through the breast, and he fell with a crash and struck the ground full with his forehead. Then Telemachus sprang away, leaving the long spear fixed in Amphinomus, for he greatly dreaded lest one of the Achaeans might run upon him with his blade, and stab him as he drew forth the spear, or smite him with a down stroke of the sword. So he started and ran and came quickly to his father, and stood by him, and spake winged words:

'Father, lo, now I will bring thee a shield and two spears and a helmet all of bronze, close fitting on the temples, and when I return I will arm myself, and likewise give arms to the swineherd and to the neatherd yonder: for it is better to be clad in full armour.'

And Odysseus of many counsels answered him saying: 'Run and bring them while I have arrows to defend me, lest they thrust me from the doorway, one man against them all.'

So he spake, and Telemachus obeyed his dear father, and went forth to the chamber, where his famous weapons were lying. Thence he took out four shields and eight spears, and four helmets of bronze, with thick plumes of horse hair, and he started to bring them and came quickly to his father. Now he girded the gear of bronze about his own body first, and in like manner the two thralls did on the goodly armour, and stood beside the wise and crafty Odysseus. Now he, so long as he had arrows to defend him, kept aiming and smote the wooers one by one in his house, and they fell thick one upon another.

But when the arrows failed the prince in his archery, he leaned his bow against the doorpost of the stablished hall, against the shining faces of the entrance. As for him he girt his fourfold shield about his shoulders and bound on his mighty head a well-wrought helmet, with horse hair crest, and terribly the plume waved aloft. And he grasped two mighty spears tipped with bronze.

Now there was in the well-builded wall a certain postern raised above the floor, and there by the topmost level of the threshold of the stablished hall, was a way into an open passage, closed by well-fitted folding doors. So Odysseus bade the goodly swineherd stand near thereto and watch the way, for thither was there but one approach. Then Agelaus spake among them, and declared his word to all:

'Friends, will not some man climb up to the postern, and give word to the people, and a cry would be raised straightway; so should this man soon have shot his latest bolt?'

Then Melanthius, the goatherd, answered him, saying: 'It may in no wise be, prince Agelaus; for the fair gate of the courtyard is terribly nigh, and perilous is the entrance to the passage, and one man, if he were valiant, might keep back a host. But come, let me bring you armour from the inner chamber, that ye may be clad in hauberks, for, methinks, within that room and not elsewhere did Odysseus and his renowned son lay by the arms.'

Therewith Melanthius, the goatherd, climbed up by the clerestory of the hall to the inner chambers of Odysseus, whence he took twelve shields and as many spears, and as many helmets of bronze with thick plumes of horse hair, and he came forth and brought them speedily, and gave them to the wooers. Then the knees of Odysseus were loosened and his heart melted within him, when he saw them girding on the armour and brandishing the long spears in their hands, and great, he saw, was the adventure. Quickly he spake to Telemachus winged words:

'Telemachus, sure I am that one of the women in the halls is stirring up an evil battle against us, or perchance it is Melanthius.'

Then wise Telemachus answered him: 'My father, it is I that have erred herein and none other is to blame, for I left the well-fitted door of the chamber open, and there has been one of them but too quick to spy it. Go now, goodly Eumaeus, and close the door of the chamber, and mark if it be indeed one of the women that does this mischief, or Melanthius, son of Dolius, as methinks it is.'

Even so they spake one to the other. And Melanthius, the goatherd, went yet again to the chamber to bring the fair armour. But the goodly swineherd was ware thereof, and quickly he spake to Odysseus who stood nigh him:

'Son of Laertes, of the seed of Zeus, Odysseus, of many devices, lo, there again is that baleful man, whom we ourselves suspect, going to the chamber; do thou tell me truly, shall I slay him if I prove the better man, or bring him hither to thee, that he may pay for the many transgressions that he has devised in thy house?"

Then Odysseus of many counsels answered saying: 'Verily, I and Telemachus will keep the proud wooers within the halls, for all their fury, but do ye twain tie his feet and arms behind his back and cast him into the chamber, and close the doors after you, and make fast to his body a twisted rope, and drag him up the lofty pillar till he be near the roof-beams, that he may hang there and live for long, and suffer grievous torment.'

So he spake, and they gave good heed and hearkened. So they went forth to the chamber, but the goatherd who was within knew not of their coming. Now he was seeking for the armour in the secret place of the chamber, but they twain stood in waiting on either side the doorposts. And when Melanthius, the goatherd, was crossing the threshold with a goodly helm in one hand, and in the other a wide shield and an old, stained with rust, the shield of the hero Laertes that he bare when he was young—but at that time it was laid by, and the seams of the straps were loosened,—then the twain rushed on him and caught him, and dragged him in by the hair, and cast him on the floor in sorrowful plight, and bound him hand and foot in a bitter bond, tightly winding each limb behind his back, even as the son of Laertes bade them, the steadfast goodly Odysseus. And they made fast to his body a twisted rope, and dragged him up the lofty pillar till he came near the roof-beams. Then didst thou speak to him and gird at him, swineherd Eumaeus:

'Now in good truth, Melanthius, shalt thou watch all night, lying in a soft bed as beseems thee, nor shall the early-born Dawn escape thy ken, when she comes forth from the streams of Oceanus, on her golden throne, in the hour when thou art wont to drive the goats to make a meal for the wooers in the halls.'

So he was left there, stretched tight in the deadly bond. But they twain got into their harness, and closed the shining door, and went to Odysseus, wise and crafty chief. There they stood breathing fury, four men by the threshold, while those others within the halls were many and good warriors. Then Athene, daughter of Zeus, drew nigh them, like Mentor in fashion and in voice, and Odysseus was glad when he saw her and spake, saying:

'Mentor, ward from us hurt, and remember me thy dear companion, that befriended thee often, and thou art of like age with me.'

So he spake, deeming the while that it was Athene, summoner of the host. But the wooers on the other side shouted in the halls, and first Agelaus son of Damastor rebuked Athene, saying:

'Mentor, let not the speech of Odysseus beguile thee to fight against the wooers, and to succour him. For methinks that on this wise we shall work our will. When we shall have slain these men, father and son, thereafter shalt thou perish with them, such deeds thou art set on doing in these halls; nay, with thine own head shalt thou pay the price. But when with the sword we shall have overcome your violence, we will mingle all thy possessions, all that thou hast at home or in the field, with the wealth of Odysseus, and we will not suffer thy sons nor thy daughters to dwell in the halls, nor thy good wife to gad about in the town of Ithaca.'

So spake he, and Athene was mightily angered at heart, and chid Odysseus in wrathful words: 'Odysseus, thou hast no more steadfast might nor any prowess, as when for nine whole years continually thou didst battle with the Trojans for high born Helen, of the white arms, and many men thou slewest in terrible warfare, and by thy device the wide-wayed city of Priam was taken. How then, now that thou art come to thy house and thine own possessions, dost thou bewail thee and art of feeble courage to stand before the wooers? Nay, come hither, friend, and stand by me, and I will show thee a thing, that thou mayest know what manner of man is Mentor, son of Alcimus, to repay good deeds in the ranks of foemen.'

She spake, and gave him not yet clear victory in full, but still for a while made trial of the might and prowess of Odysseus and his renowned son. As for her she flew up to the roof timber of the murky hall, in such fashion as a swallow flies, and there sat down.

Now Agelaus, son of Damastor, urged on the wooers, and likewise Eurynomus and Amphimedon and Demoptolemus and Peisandrus son of Polyctor, and wise Polybus, for these were in valiancy far the best men of the wooers, that still lived and fought for their lives; for the rest had fallen already beneath the bow and the thick rain of arrows. Then Agelaus spake among them, and made known his word to all:

'Friends, now at last will this man hold his unconquerable hands. Lo, now has Mentor left him and spoken but vain boasts, and these remain alone at the entrance of the doors. Wherefore now, throw not your long spears all together, but come, do ye six cast first, if perchance Zeus may grant us to smite Odysseus and win renown. Of the rest will we take no heed, so soon as that man shall have fallen.'

So he spake and they all cast their javelins, as he bade them, eagerly; but behold, Athene so wrought that they were all in vain. One man smote the doorpost of the stablished hall, and another the well-fastened door, and the ashen spear of yet another wooer, heavy with bronze, stuck fast in the wall. So when they had avoided all the spears of the wooers, the steadfast goodly Odysseus began first to speak among them:

'Friends, now my word is that we too cast and hurl into the press of the wooers, that are mad to slay and strip us beyond the measure of their former iniquities.'

So he spake, and they all took good aim and threw their sharp spears, and Odysseus smote Demoptolemus, and Telemachus Euryades, and the swineherd slew Elatus, and the neatherd Peisandrus. Thus they all bit the wide floor with their teeth, and the wooers fell back into the inmost part of the hall. But the others dashed upon them, and drew forth the shafts from the bodies of the dead.

Then once more the wooers threw their sharp spears eagerly; but behold, Athene so wrought that many of them were in vain. One man smote the doorpost of the stablished hall, and another the well-fastened door, and the ashen spear of another wooer, heavy with bronze, stuck in the wall. Yet Amphimedon hit Telemachus on the hand by the wrist lightly, and the shaft of bronze wounded the surface of the skin. And Ctesippus grazed the shoulder of Eumaeus with a long spear high above the shield, and the spear flew over and fell to the ground. Then again

Odysseus, the wise and crafty, he and his men cast their swift spears into the press of the wooers, and now once more Odysseus, waster of cities, smote Eurydamas, and Telemachus Amphimedon, and the swineherd slew Polybus, and last, the neatherd struck Ctesippus in the breast and boasted over him, saying:

'O son of Polytherses, thou lover of jeering, never give place at all to folly to speak so big, but leave thy case to the gods, since in truth they are far mightier than thou. This gift is thy recompense for the ox-foot that thou gavest of late to the divine Odysseus, when he went begging through the house.'

So spake the keeper of the shambling kine. Next Odysseus wounded the son of Damastor in close fight with his long spear, and Telemachus wounded Leocritus son of Euenor, right in the flank with his lance, and drave the bronze point clean through, that he fell prone and struck the ground full with his forehead. Then Athene held up her destroying aegis on high from the roof, and their minds were scared, and they fled through the hall, like a drove of kine that the flitting gadfly falls upon and scatters hither and thither in spring time, when the long days begin. But the others set on like vultures of crooked claws and curved beak, that come forth from the mountains and dash upon smaller birds, and these scour low in the plain, stooping in terror from the clouds, while the vultures pounce on them and slay them, and there is no help nor way of flight, and men are glad at the sport; even so did the company of Odysseus set upon the wooers and smite them right and left through the hall; and there rose a hideous moaning as their heads were smitten, and the floor all ran with blood.

Now Leiodes took hold of the knees of Odysseus eagerly, and besought him and spake winged words: 'I entreat thee by thy knees, Odysseus, and do thou show mercy on me and have pity. For never yet, I say, have

I wronged a maiden in thy halls by froward word or deed, nay I bade the other wooers refrain, whoso of them wrought thus. But they hearkened not unto me to keep their hands from evil. Wherefore they have met a shameful death through their own infatuate deeds. Yet I, the soothsayer among them, that have wrought no evil, shall fall even as they, for no grace abides for good deeds done.'

Then Odysseus of many counsels looked askance at him, and said: 'If indeed thou dost avow thee to be the soothsayer of these men, thou art like to have often prayed in the halls that the issue of a glad return might be far from me, and that my dear wife should follow thee and bear thee children; wherefore thou shalt not escape the bitterness of death.'

Therewith he caught up a sword in his strong hand, that lay where Agelaus had let it fall to the ground when he was slain, and drave it clean through his neck, and as he yet spake his head fell even to the dust.

But the son of Terpes, the minstrel, still sought how he might shun black fate, Phemius, who sang among the wooers of necessity. He stood with the loud lyre in his hand hard by the postern gate, and his heart was divided within him, whether he should slip forth from the hall and sit down by the well-wrought altar of great Zeus of the household court, whereon Laertes and Odysseus had burnt many pieces of the thighs of oxen, or should spring forward and beseech Odysseus by his knees. And as he thought thereupon this seemed to him the better way, to embrace the knees of Odysseus, son of Laertes. So he laid the hollow lyre on the ground between the mixing-bowl and the high seat inlaid with silver, and himself sprang forward and seized Odysseus by the knees, and besought him and spake winged words:

'I entreat thee by thy knees, Odysseus, and do thou show mercy on me and have pity. It will be a sorrow to thyself in the aftertime if thou slayest me who am a minstrel, and sing before gods and men. Yea none has taught me but myself, and the god has put into my heart all manner of lays, and methinks I sing to thee as to a god, wherefore be not eager to cut off my head. And Telemachus will testify of this, thine own dear son, that not by mine own will or desire did I resort to thy house to sing to the wooers at their feasts; but being so many and stronger than I they led me by constraint.'

So he spake, and the mighty prince Telemachus heard him and quickly spake to his father at his side: 'Hold thy hand, and wound not this blameless man with the sword; and let us save also the henchman Medon, that ever had charge of me in our house when I was a child, unless perchance Philoetius or the swineherd have already slain him, or he hath met thee in thy raging through the house.'

So he spake, and Medon, wise of heart, heard him. For he lay crouching beneath a high seat, clad about in the new-flayed hide of an ox and shunned black fate. So he rose up quickly from under the seat, and cast off the ox-hide, and sprang forth and caught Telemachus by the knees, and besought him and spake winged words:

'Friend, here am I; prithee stay thy hand and speak to thy father, lest he harm me with the sharp sword in the greatness of his strength, out of his anger for the wooers that wasted his possessions in the halls, and in their folly held thee in no honour.'

And Odysseus of many counsels smiled on him and said: 'Take courage, for lo, he has saved thee and delivered thee, that thou mayst know in thy heart, and tell it even to another, how far more excellent are good deeds than evil. But go forth from the halls and sit down in the court apart from the slaughter, thou and the full-voiced minstrel, till I have accomplished all that I must needs do in the house.'

Therewith the two went forth and gat them from the

hall. So they sat down by the altar of great Zeus, peering about on every side, still expecting death. And Odysseus peered all through the house, to see if any man was yet alive and hiding away to shun black fate. But he found all the sort of them fallen in their blood in the dust, like fishes that the fishermen have drawn forth in the meshes of the net into a hollow of the beach from out the grey sea, and all the fish, sore longing for the salt sea waves, are heaped upon the sand, and the sun shines forth and takes their life away; so now the wooers lay heaped upon each other. Then Odysseus of many counsels spake to Telemachus:

'Telemachus, go, call me the nurse Eurycleia, that I may tell her a word that is on my mind.'

So he spake, and Telemachus obeyed his dear father, and smote at the door, and spake to the nurse Eurycleia: 'Up now, aged wife, that overlookest all the women servants in our halls, come hither, my father calls thee and has somewhat to say to thee.'

Even so he spake, and wingless her speech remained, and she opened the doors of the fair-lying halls, and came forth, and Telemachus led the way before her. So she found Odysseus among the bodies of the dead, stained with blood and soil of battle, like a lion that has eaten of an ox of the homestead and goes on his way, and all his breast and his cheeks on either side are flecked with blood, and he is terrible to behold; even so was Odysseus stained, both hands and feet. Now the nurse, when she saw the bodies of the dead and the great gore of blood, made ready to cry aloud for joy, beholding so great an adventure. But Odysseus checked and held her in her eagerness, and uttering his voice spake to her winged words:

'Within thine own heart rejoice, old nurse, and be still, and cry not aloud; for it is an unholy thing to boast over slain men. Now these hath the destiny of the gods overcome, and their own cruel deeds, for they honoured none of earthly men, neither the bad nor yet the good, that came among them. Wherefore they have met a shameful death through their own infatuate deeds. But come, tell me the tale of the women in my halls, which of them dishonour me, and which be guiltless.'

Then the good nurse Eurycleia answered him: 'Yea now, my child, I will tell thee all the truth. Thou hast fifty women-servants in thy halls, that we have taught the ways of housewifery, how to card wool and to bear bondage. Of these twelve in all have gone the way of shame, and honour not me, nor their lady Penelope. And Telemachus hath but newly come to his strength, and his mother suffered him not to take command over the women in this house. But now, let me go aloft to the shining upper chamber, and tell all to thy wife, on whom some god hath sent a sleep.'

And Odysseus of many counsels answered her, saying: 'Wake her not yet, but bid the women come hither, who in time past behaved themselves unseemly.'

So he spake, and the old wife passed through the hall, to tell the women and to hasten their coming. Then Odysseus called to him Telemachus, and the neatherd, and the swineherd, and spake to them winged words:

'Begin ye now to carry out the dead, and bid the women help you, and thereafter cleanse the fair high seats and the tables with water and porous sponges. And when ye have set all the house in order, lead the maidens without the stablished hall, between the vaulted room and the goodly fence of the court, and there slay them with your long blades, till they shall have all given up the ghost and forgotten the love that of old they had at the bidding of the wooers, in secret dalliance.'

Even so he spake, and the women came all in a crowd together, making a terrible lament and shedding big tears. So first they carried forth the bodies of the slain, and set them beneath the gallery of the fenced court, and propped them one on another; and Odysseus himself hasted the women and directed them, and they carried forth the dead perforce. Thereafter they cleansed the fair high seats and the tables with water and porous sponges. And Telemachus, and the neatherd, and the swineherd, scraped with spades the floor of the well-builded house, and, behold, the maidens carried all forth and laid it without the doors.

Now when they had made an end of setting the hall in order, they led the maidens forth from the stablished hall, and drove them up in a narrow space between the vaulted room and the goodly fence of the court, whence none might avoid; and wise Telemachus began to speak to his fellows, saying:

'God forbid that I should take these women's lives by a clean death, these that have poured dishonour on my head and on my mother, and have lain with the wooers.'

With that word he tied the cable of a dark-prowed ship to a great pillar and flung it round the vaulted room, and fastened it aloft, that none might touch the ground with her feet. And even as when thrushes, long of wing, or doves fall into a net that is set in a thicket, as they seek to their roosting-place, and a loathly bed harbours them, even so the women held their heads all in a row, and about all their necks nooses were cast, that they might die by the most pitiful death. And they writhed with their feet for a little space, but for no long while.

Then they led out Melanthius through the doorway and the court, and cut off his nostrils and his ears with the pitiless sword, and drew forth his vitals for the dogs to devour raw, and cut off his hands and feet in their cruel anger.

Thereafter they washed their hands and feet, and went into the house to Odysseus, and all the adventure was over. So Odysseus called to the good nurse Eurycleia: 'Bring sulphur, old nurse, that cleanses all pollution and bring me fire, that I may purify the house with sulphur, and do thou bid Penelope come here with her handmaidens, and tell all the women to hasten into the hall.'

Then the good nurse Eurycleia made answer: 'Yea, my child, herein thou hast spoken aright. But go to, let me bring thee a mantle and a doublet for raiment, and stand not thus in the halls with thy broad shoulders wrapped in rags; it were blame in thee so to do.'

And Odysseus of many counsels answered her saying: 'First let a fire now be made me in the hall.'

So he spake, and the good nurse Eurycleia was not slow to obey, but brought fire and brimstone; and Odysseus thoroughly purged the women's chamber and the great hall and the court.

Then the old wife went through the fair halls of Odysseus to tell the women, and to hasten their coming. So they came forth from their chamber with torches in their hands, and fell about Odysseus, and embraced him and kissed and clasped his head and shoulders and his hands lovingly, and a sweet longing came on him to weep and moan, for he remembered them every one.

BOOK XXIII

Odysseus maketh himself known to Penelope, tells his adventures briefly, and in the morning goes to Laertes and makes himself known to him.

THEN the ancient woman went up into the upper chamber laughing aloud, to tell her mistress how her dear lord was within, and her knees moved fast for joy, and her feet stumbled one over the other; and she stood above the lady's head and spake to her, saying:

'Awake, Penelope, dear child, that thou mayest see with thine own eyes that which thou desirest day by day. Odysseus hath come, and hath got him to his own house, though late hath he come, and hath slain the proud wooers that troubled his house, and devoured his substance and oppressed his child.'

Then wise Penelope answered her: 'Dear nurse, the gods have made thee distraught, the gods that can make foolish even the wisdom of the wise, and that stablish the simple in understanding. They it is that have marred thy reason, though heretofore thou hadst a prudent heart. Why dost thou mock me, who have a spirit full of sorrow, to speak these wild words, and rousest me out of sweet slumber, that had bound me and overshadowed mine eyelids? Never yet have I slept so sound since the day that Odysseus went forth to see that evil Ilios, never to be named. Go to now, get thee down and back to the women's chamber, for if any other of the maids of my house had come and brought me such tidings, and wakened me from sleep, straightway would I have sent her back woefully to return within the women's chamber; but this time thine old age shall stand thee in good stead.'

Then the good nurse Eurycleia answered her: 'I mock thee not, dear child, but in very deed Odysseus is here, and hath come home, even as I tell thee. He is that guest on whom all men wrought such dishonour in the halls. But long ago Telemachus was ware of him, that he was within the house, yet in his prudence he hid the counsels of his father, that he might take vengeance on the violence of the haughty wooers.'

Thus she spake, and then was Penelope glad, and leaping from her bed she fell on the old woman's neck, and let fall the tears from her eyelids, and uttering her voice spake to her winged words: 'Come, dear nurse, I pray thee, tell me all truly—if indeed he hath come home as thou sayest—how he hath laid his hands on the shameless wooers, he being but one man, while they abode ever in their companies within the house.'

Then the good nurse Eurycleia answered her: 'I saw not, I wist not, only I heard the groaning of men slain. And we in an inmost place of the well-builded chambers sat all amazed, and the close-fitted doors shut in the room, till thy son called me from the chamber, for his father sent him out to that end. Then I found Odysseus standing among the slain, who around him, stretched on the hard floor, lay one upon the other; it would have comforted thy heart to see him, all stained like a lion with blood and soil of battle. And now are all the wooers gathered in an heap by the gates of the court, while he is purifying his fair house with brimstone, and hath kindled a great fire, and hath sent me forth to call thee. So come with me, that ye may both enter into your hearts' delight, for ye have suffered much affliction. And even now hath this thy long desire been fulfilled; thy lord hath come alive to his own hearth, and hath found both thee and his son in the halls; and the wooers that wrought him evil he hath slain, every man of them in his house.'

Then wise Penelope answered her: 'Dear nurse, boast not yet over them with laughter. Thou knowest how welcome the sight of him would be in the halls to all, and to me in chief, and to his son that we got between us. But this is no true tale, as thou declarest it, nay but it is one of the deathless gods that hath slain the proud wooers, in wrath at their bitter insolence and evil deeds. For they honoured none of earthly men, neither the good nor yet the bad, that came among them. Wherefore they have suffered an evil doom through their own infatuate deeds. But Odysseus, far away hath lost his homeward path to the Achaean land, and himself is lost.'

Then the good nurse Eurycleia made answer to her: 'My child, what word hath escaped the door of thy lips, in that thou saidest that thy lord, who is even now within, and by his own hearthstone, would return no more? Nay, thy heart is ever hard of belief. Go to now, and I will tell thee besides a most manifest token, even the scar of the wound that the boar on a time dealt him with his white tusk. This I spied while washing his feet, and fain I would have told it even to thee, but he laid his hand on my mouth, and in the fulness of his wisdom suffered me not to speak. But come with me and I will stake my life on it; and, if I play thee false, do thou slay me by a death most pitiful.'

Then wise Penelope made answer to her: 'Dear nurse, it is hard for thee, how wise soever, to observe the purposes of the everlasting gods. None the less let us go to my child, that I may see the wooers dead, and him that slew them.'

With that word she went down from the upper chamber, and much her heart debated, whether she should stand apart, and question her dear lord or draw nigh, and clasp and kiss his head and hands. But when she had come within and had crossed the threshold of stone, she sat down over against Odysseus, in the light of the fire, by the further wall. Now he was sitting by the tall pillar, looking down and waiting to know if perchance his noble wife would speak to him, when her eyes beheld him. But she sat long in silence, and amazement came upon her soul, and now she would look upon him steadfastly with her eyes, and now again she knew him not, for that he was clad in vile raiment. And Telemachus rebuked her, and spake and hailed her:

'Mother mine, ill mother, of an ungentle heart, why turnest thou thus away from my father, and dost not sit by him and question him and ask him all? No other woman in the world would harden her heart to stand thus aloof from her lord, who after much travail and sore had come to her in the twentieth year to his own country. But thy heart is ever harder than stone.'

Then wise Penelope answered him, saying: 'Child, my mind is amazed within me, and I have no strength to speak, nor to ask him aught, nay nor to look on him face to face. But if in truth this be Odysseus, and he hath indeed come home, verily we shall be ware of each other the more surely, for we have tokens that we twain know, even we, secret from all others.'

So she spake, and the steadfast goodly Odysseus smiled, and quickly he spake to Telemachus winged words: 'Telemachus, leave now thy mother to make trial of me within the chambers; so shall she soon come to a better knowledge than heretofore. But now I go filthy, and am clad in vile raiment, wherefore she has me in dishonour, and as yet will not allow that I am he. Let us then advise us how all may be for the very best. For whoso has slain but one man in a land, even one that leaves not many behind him to take up the feud for him, turns outlaw and leaves his kindred and his own country; but we have slain the very stay of the city, the men who were far the best of all the noble youths in Ithaca. So this I bid thee consider.'

Then wise Telemachus answered him, saying: 'Father, see thou to this, for they say that thy counsel is far the best among men, nor might any other of mortal men contend with thee. But right eagerly will we go with thee now, and I think we shall not lack prowess, so far as might is ours.'

And Odysseus of many counsels answered him saying: 'Yea now, I will tell on what wise methinks it is best. First, go ye to the bath and array you in your doublets, and bid the maidens in the chambers to take to them their garments. Then let the divine minstrel, with his loud lyre in hand, lead off for us the measure of the mirthful dance. So shall any man that hears the sound from without, whether a wayfarer or one of those that dwell around, say that it is a wedding feast. And thus the slaughter of the wooers shall not be noised abroad through the town before we go forth to our well-wooded farm-land. Thereafter shall we consider what gainful counsel the Olympian may vouchsafe us.'

So he spake, and they gave good ear and hearkened to him. So first they went to the bath, and arrayed them in doublets, and the women were apparelled, and the divine minstrel took the hollow harp, and aroused in them the desire of sweet song and of the happy dance. Then the great hall rang round them with the sound of the feet of dancing men and of fair-girdled women. And whoso heard it from without would say:

'Surely some one has wedded the queen of many wooers. Hard of heart was she, nor had she courage to keep the great house of her wedded lord continually till his coming.'

Even so men spake, and knew not how these things were ordained. Meanwhile, the house-dame Eurynome had bathed the great-hearted Odysseus within his house, and anointed him with olive-oil, and cast about him a goodly mantle and a doublet. Moreover, Athene shed great beauty from his head downwards, and made him greater and more mighty to behold, and from his head caused deep curling locks to flow, like the hyacinth flower. And as when some skilful man overlays gold upon silver, one that Hephaestus and Pallas Athene have taught all manner of craft, and full of grace is his handiwork, even so did Athene shed grace about his head and shoulders, and forth from the bath he came, in form like to the Immortals. Then he sat down again on the high seat, whence he had arisen, over against his wife, and spake to her, saying:

'Strange lady, surely to thee above all womankind the Olympians have given a heart that cannot be softened. No other woman in the world would harden her heart to stand thus aloof from her husband, who after much travail and sore had come to her, in the twentieth year, to his own country. Nay come, nurse, strew a bed for me to lie all alone, for assuredly her spirit within her is as iron.'

Then wise Penelope answered him again: 'Strange man, I have no proud thoughts nor do I think scorn of thee, nor am I too greatly astonied, but I know right well what manner of man thou wert, when thou wentest forth out of Ithaca, on the long-oared galley. But come, Eurycleia, spread for him the good bedstead outside the stablished bridal chamber that he built himself. Thither bring ye forth the good bedstead and cast bedding thereon, even fleeces and rugs and shining blankets.'

So she spake and made trial of her lord, but Odysseus in sore displeasure spake to his true wife, saying: 'Verily a bitter word is this, lady, that thou hast spoken. Who has set my bed otherwhere? Hard it would be for one, how skilled soever, unless a god were to come that might easily set it in another place, if so he would. But of men there is none living, howsoever strong in his youth, that could lightly upheave it, for a great token is wrought in the fashioning of the bed, and it was I that made it and none other. There was growing a bush of olive, long of leaf, and most goodly of growth, within the inner court, and the stem as large as a pillar. Round about this I built the chamber, till I had finished it, with stones close set, and I roofed it over well and added thereto compacted doors fitting well. Next I sheared off all the light wood of the long-leaved olive, and rough-hewed the trunk upwards from the root, and smoothed it around with the adze, well and skilfully, and made straight the line thereto and so fashioned it into the bed-post, and I bored it all with the auger. Beginning from this bed-post, I wrought at the bedstead till I had finished it, and made it fair with inlaid work of gold and of silver and of ivory. Then I made fast therein a bright purple band of oxhide. Even so I declare to thee this token, and I know not, lady, if the bedstead be yet fast in his place, or if some man has cut away the stem of the olive tree, and set the bedstead otherwhere.'

So he spake, and at once her knees were loosened, and her heart melted within her, as she knew the sure tokens that Odysseus showed her. Then she fell a weeping, and ran straight toward him and cast her hands about his neck, and kissed his head and spake, saying:

'Be not angry with me, Odysseus, for thou wert ever at other times the wisest of men. It is the gods that gave us sorrow, the gods who begrudged us that we should abide together and have joy of our youth, and come to the threshold of old age. So now be not wroth with me hereat nor full of indignation, because at the first, when I saw thee, I did not welcome thee straightway. For always my heart within my breast shuddered, for fear lest some man should come and deceive me with his words, for many they be that devise gainful schemes and evil. Nay even Argive Helen, daughter of Zeus, would not have lain with a stranger, and taken him for a lover, had she known that the warlike sons of the Achaeans would bring her home again to her own dear country. Howsoever, it was the god that set her upon this shameful deed; nor ever, ere that, did she lay up in her heart the thought of this folly, a bitter folly, whence on us too first came sorrow. But now that thou hast told all the sure tokens of our bed, which never was seen by mortal man, save by thee and me and one maiden only, the daughter of Actor, that my father gave me ere yet I had come hither, she who kept the doors of our strong bridal chamber, even now dost thou bend my soul, all ungentle as it is.'

Thus she spake, and in his heart she stirred yet a greater longing to lament, and he wept as he embraced his beloved wife and true. And even as when the sight of land is welcome to swimmers, whose well-wrought ship Poseidon hath smitten on the deep, all driven with the wind and swelling waves, and but a remnant hath escaped the grey sea-water and swum to the shore, and their bodies are all crusted with the brine, and gladly have they set foot on land and escaped an evil end; so welcome to her was the sight of her lord, and her white arms she would never quite let go from his neck. And now would the rosy-fingered Dawn have risen upon their weeping, but the goddess, grey-eyed Athene, had other thoughts. The night she held long in the utmost West, and on the other side she stayed the golden throned Dawn by the stream Oceanus, and suffered her not to harness the swift-footed steeds that bear light to men, Lampus and Phaethon, the steeds ever young, that bring the morning.

Then at the last, Odysseus of many counsels spake to his wife, saying: 'Lady, we have not yet come to the issue of all our labours; but still there will be toil unmeasured, long and difficult, that I must needs bring to a full end. Even so the spirit of Teiresias foretold to me, on that day when I went down into the house of Hades, to inquire after a returning for myself and my company. Wherefore come, lady, let us to bed, that forthwith we may take our joy of rest beneath the spell of sweet sleep.'

Then wise Penelope answered him: 'Thy bed verily shall be ready whensoever thy soul desires it, forasmuch as the gods have indeed caused thee to come back to thy stablished home and thine own country. But now that thou hast noted it and the god has put it into thy heart, come, tell me of this ordeal, for methinks the day will come when I must learn it, and timely knowledge is no hurt.'

And Odysseus of many counsels answered her saying: 'Ah, why now art thou so instant with me to declare it? Yet I will tell thee all and hide nought. Howbeit thy heart shall have no joy of it, as even I myself have no pleasure therein. For Teiresias bade me fare to many cities of men, carrying a shapen oar in my hands, till I should come to such men as know not the sea, neither eat meat savoured with salt, nor have they knowledge of ships of purple cheek nor of shapen oars, which serve for wings to ships. And he told me this with manifest token, which I will not hide from thee. In the day when another wayfarer should meet me and say that I had a winnowing fan on my stout shoulder, even then he bade me make fast my shapen oar in the earth, and do goodly sacrifice to the lord Poseidon, even with a ram and a bull and a boar, the mate of swine, and depart for home, and offer holy hecatombs to the deathless gods, that keep the wide heaven, to each in order due. And from the sea shall mine own death come, the gentlest death that may be, which shall end me, foredone with smooth old age, and the folk shall dwell happily around. All this, he said, was to be fulfilled.'

Then wise Penelope answered him saying: 'If indeed the gods will bring about for thee a happier old age at the last, then is there hope that thou mayest yet have an escape from evil.'

Thus they spake one to the other. Meanwhile, Eurynome and the nurse spread the bed with soft coverlets, by the light of the torches burning. But when they had busied them and spread the good bed, the ancient nurse went back to her chamber to lie down, and Eurynome, the bower-maiden, guided them on their way to the couch, with torches in her hands, and when she had led them to the bridal-chamber she departed. And so they came gladly to the rites of their bed, as of old. But Telemachus, and the neatherd, and the swineherd stayed their feet from dancing, and made the women to cease, and themselves gat them to rest through the shadowy halls.

Now when the twain had taken their fill of sweet love, they had delight in the tales, which they told one to the other. The fair lady spoke of all that she had endured in the halls at the sight of the ruinous throng of wooers, who for her sake slew many cattle, kine and goodly sheep; and many a cask of wine was broached. And in turn, Odysseus, of the seed of Zeus, recounted all the griefs he had wrought on men, and all his own travail and sorrow and she was delighted with the story, and sweet sleep fell not upon her eyelids till the tale was ended.

He began by setting forth how he overcame the Cicones, and next arrived at the rich land of the Lotuseaters, and all that the Cyclops wrought, and what a price he got from him for the good companions that he devoured, and showed no pity. Then how he came to Aeolus, who received him gladly and sent him on his way; but it was not yet ordained that he should reach his own country, for the stormwind seized him again, and bare him over the teeming seas, making grievous moan. Next how he came to Telepylus of the Laestrygonians, who brake his ships and slew all his goodly-greaved companions, and Odysseus only escaped with his black ship. Then he told all the wiles and many contrivances of Circé, and how in a benched ship he fared to the dank house of Hades, to seek to the soul of Theban Teiresias. There he beheld all those that had been his companions, and his mother who bore him and nurtured him, while yet he was a little one. Then how he heard the song of the full-voiced Sirens, and came to the Rocks Wandering, and to terrible Charybdis, and to Scylla, that never yet have men avoided scatheless. Next he told how his company slew the kine of Helios, and how Zeus, that thunders on high, smote the swift ship with the flaming bolt, and the good crew perished all together, and he alone escaped from evil fates. And how he came to the isle Ogygia, and to the nymph Calypso, who kept him there in her hollow caves, longing to have him for her lord, and nurtured him and said that she would make him never to know death or age all his days: yet she never won his heart within his breast. Next how with great toil he came to the Phaeacians, who gave him all worship heartily, as to a god, and sent him with a ship to his own dear country, with gifts of bronze, and of gold, and raiment in plenty. This was the last word of the tale, when sweet sleep came speedily upon him, sleep that loosens the limbs of men, unknitting the cares of his soul.

Then the goddess, grey-eyed Athene, turned to new thoughts. When she deemed that Odysseus had taken his fill of love and sleep, straightway she aroused from out Oceanus the golden throned Dawn, to bear light to men. Then Odysseus gat him up from his soft bed, and laid this charge on his wife, saying:

'Lady, already have we had enough of labours, thou and I; thou, in weeping here, and longing for my troublous return, I, while Zeus and the other gods bound me fast in pain, despite my yearning after home, away from mine own country. But now that we both have come to the bed of our desire, take thou thought for the care of my wealth within the halls. But as for the sheep that the proud wooers have slain, I myself will lift many more as spoil, and others the Achaeans will give, till they fill all my folds. But now, behold, I go to the well-wooded farm-land, to see my good father, who for love of me has been in sorrow continually. And this charge I lay on thee, lady, too wise though thou art to need it. Quickly will the bruit go forth with the rising sun, the bruit concerning the wooers' whom I slew in the halls. Wherefore ascend with the women thy handmaids into the upper chamber, and sit there and look on no man, nor ask any question.'

Therewith he girded on his shoulder his goodly armour, and roused Telemachus and the neatherd and the swine-herd, and bade them all take weapons of war in their hands. So they were not disobedient to his word, but clad them-selves in mail, and opened the doors and went forth, and Odysseus led the way. And now there was light over all the earth; but them Athene hid in night, and quickly con-ducted out of the town.

BOOK XXIV

The Ithacans bury the wooers, and sitting in council resolve on revenge. And coming near the house of Laertes, are met by Odysseus, and Laertes with Telemachus and servants, the whole number twelve, and are overcome, and submit.

Now Cyllenian Hermes called forth from the halls the souls of the wooers, and he held in his hand his wand that is fair and golden, wherewith he lulls the eyes of men, of whomso he will, while others again he even wakens out of sleep. Herewith he roused and led the souls who followed gibbering. And even as bats flit gibbering in the secret place of a wondrous cave, when one has fallen down from the cluster on the rock, where they cling each to each up aloft, even so the souls gibbered as they fared together, and Hermes, the helper, led them down the dank ways. Past the streams of Oceanus and the White Rock, past the gates of the Sun they sped and the land of dreams, and soon they came to the mead of asphodel, where dwell the souls, the phantoms of men outworn. There they found the soul of Achilles son of Peleus, and the souls of Patroclus, and of noble Antilochus, and of Aias, who in face and form was goodliest of all the Danaans after the noble son of Peleus.

So these were flocking round Achilles, and the spirit of Agamemnon, son of Atreus, drew nigh sorrowful; and about him were gathered all the other shades, as many as perished with him in the house of Aegisthus, and met their doom. Now the soul of the son of Peleus spake to him first, saying:

'Son of Atreus, verily we deemed that thou above all other heroes wast evermore dear to Zeus, whose joy is in the thunder, seeing that thou wast lord over warriors, many and mighty men, in the land of the Trojans where we Achaeans suffered affliction. But lo, thee too was deadly doom to visit early, the doom that none avoids of all men born. Ah, would that in the fulness of thy princely honour, thou hadst met death and fate in the land of the Trojans! So would all the Achaean host have builded thee a barrow, yea and for thy son thou wouldst have won great glory in the aftertime. But now it has been decreed for thee to perish by a most pitiful death.'

Then the soul of the son of Atreus answered, and spake: 'Happy art thou, son of Peleus, godlike Achilles, that didst die in Troy-land far from Argos, and about thee fell others, the best of the sons of Trojans and Achaeans, fighting for thy body; but thou in the whirl of dust layest mighty and mightily fallen, forgetful of thy chivalry. And we strove the livelong day, nor would we ever have ceased from the fight, if Zeus had not stayed us with a tempest. Anon when we had borne thee to the ships from out of the battle, we laid thee on a bier and washed thy fair flesh clean with warm water and unguents, and around thee the Danaans shed many a hot tear and shore their hair. And forth from the sea came thy mother with the deathless maidens of the waters, when they heard the tidings; and a wonderful wailing rose over the deep, and trembling fell on the limbs of all the Achaeans. Yea, and they would have sprung up and departed to the hollow ships, had not one held them back that knew much lore from of old, Nestor, whose counsel proved heretofore the best. Out of his good will he made harangue, and spake among them:

'"Hold, ye Argives, flee not, young lords of the Achaeans. Lo, his mother from the sea is she that comes, with the deathless maidens of the waters, to behold the face of her dead son."

'So he spake, and the high-hearted Achaeans ceased from their flight. Then round thee stood the daughters of the ancient one of the sea, holding a pitiful lament, and they clad thee about in raiment incorruptible. And all the nine Muses one to the other replying with sweet voices began the dirge; there thou wouldest not have seen an Argive but wept, so mightily rose up the clear chant. Thus for seventeen days and nights continually did we all bewail thee, immortal gods and mortal men. On the eighteenth day we gave thy body to the flames, and many well-fatted sheep we slew around thee, and kine of shambling gait. So thou wert burned in the garments of the gods, and in much unguents and in sweet honey, and many heroes of the Achaeans moved mail-clad around the pyre when thou wast burning, both footmen and horse, and great was the noise that arose. But when the flame of Hephaestus had utterly abolished thee, lo, in the morning we gathered together thy white bones, Achilles, and bestowed them in unmixed wine and in unguents. Thy mother gave a twy-handled golden urn, and said that it was the gift of Dionysus, and the workmanship of renowned Hephaestus. Therein lie thy white bones, great Achilles, and mingled therewith the bones of Patroclus son of Menoetias, that is dead, but apart is the dust of Antilochus, whom thou didst honour above all thy other companions, after Patroclus that was dead. Then over them did we pile a great and goodly tomb, we the holy host of Argive warriors, high on a jutting headland over wide Hellespont, that it might be far seen from off the sea by men that now are, and by those that shall be hereafter. Then thy mother asked the gods for glorious prizes in the games, and set them in the midst of the lists for the champions of the Achaeans. In days past thou hast been at the funeral games of many a hero, whenso, after some king's death, the young men gird themselves and make them ready for the meed of victory; but couldst thou have seen these gifts thou wouldst most have marvelled in spirit, such glorious prizes did the goddess set there to honour thee, even Thetis, the silver-footed; for very dear wert thou to the gods. Thus not even in death hast thou lost thy name, but to thee shall there be a fair renown for ever among all men, Achilles. But what joy have I now herein, that I have wound up the clew of war, for on my return Zeus devised for me an evil end at the hands of Aegisthus and my wife accursed?'

So they spake one to the other. And nigh them came the Messenger, the slayer of Argos, leading down the ghosts of the wooers by Odysseus slain, and the two heroes were amazed at the sight and went straight toward them. And the soul of Agamemnon, son of Atreus, knew the dear son of Melaneus, renowned Amphimedon, who had been his host, having his dwelling in Ithaca. The soul of the son of Atreus spake to him first, saying:

'Amphimedon, what hath befallen you, that ye have come beneath the darkness of earth, all of you picked men and of like age? it is even as though one should choose out and gather together the best warriors in a city. Did Poseidon smite you in your ships and rouse up contrary winds and the long waves? Or did unfriendly men, perchance, do you hurt upon the land as ye were cutting off their oxen and fair flocks of sheep, or while they fought to defend their city and the women thereof? Answer and tell me, for I avow me a friend of thy house. Rememberest thou not the day when I came to your house in Ithaca with godlike Menelaus, to urge Odysseus to follow with me to Ilios on the decked ships? And it was a full month ere we had sailed all across the wide sea, for scarce could we win to our cause Odysseus, waster of cities.'

Then the ghost of Amphimedon answered him, and spake: 'Most famous son of Atreus, king of men, Agamemnon, I remember all these things, O fosterling of Zeus, as thou declarest them, and I in turn will tell thee all the tale well and truly, even our death and evil end, on what wise it befell. We wooed the wife of Odysseus that was long afar, and she neither refused the hated bridal nor was minded to make an end, devising for us death and black fate. Also this other wile she contrived in her heart. She set up in her halls a mighty web, fine of woof and very wide, whereat she would weave, and anon she spake among us:

' "Ye princely youths, my wooers, now that goodly Odysseus is dead, do ye abide patiently, how eager soever to speed on this marriage of mine, till I finish the robe. I would not that the threads perish to no avail, even this shroud for the hero Laertes, against the day when the ruinous doom shall bring him low, of death that lays men at their length. So shall none of the Achaean women in the land count it blame in me, as well might be, were he to lie without a winding-sheet, a man that had gotten great possessions."

'So spake she, and our high hearts consented thereto. So then in the daytime she would weave the mighty web, and in the night unravel the same, when she had let place the torches by her. Thus for the space of three years she hid the thing by guile and won the minds of the Achaeans; but when the fourth year arrived and the seasons came round, as the months waned and many days were accomplished, then it was that one of her women who knew all declared it, and we found her unravelling the splendid web. Thus she finished it perforce and sore against her will. Now when she brought the robe to light, after she had woven the great web and washed it, and it shone even as sun or moon, at that very hour some evil god led Odysseus, I know not whence, to the upland farm, where the swineherd abode in his dwelling. Thither too came the dear son of divine Odysseus out of sandy Pylos, voyaging with his black ship. These twain framed an evil death for the wooers, and came to the renowned town. Odysseus verily came the later, and Telemachus went before and led the way. Now the swineherd brought Odysseus clad in vile raiment, in the likeness of a beggar, a wretched man and an old, leaning on a staff, and behold, he was clad about in sorry raiment. And none of us, not even the elders, could know him for that he was, on this his sudden appearing, but with evil words we assailed him and hurled things at him. Yet for a while he hardened his heart to endure both the hurlings and the evil words in his own halls; but at the last, when the spirit of Zeus, lord of the aegis, aroused him, by the help of Telemachus he took up all the goodly weapons, and laid them by in the inner chamber and drew the bolts. Next in his great craft he bade his wife to offer his bow and store of grey iron to the wooers to be the weapons of our contest, luckless that we were, and the beginning of death. Now not one of us could stretch the string of the strong bow; far short we fell of that might. But when the great bow came to the hands of Odysseus, then we all clamoured and forbade to give him the bow, how much soever he might speak, but Telemachus alone was instant with him and commanded him to take it. Then he took the bow into his hands, the steadfast goodly Odysseus, and lightly he strung it, and sent the arrow through the iron. Then straight he went to the threshold and there took his stand, and poured forth the swift arrows, glancing terribly around, and smote the king Antinous. Thereafter on the others he let fly his bolts, winged for death, with straight aim, and the wooers fell thick one upon another. Then was it known how that some god was their helper, for pressing on as their passion drave them, they slew the men right and left through the halls, and thence there arose a hideous moaning, as heads were smitten and the floor all ran with blood. So we perished, Agamemnon, and even now our bodies lie uncared for in the halls of Odysseus, for the friends of each one at home as yet know nought, even they who might wash the black-clotted blood out of our wounds, and lay out the bodies and wail the dirge, for that is the due of the dead.'

Then the ghost of the son of Atreus answered him: 'Ah, happy son of Laertes, Odysseus of many devices, yea, for a wife most excellent hast thou gotten, so good was the wisdom of constant Penelope daughter of Icarius, that was duly mindful of Odysseus, her wedded lord. Wherefore the fame of her virtue shall never perish, but the immortals will make a gracious song in the ears of men on earth to the fame of constant Penelope. In far other wise did the daughter of Tyndareus devise ill deeds, and slay her wedded lord, and hateful shall the song of her be among men, and an evil repute hath she brought upon all womankind, even on the upright.'

Even so these twain spake one to the other, standing in the house of Hades, beneath the secret places of the earth.

Now when those others had gone down from the city, quickly they came to the rich and well-ordered farm-land of Laertes, that he had won for himself of old, as the prize of great toil in war. There was his house, and all about it ran the huts wherein the thralls were wont to eat and dwell and sleep, bondsmen that worked his will. And in the house there was an old Sicilian woman, who diligently cared for the old man, in the upland far from the city. There Odysseus spake to his thralls and to his son, saying:

'Do ye now get you within the well-builded house, and quickly sacrifice the best of the swine for the midday meal, but I will make trial of my father, whether he will know me again and be aware of me when he sees me, or know me not, so long have I been away.'

Therewith he gave the thralls his weapons of war. Then they went speedily to the house, while Odysseus drew near to the fruitful vineyard to make trial of his father. Now he found not Dolius there, as he went down into the great garden, nor any of the thralls nor of their sons. It chanced that they had all gone to gather stones for a garden fence, and the old man at their head. So he found his father alone in the terraced vineyard, digging about a plant. He was clothed in a filthy doublet, patched and unseemly, with clouted leggings of oxhide bound about his legs, against the scratches of the thorns, and long sleeves over his hands by reason of the brambles, and on his head he wore a goatskin cap, and so he nursed his sorrow. Now when the steadfast goodly Odysseus saw his father thus wasted with age and in great grief of heart, he stood still beneath a tall pear tree and let fall a tear. Then he communed with his heart and soul, whether he should fall on his father's neck and kiss him, and tell him all, how he had returned and come to his own country, or whether he should first question him and prove him in every word. And as he thought within himself, this seemed to him the better way, namely, first to prove his father and speak to him sharply. So with this intent the goodly Odysseus went up to him. Now he was holding his head down and kept digging about the plant, while his renowned son stood by him and spake, saying:

'Old man, thou hast no lack of skill in tending a garden; lo, thou carest well for all, nor is there aught whatsoever, either plant or fig tree, or vine, yea, or olive, or pear, or garden-bed in all the close, that is not well seen to. Yet another thing will I tell thee and lay not up wrath thereat in thy heart. Thyself art scarce so well cared for, but a pitiful old age is on thee, and withal thou art withered and unkempt, and clad unseemly. It cannot be to punish thy sloth that thy master cares not for thee; there shows nothing of the slave about thy face and stature, for thou art like a kingly man, even like one who should lie soft, when he has washed and eaten well, as is the manner of the aged. But come, declare me this and plainly tell it all. Whose thrall art thou, and whose garden dost thou tend? Tell me moreover truly, that I may surely know, if it be indeed to Ithaca that I am now come, as one yonder told me who met with me but now on the way hither. He was but of little understanding, for he deigned not to tell me all nor to heed my saying, when I questioned him concerning my friend, whether indeed he is yet alive or is even now dead and within the house of Hades. For I will declare it and do thou mark and listen: once did I kindly entreat a man in mine own dear country, who came to our home, and never yet has any mortal been dearer of all the strangers that have drawn to my house from afar. He declared him to be by lineage from out of Ithaca, and said that his own father was Laertes son of Arceisius. So I led him to our halls and gave him good entertainment, with all loving-kindness, out of the plenty that was within. Such gifts too I gave him as are the due of guests; of well-wrought gold I gave him seven talents, and a mixing bowl of flowered work, all of silver, and twelve cloaks of single fold, and as many coverlets, and as many goodly mantles and doublets to boot, and besides all these, four women skilled in all fair works and most comely, the women of his choice.'

Then his father answered him, weeping: 'Stranger, thou art verily come to that country whereof thou askest, but outrageous men and froward hold it. And these thy gifts, thy countless gifts, thou didst bestow in vain. For if thou hadst found that man yet living in the land of Ithaca he would have sent thee on thy way with good return of thy presents, and with all hospitality, as is due to the man that begins the kindness. But come, declare me this and plainly tell me all; how many years are passed since thou didst entertain him, thy guest ill-fated and my child,—if ever such an one there was,—hapless man, whom far from his friends and his country's soil, the fishes, it may be, have devoured in the deep sea, or on the shore he has fallen the prey of birds and beasts. His mother wept not over him nor clad him for burial, nor his father, we that begat him.

Nor did his bride, whom men sought with rich gifts, the constant Penelope, bewail her lord upon the bier, as was meet, nor closed his eyes, as is the due of the departed. Moreover, tell me this truly, that I may surely know, who art thou and whence of the sons of men? Where is thy city and where are they that begat thee? Where now is thy swift ship moored, that brought thee thither with thy godlike company? Hast thou come as a passenger on another's ship, while they set thee ashore and went away?'

Then Odysseus of many counsels answered him, saying: 'Yea now, I will tell thee all most plainly. From out of Alybas I come, where I dwell in a house renowned, and am the son of Apheidas the son of Polypemon, the prince, and my own name is Eperitus. But some god drave me wandering hither from Sicania against my will, and yonder my ship is moored toward the upland away from the city. But for Odysseus, this is now the fifth year since he went thence and departed out of my country. Ill-fated was he, and yet he had birds of good omen when he fared away, birds on the right; wherefore I sped him gladly on his road, and gladly he departed, and the heart of us twain hoped yet to meet in friendship on a day and to give splendid gifts.'

So he spake, and on the old man fell a black cloud of sorrow. With both his hands he clutched the dust and ashes and showered them on his grey head, with ceaseless groaning. Then the heart of Odysseus was moved, and up through his nostrils throbbed anon the keen sting of sorrow at the sight of his dear father. And he sprang towards him and fell on his neck and kissed him, saying:

'Behold, I here, even I, my father, am the man of whom thou askest; in the twentieth year am I come to mine own country. But stay thy weeping and tearful lamentation, for I will tell thee all clearly, though great need there is of haste. I have slain the wooers in our halls and avenged their bitter scorn and evil deeds.'

Then Laertes answered him and spake, saying: 'If thou art indeed Odysseus, mine own child, that art come hither, show me now a manifest token, that I may be assured.'

Then Odysseus of many counsels answered him saying: 'Look first on this scar and consider it, that the boar dealt me with his white tusk on Parnassus, whither I had gone, and thou didst send me forth, thou and my lady mother, to Autolycus my mother's father, to get the gifts which when he came hither he promised and covenanted to give me. But come, and I will even tell thee the trees through all the terraced garden, which thou gavest me once for mine own, and I was begging of thee this and that, being but a little child, and following thee through the garden. Through these very trees we were going, and thou didst tell me the names of each of them. Pear trees thirteen thou gavest me and ten apple trees and figs two-score, and, as we went, thou didst name the fifty rows of vines thou wouldest give me, whereof each one ripened at divers times, with all manner of clusters on their boughs, when the seasons of Zeus wrought mightily on them from on high.'

So he spake, and straightway his knees were loosened, and his heart melted within him, as he knew the sure tokens that Odysseus showed him. About his dear son he cast his arms, and the steadfast goodly Odysseus caught him fainting to his breast. Now when he had got breath and his spirit came to him again, once more he answered and spake, saying:

'Father Zeus, verily ye gods yet bear sway on high Olympus, if indeed the wooers have paid for their infatuate pride! But now my heart is terribly afraid, lest straightway all the men of Ithaca come up against us here, and haste to send messengers everywhere to the cities of the Cephallenians.'

Then Odysseus of many counsels answered him saying: 'Take courage, and let not thy heart be careful about these matters. But come, let us go to the house that lies near the garden, for thither I sent forward Telemachus and the neatherd and the swineherd to get ready the meal as speedily as may be.'

After these words the twain set out to the goodly halls. Now when they had come to the fair-lying house, they found Telemachus and the neatherd and the swineherd carving much flesh, and mixing the dark wine. Meanwhile the Sicilian handmaid bathed high-hearted Laertes in his house, and anointed him with olive-oil, and cast a fair mantle about him. Then Athene drew nigh, and made greater the limbs of the shepherd of the people, taller she made him than before and mightier to behold. Then he went forth from the bath, and his dear son marvelled at him, beholding him like to the deathless gods in presence. And uttering his voice he spake to him winged words:

'Father, surely one of the gods that are from everlasting hath made thee goodlier and greater to behold.'

Then wise Laertes answered him, saying: 'Ah, would to father Zeus and Athene and Apollo, that such as I was when I took Nericus, the stablished castle on the foreland of the continent, being then the prince of the Cephallenians, would that in such might, and with mail about my shoulders, I had stood to aid thee yesterday in our house, and to beat back the wooers; so should I have loosened the knees of many an one of them in the halls, and thou shouldest have been gladdened in thine inmost heart!'

So they spake each with the other. But when the others had ceased from their task and made ready the feast, they sat down all orderly on chairs and on high seats. Then they began to put forth their hands on the meat, and the old man Dolius drew nigh, and the old man's sons withal came tired from their labour in the fields, for their mother, the aged Sicilian woman, had gone forth and called them, she that saw to their living and diligently cared for the old man, now that old age had laid hold on him. So soon as they looked on Odysseus and took knowledge of him, they stood still in the halls in great amazement. But Odysseus addressed them in gentle words, saying:

'Old man, sit down to meat and do ye forget your marvelling, for long have we been eager to put forth our hands on the food, as we abode in the hall always expecting your coming.'

So he spake, and Dolius ran straight toward him stretching forth both his hands, and he grasped the hand of Odysseus and kissed it on the wrist, and uttering his voice spake to him winged words:

'Beloved, forasmuch as thou hast come back to us who sore desired thee, and no longer thought to see thee, and the gods have led thee home again;—hail to thee and welcome manifold, and may the gods give thee all good fortune! Moreover tell me this truly, that I may be assured, whether wise Penelope yet knows well that thou hast come back hither, or whether we shall despatch a messenger.'

Then Odysseus of many counsels answered saying: 'Old man, already she knows all; what need to busy thyself herewith?'

Thereon the other sat him down again on his polished settle. And in like wise the sons of Dolius gathered about the renowned Odysseus, and greeted him well and clasped his hands, and then sat down all orderly by Dolius their father.

So they were busy with the meal in the halls. Now Rumour the messenger went swiftly all about the city, telling the tale of the dire death and fate of the wooers. And the people heard it, and all at once gathered together from every side with sighing and groaning before the house of Odysseus. And each brought forth his dead from the halls, and buried them; but those that came out of other cities they placed on swift ships and sent with fisher-folk, each to be carried to his own home. As for them they all fared together to the assembly-place, in sorrow of heart. When they were all gathered and come together, Eupeithes arose and spake among them, for a comfortless grief lay heavy on his heart for his son Antinous, the first man that goodly Odysseus had slain. Weeping for him he made harangue and spake among them:

'Friends, a great deed truly hath this man devised against the Achaeans. Some with his ships he led away, many men and noble, and his hollow ships hath he lost, and utterly lost of his company, and others again, and those far the best of the Cephallenians he hath slain on his coming home. Up now, before ever he gets him swiftly either to Pylos or to fair Elis, where the Epeians bear sway, let us go forth; else even hereafter shall we have shame of face for ever. For a scorn this is even for the ears of men unborn to hear, if we avenge not ourselves on the slayers of our sons and of our brethren. Life would no more be sweet to me, but rather would I die straightway and be with the departed. Up, let us be going, lest these fellows be beforehand with us and get them over the sea.'

Thus he spake weeping, and pity fell on all the Achaeans. Then came near to them Medon and the divine minstrel, forth from the halls of Odysseus, for that sleep had let them go. They stood in the midst of the gathering, and amazement seized every man. Then Medon, wise of heart, spake among them, saying:

'Hearken to me now, ye men of Ithaca, for surely Odysseus planned not these deeds without the will of the gods. Nay I myself beheld a god immortal, who stood hard by Odysseus, in the perfect semblance of Mentor; now as a deathless god was he manifest in front of Odysseus, cheering him, and yet again scaring the wooers he stormed through the hall, and they fell thick one on another.'

Thus he spake, and pale fear gat hold of the limbs of all. Then the old man, the lord Halitherses, spake among them, the son of Mastor, for he alone saw before and after. Out of his good will he made harangue and spake among them, saying:

'Hearken to me now, ye men of Ithaca, to the word that I will say. Through your own cowardice, my friends, have these deeds come to pass. For ye obeyed not me, nor Mentor, the shepherd of the people, to make your sons cease from their foolish ways. A great villainy they wrought in their evil infatuation, wasting the wealth and holding in no regard the wife of a prince, while they deemed that he would never more come home. And now let things be on this wise, and obey my counsel. Let us not go forth against him, lest haply some may find a bane of their own bringing.'

So he spake, but they leapt up with a great cry, the more part of them, while the rest abode there together; for his counsel was not to the mind of the more part, but they gave ear to Eupeithes, and swiftly thereafter they rushed for their armour. So when they had arrayed them in shining mail, they assembled together in front of the spacious town. And Eupeithes led them in his witlessness, for he thought to avenge the slaying of his son, yet himself was never to return, but then and there to meet his doom.

Now Athene spake to Zeus, the son of Cronos, saying: 'O Father, our father Cronides, throned in the highest, answer and tell me what is now the hidden counsel of thy heart? Wilt thou yet further rouse up evil war and the terrible din of battle, or art thou minded to set them at one again in friendship?'

Then Zeus, the gatherer of the clouds, answered her saying: 'My child, why dost thou thus straitly question me, and ask me this? Nay, didst not thou thyself devise this very thought, namely, that Odysseus should indeed take vengeance on these men at his coming? Do as thou wilt, but I will tell thee of the better way. Now that goodly Odysseus hath wreaked vengeance on the wooers, let them make a firm covenant together with sacrifice, and let him be king all his days, and let us bring about oblivion of the slaying of their children and their brethren; so may both sides love one another as of old, and let peace and wealth abundant be their portion.'

Therewith he roused Athene to yet greater eagerness, and from the peaks of Olympus she came glancing down.

Now when they had put from them the desire of honey-sweet food, the steadfast goodly Odysseus began to speak among them, saying:

'Let one go forth and see, lest the people be already drawing near against us.'

So he spake, and the son of Dolius went forth at his bidding, and stood on the outer threshold and saw them all close at hand. Then straightway he spake to Odysseus winged words:

'Here they be, close upon us! Quick, let us to arms!'

Thereon they rose up and arrayed them in their harness, Odysseus and his men being four, and the six sons of Dolius, and likewise Laertes and Dolius did on their armour, grey-headed as they were, warriors through stress of need. Now when they had clad them in shining mail, they opened the gates and went forth and Odysseus led them.

Then Athene, daughter of Zeus, drew near them in the likeness of Mentor, in fashion and in voice. And the steadfast goodly Odysseus beheld her and was glad, and straightway he spake to Telemachus his dear son:

'Telemachus, soon shalt thou learn this, when thou thyself art got to the place of the battle where the best men try the issue,—namely, not to bring shame on thy father's house, on us who in time past have been eminent for might and hardihood over all the world.'

Then wise Telemachus answered him, saying: 'Thou shalt see me, if thou wilt, dear father, in this my mood no whit disgracing thy line, according to thy word.'

So spake he, and Laertes was glad and spake, saying: 'What a day has dawned for me, kind gods; yea, a glad man am I! My son and my son's son are vying with one another in valour.'

Then grey-eyed Athene stood beside Laertes, and spake to him: 'O son of Arceisius that art far the dearest of all my friends, pray first to the grey-eyed maid and to father Zeus, then swing thy long spear aloft and hurl it straightway.'

Therewith Pallas Athene breathed into him great strength. Then he prayed to the daughter of mighty Zeus, and straightway swung his long spear aloft and hurled it, and smote Eupeithes through his casque with the cheek-piece of bronze. The armour kept not out the spear that went clean through, and he fell with a crash, and his arms rattled about his body. Then Odysseus and his renowned son fell on the fore-fighters, and smote them with swords and two-headed spears. And now would they have slain them all and cut off their return, had not Athene called aloud, the daughter of Zeus lord of the aegis, and stayed all the host of the enemy, saying:

'Hold your hands from fierce fighting, ye men of Ithaca, that so ye may be parted quickly, without bloodshed.'

So spake Athene, and pale fear gat hold of them all. The arms flew from their hands in their terror and fell all upon the ground, as the goddess uttered her voice. To the city they turned their steps, as men fain of life, and the steadfast goodly Odysseus with a terrible cry gathered himself together and hurled in on them, like an eagle of lofty flight. Then in that hour the son of Cronos cast forth a flaming bolt, and it fell at the feet of the grey-eyed goddess, the daughter of the mighty Sire. Then grey-eyed Athene spake to Odysseus, saying:

'Son of Laertes, of the seed of Zeus, Odysseus of many devices, refrain thee now and stay the strike of even-handed war, lest perchance the son of Cronos be angry with thee, even Zeus of the far-borne voice.'

So spake Athene, and he obeyed and was glad at heart. And thereafter Pallas Athene set a covenant between them with sacrifice, she, the daughter of Zeus lord of the aegis, in the likeness of Mentor, both in fashion and in voice.

Homer, thy song men liken to the sea,
With every note of music in his tone,
With tides that wash the dim dominion
Of Hades, and light waves that laugh in glee
Around the isles enchanted: nay, to me
Thy verse seems as the River of source unknown
That glasses Egypt's temples overthrown,
In his sky-nurtur'd stream, eternally.
No wiser we than men of heretofore
To find thy mystic fountains guarded fast;
Enough—thy flood makes green our human shore
As Nilus, Egypt, rolling down his vast,
His fertile waters, murmuring evermore
Of gods dethroned, and empires of the Past.

A. L.